fundamentals
of
LINEAR
ALGEBRA

The Appleton-Century Mathematics Series

Raymond W. Brink, John M. H. Olmsted & Fred B. Wright, Editors

A. H. LIGHTSTONE

Queen's University

fundamentals
of
LINEAR
ALGEBRA

APPLETON-CENTURY-CROFTS

EDUCATIONAL DIVISION

MEREDITH CORPORATION NEW YORK

PREFACE

This brief treatment of linear algebra and geometry is intended for use in a one-semester course, where time does not permit a thorough development of the subject. In a sense, this book constitutes an introduction to abstract mathematics. It is assumed that the reader is familiar with elementary notions of set theory.

In an effort to break down the usual "compartmentalized" view of mathematics, considerable emphasis is placed on interconnecting algebra and geometry. There is obvious pedagogical value in using ideas about vector spaces in the simple situation of geometry; the student has an opportunity to familiarize himself with vector concepts by actually using them in a meaningful situation. Also, the geometric problem of finding a vector orthogonal to given vectors, leads to a useful generalization of the vector product, a purely algebraic concept.

The associative law of matrix multiplication provides an opportunity to gain some insight into the nature of matrix multiplication. Two proofs of this theorem are presented, which hinge on methods of characterizing matrix multiplication. The point is that the algebraic properties of matrix multiplication yield easily when this operation is expressed in terms of row or column vectors, rather than individual entries of a matrix.

Quadric surfaces are analysed in terms of three parameters, a quadratic form, a vector, and a scalar. This analysis is facilitated by the notion of a *matrix with multipliers*, an idea that is also used in proving the associative law of matrix multiplication.

The first five chapters of this book have grown out of the corresponding chapters of *Concepts of Calculus II*, (c) 1966, Harper & Row, Publishers, New York, N.Y. The author is grateful to the publisher for permission to use this material here. In that book the chapters on linear algebra were relatively brief, serving as an introduction to the topic for use in the subsequent portions of the book. In the present work, however, these topics are treated in more detail, and greater use is made of algebraic techniques, to assist the reader in developing the algebraic viewpoint.

A. H. L.

CONTENTS

Preface

1 MATRICES 1

1.1 The algebra of n-tuples   1
1.2 Linear systems; reducing a matrix   6
1.3 The mapping determinant   13
1.4 Properties of determinant   17
1.5 Second-level minors   24
1.6 Principle of duality; det   27

2 VECTORS AND LINEAR SYSTEMS 33

2.1 Subspaces and linear combinations   33
2.2 Basis and dimension   38
2.3 More about linear systems   43
2.4 Characterizing the solution set of a linear system 46
2.5 Computing the rank of a matrix   51
2.6 Rank and the mapping determinant   53

3 MATRIX ALGEBRA 57

3.1 The dot product   57
3.2 Length and angle   62
3.3 Matrix algebra   70
3.4 Inverses   77
3.5 Elementary matrices; mixed matrices   82

4 LINES 89

4.1 Three-dimensional Euclidean space   89
4.2 The line through two points   92

4.3	Direction and directed lines	95
4.4	Directed distance	99
4.5	Perpendicular lines; the vector product	102

5   PLANES   109

5.1	Planes and hyperplanes	109
5.2	Normal to a plane	112
5.3	Intersection of planes	115
5.4	Distance between a point and a plane	119

6   MODERN ALGEBRA   123

6.1	Algebraic systems	123
6.2	Groups	128
6.3	Rings	136
6.4	Fields	141
6.5	Isomorphic algebraic systems	145

7   VECTOR SPACES   149

7.1	Vector spaces	149
7.2	Steinitz Replacement Theorem	157
7.3	Change of basis	162

8   POLYNOMIALS   173

8.1	Vector space of polynomials	173
8.2	Ring of polynomials	176
8.3	Polynomial functions	182
8.4	The Division Theorem	185
8.5	Matric polynominals and polynomial matrices	190

9   LINEAR OPERATORS   197

9.1	Linear transformations	197
9.2	Linear operators	202
9.3	Algebra of linear operators	207

10   CHARACTERISTIC POLYNOMIALS   213

10.1	Characteristic vectors	213
10.2	The characteristic polynomial of a matrix	217
10.3	Similar matrices	219

10.4   The Cayley-Hamilton Theorem   223
10.5   Computing characteristic polynomials   227

11   **INNER PRODUCT SPACES**   233

11.1   Bilinear forms   233
11.2   Real inner product spaces   239
11.3   Properties of real inner product spaces   244
11.4   Quadratic forms   247

12   **QUADRIC SURFACES**   253

12.1   Quadric surfaces   253
12.2   Intersection of a quadric surface and a line   262
12.3   Diametral planes; centers   264
12.4   Principal planes   270

Table I   Arccos   277

Table II   Cos   283

Answers and Hints   313

Index of Mathematical Expressions   333

Index   337

1

MATRICES

1.1 THE ALGEBRA OF n-TUPLES

Linear algebra is largely a discussion of the algebraic properties of ordered n-tuples; so, much of this book involves ordered n-tuples. Clearly, time spent considering the basic properties of ordered n-tuples is well invested. An ordered n-tuple is an object that possesses n terms, a first term, a second term, . . . , an nth term. For example, $(2, 5, -4)$ is an ordered 3-tuple, $(1, 6, 0, 1, 1)$ is an ordered 5-tuple, and (3) is an ordered 1-tuple. Notice that the terms of an ordered n-tuple need not be distinct. On the other hand, a *set* is composed of distinct objects; the set $\{1, 6, 0, 1, 1\}$ has exactly three members; indeed $\{1, 6, 0, 1, 1\} = \{1, 6, 0\}$. Notice that parentheses are used for n-tuples whereas braces are used for sets. The fundamental statement that we can make about an n-tuple is that an object is its kth term, where $k \in \{1, \ldots, n\}$, whereas the fundamental statement that we can make about a set is that an object is a member of the set. For example, we can assert that $3 \in \{2, 3, 7, 9\}$, that $5 \in \{2, 3, 7, 9\}$, that 4 is the second term of $(2, 4, -1)$, and that 6 is the third term of $(2, 4, -1)$. Clearly, two of these statements are true and two are false. We emphasize that an ordered n-tuple possesses *terms* whereas a set possesses *members*.

Throughout this book we are frequently involved with real numbers and natural numbers. Therefore, it is useful to develop a brief way of asserting that an object is a real number, or is a natural number. The set theory symbol $\in$ is the key to our shorthand. Let R denote the set of all real numbers and let N denote the set of all natural numbers; so, we can assert that a is a real number and that b is a natural number by writing $a \in R$ and $b \in N$, respectively. Similarly, let us agree to denote the set of all ordered n-tuples of real numbers by R_n; so, $\alpha \in R_n$ means that α is an ordered n-tuple of real numbers.

We propose now to *add* ordered *n*-tuples. Let $(a_1, \ldots, A_n) \in R_n$ and let $(b_1, \ldots, b_n) \in R_n$; the idea is to add corresponding terms.

Definition 1.1.1: $(a_1, \ldots, a_n) + (b_1, \ldots, b_n) = (a_1 + b_1, \ldots, a_n + b_n)$, whenever $(a_1, \ldots, a_n) \in R_n$ and $(b_1, \ldots, b_n) \in R_n$.

Notice that the $+$ on the left-hand side does not possess the same significance as the $+$'s that appear on the right-hand side. The first denotes a binary operation on R_n; whereas the other $+$'s denote a binary operation on R, the usual addition. Of course it is clear from the context whether we are adding ordered tuples or real numbers.

Next, we introduce a mapping of $R \times R_n$ into R_n; i.e., we propose to associate with each real number and ordered *n*-tuple some ordered *n*-tuple. Let $k \in R$ and let $(a_1, \ldots, a_n) \in R_n$; the idea is to multiply each term by k. This mapping is denoted by $\circ$.

Definition 1.1.2: $k \circ (a_1, \ldots, a_n) = (ka_1, \ldots, ka_n)$ whenever $k \in R$ and $(a_1, \ldots, a_n) \in R_n$.

This mapping is called *scalar multiplication*. You see, real numbers are sometimes called *scalars* (this is a good habit to develop), whereas ordered *n*-tuples are called *vectors* or *n-vectors*.

Finally, we exhibit an *n*-vector that possesses special significance.

Definition 1.1.3: $\mathbf{0} = \underbrace{(0, \ldots, 0)}_{n \text{ 0's}}$.

Notice that we use heavy type for the $\mathbf{0}$ on the left-hand side and light type for the 0's on the right-hand side; this convention helps us to distinguish between the scalar 0 and the vector $\mathbf{0}$.

Here are some examples of the preceding definitions.

Example 1: $(2, -1, 3, 4) + (3, 4, 0, 2) = (5, 3, 3, 6)$.

Example 2: $(-3, 4, 0, 5, 1) + (0, 1, 1, -2, 3) = (-3, 5, 1, 3, 4)$.

Example 3: $(4, 1) + (-2, 3) = (2, 4)$.

Example 4: $(4, 1) + (-2, 3, 0)$ has no significance.

Example 5: $5 \circ (3, 2, -1, 6) = (15, 10, -5, 30)$.

Example 6: $-1 \circ (2, -3) = (-2, 3)$.

Example 7: $3 \circ (4) = (12)$.

We are now ready to explore the algebra of ordered *n*-tuples. Let us agree to use Greek letters as place-holders (or symbols) for vectors, and to use Latin letters as place-holders (or symbols) for scalars.

First, we point out that $+$ is associative.

Lemma 1.1.1: $\alpha + (\beta + \gamma) = (\alpha + \beta) + \gamma$ whenever $\{\alpha, \beta, \gamma\} \subset R_n$.

Proof: Let $\alpha = (a_1, \ldots, a_n)$, $\beta = (b_1, \ldots, b_n)$, and let $\gamma = (c_1, \ldots, c_n)$. Now $\alpha + (\beta + \gamma) = (a_1 + (b_1 + c_1), \ldots, a_n + (b_n + c_n))$, and $(\alpha + \beta) + \gamma = ((a_1 + b_1) + c_1, \ldots, (a_n + b_n) + c_n)$. But $+$ is associative on R, i.e., $a + (b + c) = (a + b) + c$ whenever $\{a, b, c\} \subset R$. Thus $(a_1 + (b_1 + c_1), \ldots, a_n + (b_n + c_n)) = ((a_1 + b_1) + c_1, \ldots, (a_n + b_n) + c_n)$; so $\alpha + (\beta + \gamma) = (\alpha + \beta) + \gamma$. This establishes our lemma.

Next, we prove that **0** is a *right identity*.

Lemma 1.1.2: $\alpha + \mathbf{0} = \alpha$ whenever $\alpha \in R_n$.

Proof: Let $\alpha = (a_1, \ldots, a_n)$; now $\alpha + \mathbf{0} = (a_1, \ldots, a_n) + (0, \ldots, 0) = (a_1 + 0, \ldots, a_n + 0) = (a_1, \ldots, a_n)$ since $a + 0 = a$ whenever $a \in R$. Thus $\alpha + \mathbf{0} = \alpha$.

Let us prove that each *n*-vector possesses a *right inverse*.

Lemma 1.1.3:   Corresponding to each *n*-vector α there is an *n*-vector β such that $\alpha + \beta = \mathbf{0}$.

Proof: Let $\alpha = (a_1, \ldots, a_n)$ be any *n*-vector and let $\beta = (-a_1, \ldots, -a_n)$. Recall that $-a$ denotes the real number b such that $a + b = 0$. Thus $\alpha + \beta = (a_1 + (-a_1), \ldots, a_n + (-a_n)) = (0, \ldots, 0) = \mathbf{0}$.

Notice that vector addition is commutative.

Lemma 1.1.4: $\alpha + \beta = \beta + \alpha$ whenever $\{\alpha, \beta\} \subset R_n$.

Proof: Use the fact that scalar addition is commutative.

If you are familiar with the *group* concept you will appreciate the significance of the preceding lemmas; namely, that $(R_n, +, \mathbf{0})$ is an abelian group.

Next, we present some algebraic properties of scalar multiplication.

Lemma 1.1.5: $a \circ (\beta + \gamma) = a \circ \beta + a \circ \gamma$ whenever $\{\beta, \gamma\} \subset R_n$ and $a \in R$.

Proof: Use the fact that multiplication distributes over addition in the real number system, i.e., $a(b + c) = ab + ac$ whenever $\{a, b, c\} \subset R$.

Lemma 1.1.6: $(a + b) \circ \gamma = a \circ \gamma + b \circ \gamma$ whenever $\{a, b\} \subset R$ and $\gamma \in R_n$.

Proof: Again, this result depends upon a distributive law for the real number system. The details are left as an exercise.

Lemma 1.1.7: $(ab) \circ \gamma = a \circ (b \circ \gamma)$ whenever $\{a, b\} \subset R$ and $\gamma \in R_n$.

Proof: Use the fact that multiplication is associative, i.e., $a(bc) = (ab)c$ whenever $\{a, b, c\} \subset R$.

Lemma 1.1.8: $1 \circ \gamma = \gamma$ whenever $\gamma \in R_n$.

Proof: Here, we need the fact that 1 is a multiplicative identity for the real number system; i.e., $1 \cdot a = a$ whenever $a \in R$.

In view of these lemmas, mathematicians say that ordered n-tuples form a *vector space;* indeed, any mathematical system for which the preceding eight lemmas are true, is said to be a vector space. In order to spell out this notion accurately we need two elementary concepts of modern algebra, the notion of an *abelian group* and the notion of a *field.* In Section 7.1 we shall see that each vector space involves an underlying field as well as an abelian group. Perhaps you are curious about this idea; if so, read Chapter 6 quickly and consider Definition 7.1.1.

The symbol $\circ$ for scalar multiplication is usually suppressed. So far we have carefully avoided this convention for the sake of clarity; we need a certain familiarity with scalar multiplication before treating it so lightly. The following example indicates the advantage of suppressing $\circ$.

Example 8:   Simplify $3(2, -1, 4) + 2(0, 5, 3) + -4(1, -1, 0)$.

Solution: First we point out that we have suppressed the parentheses that indicate the order in which the vector additions are to be carried out. This convention is justified by the fact that vector addition is associative (see Lemma 1.1.1); i.e., no matter how we insert parentheses we arrive at the same vector. Now

$$3(2, -1, 4) + 2(0, 5, 3) + -4(1, -1, 0)$$
$$= (6, -3, 12) + (0, 10, 6) + (-4, 4, 0)$$
$$= (2, 11, 18).$$

There is one more convention that we wish to introduce right now. Let us agree that n-tuple and ordered n-tuple have exactly the same significance. If we wish to refer to a set with exactly n members we call it a "set with n members," not an "n-tuple." Of course, "n-tuple" should not suggest "set with n members," since an n-tuple may involve only one object; for example, consider the 3-tuple $(5, 5, 5)$.

The mathematical system that we have developed in this section is used throughout this book; so, it is helpful to give it a name, say $\mathcal{R}_n$. Thus, $\mathcal{R}_n$ is the mathematical system that involves R_n and the mappings $+$ and $\circ$. The point is this: when you see R_n think of n-tuples of real numbers; when you see $\mathcal{R}_n$ think of R_n and the mappings $+$ and $\circ$ presented in Definition 1.1.1 and Definition 1.1.2. We present a precise definition of $\mathcal{R}_n$ in Section 7.1.

EXERCISES

1. Simplify each of the following expressions.

    (a) $(5, 7, 3) + (4, -1, -2)$

    (b) $(2, 1, 0, 4) + (-1, 1, 1, 1)$

    (c) $(4, 1, 2, -5, 6) + (-4, -1, -2, 5, -6)$

    (d) $3 \circ (5, 7, -1) + 7 \circ (-2, -3, 1)$

    (e) $-1 \circ (2, 4) + 3 \circ (1, 5)$

    (f) $-2 \circ (1) + -4 \circ (3)$

2. Prove Lemma 1.1.4.

3. Let $\{\alpha, \beta\} \subset R_n$ and suppose that $\alpha + \beta = \mathbf{0}$. Show that $\beta + \alpha = \mathbf{0}$.

4. Prove that corresponding to each *n*-vector α there is an *n*-vector β such that $\beta + \alpha = \mathbf{0}$.

5. Let $\{\alpha, \beta, \gamma\} \subset R_n$ and suppose that $\alpha + \gamma = \beta + \gamma$. Prove that $\alpha = \beta$.

6. Prove Lemma 1.1.5.

7. Prove Lemma 1.1.6.

8. Prove Lemma 1.1.7.

9. Prove Lemma 1.1.8.

10. Prove that $\mathbf{0} \circ \gamma = \mathbf{0}$ whenever $\gamma \in R_n$.

11. Prove that $\gamma + -1 \circ \gamma = \mathbf{0}$ whenever $\gamma \in R_n$.

12. Given that a is a nonzero scalar and that $a \circ \gamma = \mathbf{0}$, show that $\gamma = \mathbf{0}$.

13. Let a be a nonzero scalar and let β and γ be *n*-vectors such that $a \circ \beta = \gamma$; prove that $\beta = (1/a) \circ \gamma$.

14. Simplify each of the following expressions.

    (a) $4(2, -1) + 3(1, 0) + 2(4, -3)$

    (b) $-3(2, 2) + 5(4, -3) + 7(1, 5) + 2(3, 3)$

    (c) $2(1, 1, 1) + 3(4, 4, 0) + (2, 1, -1) + -1(1, 1, 0)$

    (d) $2(1, 3, 5, -7) + -2(2, 1, 0, 0) + -3(2, -2, 1, -1)$
              $+ (1, 0, 0, 2) + 3(2, -2, 1, 5)$

15. Consider any equation of the form

$$a_1 x_1 + \cdots + a_n x_n = b$$

where $x_1, \ldots, x_n$ are the unknowns and $a_1, \ldots, a_n, b$ are real numbers. Equations of this sort can be *added* by adding corresponding coefficients, and can be *multiplied* by a scalar k by multiplying each of its coefficients by k. Let $\mathbf{0}$ denote the equation $0x_1 + \cdots + 0x_n = 0$. Show that these operations possess the properties given in the eight lemmas of this section.

1.2 LINEAR SYSTEMS; REDUCING A MATRIX

Consider the familiar problem of finding all n-tuples of real numbers, say $(x_1, x_2, \ldots, x_n)$, such that:

(1)
$$\begin{cases} a_{11}x_1 + a_{12}x_2 + \cdots + a_{1n}x_n = b_1 \\ a_{21}x_1 + a_{22}x_2 + \cdots + a_{2n}x_n = b_2 \\ \qquad\qquad\quad \cdot \\ \qquad\qquad\quad \cdot \\ \qquad\qquad\quad \cdot \\ a_{m1}x_1 + a_{m2}x_2 + \cdots + a_{mn}x_n = b_m \end{cases}$$

where the a's and b's are given real numbers. Notice that we are faced with m equations in the n unknowns $x_1, x_2, \ldots, x_n$. Our problem is to determine the solution set of the given system; i.e., the set $\{(c_1, c_2, \ldots, c_n) \mid (c_1, c_2, \ldots, c_n) \in R_n$ and $(c_1, c_2, \ldots, c_n)$ satisfies each equation of (1)}. Of course, you have considered this problem in high school and already possess a technique for solving it. Our purpose here is to develop an efficient method of carrying out this technique; in Chapter 2 we investigate the theory which underlies this problem.

We now introduce a useful equivalence relation on systems of equations which involve the same number of unknowns. Notice that the system (1) is an *ordered* set of equations; the system possesses a first equation, a second equation, . . . , and an mth equation. Any system of equations such as (1) is said to be a *linear* system because each term on the left-hand side of each equation has the form ax where a is a scalar and x is an unknown.

Definition 1.2.1: Two linear systems which have the same solution set are said to be *equivalent;* each linear system is said to be equivalent to itself.

Example 1: The linear systems

$$\begin{cases} 3x_1 - x_2 = 1 \\ 2x_1 + x_2 = 4 \\ x_1 + 2x_2 = 5 \end{cases} \quad \text{and} \quad \begin{cases} x_1 - x_2 = -1 \\ x_1 + x_2 = 3 \end{cases}$$

are equivalent since each system has solution set $\{(1, 2)\}$.

Example 2: The linear systems

$$\begin{cases} x_1 + x_2 - x_3 = 0 \\ \quad\;\; x_2 + x_3 = 0 \end{cases} \quad \text{and} \quad \begin{cases} x_1 \qquad\quad - 2x_3 = 0 \\ x_1 + 2x_2 \qquad\; = 0 \end{cases}$$

are equivalent since each system has solution set $\{(2t, -t, t) \mid t \in R\}$. Notice that this solution set has infinitely many members.

Example 3: The linear systems

$$\begin{cases} x_1 + 2x_2 - x_3 = 2 \\ x_1 + x_2 - 2x_3 = 0 \\ 2x_1 - x_2 - 2x_3 = -1 \\ x_1 + x_2 + x_3 = 2 \end{cases} \quad \text{and} \quad \begin{cases} x_1 - 2x_2 + x_3 = 1 \\ 2x_1 - 4x_2 + 2x_3 = 3 \end{cases}$$

are equivalent since each system has solution set $\varnothing$, the empty set.

It is possible to transform a linear system into an equivalent system whose solution set is easily found. This is achieved as the final result of a series of remarkably simple transformations. The basic question is this: how can we obtain an equivalent system from a given system? Now, there are three fundamental transformations which produce an equivalent system from a given system, as follows:

(i) Interchange any two equations.

(ii) Multiply any equation by a nonzero real number.

(iii) Add one equation to another equation; i.e., replace one equation by the equation obtained from it by adding another of the equations to it.

It is a simple matter to verify that each of these transformations transforms a linear system into an equivalent linear system (this is left as an exercise). Let us see how we can apply these transformations with a minimum of effort. The main idea is to avoid writing down symbols that are not necessary to our procedure. Now the x's, the $+$'s, and the $=$'s do not vary throughout the system of equations (1); let us agree to delete these symbols. This means that we represent the linear system (1) by writing:

$$
\begin{matrix}
a_{11} & a_{12} & \cdots & a_{1n} & b_1 \\
a_{21} & a_{22} & \cdots & a_{2n} & b_2 \\
& & \cdot & & \\
& & \cdot & & \\
& & \cdot & & \\
a_{m1} & a_{m2} & \cdots & a_{mn} & b_m
\end{matrix}
$$

We want to separate the above array of numbers from the rest of the world, so we surround it by parentheses, thus:

$$
\begin{pmatrix}
a_{11} & a_{12} & \cdots & a_{1n} & b_1 \\
a_{21} & a_{22} & \cdots & a_{2n} & b_2 \\
& & \cdot & & \\
& & \cdot & & \\
& & \cdot & & \\
a_{m1} & a_{m2} & \cdots & a_{mn} & b_m
\end{pmatrix}.
$$

An array of numbers of this sort is called a *matrix*. We sometimes want to indicate the number of rows and columns of a given matrix; a matrix which has r rows and s columns is said to be an $r \times s$ matrix. The matrix given above is an $m \times n + 1$ matrix. It is easy to recapture the system of equations represented by a matrix. Consider the following example.

Example 4: The 3×4 matrix

$$
\begin{pmatrix}
1 & 3 & 2 & -1 \\
-1 & 2 & -1 & -4 \\
2 & 1 & 2 & 3
\end{pmatrix}
$$

represents the linear system,

$$
\begin{cases}
x_1 + 3x_2 + 2x_3 = -1 \\
-x_1 + 2x_2 - x_3 = -4 \\
2x_1 + x_2 + 2x_3 = 3
\end{cases}
$$

Let us solve this linear system. To assert that two linear systems are equivalent we shall insert the symbol $\sim$ between them. Now

$$\begin{pmatrix} 1 & 3 & 2 & -1 \\ -1 & 2 & -1 & -4 \\ 2 & 1 & 2 & 3 \end{pmatrix} \sim \begin{pmatrix} 1 & 3 & 2 & -1 \\ 0 & 5 & 1 & -5 \\ 2 & 1 & 2 & 3 \end{pmatrix} \sim \begin{pmatrix} -2 & -6 & -4 & 2 \\ 0 & 5 & 1 & -5 \\ 2 & 1 & 2 & 3 \end{pmatrix}$$

$$\sim \begin{pmatrix} -2 & -6 & -4 & 2 \\ 0 & 5 & 1 & -5 \\ 0 & -5 & -2 & 5 \end{pmatrix} \sim \begin{pmatrix} -2 & -6 & -4 & 2 \\ 0 & 5 & 1 & -5 \\ 0 & 0 & -1 & 0 \end{pmatrix} \sim \begin{pmatrix} -5 & -15 & -10 & 5 \\ 0 & 5 & 1 & -5 \\ 0 & 0 & -1 & 0 \end{pmatrix}$$

$$\sim \begin{pmatrix} -5 & -15 & -10 & 5 \\ 0 & 15 & 3 & -15 \\ 0 & 0 & -1 & 0 \end{pmatrix} \sim \begin{pmatrix} -5 & 0 & -7 & -10 \\ 0 & 15 & 3 & -15 \\ 0 & 0 & -1 & 0 \end{pmatrix} \sim \begin{pmatrix} -5 & 0 & -7 & -10 \\ 0 & 5 & 1 & -5 \\ 0 & 0 & -1 & 0 \end{pmatrix}$$

$$\sim \begin{pmatrix} -5 & 0 & -7 & -10 \\ 0 & 5 & 0 & -5 \\ 0 & 0 & -1 & 0 \end{pmatrix} \sim \begin{pmatrix} -5 & 0 & -7 & -10 \\ 0 & 5 & 0 & -5 \\ 0 & 0 & 7 & 0 \end{pmatrix} \sim \begin{pmatrix} -5 & 0 & 0 & -10 \\ 0 & 5 & 0 & -5 \\ 0 & 0 & 7 & 0 \end{pmatrix}$$

$$\sim \begin{pmatrix} 1 & 0 & 0 & 2 \\ 0 & 5 & 0 & -5 \\ 0 & 0 & 7 & 0 \end{pmatrix} \sim \begin{pmatrix} 1 & 0 & 0 & 2 \\ 0 & 1 & 0 & -1 \\ 0 & 0 & 7 & 0 \end{pmatrix} \sim \begin{pmatrix} 1 & 0 & 0 & 2 \\ 0 & 1 & 0 & -1 \\ 0 & 0 & 1 & 0 \end{pmatrix}.$$

Thus the given linear system is equivalent to the system

$$x_1 = 2, \; x_2 = -1, \; x_3 = 0 .$$

Of course, $\{(2, -1, 0)\}$ is the solution set of this system. We have carefully listed each step in the simplification of the given system, so that each transformation is visible. It is easy to carry out several transformations mentally, indicating on paper the result of three or four transformations. In this way, the amount of writing is greatly reduced. Certainly, this requires some practice at handling our basic transformations; but this is all to the good. To illustrate the technique, we simplify the linear system of Example 4 once again, this time doing mentally whatever we can.

Example 5:

$$\begin{pmatrix} 1 & 3 & 2 & -1 \\ -1 & 2 & -1 & -4 \\ 2 & 1 & 2 & 3 \end{pmatrix} \sim \begin{pmatrix} 1 & 3 & 2 & -1 \\ 0 & 5 & 1 & -5 \\ 0 & -5 & -2 & 5 \end{pmatrix} \sim \begin{pmatrix} 1 & 3 & 2 & -1 \\ 0 & 5 & 0 & -5 \\ 0 & 0 & -1 & 0 \end{pmatrix}$$

$$\sim \begin{pmatrix} 1 & 0 & 2 & 2 \\ 0 & 1 & 0 & -1 \\ 0 & 0 & 1 & 0 \end{pmatrix} \sim \begin{pmatrix} 1 & 0 & 0 & 2 \\ 0 & 1 & 0 & -1 \\ 0 & 0 & 1 & 0 \end{pmatrix}.$$

The procedure that was followed here may not be clear. Look at the first column of the second matrix; note that all entries but one are zero. The same is true of the second column of the fourth matrix, and also of the third column of the fifth matrix. We have reduced the matrix; i.e., we have obtained an equivalent matrix with

1's down the main diagonal and 0's off the main diagonal, with the exception of the entries in the final column.

In general, to reduce the matrix

$$\begin{pmatrix} a_{11} & a_{12} & \cdots & a_{1n} \\ a_{21} & a_{22} & \cdots & a_{2n} \\ & & \cdot & \\ & & \cdot & \\ & & \cdot & \\ a_{m1} & a_{m2} & \cdots & a_{mn} \end{pmatrix}$$

we operate on the first column so as to produce all 0's with at most one exception, namely the entry in the first row and first column. This is achieved as follows. If each entry of the first column is 0, there is nothing to do. Otherwise, we carry out a row interchange so that in the resulting system the entry in the first column and first row is not 0. Let us assume that $a_{11} \neq 0$; multiply the first row by $1/a_{11}$; in the resulting system the entry in the first row and first column is 1. Next, multiply the first row by $-a_{i1}$, where $i \neq 1$ and $a_{i1} \neq 0$, and add the first row to the ith row, then divide the first row by $-a_{i1}$. Do this for each i such that $i \neq 1$ and $a_{i1} \neq 0$. So we obtain a column of 0's except for the entry in the first row, which is called the *pivot* for this column. We have obtained a system equivalent to the given system whose first column consists of 0's with at most one exception, its pivot. Next, we transfer our attention to the second column. If the entry in the first row is its only nonzero entry, there is nothing to do. Otherwise, we interchange the second row with one of the following rows so that in the resulting system the entry in the second column and second row is not 0 (this is called the *pivot* for this column). A suitable row multiplication produces 1 in this position. Adding suitable multiples of the second row to the other rows, we obtain an equivalent system such that each entry of the second column is 0 except for its pivot. We continue in this fashion until we run out of rows or columns. Notice that our transformations do not affect the zero entries of the preceding columns. We point out that our procedure centers around the entries a_{ii} of the main diagonal. Of course, our procedure stops once we run out of rows; so we may not be able to treat each column of our matrix. In particular, if $m < n$ then we will not reach the final $n - m$ columns unless we meet columns of 0's along the way. It is convenient to obtain 1 or -1 in the pivotal position on the main diagonal before treating the column involved. Rather than divide the row by the entry in the pivotal position, it may be more convenient to obtain 1 there by adding multiples of the other rows to that row. We now illustrate this reduction procedure.

Example 6:   Reduce the matrix

$$\begin{pmatrix} 0 & 1 & 3 & 2 \\ 1 & 3 & -1 & 0 \\ 2 & 1 & 4 & 2 \\ 1 & -7 & 11 & 4 \end{pmatrix}.$$

Solution:

$$\begin{pmatrix} 0 & 1 & 3 & 2 \\ 1 & 3 & -1 & 0 \\ 2 & 1 & 4 & 2 \\ 1 & -7 & 11 & 4 \end{pmatrix} \sim \begin{pmatrix} 1 & 3 & -1 & 0 \\ 0 & 1 & 3 & 2 \\ 0 & -5 & 6 & 2 \\ 0 & -10 & 12 & 4 \end{pmatrix} \sim \begin{pmatrix} 1 & 0 & -10 & -6 \\ 0 & 1 & 3 & 2 \\ 0 & 0 & 21 & 12 \\ 0 & 0 & 0 & 0 \end{pmatrix}$$

$$\sim \begin{pmatrix} 1 & 0 & -10 & -6 \\ 0 & 1 & 3 & 2 \\ 0 & 0 & 1 & 4/7 \\ 0 & 0 & 0 & 0 \end{pmatrix} \sim \begin{pmatrix} 1 & 0 & 0 & -2/7 \\ 0 & 1 & 0 & 2/7 \\ 0 & 0 & 1 & 4/7 \\ 0 & 0 & 0 & 0 \end{pmatrix}.$$

Example 7: Reduce the matrix

$$\begin{pmatrix} 3 & 1 & -2 & 1 \\ 2 & 2 & -1 & 3 \\ 1 & 0 & 3 & 11 \\ 2 & 1 & 1 & 7 \end{pmatrix}.$$

Solution:

$$\begin{pmatrix} 3 & 1 & -2 & 1 \\ 2 & 2 & -1 & 3 \\ 1 & 0 & 3 & 11 \\ 2 & 1 & 1 & 7 \end{pmatrix} \sim \begin{pmatrix} 1 & 0 & 3 & 11 \\ 0 & 1 & -11 & -32 \\ 0 & 2 & -7 & -19 \\ 0 & 1 & -5 & -15 \end{pmatrix}$$

$$\sim \begin{pmatrix} 1 & 0 & 3 & 11 \\ 0 & 1 & -11 & -32 \\ 0 & 0 & 15 & 45 \\ 0 & 0 & 6 & 17 \end{pmatrix} \sim \begin{pmatrix} 1 & 0 & 0 & 2 \\ 0 & 1 & 0 & 1 \\ 0 & 0 & 1 & 3 \\ 0 & 0 & 0 & -1 \end{pmatrix}.$$

Question: What can you say about the solution set of the linear system represented by the matrix of Example 7?

Example 8: Solve the linear system:

$$\begin{cases} x_1 + x_2 & = -3 \\ 2x_1 - 2x_2 - x_3 = -8 \\ 4x_1 \quad\quad - x_3 = -14 \\ x_1 - 3x_2 - x_3 = -5 \end{cases}.$$

Solution: We reduce the matrix that represents the given system:

$$\begin{pmatrix} 1 & 1 & 0 & -3 \\ 2 & -2 & -1 & -8 \\ 4 & 0 & -1 & -14 \\ 1 & -3 & -1 & -5 \end{pmatrix} \sim \begin{pmatrix} 1 & 1 & 0 & -3 \\ 0 & -4 & -1 & -2 \\ 0 & -4 & -1 & -2 \\ 0 & -4 & -1 & -2 \end{pmatrix}$$

$$\sim \begin{pmatrix} 1 & 1 & 0 & -3 \\ 0 & 4 & 1 & 2 \\ 0 & 0 & 0 & 0 \\ 0 & 0 & 0 & 0 \end{pmatrix} \sim \begin{pmatrix} 4 & 0 & -1 & -14 \\ 0 & 4 & 1 & 2 \\ 0 & 0 & 0 & 0 \\ 0 & 0 & 0 & 0 \end{pmatrix}.$$

We conclude that the given system is equivalent to the linear system

$$\begin{cases} 4x_1 - x_3 = -14 \\ 4x_2 + x_3 = 2 \end{cases}.$$

This system has infinitely many solutions. Let us assign a value to the unknown x_3, say t. Then $x_1 = (t - 14)/4$ and $x_2 = (t - 2)/-4$. We conclude that the solution set of the given system is $\left\{ \left(\dfrac{t - 14}{4}, \dfrac{t - 2}{-4}, t \right) \mid t \in R \right\}$. Notice that this solution set is infinite.

It is convenient to extend our equivalence relation on linear systems to the matrices that represent linear systems. Thus, let A and B be any matrices; we shall say that A is *equivalent* to B, and write $A \sim B$, if and only if the systems represented by A and B are equivalent. We now list the fundamental matrix transformations that produce an equivalent matrix from a given matrix:

(*i*)   interchange two rows
(*ii*) multiply a row by a nonzero real number
(*iii*) add one row to another row.

The transformations (*ii*) and (*iii*) are familiar. Indeed, they are the operations of scalar multiplication and vector addition presented in Section 1.1. We find it useful to regard the rows of an $m \times n$ matrix as n-vectors; these n-vectors are said to be the *row vectors* of the matrix. Similarly, we regard the columns of an $m \times n$ matrix as m-vectors; these m-vectors are said to be the *column vectors* of the matrix.

We point out that a linear system may have

(*a*)   no solution,
(*b*)   one solution,
(*c*)   infinitely many solutions.

A linear system is said to be *inconsistent* if it has no solution. Example 8 exhibits a linear system which is *redundant* in the sense that some of its equations can be dropped without affecting its solution set.

EXERCISES

1. Determine the solution set of the linear system:

$$x_1 + 2x_2 = -1, \quad 2x_1 - x_2 = 3 .$$

2. Determine the solution set of the linear system:

$$x_1 - x_2 + x_3 = 0, \quad x_1 + x_2 - x_3 = 2, \quad x_1 + x_2 = 3 .$$

3. Determine the solution set of the linear system:

$$x_1 - x_2 - 2x_3 = 5, \quad x_1 + x_2 - x_3 = 4, \quad x_1 + x_3 = 0, \quad x_2 + x_3 = 1 .$$

4. Exhibit two members of the solution set of the linear system:

$$x_1 - x_2 + x_3 = 3, \quad 2x_1 + x_2 - 2x_3 = 2 .$$

5. Exhibit three members of the solution set of the linear system:

$$2x_1 - x_2 + x_3 = 0, \quad x_1 + x_2 - 3x_3 = 2 .$$

6. Show that the following linear systems are equivalent:

   (i) $x_1 + x_2 = 4, \quad 2x_1 - x_2 = -1, \quad 3x_1 - 2x_2 = -3$

   (ii) $2x_1 + x_2 = 5, \quad x_1 + 3x_2 = 10.$

7. Show that the following linear systems are equivalent:

   (i) $x_1 - x_2 + x_3 = 6, \quad 2x_1 + x_2 - x_3 = -3, \quad x_1 + 2x_2 + 2x_3 = 3$

   (ii) $3x_1 - x_2 - x_3 = 2, \quad x_1 + x_2 + x_3 = 2, \quad 2x_1 + x_2 = 0.$

8. Prove that each of the three basic transformations transforms a linear system into an equivalent linear system.

9. Prove that the binary relation $\sim$ is reflective, symmetric, and transitive. *Note:* A binary relation R is *reflexive* provided that $x \, R \, x$ for each x, R is *symmetric* provided that $y \, R \, x$ whenever $x \, R \, y$, and R is *transitive* provided that $x \, R \, z$ whenever $x \, R \, y$ and $y \, R \, z$.

10. Prove that the linear system obtained from a given linear system by subtracting one of its equations from another equation, is equivalent to the given system.

11. By applying the fundamental matrix transformations, prove that:

$$\begin{pmatrix} a_{11} & a_{12} & \ldots & a_{1n} \\ a_{21} & a_{22} & \ldots & a_{2n} \\ & & \cdot & \\ & & \cdot & \\ & & \cdot & \\ a_{m1} & a_{m2} & \ldots & a_{mn} \end{pmatrix} \sim \begin{pmatrix} a_{11} + ka_{21} & a_{12} + ka_{22} & \ldots & a_{1n} + ka_{2n} \\ a_{21} & a_{22} & & a_{2n} \\ & & \cdot & \\ & & \cdot & \\ & & \cdot & \\ a_{m1} & a_{m2} & & a_{mn} \end{pmatrix}$$

whenever k is a real number.

Reduce the following matrices.

12. $\begin{pmatrix} 1 & 1 & -2 & 5 \\ 1 & 1 & -1 & 4 \\ 1 & 0 & 1 & 0 \\ 0 & 1 & 1 & 1 \end{pmatrix}.$

13. $\begin{pmatrix} 1 & 2 & -1 \\ 2 & -1 & 3 \\ 2 & 2 & 1 \\ -1 & -3 & 2 \end{pmatrix}.$

14.
$$\begin{pmatrix} 3 & -2 & -4 & 2 \\ 1 & 3 & -1 & 1 \\ 2 & 1 & 3 & 7 \\ -1 & 1 & 3 & 1 \\ 2 & 3 & 0 & 4 \end{pmatrix}.$$

15. Solve the linear system:

$$\begin{cases} 2x_1 + x_2 - x_3 - 2x_4 = 11 \\ 3x_1 - x_2 + x_3 - x_4 = 8 \\ -x_1 + x_2 - x_3 \qquad = -1 \\ x_1 + x_2 + x_3 + x_4 = -2 \end{cases}.$$

1.3 THE MAPPING DETERMINANT

People who are experienced at handling matrices know that a certain method of associating a real number with *square* matrices occupies a central position in the theory of matrices. The real number associated with a square matrix is said to be the *determinant* of the matrix; we shall denote the mapping involved by the same term. Our purpose, here, is to define this mapping. There are several methods of achieving this goal; none are particularly simple. Here, we present an *inductive* definition; we begin by defining the determinant of any 1×1 matrix, and then we go on to define the determinant of any $n + 1 \times n + 1$ matrix in terms of the determinants of several $n \times n$ matrices, whenever $n \in N$. It is well-known that this is an acceptable method of presenting a definition. First, we mention that the real number that the mapping *determinant* associates with a square matrix A is denoted by $|A|$ or by replacing the parentheses around the entries of A by a pair of vertical lines. We now present our inductive definition of this mapping.

Definition 1.3.1: There are two parts to this definition:

(*i*) Let $A = (a)$ be any 1×1 matrix; then $|A| = a$ (in other words, our mapping associates the entry of a 1×1 matrix with the matrix).

(*ii*) Let $A = \begin{pmatrix} a_{11} & \cdots & a_{1,n+1} \\ & \cdot & \\ & \cdot & \\ & \cdot & \\ a_{n+1,1} & \cdots & a_{n+1,n+1} \end{pmatrix}$ be any $n + 1 \times n + 1$ matrix, where

$n \in N$; then $|A| = a_{11} M_{11} - a_{12} M_{12} + \cdots + (-1)^n a_{1,n+1} M_{1,n+1}$ where, for each j, M_{1j} is the determinant of the $n \times n$ matrix obtained from A by deleting its first row and jth column.

The first part of this definition is certainly simple; it is the second part that is complicated. Notice that the determinant of an $n + 1 \times n + 1$ matrix is expressed in terms of the determinants of certain $n \times n$ matrices constructed from the given matrix. Any matrix which is obtained from a given matrix by deleting certain rows or columns of the given matrix, is said to be a *submatrix* of that matrix. So, the determinant of an $n + 1 \times n + 1$ matrix is expressed in terms of the entries of its first row and the determinants of certain of its submatrices. We now present several examples.

Example 1: Compute $\begin{vmatrix} a & b \\ c & d \end{vmatrix}$.

Solution: We apply the second part of Definition 1.3.1: $\begin{vmatrix} a & b \\ c & d \end{vmatrix} = a|d| - b|c| = ad - bc$ by the first part of Definition 1.3.1. Notice that here $|d|$ denotes the number that *determinant* associates with the matrix (d) and not the absolute value of d.

Example 2: Compute $\begin{vmatrix} a_1 & a_2 & a_3 \\ b_1 & b_2 & b_3 \\ c_1 & c_2 & c_3 \end{vmatrix}$.

Solution: By the second part of Definition 1.3.1

$$\begin{vmatrix} a_1 & a_2 & a_3 \\ b_1 & b_2 & b_3 \\ c_1 & c_2 & c_3 \end{vmatrix} = a_1 \begin{vmatrix} b_2 & b_3 \\ c_2 & c_3 \end{vmatrix} - a_2 \begin{vmatrix} b_1 & b_3 \\ c_1 & c_3 \end{vmatrix} + a_3 \begin{vmatrix} b_1 & b_2 \\ c_1 & c_2 \end{vmatrix}$$

$$= a_1(b_2c_3 - b_3c_2) - a_2(b_1c_3 - b_3c_1) + a_3(b_1c_2 - b_2c_1)$$

by Example 1.

Example 3: Compute $\begin{vmatrix} 5 & 2 & -3 \\ 1 & 4 & 0 \\ 6 & 7 & -8 \end{vmatrix}$.

Solution: It is a waste of time to memorize the formula of Example 2; rather, we apply our basic definition. Thus, by the second part of Definition 1.3.1

$$\begin{vmatrix} 5 & 2 & -3 \\ 1 & 4 & 0 \\ 6 & 7 & -8 \end{vmatrix} = 5 \begin{vmatrix} 4 & 0 \\ 7 & -8 \end{vmatrix} - 2 \begin{vmatrix} 1 & 0 \\ 6 & -8 \end{vmatrix} - 3 \begin{vmatrix} 1 & 4 \\ 6 & 7 \end{vmatrix}$$

$$= 5(-32) - 2(-8) - 3(-17) \qquad \text{by Example 1}$$

$$= -160 + 16 + 51$$

$$= -93 \ .$$

Example 4: Express $\begin{vmatrix} 2 & 1 & 5 & -3 \\ 4 & 0 & -2 & 1 \\ 1 & 3 & 8 & 7 \\ 0 & -4 & -3 & 6 \end{vmatrix}$ as the sum of the determinants of four

3×3 matrices.

Solution: By the second part of Definition 1.3.1

$$\begin{vmatrix} 2 & 1 & 5 & -3 \\ 4 & 0 & -2 & 1 \\ 1 & 3 & 8 & 7 \\ 0 & -4 & -3 & 6 \end{vmatrix} = 2\begin{vmatrix} 0 & -2 & 1 \\ 3 & 8 & 7 \\ -4 & -3 & 6 \end{vmatrix} - \begin{vmatrix} 4 & -2 & 1 \\ 1 & 8 & 7 \\ 0 & -3 & 6 \end{vmatrix}$$

$$+ 5\begin{vmatrix} 4 & 0 & 1 \\ 1 & 3 & 7 \\ 0 & -4 & 6 \end{vmatrix} + 3\begin{vmatrix} 4 & 0 & -2 \\ 1 & 3 & 8 \\ 0 & -4 & -3 \end{vmatrix}.$$

Although it is easy to work out $|A|$ in case A is a 2×2 or a 3×3 matrix, it is clear that it is not practical to rely on our two-part definition when computing the determinant of an $n \times n$ matrix where $n > 3$. Instead, we shall present certain properties of our mapping that enable us to compute $|A|$ by a process similar to that of reducing a matrix. We do this in the next section.

We must improve our notation for a matrix. What we need is a method of denoting any $m \times n$ matrix without listing each term of the matrix; yet we want to retain the ability to refer to a particular entry of the matrix at will. These goals are achieved by the following convention. We shall denote the $m \times n$ matrix whose entry in the ith row and jth column is a_{ij} whenever $1 \le i \le m$ and $1 \le j \le n$, by writing (a_{ij}). Actually a_{ij} is a rule that leads us from (i, j) to the real number that occupies this position of the matrix; i.e., a_{ij} denotes a mapping of $\{1, \ldots, m\} \times \{1, \ldots, n\}$ into R. Of course, this method of denoting a matrix does not disclose the dimensions of the matrix; however, this will seldom bother us. The main idea is to develop an efficient notation so as to write as little as possible; thus, the ideas under discussion come through more sharply.

Throughout this book we find it convenient to extend the summation convention $\sum_{i=1}^{n} a_i$, where a_i is an expression, as follows. Let I be a finite set, called an *index* set, and let a_i be an expression whose only place-holder is i, and such that the operation of replacing i throughout a_i by a member of I produces a real number (we point out that i need not occur in a_i; in this case, substituting a member of I for i produces a_i itself). The idea is to sum all the numbers obtained from a_i by replacing i by a member of I. Since addition is associative and commutative, we can carry out the summation in any order. Let us agree to denote this operation by writing $\sum_{i \in I} a_i$; of course, virtually any symbol can be used for the place-holder i or for the index set. To illustrate, let $I = \{2, 5, 6\}$ and let $a_i = 3 - 2i + i^2$; then $\sum_{i \in I} a_i = 3 + 18 + 27 = 48$. We point out that the index set I need not be a set of numbers; for example, I can be a set of functions. Let F be the set whose members are the functions $\{(a, 5) \mid a \in R\}$, $\{(a, a) \mid a \in R\}$, $\{(a, 2a) \mid a \in R\}$, and $\{(a, a^2) \mid a \in R\}$. Then $\sum_{f \in F} f(4) = 5 + 4 + 8 + 16 = 33$. We mention that we can use this convention for multiplication, instead of addition; indeed for any commutative and associative binary operation. Of course, in the case of multiplication we shall use $\prod$ in place of $\sum$; so $\prod_{i \in I} a_i$ denotes the product of all the numbers obtained from the expression a_i by substituting a member of I for i.

It is useful to extend this idea a little further. Our object is to characterize the double sum $\sum\limits_{j=1}^{n} \sum\limits_{i=1}^{n} a_{ij}$. To this purpose we need the set $\{1, \ldots, n\} \times \{1, \ldots, n\}$, where $n \in N$. Let us agree to denote this set by C_n.

Definition 1.3.2: $C_n = \{1, \ldots, n\} \times \{1, \ldots, n\}$ whenever $n \in N$.

For example, $C_1 = \{(1, 1)\}$ and $C_2 = \{(1, 1), (1, 2), (2, 1), (2, 2)\}$.

Now, let a_{ij} be an expression involving two place-holders i and j, such that a_{ij} yields a real number whenever i and j are replaced by natural numbers. Clearly,

$$\sum_{=1}^{n} \sum_{i=1}^{n} a_{ij} = \sum_{j=1}^{n} (a_{1j} + \cdots + a_{nj})$$

$$= (a_{11} + \cdots + a_{n1}) + \cdots + (a_{1n} + \cdots + a_{nn})$$

$$= \sum_{(i,j) \in C_n} a_{ij}.$$

So, the double sum $\sum\limits_{j=1}^{n} \sum\limits_{i=1}^{n} a_{ij}$ is expressed by $\sum\limits_{(i,j) \in C_n} a_{ij}$, which we can regard as a single sum indexed by C_n.

To simplify our notation we sometimes abbreviate the indexing set involved in a sum of this sort. For example, if the indexing set is $\{(i, j) \mid i < j \text{ and } (i, j) \in C_n\}$, a subset of C_n, we merely write $\sum\limits_{i<j} a_{ij}$.

EXERCISES

Compute each of the following by applying Definition 1.3.1.

1. $\begin{vmatrix} 3 & -4 \\ 2 & 1 \end{vmatrix}$

2. $\begin{vmatrix} 5 & 0 \\ -1 & 2 \end{vmatrix}$

Compute each of the following by applying Definition 1.3.1 and the formula of Example 1.

3. $\begin{vmatrix} 2 & 3 & -1 \\ 4 & 2 & 0 \\ 5 & -1 & -2 \end{vmatrix}$

4. $\begin{vmatrix} -1 & -2 & 2 \\ 0 & 1 & 5 \\ -3 & 4 & -2 \end{vmatrix}$

5. $\begin{vmatrix} -3 & 0 & 2 \\ 0 & 1 & 1 \\ -2 & 2 & 2 \end{vmatrix}$

6. $\begin{vmatrix} 2 & -3 & -4 \\ 1 & 0 & 0 \\ -1 & 5 & 7 \end{vmatrix}$

7. $\begin{vmatrix} 2 & 0 & -1 & -1 \\ 0 & -1 & 3 & 3 \\ -1 & 0 & 4 & 4 \\ 0 & 1 & 1 & 1 \end{vmatrix}$

8. $\begin{vmatrix} -1 & 0 & 0 & -3 \\ 0 & 5 & 7 & 11 \\ 2 & 4 & 6 & -2 \\ 0 & -1 & 0 & 0 \end{vmatrix}$

9. $\begin{vmatrix} 1 & 0 & 0 & 2 & 3 \\ 0 & -1 & 0 & -1 & 1 \\ 2 & 0 & 0 & 1 & 0 \\ 0 & 1 & 0 & 1 & -1 \\ 0 & -2 & 1 & 0 & 0 \end{vmatrix}$ 10. $\begin{vmatrix} 1 & -1 & 0 & 0 & 2 \\ 3 & 0 & 0 & 1 & 0 \\ 0 & 1 & 2 & 0 & 0 \\ 0 & -2 & -3 & 0 & 5 \\ -1 & 0 & 0 & 4 & 0 \end{vmatrix}$

1.4   PROPERTIES OF DETERMINANT

In this section we establish several properties of our mapping *determinant* that help us to compute $|A|$ whenever A is a square matrix. Now, it is usually true that when a concept has been defined inductively, its properties can be established by mathematical induction. Remember that a proof by mathematical induction demonstrates that each natural number possesses a specified property. So, to apply mathematical induction we must formulate a property which is meaningful for natural numbers in the sense that for each natural number we can put the question "does this natural number have the property?" and expect an answer "yes" or "no". Returning to our mapping determinant, we can demonstrate that each square matrix possesses a specified property by considering the following property P of natural numbers. We say that a natural number n has property P if each $n \times n$ matrix possesses the specified property of matrices. Thus we can prove that each square matrix has the given property by demonstrating, using mathematical induction, that each natural number has property P; so we must establish that 1 has property P and that $k + 1$ has property P whenever k has property P.

Let us use this technique to establish some important properties of our mapping determinant.

Lemma 1.4.1:   Let $A = (a_{ij})$ be an $n \times n$ matrix such that $a_{ij} = \begin{cases} c_i \text{ if } i = j \\ 0 \text{ if } i \neq j \end{cases}$ then $|A| = c_1 c_2 \dots c_n$.

Proof: First we introduce some terminology; we say that a square matrix is a *diagonal* matrix if each entry off the main diagonal is zero. Thus, our lemma asserts that the determinant of a diagonal matrix is the product of its diagonal entries. We now introduce a corresponding property of natural numbers. We say that a natural number, say t, has property P if the determinant of each $t \times t$ diagonal matrix is the product of its diagonal entries. Clearly 1 has property P since $|a| = a$. Assume that k is a natural number with property P; we must prove that $k + 1$ also has property P. Consider any $k + 1 \times k + 1$ diagonal matrix and let $(d_1, d_2, \dots, d_{k+1})$ be its main diagonal. Clearly,

$$\begin{vmatrix} d_1 & & & \\ & d_2 & & 0 \\ & & \ddots & \\ 0 & & & d_{k+1} \end{vmatrix} = d_1 \begin{vmatrix} d_2 & & & \\ & d_3 & & 0 \\ & & \ddots & \\ 0 & & & d_{k+1} \end{vmatrix} \qquad \text{by Definition 1.3.1,}$$

$$= d_1(d_2 d_3 \cdots d_{k+1}) \qquad \text{since } k \text{ has property } P \ .$$

This establishes that $k + 1$ has property P whenever k has property P. We conclude, by mathematical induction, that each natural number has property P. So, the determinant of each diagonal matrix is the product of its diagonal entries.

Note: The diagonal matrix with main diagonal $(a_1, \ldots, a_n)$ is denoted by diag $(a_1, \ldots, a_n)$.

We have observed that the rows of an $m \times n$ matrix may be regarded as n-vectors and that its columns may be regarded as m-vectors. It is helpful to use vector language and vector ideas in connection with matrices. We use the following notation. Let A be any $m \times n$ matrix; we denote the ith row vector of A by A_i, $i = 1, \ldots, m$, and we denote the jth column vector of A by $_jA$, $j = 1, \ldots, n$.

For example, let $A = \begin{pmatrix} 2 & 0 & 5 & 4 \\ 3 & 1 & -2 & 7 \\ -1 & 4 & 3 & -6 \end{pmatrix}$; then $A_2 = (3, 1, -2, 7)$ and $_3A = (5, -2, 3)$.

Lemma 1.4.2: Let A be a square matrix such that $A_i = \mathbf{0}$ for some i; then $|A| = 0$.

Proof: First, we point out that $|A| = 0$ if $A_1 = \mathbf{0}$ since this means that each entry of the first row of A is 0, so $|A| = 0$ by Definition 1.3.1. Next, we consider a square matrix A such that $A_i = \mathbf{0}$ where $i \neq 1$. Applying mathematical induction and the first part of this proof, it is easy to demonstrate that $|A| = 0$. The details are left as an exercise.

Lemma 1.4.3: Let A be a square matrix such that $_iA = \mathbf{0}$ for some i; then $|A| = 0$.

Proof: Apply mathematical induction.

It is possible to generalize the result of Lemma 1.4.1 by introducing the notion of a *triangular* matrix. A square matrix is said to be *triangular* if each entry above the main diagonal is 0, or if each entry below the main diagonal is 0. For example, each of the following matrices is triangular:

$$\begin{pmatrix} 2 & 0 & 0 & 0 \\ -3 & 4 & 0 & 0 \\ 0 & 5 & 6 & 0 \\ 1 & 2 & -2 & 3 \end{pmatrix}, \begin{pmatrix} 1 & 5 & 2 & 4 \\ 0 & 3 & 4 & 8 \\ 0 & 0 & 3 & -7 \\ 0 & 0 & 0 & 9 \end{pmatrix}, \begin{pmatrix} 0 & 0 & 0 \\ 0 & 0 & 0 \\ 2 & 0 & 0 \end{pmatrix}, \begin{pmatrix} 0 & 0 \\ 0 & 0 \end{pmatrix}, \quad (7) \cdot$$

It is useful to classify triangular matrices as follows. We say that a square matrix is *upper* triangular if each entry above the main diagonal is 0; we shall say that a square matrix is *lower* triangular if each entry below the main diagonal is 0.

Theorem 1.4.1: $|A| = c_1 \cdots c_n$ if A is triangular with main diagonal $(c_1, \ldots, c_n)$.

Proof: It is a simple exercise in mathematical induction to prove that each upper triangular matrix has this property; this is left as an exercise. Next, we prove that each lower triangular matrix has this property. We apply mathematical induction, our basic technique. Clearly, 1 has the property since the diagonal entry of a 1×1 matrix (a) is a, and a is the determinant of this matrix. Assume that k is a natural number with the property; we must prove that $k + 1$ also has the property. So, we are assuming that each lower triangular $k \times k$ matrix possesses the property of the theorem. Consider any lower triangular $k + 1 \times k + 1$ matrix, say

$$A = \begin{pmatrix} a_{11} & a_{12} & \cdots & a_{1,k+1} \\ 0 & a_{22} & \cdots & a_{2,k+1} \\ 0 & 0 & \cdots & a_{3,k+1} \\ & & \cdot & \\ & & \cdot & \\ & & \cdot & \\ 0 & 0 & \cdots & a_{k+1,k+1} \end{pmatrix}.$$

Now, $|A| = a_{11} M_{11} - a_{12} M_{12} + \cdots + (-1)^{k+2} a_{1,k+1} M_{1,k+1}$ by Definition 1.3.1

$\quad\quad = a_{11} M_{11}$ since $M_{1j} = 0$ whenever $j \neq 1$, by Lemma 1.4.3

$\quad\quad = a_{11} a_{22} \ldots a_{k+1,k+1}$

since $M_{11} = a_{22} \ldots a_{k+1,k+1}$ by the induction assumption. We point out that the submatrix of A obtained by deleting A_1 and $_1A$ is $k \times k$ and is lower triangular; so, by the induction assumption, the determinant of this submatrix is the product of its diagonal entries. We have established that $k + 1$ has the property whenever k has the property. So, by mathematical induction, each natural number has the property. This proves that each lower triangular matrix has the property of the theorem.

Theorem 1.4.2: Let A be any square matrix, let k be any real number, and let B be the matrix obtained from A by multiplying each entry of one row vector of A by k (i.e., replacing A_i by kA_i for some i). Then $|B| = k|A|$.

Proof: Apply mathematical induction.

Later we need the following terminology which centers around the construction involved in Definition 1.3.1. Let $n > 1$ and let A be any $n \times n$ matrix. The determinant of the submatrix of A obtained by deleting A_i and $_jA$ is said to be the *minor* of the position (i, j) in A; this scalar is denoted by M_{ij}. We are much more interested in the scalar $(-1)^{i+j} M_{ij}$ which is said to be the *cofactor* of the position (i, j) in A; this scalar is denoted by A_{ij}. Notice our convention: if A is a square matrix then A_{ij} denotes the cofactor of the position (i, j) in A, whereas a_{ij} denotes the entry of A that occupies that position. Using cofactors the second part of Definition 1.3.1 can be expressed as follows.

Lemma 1.4.4: Let $A = (a_{ij})$ be any $n \times n$ matrix, $n > 1$; then $|A| = a_{11} A_{11} + \cdots + a_{1n} A_{1n}$.

It is important to notice that the cofactor $A_{1j} = B_{1j}, j = 1, \ldots, n$, if A and B are $n \times n$ matrices such that $A_i = B_i, i = 2, \ldots, n$. This observation is the key to the following lemma.

Lemma 1.4.5: Let B be the matrix obtained from an $n \times n$ matrix A by replacing A_1 by an n-vector β, and let C be the matrix obtained from A by replacing A_1 by $A_1 + \beta$. Then $|C| = |A| + |B|$.

Proof: Let $A_1 = (a_1, \ldots, a_n)$ and let $\beta = (b_1, \ldots, b_n)$. By construction $A_{1j} = B_{1j} = C_{1j}, j = 1, \ldots, n$. Thus

$$|C| = (a_1 + b_1)C_{11} + \cdots + (a_n + b_n)C_{1n} \qquad \text{by Lemma 1.4.4}$$

$$= (a_1 C_{11} + \cdots + a_n C_{1n}) + (b_1 C_{11} + \cdots + b_n C_{1n})$$

$$= |A| + |B| \qquad\qquad\qquad\qquad \text{by Lemma 1.4.4.}$$

We now extend this result.

Lemma 1.4.6: Let $i \in \{1, \ldots, n\}$, let B be the matrix obtained from an $n \times n$ matrix A by replacing A_i by an n-vector β, and let C be the matrix obtained from A by replacing A_i by $A_i + \beta$. Then $|C| = |A| + |B|$.

Proof: Apply mathematical induction.

Here is a very useful fact.

Theorem 1.4.3: Let A be any $n \times n$ matrix, $n > 1$, and let B be the matrix obtained from A by interchanging two row vectors of A. Then $|B| = -|A|$.

Comment: Our proof of this theorem is rather complicated and is postponed until Section 1.5.

The following corollary is useful.

Corollary 1.4.1: Let A be a square matrix such that $A_i = A_j$ where $i \neq j$. Then $|A| = 0$.

Proof: Let B be the matrix obtained from A by interchanging A_i and A_j; clearly B is A. Therefore, by Theorem 1.4.3, $|A| = -|A|$; so $|A| = 0$.
We now consider a special case of Lemma 1.4.6.

Lemma 1.4.7: Let C be the matrix obtained from a square matrix A by replacing A_i by $A_i + A_j$ where $i \neq j$. Then $|C| = |A|$.

Proof: Let B be the matrix obtained from A by replacing A_i by A_j. Then

$$|C| = |A| + |B| \qquad \text{by Lemma 1.4.6}$$

$$= |A| \qquad\qquad \text{by Corollary 1.4.1 (since } B_i = B_j) \ .$$

The following theorem is the basis of our technique for computing the determinant of a square matrix.

Theorem 1.4.4: Let C be the matrix obtained from a square matrix A by replacing A_i by $A_i + kA_j$ where k is a scalar and $i \neq j$. Then $|C| = .|A|$.

Proof: Let B be the matrix obtained from A by replacing A_i by kA_j, and let D be the matrix obtained from A by replacing A_i by A_j. Then

$$|C| = |A| + |B| \qquad \text{by Lemma 1.4.6}$$

$$= |A| + k|D| \qquad \text{by Theorem 1.4.2}$$

$$= |A| \qquad \text{by Corollary 1.4.1 (since } D_i = D_j) \ .$$

This completes our proof.

Next, consider Lemma 1.4.4 which asserts that $|A|$ can be expressed in terms of the entries of A_1 and the cofactors of the corresponding positions of A. We claim that any row vector of A can be used for this purpose.

Theorem 1.4.5: Let $n > 1$, let $A = (a_{ij})$ be any $n \times n$ matrix, and let $r \in \{1, \ldots, n\}$. Then $|A| = a_{r1} A_{r1} + \cdots + a_{rn} A_{rn}$.

Proof: Our plan is to interchange A_r with each of the $r - 1$ row vectors of A that precedes it. Call the resulting matrix B. By construction, $A_{rj} = (-1)^{r-1} B_{1j}$, $j = 1, \ldots, n$. Now

$$|A| = (-1)^{r-1}|B| \qquad \text{by Theorem 1.4.3}$$

$$= (-1)^{r-1}(a_{r1} B_{11} + \cdots + a_{rn} B_{1n}) \qquad \text{by Lemma 1.4.4}$$

$$= a_{r1} A_{r1} + \cdots + a_{rn} A_{rn} \ .$$

This completes our proof.

Let us illustrate the value of this result.

Example 1:

$$\begin{vmatrix} 2 & 1 & 3 & -4 \\ -3 & 4 & 1 & 2 \\ 5 & 0 & 0 & 0 \\ 2 & 3 & 0 & -1 \end{vmatrix} = 5\begin{vmatrix} 1 & 3 & -4 \\ 4 & 1 & 2 \\ 3 & 0 & -1 \end{vmatrix} \qquad \text{by Theorem 1.4.5 } (r = 3) \ .$$

Next, we mention that Theorem 1.4.3 and Theorem 1.4.4 enable us to transform a square matrix into a matrix in triangular form with the property that the determinants of these matrices are related by a factor of $(-1)^s$ where s is the number of applications of Theorem 1.4.3 involved in the reduction process. The calculations can be simplified by utilizing Theorem 1.4.2. Now, the determinant of a triangular matrix is the product of its diagonal entries; so the theorems of this section provide us with an effective method of computing the determinant of a given matrix. We now illustrate our technique.

Example 2: Compute $|A|$ where

$$A = \begin{pmatrix} 1 & 5 & 0 & 3 & -4 \\ 2 & 3 & 7 & -1 & 6 \\ -3 & -10 & 2 & 4 & 3 \\ 0 & -2 & 3 & 1 & 5 \\ 4 & 15 & 2 & 13 & -9 \end{pmatrix} \ .$$

Solution:

$$|A| = \begin{vmatrix} 1 & 5 & 0 & 3 & -4 \\ 0 & -7 & 7 & -7 & 14 \\ 0 & 5 & 2 & 13 & -9 \\ 0 & -2 & 3 & 1 & 5 \\ 0 & -5 & 2 & 1 & 7 \end{vmatrix}$$ by Theorem 1.4.4

$$= 7 \begin{vmatrix} 1 & 5 & 0 & 3 & -4 \\ 0 & -1 & 1 & -1 & 2 \\ 0 & 0 & 7 & 8 & 1 \\ 0 & 0 & 1 & 3 & 1 \\ 0 & 0 & 4 & 14 & -2 \end{vmatrix}$$ by Theorem 1.4.2 and Theorem 1.4.4

$$= -7 \begin{vmatrix} 1 & 5 & 0 & 3 & -4 \\ 0 & -1 & 1 & -1 & 2 \\ 0 & 0 & 1 & 3 & 1 \\ 0 & 0 & 0 & -13 & -6 \\ 0 & 0 & 0 & 2 & -6 \end{vmatrix}$$ by Theorem 1.4.3 and Theorem 1.4.4

$$= 14 \begin{vmatrix} 1 & 5 & 0 & 3 & -4 \\ 0 & -1 & 1 & -1 & 2 \\ 0 & 0 & 1 & 3 & 1 \\ 0 & 0 & 0 & 1 & -3 \\ 0 & 0 & 0 & -13 & -6 \end{vmatrix}$$ by Theorem 1.4.3 and Theorem 1.4.2

$$= 14 \begin{vmatrix} 1 & 5 & 0 & 3 & -4 \\ 0 & -1 & 1 & -1 & 2 \\ 0 & 0 & 1 & 3 & 1 \\ 0 & 0 & 0 & 1 & -3 \\ 0 & 0 & 0 & 0 & -45 \end{vmatrix}$$ by Theorem 1.4.4

$$= 14 \times 45$$ by Theorem 1.4.1

$$= 630.$$

The technique illustrated in Example 2 can be simplified by applying the following result.

Lemma 1.4.8: Let A be any $n \times n$ matrix such that $_1A = (a_{11}, 0, \ldots, 0)$; then $|A| = a_{11} A_{11}$.

Proof: Let $A = (a_{ij})$; then $|A| = a_{11} A_{11} + \cdots + a_{1n} A_{1n}$ by Lemma 1.4.4

$$= a_{11} A_{11}$$ by Lemma 1.4.3.

Notice that this result enables us to reduce the size of the arrays that appear in our reduction procedure. We now illustrate this idea.

Example 3: Compure $|A|$ where

$$A = \begin{pmatrix} 1 & 4 & 3 & -1 \\ 2 & 6 & -2 & 5 \\ -1 & 5 & 3 & 2 \\ 3 & 4 & 2 & -3 \end{pmatrix}.$$

Solution:

$$|A| = \begin{vmatrix} 1 & 4 & 3 & -1 \\ 0 & -2 & -8 & 7 \\ 0 & 9 & 6 & 1 \\ 0 & -8 & -7 & 0 \end{vmatrix} \quad \text{by Theorem 1.4.4}$$

$$= \begin{vmatrix} -2 & -8 & 7 \\ 1 & -26 & 29 \\ 0 & 25 & -28 \end{vmatrix} \quad \text{by Lemma 1.4.8 and Theorem 1.4.4}$$

$$= - \begin{vmatrix} 1 & -26 & 29 \\ 0 & -60 & 65 \\ 0 & 25 & -28 \end{vmatrix} \quad \text{by Theorem 1.4.3 and Theorem 1.4.4}$$

$$= - \begin{vmatrix} -60 & 65 \\ 25 & -28 \end{vmatrix} \quad \text{by Lemma 1.4.8}$$

$$= - \begin{vmatrix} -10 & 9 \\ 5 & -10 \end{vmatrix} \quad \text{by Theorem 1.4.4 (applied twice)}$$

$$= -55 .$$

EXERCISES

Compute the determinant of each of the following matrices.

1. $\begin{pmatrix} 1 & -2 & 4 & 2 \\ 0 & 3 & 5 & -1 \\ 1 & 1 & 3 & 3 \\ 2 & 3 & 2 & -2 \end{pmatrix}$

2. $\begin{pmatrix} -1 & 3 & -2 & 5 \\ 2 & 2 & 1 & 1 \\ -2 & 1 & 0 & 2 \\ 4 & -2 & 1 & 1 \end{pmatrix}$

3. $\begin{pmatrix} 1 & 2 & -1 & 2 & 1 \\ 2 & 4 & 3 & -1 & -1 \\ -1 & 0 & -1 & 0 & -1 \\ -2 & 3 & 1 & 3 & 1 \\ 0 & 2 & 0 & 2 & 0 \end{pmatrix}$

4. $\begin{pmatrix} -1 & 1 & 2 & -3 & -5 \\ 3 & 5 & 3 & 5 & 3 \\ 2 & 2 & 1 & 1 & -1 \\ 5 & 3 & 1 & 3 & 5 \\ 0 & -2 & -1 & -2 & -1 \end{pmatrix}$

5. $\begin{pmatrix} 2 & -1 & 1 & -1 & 1 \\ -4 & 0 & -1 & 3 & 3 \\ 4 & 1 & 2 & -2 & -2 \\ 8 & -5 & 5 & -6 & 4 \\ 10 & -6 & 4 & 0 & 3 \end{pmatrix}$

6. $\begin{pmatrix} 3 & 1 & -1 & 1 & -1 \\ 6 & 0 & 1 & -1 & 1 \\ 12 & 6 & -2 & 5 & -3 \\ -6 & -2 & 4 & -3 & 0 \\ 3 & 2 & 0 & 5 & -4 \end{pmatrix}$

7. Find a scalar a such that

$$\begin{vmatrix} -1 & 3 & 0 & 2 \\ 0 & 1 & 1 & -1 \\ 1 & -2 & 5 & 3 \\ 4 & -10 & 2 & a \end{vmatrix} = 88 .$$

8. Prove Lemma 1.4.2.

9. Prove Lemma 1.4.3.

10. Prove Theorem 1.4.2.

11. Prove Lemma 1.4.6.

12. Verify that Theorem 1.4.3 is true for each 2×2 matrix and for each 3×3 matrix.

1.5 SECOND-LEVEL MINORS

The purpose of this section is to establish the important result contained in Theorem 1.4.3; to this purpose we need the notion of a *second-level minor* of a matrix. Now, a minor of a matrix A is the determinant of a submatrix of A obtained by deleting a row and column of A. A *second-level minor* of A is the determinant of a submatrix of A obtained by deleting two rows and two columns of A. For example, let

$$B = \begin{pmatrix} 2 & 5 & -1 & 3 \\ 0 & 1 & 4 & 2 \\ 3 & -1 & 0 & 6 \\ 1 & 2 & -1 & 2 \end{pmatrix} .$$

Deleting B_2, B_3, $_1B$, and $_3B$ produces the submatrix $\begin{pmatrix} 5 & 3 \\ 2 & 2 \end{pmatrix}$ whose determinant is 4; think of this as the minor of the positions $(2 , 1)$ and $(3 , 3)$. Thus, 4 is the second-level minor of B with respect to the positions $(2 , 1)$ and $(3 , 3)$. Notice that this minor is also the minor of B with respect to the positions $(2 , 3)$ and $(3 , 1)$, since the submatrix involved is the same as before.

We mention that $|A|$, where A is any square matrix, can be expressed in terms of certain of the second-level minors of A; namely those obtained by deleting A_1, A_2, and two column vectors of A, i.e., the minors of the positions $(1 , i)$ and $(2 , j)$ where $i \neq j$. Let us illustrate this statement.

Example 1:

$$\begin{vmatrix} 1 & 0 & 2 & 4 \\ -1 & 1 & 0 & 5 \\ 0 & 2 & 3 & 1 \\ 1 & 1 & 0 & 0 \end{vmatrix} = \begin{vmatrix} 1 & 0 & 5 \\ 2 & 3 & 1 \\ 1 & 0 & 0 \end{vmatrix} + 2\begin{vmatrix} -1 & 1 & 5 \\ 0 & 2 & 1 \\ 1 & 1 & 0 \end{vmatrix} - 4\begin{vmatrix} -1 & 1 & 0 \\ 0 & 2 & 3 \\ 1 & 1 & 0 \end{vmatrix}$$

$$= \begin{vmatrix} 3 & 1 \\ 0 & 0 \end{vmatrix} + 5\begin{vmatrix} 2 & 3 \\ 1 & 0 \end{vmatrix} - 2\begin{vmatrix} 2 & 1 \\ 1 & 0 \end{vmatrix} - 2\begin{vmatrix} 0 & 1 \\ 1 & 0 \end{vmatrix} + 10\begin{vmatrix} 0 & 2 \\ 1 & 1 \end{vmatrix}$$

$$+ 4\begin{vmatrix} 2 & 3 \\ 1 & 0 \end{vmatrix} + 4\begin{vmatrix} 0 & 3 \\ 1 & 0 \end{vmatrix}$$

$$= -55 \; .$$

Obviously this is not an efficient way to compute the determinant of a matrix. The purpose of Example 1 is merely to illustrate the notion of a second-level minor and the fact that the determinant of a matrix can be represented in this fashion. This fact is crucial to our proof of Theorem 1.4.3.

Since the minors of positions in the first two rows of a matrix are especially important, let us agree that M_i^j denotes the minor of $(1, i)$ and $(2, j)$ whenever $i \neq j$. Thus, for the matrix of Example 1, $M_2^4 = \begin{vmatrix} 0 & 3 \\ 1 & 0 \end{vmatrix} = -3$ and $M_1^2 = \begin{vmatrix} 3 & 1 \\ 0 & 0 \end{vmatrix} = 0$. Of course $M_i^j = M_j^i$ for any matrix, since the submatrices involved are the same for both minors.

The following lemma shows explicitly how the determinant of a square matrix can be expressed in terms of the entries of its first two rows, and certain of its second-level minors.

Lemma 1.5.1: Let $A = (a_{ij})$ be any $n \times n$ matrix, $n > 1$; then

$$|A| = a_{11}(a_{22} M_1^2 - a_{23} M_1^3 + \cdots + (-1)^n a_{2n} M_1^n) + \cdots +$$

$$+ (-1)^{n+1} a_{1n}(a_{21} M_n^1 - a_{22} M_n^2 + \cdots + (-1)^n a_{2,n-1} M_n^{n-1})$$

Notice that each of the second-level minors M_i^j occurs twice in this expansion; indeed if $i < j$ then $(-1)^{i+j+1}a_{1i} a_{2j} + (-1)^{i+j}a_{1j} a_{2i}$ is the coefficient of M_i^j. This observation establishes our next lemma.

Lemma 1.5.2: Let $A = (a_{ij})$ be any $n \times n$ matrix, $n > 1$; then

$$|A| = \sum_{i<j} [(-1)^{i+j+1}a_{1i} a_{2j} + (-1)^{i+j}a_{1j} a_{2i}]M_i^j \; .$$

We are now ready to prove Theorem 1.4.3. First, we establish the special case in which the first two row vectors of the matrix involved are interchanged.

Lemma 1.5.3: Let A be any $n \times n$ matrix, $n > 1$, and let B be obtained from A by interchanging A_1 and A_2. Then $|B| = -|A|$.

Proof: The point is that M_i^j for A is the same as M_i^j for B. Now, let $A = (a_{ij})$ clearly

$$|B| = \sum_{i<j} [(-1)^{i+j+1}a_{2i}\,a_{1j} + (-1)^{i+j}a_{2j}\,a_{1i}]M_i^j \qquad \text{by Lemma 1.5.2}$$

$$= -|A| \ . \qquad \text{by Lemma 1.5.2}$$

This establishes our lemma.

Our result can be extended as follows.

Lemma 1.5.4: Let A be any $n \times n$ matrix, $n > 1$, and let B be obtained from A by interchanging two adjacent rows. Then $|B| = -|A|$.

Proof: Let B be obtained from A by interchanging A_j and A_{j+1}. The idea is to express $|A|$ and $|B|$ in terms of their $(j-1)$-level minors. Now, the coefficients of corresponding minors are identical; moreover, by Lemma 1.5.3, each $(j-1)$-level minor for $|B|$ is the negative of the corresponding minor for $|A|$. Thus $|B| = -|A|$. This establishes Lemma 1.5.4.

We can now demonstrate our main result, Theorem 1.4.3.

Theorem 1.4.3: Let A be any $n \times n$ matrix, $n > 1$, and let B be obtained from A by interchanging two row vectors of A. Then $|B| = -|A|$.

Proof: Let B be obtained from A by interchanging A_i and A_j where $i < j$. Interchange A_i with each of the row vectors between it and A_j; this requires $j - i - 1$ interchanges of the type handled by Lemma 1.5.4. Next, interchange A_j with each of the row vectors between it and A_{i-1}; this requires $j - i$ interchanges of the type handled by Lemma 1.5.4. Altogether, $j - i - 1 + j - i$ "adjacent" interchanges are required to interchange A_i and A_j. So, by Lemma 1.5.4,

$$|B| = (-1)^{2(j-i)-1}|A| = -|A| \ .$$

This completes our proof.

EXERCISES

1. Use the minors of the positions $(1, i)$ and $(2, j)$, where $i \neq j$, to evaluate:

(a) $\begin{vmatrix} 2 & 1 & 3 \\ 1 & 4 & 0 \\ -2 & 0 & 1 \end{vmatrix};$
(b) $\begin{vmatrix} 3 & 2 & 0 & 1 \\ 4 & 0 & 10 & 5 \\ -1 & 2 & 0 & 1 \\ 1 & 1 & 0 & -1 \end{vmatrix}.$

2. Verify Lemma 1.5.2 for the case that $n = 4$.

1.6 PRINCIPLE OF DUALITY; det

We now introduce the important notion of the *transpose* of a matrix. This is the matrix B obtained from a given matrix A by interchanging its rows and columns; i.e., the rows of B are the columns of A, and the columns of B are the rows of A. The transpose of A is denoted by A^t.

Definition 1.6.1: Let A be any $m \times n$ matrix; then A^t denotes the $n \times m$ matrix whose ith row vector is $_iA$, $i = 1, \ldots, n$.

$$\text{For example,} \quad \begin{pmatrix} 2 & -1 & 3 \\ 0 & -2 & 5 \end{pmatrix}^t = \begin{pmatrix} 2 & 0 \\ -1 & -2 \\ 3 & 5 \end{pmatrix}.$$

The following fact is extremely useful.

Theorem 1.6.1: $|A^t| = |A|$ whenever A is a square matrix.

Proof: We use mathematical induction. Clearly each 1×1 matrix has the property of the theorem. Assuming that each $(n - 1) \times (n - 1)$ matrix has this property, we must show that each $n \times n$ matrix also has the property. Let $A = (a_{ij})$ be any $n \times n$ matrix and let $B = A^t$; now, for each i,

$$|B| = a_{1i} B_{i1} + \cdots + a_{ni} B_{in} \qquad \text{by Theorem 1.4.5}$$

so
$$n|B| = \sum_{i=1}^{n} (a_{1i} B_{i1} + \cdots + a_{ni} B_{in}) = \sum_{(i,j) \in C_n} a_{ji} B_{ij} .$$

Notice that the submatrix of B involved in computing B_{ij} is the transpose of the submatrix of A involved in computing A_{ji}; so, by our induction assumption, these submatrices have the same determinant, and it follows that $B_{ij} = A_{ji}$ whenever $(i, j) \in C_n$. Thus

$$n|B| = \sum_{(i,j) \in C_n} a_{ji} B_{ij} = \sum_{(i,j) \in C_n} a_{ji} A_{ji} = n|A| \qquad \text{by Theorem 1.4.5 .}$$

Therefore, $|B| = |A|$, i.e., $|A^t| = |A|$. This completes our proof.

PRINCIPLE OF DUALITY: Let P be a proposition about the mapping determinant which expresses $|A|$ in terms of operations on the rows or columns of A, whenever A is a square matrix. Let $\mathfrak{D}(P)$ (read "the dual of P") be the proposition obtained from P by interchanging the words "row" and "column" throughout P. Then $\mathfrak{D}(P)$ is true if and only if P is true.

Proof: There are two parts to our proof.

1. Assume that P is true. We wish to show that $\mathfrak{D}(P)$ is true. Let A be any square matrix; we must show that $|A|$ is obtained by applying $\mathfrak{D}(P)$ to A. Let us apply P to A^t; thus, $|A^t|$ is obtained by carrying out certain operations on the rows and columns of A^t. By Theorem 1.6.1, $|A^t| = |A|$; so, $|A|$ is obtained by carrying out certain operations on the rows and columns of A^t. But the rows of A^t are the

columns of A, and the columns of A^t are the rows of A. Thus $|A|$ is obtained by applying $\mathfrak{D}(P)$ to A. We conclude that $\mathfrak{D}(P)$ is true.

2.   Assume that $\mathfrak{D}(P)$ is true. By the first part of this proof, $\mathfrak{D}(\mathfrak{D}(P))$ is true. But $\mathfrak{D}(\mathfrak{D}(P)) = P$. Thus, P is true.

To illustrate our Principle of Duality we consider the results of Section 1.4. Notice that Lemma 1.4.3 is the dual of Lemma 1.4.2.

Lemma 1.6.1:   Let A be any square matrix, let k be any real number, and let B be the matrix obtained from A by multiplying each entry of one column vector of A by k (i.e., replacing $_iA$ by $k \, _iA$ for some i). Then $|B| = k|A|$.

Proof: This is the dual of Theorem 1.4.2; by the Principle of Duality our lemma is true.

Lemma 1.6.2:   Let $A = (a_{ij})$ be any $n \times n$ matrix, $n > 1$; then $|A| = a_{11} A_{11} + \cdots + a_{n1} A_{n1}$.

Proof: This is the dual of Lemma 1.4.4; by the Principle of Duality our lemma is true.

Lemma 1.6.3:   Let $n > 1$ and let B be the matrix obtained from an $n \times n$ matrix A by interchanging two column vectors of A. Then $|B| = -|A|$.

Proof: This is the dual of Theorem 1.4.3; so it is true by the Principle of Duality.

Lemma 1.6.4:   Let A be a square matrix such that $_iA = {}_jA$ where $i \neq j$. Then $|A| = 0$.

Proof: This is the dual of Corollary 1.4.1; so it is true by the Principle of Duality.

Lemma 1.6.5:   Let C be the matrix obtained from a square matrix A by replacing $_iA$ by $_iA + k \, _jA$ where k is a scalar and $i \neq j$. Then $|C| = |A|$.

Proof: This is the dual of Theorem 1.4.4; so it is true by the Principle of Duality.

In view of the Principle of Duality and Theorem 1.4.5 we can use a column vector of a square matrix A to compute $|A|$.

Lemma 1.6.6:   Let $n > 1$, let $A = (a_{ij})$ be any $n \times n$ matrix, and let $r \in \{1, \ldots, n\}$. Then $|A| = a_{1r} A_{1r} + \cdots + a_{nr} A_{nr}$.

Proof: This is the dual of Theorem 1.4.5; so it is true by the Principle of Duality.

Later, we shall need the following result.

Theorem 1.6.2:   Let $A = (a_{ij})$ be any $n \times n$ matrix and let r and s be distinct members of $\{1, \ldots, n\}$. Then $a_{s1} A_{r1} + \cdots + a_{sn} A_{rn} = 0$.

Proof: Let B be the $n \times n$ matrix obtained from A by replacing A_r by A_s. By construction $B_{rj} = A_{rj}, j = 1, \ldots, n$. Now

$$|B| = a_{s1} B_{r1} + \cdots + a_{sn} B_{rn} \qquad \text{by Theorem 1.4.5}$$

$$= a_{s1} A_{r1} + \cdots + a_{sn} A_{rn} .$$

But $B_r = B_s$; so $|B| = 0$ by Corollary 1.4.1. We conclude that $a_{s1} A_{r1} + \cdots + a_{sn} A_{rn} = 0$.

We exhibit the dual of Theorem 1.6.2.

Corollary 1.6.1: Let $A = (a_{ij})$ be any $n \times n$ matrix and let r and s be distinct members of $\{1, \ldots, n\}$. Then $a_{1s} A_{1r} + \cdots + a_{ns} A_{nr} = 0$.

Proof: Principle of Duality.

Although our notation is quite suitable for computing the determinant of a specific square matrix, it is not adequate for theoretical investigations. Notice that our theorems about determinant involve a matrix which is constructed from a given matrix; the theorem announces the relationship between the determinants of these matrices. We require a notation which is capable of disclosing the matrices involved while expressing the relationship between their determinants. The advantage consists in the uninterrupted flow of simplification that results.

Actually, we propose to introduce a mapping which associates a scalar with each n-tuple of n-vectors, whenever $n \in N$; this mapping is called *det*.

Definition 1.6.2: Let $n \in N$ and let $(\alpha_1, \ldots, \alpha_n)$ be any n-tuple of n-vectors. Then *det* $(\alpha_1, \ldots, \alpha_n)$ denotes $|A|$ where A is the $n \times n$ matrix such that $A_i = \alpha_i, i = 1, \ldots, n$.

For example, $\det((2, 4), (0, 1)) = 2$ and $\det((1, 0, 0), (2, 3, 0), (1, -2, -4)) = -12$.

The difference between det and determinant is that the domain of det consists of all n-tuples of n-vectors, whereas the domain of determinant consists of all square matrices. So the distinction between these mappings reduces to the distinction between a square matrix A and the n-tuple $(A_1, \ldots, A_n)$ that characterizes A. Although this point is subtle, it is necessary to appreciate that the mappings det and determinant are not the same.

To illustrate our notation we now formulate some of our earlier results in this language.

Theorem 1.4.3: Let $\alpha_1, \ldots, \alpha_n$ be n-vectors; then

$$\det(\alpha_1, \ldots, \alpha_j, \ldots, \alpha_i, \ldots, \alpha_n) = -\det(\alpha_1, \ldots, \alpha_i, \ldots, \alpha_j, \ldots, \alpha_n) .$$

Theorem 1.4.4: Let $\alpha_1, \ldots, \alpha_n$ be n-vectors and let k be a scalar; then

$$\det(\alpha_1, \ldots, \alpha_i + k\alpha_j, \ldots, \alpha_j, \ldots, \alpha_n) = \det(\alpha_1, \ldots, \alpha_i, \ldots, \alpha_j, \ldots, \alpha_n) .$$

Corollary 1.4.1: Let $\alpha_1, \ldots, \alpha_n$ be n-vectors; then

$$\det(\alpha_1, \ldots, \alpha_i, \ldots, \alpha_i, \ldots, \alpha_n) = 0 .$$

Lemma 1.4.6: Let $\alpha_1, \ldots, \alpha_n, \beta$ be n-vectors; then

$$\det(\alpha_1, \ldots, \alpha_i + \beta, \ldots, \alpha_n) = \det(\alpha_1, \ldots, \alpha_i, \ldots, \alpha_n) + \det(\alpha_1, \ldots, \beta, \ldots, \alpha_n).$$

We illustrate the power of this approach in Section 10.5 where we show how to compute each coefficient of the characteristic polynomial of a matrix, and in Theorem 3.3.5 where we prove that $|AB| = |A||B|$. Here, we present an example that illustrates the idea of a "flow of equations."

Example 1: Let $\{\alpha, \beta\} \subset R_2$; then

$$\det(\alpha + 2\beta, \alpha - 2\beta) = \det(\alpha, \alpha) + \det(\alpha, -2\beta) + \det(2\beta, \alpha) + \det(2\beta, -2\beta)$$
$$\text{by Lemma 1.4.6}$$

$$= \det(\alpha, \alpha) - 2\det(\alpha, \beta) + 2\det(\beta, \alpha) - 4\det(\beta, \beta)$$
$$\text{by Theorem 1.4.2}$$

$$= -2\det(\alpha, \beta) + 2\det(\beta, \alpha)$$
$$\text{by Corollary 1.4.1}$$

$$= -4\det(\alpha, \beta).$$

Next, we establish a connection between *permutations* and our mapping determinant. By a *permutation* of $\{1, \ldots, n\}$, where $n \in N$, we mean any one-one mapping of $\{1, \ldots, n\}$ onto $\{1, \ldots, n\}$; for example, $\{(1, 3), (2, 2), (3, 1)\}$ is a permutation of $\{1, 2, 3\}$. We use the following notation in our next theorem. First, we denote the n-vectors $(1, 0, \ldots, 0), \ldots, (0, \ldots, 0, 1)$ by $\epsilon_1, \ldots, \epsilon_n$, respectively. Thus, ϵ_i is the n-vector whose ith term is 1, whereas its other terms are 0, $i = 1, \ldots, n$. Notice that the vector denoted by ϵ_i depends upon the choice of n involved in the discussion; for example, $\epsilon_3 = (0, 0, 1)$ if $n = 3$, whereas $\epsilon_3 = (0, 0, 1, 0)$ if $n = 4$. Let us agree to denote the set of all mappings of $\{1, \ldots, n\}$ into $\{1, \ldots, n\}$ by M_n, and to denote the set of all permutations of $\{1, \ldots, n\}$ by P_n.

We now present our theorem.

Theorem 1.6.3: Let $A = (a_{ij})$ be any $n \times n$ matrix; then

$$|A| = \sum_{\Pi \in P_n} a_{1,\Pi(1)} \times \cdots \times a_{n,\Pi(n)} \times \det(\epsilon_{\Pi(1)}, \ldots, \epsilon_{\Pi(n)}).$$

Proof: Notice that $A_i = a_{i1}\epsilon_1 + \cdots + a_{in}\epsilon_n$, $i = 1, \ldots, n$. Thus

$$|A| = \det(A_1, \ldots, A_n)$$

$$= \det(a_{11}\epsilon_1 + \cdots + a_{1n}\epsilon_n, \ldots, a_{n1}\epsilon_1 + \cdots + a_{nn}\epsilon_n)$$

$$= \sum_{\mu \in M_n} \det(a_{1,\mu(1)}\epsilon_{\mu(1)}, \ldots, a_{n,\mu(n)}\epsilon_{\mu(n)}) \qquad \text{by Lemma 1.4.6.}$$

This sum has n^n terms; we can reduce it to $n!$ terms by applying Corollary 1.4.1. Notice that $\det(a_{1,\mu(1)}\epsilon_{\mu(1)}, \ldots, a_{n,\mu(n)}\epsilon_{\mu(n)}) = 0$ if there are distinct natural numbers i and j such that $\mu(i) = \mu(j)$. In other words, a term drops out of our sum if the mapping involved is *not* a permutation of $\{1, \ldots, n\}$. So

$$|A| = \sum_{\Pi \in P_n} \det(a_{1,\Pi(1)} \, \epsilon_{\Pi(1)}, \ldots, a_{n,\Pi(n)} \, \epsilon_{\Pi(n)})$$

$$= \sum_{\Pi \in P_n} a_{1,\Pi(1)} \times \cdots \times a_{n,\Pi(n)} \times \det(\epsilon_{\Pi(1)}, \ldots, \epsilon_{\Pi(n)}) \ .$$

This completes our proof.

In connection with Theorem 1.6.3 we point out that there is a simple way of computing $\det(\epsilon_{\Pi(1)}, \ldots, \epsilon_{\Pi(n)})$ where $\Pi \in P_n$. In particular, we mention that this scalar is either 1 or -1. It is customary to denote $\det(\epsilon_{\Pi(1)}, \ldots, \epsilon_{\Pi(n)})$ by *sgn* Π, so *sgn* is a mapping of P_n into $\{-1, 1\}$.

Finally, we display the relationship between $|B|$ and the determinant of a matrix obtained from B by permuting its row vectors. We shall need this result in Chapter 3.

Lemma 1.6.7: Let B be any $n \times n$ matrix and let $\Pi \in P_n$; then $\det(B_{\Pi(1)}, \ldots, B_{\Pi(n)}) = $ sgn $\Pi \times |B|$.

Proof: Clearly, there is a natural number s such that the matrix with row vectors $B_{\Pi(1)}, \ldots, B_{\Pi(n)}$ is transformed into B by means of s row interchanges. Thus, by Theorem 1.4.3, $\det(B_{\Pi(1)}, \ldots, B_{\Pi(n)}) = (-1)^s |B|$. Notice that the matrix with row vectors $\epsilon_{\Pi(1)}, \ldots, \epsilon_{\Pi(n)}$ is transformed into $I_n = \mathrm{diag}(1, \ldots, 1)$, the matrix whose row vectors are $\epsilon_1, \ldots, \epsilon_n$, by means of s row interchanges. So $\det(\epsilon_{\Pi(1)}, \ldots, \epsilon_{\Pi(n)}) = (-1)^s$. Thus

$$\det(B_{\Pi(1)}, \ldots, B_{\Pi(n)}) = \det(\epsilon_{\Pi(1)}, \ldots, \epsilon_{\Pi(n)}) \times |B|$$

$$= \text{sgn } \Pi \times |B| \ .$$

This completes our proof.

EXERCISES

1. Prove that $(A^t)^t = A$ whenever A is a matrix.

2. State the dual of:

   (a) Lemma 1.4.2,
   (b) Lemma 1.4.3.

3. State the dual of:

   (a) Lemma 1.4.5,
   (b) Lemma 1.4.6,
   (c) Lemma 1.4.7,
   (d) Lemma 1.4.8.

4. Use Theorem 1.4.5 to compute:

(a) $\begin{vmatrix} 3 & 1 & -2 \\ 5 & 6 & -3 \\ 7 & 0 & 0 \end{vmatrix}$;

(b) $\begin{vmatrix} -2 & 2 & 4 \\ 5 & 0 & 0 \\ 3 & 1 & -1 \end{vmatrix}$;

(c) $\begin{vmatrix} 4 & 1 & 5 & -1 \\ 1 & 0 & 0 & 0 \\ 8 & 4 & 7 & 2 \\ -6 & 1 & 0 & 0 \end{vmatrix}$;

(d) $\begin{vmatrix} 3 & -7 & 6 & 4 \\ 5 & 2 & 7 & 1 \\ 8 & 3 & 0 & 0 \\ 1 & 0 & 0 & 0 \end{vmatrix}$.

5. Use Lemma 1.6.6 to compute:

(a) $\begin{vmatrix} 2 & 4 & 1 \\ 5 & 2 & 0 \\ -3 & 0 & 0 \end{vmatrix}$;

(b) $\begin{vmatrix} 7 & -1 & 2 \\ 4 & 0 & 3 \\ 2 & 0 & -2 \end{vmatrix}$;

(c) $\begin{vmatrix} 7 & 1 & -2 & 1 \\ -1 & 5 & 0 & 6 \\ 3 & 0 & 0 & 4 \\ 4 & 0 & 0 & -2 \end{vmatrix}$;

(d) $\begin{vmatrix} 4 & 2 & -3 & 7 \\ 3 & 0 & 0 & 0 \\ 1 & 0 & 2 & 1 \\ 2 & 0 & -1 & 6 \end{vmatrix}$.

6. Use Theorem 1.4.5 and Lemma 1.5.6 to compute:

(a) $\begin{vmatrix} 4 & 1 & 3 & 5 \\ 2 & -2 & 0 & 3 \\ -2 & 3 & 0 & -1 \\ 1 & 0 & 0 & 0 \end{vmatrix}$

(b) $\begin{vmatrix} 3 & 2 & 1 & 4 \\ 2 & 0 & 0 & 0 \\ -4 & 5 & -3 & 0 \\ 7 & -6 & 2 & 0 \end{vmatrix}$.

7. Compute each of the following:

(a) det((6,1,7 , 4) , (3 , 0 , 0 , 0) , (5 , 0 , 2 , −1) , (8 , 0 , −4 , 2)) .

(b) det((2 , −1 , 3 , 4 , 1) , (1 , 0 , 0 , 0 , 0) , (4 , 1 , 0 , 5 , 1) , (−3 , 2 , 0 , 1 , 2) , (7 , 1 , 0 , −1 , 3)) .

8. Let $\{\alpha , \beta\} \subset R_2$ and let $\{a , b\} \subset R$; prove that $\det(a\alpha , b\beta) = ab \det(\alpha , \beta)$.

9. Let $\{\alpha , \beta , \gamma\} \subset R_2$ and let $k \in R$; prove that $\det(k\alpha + \beta , \gamma) = k \det(\alpha , \gamma) + \det(\beta , \gamma)$.

10. A matrix A is said to be *symmetric* if $A = A^t$. Prove that B^t is symmetric whenever B is symmetric.

2

VECTORS AND
LINEAR SYSTEMS

2.1 SUBSPACES AND LINEAR COMBINATIONS

In this section we introduce some important concepts of linear algebra. In Section 1.1 we discussed the algebra of n-tuples; in particular, we exhibited the basic properties of vector addition and scalar multiplication. We now continue the development begun there. First, we present the notion of a *subspace* of $\mathcal{R}_n$; this algebraic concept has a bearing on geometry (see Chapters 4 and 5).

Definition 2.1.1: *A subset of R_n, say W, is said to be a* subspace *of $\mathcal{R}_n$ if and only if:*

   (i)   *W is nonempty.*
  (ii)   *$\alpha + \beta \in W$ whenever $\{\alpha, \beta\} \subset W$.*
 (iii)   *$k\alpha \in W$ whenever $\alpha \in W$ and $k \in R$.*

This means that W is a subspace of $\mathcal{R}_n$ if and only if W is a nonempty subset of R_n and is closed under vector addition and scalar multiplication.

Example 1: Show that $\{t(1, 0, 0) \mid t \in R\}$ is a subspace of $\mathcal{R}_3$.

Solution: Let $W = \{t(1, 0, 0) \mid t \in R\}$; clearly, W is a nonempty subset of R_3. Let $\{\alpha, \beta\} \subset W$; in view of the definition of W, there are scalars a and b such that $\alpha = a(1, 0, 0)$ and $\beta = b(1, 0, 0)$. Thus

$$\alpha + \beta = (a, 0, 0) + (b, 0, 0) = (a + b, 0, 0) = (a + b)(1, 0, 0)$$

so $\alpha + \beta \in W$. Let $k \in R$; then

$$k\alpha = k(a, 0, 0) = (ka, 0, 0) = (ka)(1, 0, 0)$$

so $k\alpha \in W$. Thus W is a subspace of $\mathcal{R}_3$.

Next, consider the problem of determining the smallest subspace of $\mathcal{R}_n$ that contains a given n-vector, say α. Let W be the required subspace. By (iii) each scalar multiple of α is a member of W, i.e., $\{t\alpha \mid t \in R\} \subset W$. But it is easy to verify that $\{t\alpha \mid t \in R\}$ is itself a subspace of $\mathcal{R}_n$. We conclude that $W = \{t\alpha \mid t \in R\}$.

Similarly, let us find the smallest subspace of $\mathcal{R}_n$ that contains distinct n-vectors α and β. Let W be the required subspace. By (iii), $\{s\alpha \mid s \in R\} \subset W$ and $\{t\beta \mid t \in R\} \subset W$. So, by (ii),

$$\{s\alpha + t\beta \mid s \text{ and } t \text{ are scalars}\} \subset W$$

But $\{s\alpha + t\beta \mid s \text{ and } t \text{ are scalars}\}$ is itself a subspace of $\mathcal{R}_n$. We conclude that this is the smallest subspace of $\mathcal{R}_n$ that contains α and β.

Finally, in this connection, let us determine the smallest subspace of $\mathcal{R}_n$, say W, that contains distinct vectors $\alpha_1, \ldots, \alpha_m$. In view of (ii) and (iii) it is clear that $t_1 \alpha_1 + \cdots + t_m \alpha_m \in W$ whenever $t_1, \ldots, t_m$ are scalars. Thus

$$\{t_1 \alpha_1 + \cdots + t_m \alpha_m \mid t_1, \ldots, t_m \text{ are scalars}\} \subset W .$$

Again, it is easy to verify that $\{t_1 \alpha_1 + \cdots + t_m \alpha_m \mid t_1, \ldots, t_m \text{ are scalars}\}$ is itself a subspace of $\mathcal{R}_n$. We conclude that this is the smallest subspace of $\mathcal{R}_n$ that contains the given vectors.

Notice that our construction for the smallest subspace that contains distinct vectors $\alpha_1, \ldots, \alpha_m$ involves the operation of multiplying each of the given vectors by a scalar and adding the resulting vectors; i.e., we form $t_1 \alpha_1 + \cdots + t_m \alpha_m$, a vector sum of scalar products. It is convenient to introduce a name for this operation; we say that the vector $t_1 \alpha_1 + \cdots + t_m \alpha_m$ is a *linear combination* of $\alpha_1, \ldots, \alpha_m$. Let us formalize this concept.

Definition 2.1.2: Let $\alpha_1, \ldots, \alpha_s$ be distinct n-vectors; γ is said to be a *linear combination* of $\alpha_1, \ldots, \alpha_s$ if and only if there are scalars $k_1, \ldots, k_s$, not necessarily distinct, such that $\gamma = k_1 \alpha_1 + \cdots + k_s \alpha_s$.

Example 2: $(2, 11, 18)$ is a linear combination of $(2, -1, 4)$, $(0, 5, 3)$, $(1, -1, 0)$. For the details see Example 8, Section 1.1.

It turns out that each subspace of $\mathcal{R}_n$ is the set of all linear combinations of certain vectors; these vectors are said to *span* the subspace. Clearly, we obtain a grip on a subspace W by finding vectors $\alpha_1, \ldots, \alpha_m$ that span W. Now, if one of the α's is a linear combination of the other α's, it can be verified that the remaining α's span W. In this sense the original list $\alpha_1, \ldots, \alpha_m$ is redundant; the technical term is *linearly dependent*. We now formalize this idea.

Definition 2.1.3: Distinct n-vectors $\alpha_1, \ldots, \alpha_s$ are said to be *linearly dependent* if and only if one of the α's is $\mathbf{0}$ or is a linear combination of the other α's. The empty list is *not* linearly dependent.

Our definition is somewhat more complicated than is suggested by the preceding discussion. The point is this: we want our concept to cover the case of a list with exactly one member. Thus, the list $\mathbf{0}$ is linearly dependent, whereas if $\alpha \neq \mathbf{0}$ then the list α is not linearly dependent.

Example 3: $(2, 11, 18)$, $(2, -1, 4)$, $(0, 5, 3)$, $(1, -1, 0)$ are linearly dependent.

Frequently we are interested in vectors which are *not* linearly dependent. To put things affirmatively we introduce the term *linearly independent*.

Definition 2.1.4: Distinct n-vectors $\alpha_1, \ldots, \alpha_s$ are said to be *linearly independent* if and only if $\alpha_1, \ldots, \alpha_s$ are not linearly dependent. The empty list is linearly independent.

Example 4: $(1, 0)$, $(0, 1)$ are linearly independent.

Example 5: $(2, -1, 4)$, $(0, 5, 3)$, $(1, -1, 0)$ are linearly independent.

Notice that the concepts of *linear combination, linearly dependent, linearly independent* are closely interrelated. These ideas must be mastered since we use them throughout this book. We now present a useful test for linear dependence.

TEST FOR LINEAR DEPENDENCE: Distinct n-vectors $\alpha_1, \ldots, \alpha_s$ are linearly dependent if and only if there are scalars $k_1, \ldots, k_s$, not all zero, such that $k_1 \alpha_1 + \cdots + k_s \alpha_s = \mathbf{0}$.

Proof: There are two parts to our proof.

1. Assume that $\alpha_1, \ldots, \alpha_s$ are linearly dependent. Then some α, say α_1, is $\mathbf{0}$ or is a linear combination of the other α's. If $\alpha_1 = \mathbf{0}$ then $1\alpha_1 + 0\alpha_2 + \cdots + 0\alpha_s = \mathbf{0}$; so scalars exist as required. If α_1 is a linear combination of the other α's, then there are scalars $k_2, \ldots, k_s$ such that $\alpha_1 = k_2 \alpha_2 + \ldots + k_s \alpha_s$; so $(-1)\alpha_1 + k_2 \alpha_2 + \ldots + k_s \alpha_s = \mathbf{0}$. We conclude that scalars exist as required.

2. Assume that there are scalars $k_1, \ldots, k_s$, not all zero, such that $k_1 \alpha_1 + \cdots + k_s \alpha_s = \mathbf{0}$. If $s = 1$, than $k_1 \alpha_1 = \mathbf{0}$ and $k_1 \neq 0$; so $\alpha_1 = \mathbf{0}$. But $\mathbf{0}$ is linearly dependent. Next, suppose that $s > 1$. Let $k_1 \neq 0$; now,

$$(-k_1)\alpha_1 = k_2 \alpha_2 + \cdots + k_s \alpha_s$$

so $$\alpha_1 = (k_2/-k_1)\alpha_2 + \cdots + (k_s/-k_1)\alpha_s \ .$$

Thus α_1 is a linear combination of $\alpha_2, \ldots, \alpha_s$; we conclude that $\alpha_1, \ldots, \alpha_s$ are linearly dependent. This completes our proof.

Since $\alpha_1, \ldots, \alpha_s$ are either linearly dependent or linearly independent, our test for linear dependence provides us with a test for linear independence in the following sense: distinct n-vectors $\alpha_1, \ldots, \alpha_s$ are linearly independent if and only if the test for linear dependence informs us that $\alpha_1, \ldots, \alpha_s$ are not linearly dependent. This can be put positively as follows.

TEST FOR LINEAR INDEPENDENCE: Distinct n-vectors $\alpha_1, \ldots, \alpha_s$ are linearly independent if and only if $k_1 \alpha_1 + \cdots + k_s \alpha_s \neq 0$ whenever the k's are not all zero.

We now illustrate these tests.

Example 6: Show that $(2, 5, -1, 1)$, $(1, 4, 0, 2)$, $(6, 15, -3, 3)$ are linearly dependent.

Solution: Notice that $-3(2, 5, -1, 1) + 0(1, 4, 0, 2) + 1(6, 15, -3, 3)$ $= 0$; therefore, by the Test for Linear Dependence, the given vectors are linearly dependent.

Example 7: Show that $(1, 0, 0, 0, 0)$, $(0, 1, 0, 0, 0)$, $(0, 0, 1, 0, 0)$ are linearly independent.

Solution: Let a, b, and c be scalars such that

$$a(1, 0, 0, 0, 0) + b(0, 1, 0, 0, 0) + c(0, 0, 1, 0, 0) = 0,$$

then $(a, b, c, 0, 0) = (0, 0, 0, 0, 0)$; so $a = b = c = 0$. Therefore, by the Test for Linear Independence, the given vectors are linearly independent.

A word of warning! The ideas contained in this section should not be regarded as a complete description of $\Re_n$. Indeed, here we have presented only a few basic ideas and have barely penetrated into the theory. Moreover, the important concepts of *linear combination* and *linear dependence* have been discussed at an intuitive level in order to being out the content and purpose of these ideas. In Chapter 7 we penetrate more deeply into the underlying theory; there we shall operate in the more general setting of vector spaces. To this purpose it is necessary to sharpen the basic ideas that have been presented here; this we do in Section 2.2.

EXERCISES

1. Show that $\{s(1, 0, 0) + t(0, 1, 0) \mid s, t \text{ are scalars}\}$ is a subspace of $\Re_3$.

2. Given that α and β are distinct n-vectors, show that $\{s\alpha + t\beta \mid s, t \text{ are scalars}\}$ is a subspace of $\Re_n$.

3. (a) Show that $\{(a, 0) \mid a \in R\}$ is a subspace of $\Re_2$.
   (b) Show that $\{(0, b) \mid b \in R\}$ is a subspace of $\Re_2$.
   (c) Given that $m \in R$, show that $\{(a, b) \mid (a, b) \in R_2 \text{ and } b = ma\}$ is a subspace of $\Re_2$.

4. (a) Show that $W = \{(a, b) \mid (a, b) \in R_2 \text{ and } b = 2a + 5\}$ is *not* a subspace of $\Re_2$.

(b)   Find a vector, say β, such that $\{\alpha + \beta \mid \alpha \in W\}$ is a subspace of $\mathfrak{R}_2$.

5. Show that $\{(a, b, c) \mid (a, b, c) \in R_3$ and $2a - b + c = 0\}$ is a subspace of $\mathfrak{R}_3$.

6. (a)   Show that $W = (a, b, c) \mid (a, b, c) \in R_3$ and $2a - b + c = 10\}$ is *not* a subspace of $\mathfrak{R}_3$.
    (b)   Find a vector, say β, such that $\{\alpha + \beta \mid \alpha \in W\}$ is a subspace of $\mathfrak{R}_3$.

7. Show that $\{(a, b, c, d) \mid (a, b, c, d) \in R_4$ and $3a - 2b + 2c - d = 0\}$ is a subspace of $\mathfrak{R}_4$.

8. (a)   Show that $W = \{(a, b, c, d) \mid (a, b, c, d) \in R_4$ and $3a - 2b + 2c - d = 10\}$ is *not* a subspace of $\mathfrak{R}_4$.
    (b)   Find a vector, say β, such that $\{\alpha + \beta \mid \alpha \in W\}$ is a subspace of $\mathfrak{R}_4$.

9. Let W_1 and W_2 be subspaces of $\mathfrak{R}_n$.
    (a)   Show that $W_1 \cap W_2$ is a subspace of $\mathfrak{R}_n$.
    (b)   Show that $\{\alpha_1 + \alpha_2 \mid \alpha_1 \in W_1$ and $\alpha_2 \in W_2\}$ is a subspace of $\mathfrak{R}_n$.

    Note: This subspace is called the *sum* of W_1 and W_2 and is denoted by $W_1 + W_2$.

10. Let W_1 and W_2 be subspaces of $\mathfrak{R}_n$ such that $W_1 + W_2 = R_n$ and $W_1 \cap W_2 = \{0\}$. Prove that corresponding to each n-vector γ there are unique members of W_1 and W_2, say α_1 and α_2, such that $\gamma = \alpha_1 + \alpha_2$.

11. Show that $(1, 0, 0), (0, 1, 0), (1, 1, 0)$ are linearly dependent.

12. Show that $(1, 2, -3), (2, 0, -1), (7, 6, -11)$ are linearly dependent.

13. Find k, given that $(k, 0, 0), (0, k, 0), (0, 0, k)$ are linearly dependent.

14. Show that $(3, 0, 1, -1), (2, -1, 0, 1), (1, 1, 1, -2)$ are linearly dependent.

15. Show that $(5, 6, 0)$ is a linear combination of $(-1, 2, 0), (3, 1, 2), (4, -1, 0), (0, 1, -1)$.

16. Show that $(0, 1, 3, -2)$ is a linear combination of $(1, 0, 2, -1), (2, -1, 1, 0), (3, -2, 0, -2)$.

17. Use the Test for Linear Independence to prove that $(1, 0, 0, 0), (0, 1, 0, 0), (0, 0, 1, 0), (0, 0, 0, 1)$ are linearly independent.

18. Let T be a mapping of R_n into R_n such that $T(k\alpha + \beta) = kT(\alpha) + T(\beta)$ whenever k is a scalar and $\{\alpha, \beta\} \subset R_n$.

    (a)   Prove that $T(0) = 0$.
    (b)   Prove that $T(\alpha + \beta) = T(\alpha) + T(\beta)$ whenever $\{\alpha, \beta\} \subset R_n$.
    (c)   Prove that $T(k\alpha) = kT(\alpha)$ whenever k is a scalar and α is a vector.
    (d)   Prove that $\{\gamma \mid T(\gamma) = 0\}$ is a subspace of $\mathfrak{R}_n$.

2.2 BASIS AND DIMENSION

So far we have limited our notions of *linear combination, linear dependence*, and *linear independence* to a list of finitely many vectors. Can these concepts be extended to infinitely many vectors? This question raises another question. Does the property of being linearly dependent belong to the vectors involved individually, or as a whole? Consider Definition 2.1.3; there we declare that distinct vectors $\alpha_1, \ldots, \alpha_s$ are linearly dependent if and only if one of these vectors is $\mathbf{0}$ or is a linear combination of the others. Notice that a set has not been exhibited directly; rather, we are presented with certain vectors, namely $\alpha_1, \ldots, \alpha_s$. We must admit there is a certain directness and ease of expression gained by referring directly to the vectors $\alpha_1, \ldots, \alpha_s$ involved, and suppressing the set $\{\alpha_1, \ldots, \alpha_s\}$. This is worthwhile when we first meet this important concept (moreover, we use this device in other areas where it is harmless and helpful). However, we will pay a terrible price if we persist in thinking in these terms. The fact of the matter is that we are dealing with a *set* of vectors; *linear dependence* is a property possessed by some sets, not by vectors. This fact is obscured when we get at the set involved by informally listing its members in the manner of Definition 2.1.3.

The main point of this discussion, which by now must be clear, is that it is a *set* of vectors which is linearly dependent or linearly independent, not the vectors themselves. This point of view is in line with a fundamental principle of exposition that we have already applied in this book, and shall continue to apply wherever possible. Namely, we organize our subject-matter so that we handle large chunks of material at a time, instead of treating each fundamental object individually. Our proposal to consider a set, rather than the individual members of a set, is in line with this principle. Putting this principle another way, we must recognize those objects that are basic to a discussion; here, we claim that a set of vectors is the fundamental object, not the vectors themselves. We have followed this principle in expressing a matrix in terms of its row vectors or column vectors, and in presenting the mapping det (we intend to exploit the former idea throughout Chapter 3).

To clarify our stand we now present revised definitions of the concepts introduced in Definitions 2.1.2, 2.1.3, and 2.1.4. At the same time we generalize these ideas so that they apply to infinite sets as well as finite sets. Notice that the term "linear combination" applies to a set, rather than to individual vectors.

Definition 2.2.1: Let $A \subset R_n$ and let $\gamma \in R_n$; then γ is said to be a *linear combination of A* if and only if there is a natural number s, a subset of A with s members, say $\{\alpha_1, \ldots, \alpha_s\}$, and corresponding scalars $k_1, \ldots, k_s$, not necessarily distinct, such that $\gamma = k_1 \alpha_1 + \cdots + k_s \alpha_s$.

Before clarifying the term *linearly dependent* it is convenient to introduce a symbol for the set of all linear combinations of a set of vectors.

Definition 2.2.2: Let $A \subset R_n$; then LA denotes the set of all linear combinations of A. We say that A *spans* LA, or that LA is *spanned* by A.

Here are our revised definitions of the terms *linearly dependent*, and *linearly independent*.

Definition 2.2.3: Let $A \subset R_n$; then A is said to be *linearly dependent* if and only if $0 \in A$ or there is a member of A, say γ, such that $\gamma \in L(A - \{\gamma\})$.

Definition 2.2.4: Let $A \subset R_n$; then A is said to be *linearly independent* if and only if A is not linearly dependent.

It is clear from these definitions that the empty set is linearly independent, that $\{0\}$ is linearly dependent, and that $\{\alpha\}$ is linearly independent whenever α is a nonzero vector.

The preceding definitions have been formulated so that they apply to infinite sets as well as finite sets. Frequently, however, we want to know whether a finite set is linearly dependent. For this reason, we now formulate the Test for Linear Dependence of Section 2.1 in the sharpened language of this section.

TEST FOR LINEAR DEPENDENCE: Let $A = \{\alpha_1, \ldots, \alpha_m\}$ be a subset of R_n with m members, where $m \in N$. Then A is linearly dependent if and only if there are scalars $k_1, \ldots, k_m$, not all zero, such that $k_1 \alpha_1 + \cdots + k_m \alpha_m = 0$.

Proof: This is left as an exercise (see the proof that appears in Section 2.1).

It is an interesting fact that a set of vectors is linearly dependent if and only if it possesses a finite, linearly dependent subset (this helps explain our conventions regarding the empty set and a set with one member). In particular, an infinite set is linearly dependent if and only if it possesses a finite, linearly dependent subset. For completeness, we now present this theorem.

TEST FOR LINEAR DEPENDENCE OF INFINITE SETS: An infinite subset of R_n, say A, is linearly dependent if and only if A possesses a finite, linearly dependent subset.

Proof: There are two parts to the proof.

1. Assume that A has a finite, linearly dependent subset, say B. Then $0 \in B$ or there is a member of B, say γ, such that $\gamma \in L(B - \{\gamma\})$. In the former case $0 \in A$; in the latter case $\gamma \in A$ and $\gamma \in L(A - \{\gamma\})$. Thus, A is linearly dependent.

2. Assume that A is linearly dependent. Then $0 \in A$ or there is a member of A, say γ, such that $\gamma \in L(A - \{\gamma\})$. In the former case $\{0\}$ is a finite, linearly dependent subset of A; in the latter case it follows from Definition 2.2.1 that there is a finite subset of $A - \{\gamma\}$, say C, such that $\gamma \in LC$. So $C \cup \{\gamma\}$ is a finite, linearly dependent subset of A. This completes our proof.

Now that we have sharpened our basic terminology we present two important ideas, the notion of a *basis* for a subspace, and the notion of the *dimension* of a subspace.

Definition 2.2.5: Let W be a subspace of $\mathfrak{R}_n$ and let $B \subset W$; then B is said to be a *basis* for W if and only if

(*i*) $W = LB$.
(*ii*) B is linearly independent.

Thus, each linearly independent subset of a subspace W that spans W, is a basis for W. For example, $\{(1, 0, 0), (0, 1, 0), (0, 0, 1)\}$ is a basis for R_3. Also, $\{(1, 0, 0, 0), (1, 1, 0, 0), (1, 0, 1, 0)\}$ is a basis for $\{(a, b, c, 0) \mid a, b, c$ are scalars$\}$, a subspace of $\mathfrak{R}_4$.

Notice that $\{0\}$ is the only subspace of $\mathfrak{R}_n$ which does not possess a basis; for this reason, we call $\{0\}$ the *trivial* subspace of $\mathfrak{R}_n$. We now present our definition of *dimension*.

Definition 2.2.6: The *dimension* of a nontrivial subspace W of $\mathfrak{R}_n$ is the largest natural number t such that W has a basis with t members; the dimension of $\{0\}$ is 0.

Here are some basic facts.

Lemma 2.2.1: Let A and B be subsets of R_n such that $A \subset B$; then $LA \subset LB$.

Proof: By Definition 2.2.1 if $\gamma \in LA$ then $\gamma \in LB$.

Lemma 2.2.2: Let $A \subset R_n$ and let $\gamma \in LA$; then $L(A \cup \{\gamma\}) = LA$.

Proof: By Lemma 2.2.1, $LA \subset L(A \cup \{\gamma\})$. We must prove that $L(A \cup \{\gamma\}) \subset LA$. Let $\beta \in L(A \cup \{\gamma\})$; then

$$\beta = k\gamma + \sum_{i=1}^{s} k_i \alpha_i$$

where $\{\alpha_1, \ldots, \alpha_s\} \subset A$ and $k, k_1, \ldots, k_s$ are scalars. But $\gamma \in LA$; so $\gamma = \sum_{i=1}^{m} c_i \beta_i$ where $\{\beta_1, \ldots, \beta_m\} \subset A$ and $c_1, \ldots, c_m$ are scalars. Thus $\beta = k \sum_{i=1}^{m} c_i \beta_i + \sum_{i=1}^{s} k_i \alpha_i = \sum_{i=1}^{m} (kc_i)\beta_i + \sum_{i=1}^{s} k_i \alpha_i$. We conclude that $\beta \in LA$; so $L(A \cup \{\gamma\}) \subset LA$. Thus $L(A \cup \{\gamma\}) = LA$.

Proofs of the next four lemmas are to be found in Section 7.2 where they are considered in a more general setting. Each of these lemmas is a consequence of the *Steinitz Replacement Theorem* which is stated and proved in Section 7.2. This interesting and important result is placed in Chapter 7 only as a matter of convenience, and could just as well be considered here. If time permits read Section 7.2 now, replacing **V** by $\mathfrak{R}_n$ and V by R_n.

Lemma 2.2.3: Let W be a subspace of $\mathfrak{R}_n$ that possesses a basis with t members; then dim $W = t$.

Comment: For a proof see Corrollary 7.2.1.

Lemma 2.2.4: Let W be a subspace of $\mathfrak{R}_n$ that possesses a basis with t members. Then each linearly independent subset of W with t members is a basis for W.

Comment: For a proof see Corrollary 7.2.2.

Lemma 2.2.5: Let $A \subset R_n$ and let B be a subset of LA with more members than A. Then B is linearly dependent.

Comment: For a proof see Corollary 7.2.3.

This lemma has an immediate corollary.

Corollary 2.2.1: Each linearly independent subset of R_n has at most n members.

Proof: Now, $\{\epsilon_1 , \ldots , \epsilon_n\}$ is a basis for R_n. By Lemma 2.2.5 each subset of R_n with more than n members is linearly dependent.

Lemma 2.2.6: Each nontrivial subspace of $\mathcal{R}_n$ possesses a basis.

Comment: For a proof see Theorem 7.2.2.

We shall need the following lemma in connection with Theorem 2.3.1.

Lemma 2.2.7: Let W_1 and W_2 be subspaces of $\mathcal{R}_n$ such that $W_1 \subset W_2$. Then $W_1 = W_2$ if and only if $\dim W_1 = \dim W_2$.

Proof: There are two parts to our proof.

1. Assume that $W_1 = W_2$. Then certainly $\dim W_1 = \dim W_2$.
2. Assume that $\dim W_1 = \dim W_2$. Let B be a basis for W_1; in particular $B \subset W_1$, so $B \subset W_2$. Thus, by Lemma 2.2.4, B is a basis for W_2. So $W_2 = LB = W_1$. This completes our proof.

We now present a simple algorithm that yields a basis for W, any nontrivial subspace of $\mathcal{R}_n$. Our procedure is based on the following lemma whose proof is left as an exercise.

Lemma 2.2.8: Let A be any linearly independent subset of a subspace W, and let $\beta \in W - LA$. Then $A \bigcup \{\beta\}$ is linearly independent.

Returning to our algorithm, choose any nonzero member of W, say α_1; of course $\{\alpha_1\}$ is linearly independent. If $W - L\{\alpha_1\} \neq \varnothing$ choose $\alpha_2 \in W - L\{\alpha_1\}$; by Lemma 2.2.8, $\{\alpha_1 , \alpha_2\}$ is linearly independent. If $W - L\{\alpha_1 , \alpha_2\} \neq \varnothing$ choose $\alpha_3 \in W - L\{\alpha_1 , \alpha_2\}$; by Lemma 2.2.8, $\{\alpha_1 , \alpha_2 , \alpha_3\}$ is linearly independent. Now, by Corollary 2.2.1, our procedure must come to an end within n steps; i.e., there is a natural number m, $m \leq n$, such that $\{\alpha_1 , \ldots , \alpha_m\}$ is linearly independent and $W = L\{\alpha_1 , \ldots , \alpha_m\}$. So $\{\alpha_1 , \ldots , \alpha_m\}$ is a basis for W.

Here are some examples.

Example 1: Find a basis for R_4.

Solution: Now $(1 , 0 , 0 , 0) \in R_4$. Clearly $(0 , 1 , 0 , 0) \notin L\{(1 , 0 , 0 , 0)\}$; so $\{(1 , 0 , 0 , 0), (0 , 1 , 0 , 0)\}$ is linearly independent. Also, $(0 , 0 , 1 , 0)$

$\notin L\{(1,0,0,0),(0,1,0,0)\}$; so $\{(1,0,0,0),(0,1,0,0),(0,0,1,0)\}$ is linearly independent. Finally, $(0,0,0,1) \notin L\{(1,0,0,0),(0,1,0,0),(0,0,1,0)\}$; so $\{(1,0,0,0),(0,1,0,0),(0,0,1,0),(0,0,0,1)\}$ is linearly independent. We conclude that $\{(1,0,0,0),(0,1,0,0),(0,0,1,0),(0,0,0,1)\}$ is a basis for R_4.

Example 2: Find a basis for $W = L\{(1,2,4,0,2),(2,-1,1,1,3),(-1,3,3,-1,-1),(4,3,9,1,7)\}$.

Solution: We point out that A is a basis for LA if and only if A is linearly independent. So, in view of Lemma 2.2.2, B is a basis for W if B is a linearly independent subset of $\{(1,2,4,0,2),(2,-1,1,1,3),(-1,3,3,-1,-1),(4,3,9,1,7)\}$ such that the remaining members of this set are linear combinations of B. We shall apply the procedure described above to construct B. Clearly, $(2,-1,1,1,3) \notin L\{(1,2,4,0,2)\}$; so $\{(1,2,4,0,2),(2,-1,1,1,3)\}$ is linearly independent. Now, $(-1,3,3,-1,-1) \in L\{(1,2,4,0,2),(2,-1,1,1,3)\}$ if and only if the linear system

$$\begin{cases} x + 2y = -1 \\ 2x - y = 3 \\ 4x + y = 3 \\ y = -1 \\ 2x + 3y = -1 \end{cases}$$

has a solution. But $(1,-1)$ is a solution of this linear system; so $(-1,3,3,-1,-1) \in L\{(1,2,4,0,2),(2,-1,1,1,3)\}$. In the same way it is easy to see that $(4,3,9,1,7) \in L\{(1,2,4,0,2),(2,-1,1,1,3)\}$. Considering Lemma 2.2.2, we conclude that $\{(1,2,4,0,2),(2,-1,1,1,3)\}$ is a basis for W.

EXERCISES

1. Prove that $LLA = LA$ whenever $A \subset R_n$.

2. Use Definition 2.2.3 to show that the empty set is linearly independent.

3. Use Definition 2.2.3 to show that $\{\alpha\}$ is linearly independent whenever $\alpha \neq \mathbf{0}$.

4. Establish the Test for Linear Dependence of this Section.

5. Show that $\{(1,0,0),(0,1,0),(0,0,1),(1,0,0)\}$ is linearly independent.

6. Show that $\{\alpha, \beta, \alpha\}$ is linearly dependent if and only if $\{\alpha, \beta\}$ is linearly dependent.

7. Let $W = \{(a,b) \mid (a,b) \in R_2 \text{ and } b = 3a\}$.

   (a) Find a basis for W.
   (b) Find the dimension of W.

8.   Let $W = \{(a, b, c) \mid (a, b, c) \in R_3 \text{ and } 2a + b + 3c = 0\}$.

(a)   Find a basis for W.
(b)   Determine the dimension of W.

9.   Let $W = \{(a, b, c) \mid (a, b, c) \in R_3 \text{ and } a + b = 0\}$.

(a)   Find a basis for W.
(b)   Determine the dimension of W.

10.   Let $W = \{(a, b, c, d) \mid (a, b, c, d) \in R_4 \text{ and } a + b + c + d = 0\}$.

(a)   Find a basis for W.
(b)   Determine the dimension of W.

11.   Prove that each subset of a linearly independent set is linearly independent.

12.   Prove that each superset of a linearly dependent set is linearly dependent.

13.   Let A be any linearly independent subset of a subspace W, and let $\beta \in W - LA$. Prove that $A \cup \{\beta\}$ is linearly independent.

14.   Let A be linearly independent, let $\beta \in LA$, and let $\alpha \neq \beta$ be a member of A such that $\alpha \in LC$ where $C = (A - \{\alpha\}) \cup \{\beta\}$.

(a)   Prove that $\beta \notin A$.
(b)   Prove that $0 \notin C$.

2.3 MORE ABOUT LINEAR SYSTEMS

In this section we establish a criterion for the existence of a solution of a linear system. First, we need some terminology. Consider the following linear system consisting of m equations in n unknowns $x_1, \ldots, x_n$:

(1)
$$\begin{cases} a_{11} x_1 + \cdots + a_{1n} x_n = b_1 \\ \quad \cdot \\ \quad \cdot \\ \quad \cdot \\ a_{m1} x_1 + \cdots + a_{mn} x_n = b_m \end{cases}$$

We associate two matrices with this linear system. First, the matrix that represents (1) in the sense of Section 1.2; we call this matrix the *augmented* matrix of (1). The second matrix that we need is the matrix of coefficients of the unknowns, namely the $m \times n$ matrix $A = (a_{ij})$; we call A the *coefficient* matrix of (1). Notice that the augmented matrix of (1) is the $m \times n + 1$ matrix whose ith column vector is $_iA$, $i = 1, \ldots, n$, and whose $n + 1$st column vector is $\beta = (b_1, \ldots, b_m)$.

We find it useful to associate a nonnegative integer with each matrix, called the *rank* of the matrix.

Definition 2.3.1:   Let A be any $m \times n$ matrix; then the dimension of the subspace $L\{_1A, \ldots, _nA\}$ is said to be the *rank* of A.

In other words, the rank of a matrix is the maximum number of linearly independent column vectors of the matrix. For example, rank $\begin{pmatrix} 1 & 0 & 0 & 0 \\ 0 & 0 & 0 & 0 \\ 0 & 1 & 0 & 0 \\ 0 & 0 & 0 & 0 \end{pmatrix} = 2$ since $\{(1, 0, 0, 0), (0, 0, 1, 0)\}$ is linearly independent, whereas $\{(1, 0, 0, 0), (0, 0, 1, 0), \mathbf{0}\}$ is linearly dependent.

In Theorem 2.3.1 we exhibit our main criterion for the *existence* of a solution of a linear system; notice that our criterion involves the ranks of the coefficient matrix and the augmented matrix of the linear system. The key to this result is the following lemma, which asserts that a linear system possesses a solution if and only if the last column vector of its augmented matrix is a linear combination of its other column vectors.

Lemma 2.3.1: A linear system, say (1), possesses a solution if and only if $\beta \in L\{_1A, \ldots, _nA\}$.

Proof: The main idea is that our linear system (1) can be reduced to a single *vector* equation. This is achieved by utilizing the column vectors of the augmented matrix to form the following vector equation:

$$(2) \qquad\qquad x_1\,_1A + \cdots + x_n\,_nA = \beta.$$

We point out that (2) involves the vector space $\mathfrak{R}_m$, i.e., the operations of vector addition and scalar multiplication that appear in (2) are operations associated with $\mathfrak{R}_m$; in particular $\{_1A, \ldots, _nA, \beta\} \subset R_m$. Notice that (2) expands to the m scalar equations that constitute (1); thus, the vector equation (2) is a short way of writing the linear system (1). Now, take a good close look at (2). The unknowns of this equation are the scalars $x_1, \ldots, x_n$; so, if (2) has a solution then $\beta \in L\{_1A, \ldots, _nA\}$, whereas if $\beta \in L\{_1A, \ldots, _nA\}$ then (2) has a solution. This establishes Lemma 2.3.1.

We now present our main result.

Theorem 2.3.1: A linear system has a solution if and only if its coefficient matrix and augmented matrix have the same rank.

Proof: Consider any linear system, say (1). There are two parts to our proof.

1. Assume that (1) has a solution. Then, by Lemma 2.3.1, $\beta \in L\{_1A, \ldots, _nA\}$; so, by Lemma 2.2.2, $L\{_1A, \ldots, _nA, \beta\} = L\{_1A, \ldots, _nA\}$. Thus, the coefficient matrix and the augmented matrix of (1) have the same rank.

2. Assume that $\dim L\{_1A, \ldots, _nA\} = \dim L\{_1A, \ldots, _nA, \beta\}$. Then, by Lemma 2.2.7, $L\{_1A, \ldots, _nA\} = L\{_1A, \ldots, _nA, \beta\}$; so $\beta \in L\{_1A, \ldots, _nA\}$. Therefore, by Lemma 2.3.1, the linear system (1) has a solution. This completes our proof.

We emphasize that the key to this section is the fact that a linear system is represented, indeed abbreviated, by a single vector equation. The fact is that (2) is (1); in particular (1) and (2) have the same solution set. So $(c_1, \ldots, c_n)$ is a solution of (1) if and only if β is the corresponding linear combination of $\{_1A, \ldots, _nA\}$, i.e., $\beta = c_1 {}_1A + \cdots + c_n {}_nA$. Once again, we have demonstrated the merit of our basic philosophy: namely, to think in terms of large chunks of mathematical material.

In order to use the criterion developed in this section (Theorem 2.3.1) we need a simple method of computing the rank of a matrix. In Section 2.5 we develop an appropriate technique.

EXERCISES

Determine the rank of each of the following matrices.

1. $\begin{pmatrix} 2 & 1 & 1 \\ 0 & 0 & 1 \\ 0 & 0 & 1 \end{pmatrix}$

2. $\begin{pmatrix} -1 & -2 & -3 \\ 2 & 4 & 6 \\ 1 & 2 & 3 \\ 3 & 6 & 9 \end{pmatrix}$

3. $\begin{pmatrix} 2 & 1 & 1 & 2 \\ 0 & 1 & 0 & 0 \\ 0 & 0 & 1 & 2 \end{pmatrix}$

4. $\begin{pmatrix} 5 & 3 & 0 & 1 \\ 1 & 0 & 0 & 0 \\ 0 & 0 & 0 & 0 \end{pmatrix}$

5. $\begin{pmatrix} 3 & 0 & 1 & -2 & 4 & 5 \\ 0 & 1 & 2 & 1 & 1 & -3 \\ 0 & 0 & 0 & 0 & 0 & 0 \\ 0 & 0 & 0 & 0 & 0 & 0 \\ 0 & 0 & 0 & 0 & 0 & 0 \end{pmatrix}$

6. Consider an $m \times n$ matrix whose final t rows consist of 0's only. Prove that the rank of this matrix does not exceed $m - t$.

7. Does the following linear system have a solution?

$$\begin{cases} -x_1 - 2x_2 - 3x_3 = 1 \\ 2x_1 + 4x_2 + 6x_3 = 2 \\ x_1 + 2x_2 + 3x_3 = 0 \end{cases}$$

8. Show that the linear system (1) of the text has at least one solution if $b_i = 0$, $i = 1, \ldots, m$.

9. Show that $(4, -1, 2) \in L\{(1, 2, -1), (2, 1, 0)\}$. Set up the problem as a linear system.

10. Let $\{\alpha_1, \ldots, \alpha_n, \beta\} \subset R_m$. Prove that $\beta \in L\{\alpha_1, \ldots, \alpha_n\}$ if and only if the $m \times n$ matrix whose ith column vector is α_i, $i = 1, \ldots, n$, has the same rank as the $m \times n + 1$ matrix whose ith column vector is α_i, $i = 1, \ldots, n$, and whose $n + 1$st column vector is β.

2.4   CHARACTERIZING THE SOLUTION SET OF A LINEAR SYSTEM

Here we develop a method of characterizing the vector solutions of a linear system; we also present a criterion for the existence of a *unique* solution of a linear system. Now, with each linear system, say (1) of Section 2.3, we associate the following *homogeneous* linear system:

$$(3) \qquad \begin{cases} a_{11}\,x_1 + \cdots + a_{1n}\,x_n = 0 \\ \qquad\qquad \vdots \\ a_{m1}\,x_1 + \cdots + a_{mn}\,x_n = 0 \end{cases}$$

This linear system consists of m equations in n unknowns $x_1, \ldots, x_n$. The coefficient matrix of (3) is the $m \times n$ matrix $A = (a_{ij})$. Notice that (3) reduces to the single *vector* equation

$$(4) \qquad\qquad x_1\,_1A + \cdots + x_n\,_nA = \mathbf{0}\ .$$

As we observed in Section 2.3, this vector equation expands to the m scalar equations that constitute (3). Accordingly, (3) and (4) have the same solution set. This establishes the following lemma.

Lemma 2.4.1: $(c_1, \ldots, c_n)$ is a solution of (3) if and only if $c_1\,_1A + \cdots + c_n\,_nA = \mathbf{0}$.

Using Lemma 2.4.1 it is easy to prove the following theorem.

Theorem 2.4.1:   The set of all solutions of (3) is a subspace of $\Re_n$.

Proof: Consider Definition 2.1.1.

Next, we characterize the dimension of the set of all solutions of (3) in terms of the rank of its coefficient matrix. In the process, we exhibit a basis for this subspace. Here is our result.

Theorem 2.4.2:   The dimension of the set of all solutions of (3) is $n - r$, where r is the rank of the coefficient matrix of (3).

Proof: Let W be the subspace of all solutions of (3). By assumption, rank $A = r$, where A is the coefficient matrix of (3); we may assume that $\{_1A, \ldots, _rA\}$ has r members and is linearly independent (otherwise we renumber the unknowns of (3)). So $_iA \in L\{_1A, \ldots, _rA\}$, $i = r + 1, \ldots, n$. In particular, let $_iA = k_1\,_1A + \cdots + k_r\,_rA$ where $i > r$; then

$$k_1\,_1A + \cdots + k_r\,_rA - \,_iA = \mathbf{0}\,.$$

So, by Lemma 2.4.1,

$$(k_1, \ldots, k_r, 0, \ldots, 0, \underbrace{-1}_{i\text{th term}}, 0, \ldots, 0) \in W\ .$$

In this manner we obtain $n - r$ vector solutions of (3), one from each of $_{r+1}A$, ... , $_nA$, which we denote by γ_1 , ... , γ_{n-r} respectively. So

$$\gamma_{i-r} = (k_1 , \ldots , k_r , 0 , \ldots , 0 , \underbrace{-1}_{i\text{th term}} , 0 , \ldots , 0), \qquad i = r + 1 , \ldots , n;$$

the first r terms of γ_{i-r} are the scalars k_1 , ... , k_r such that $_iA = k_1 {}_1A + \cdots + k_r {}_rA$. We claim that $\{\gamma_1 , \ldots , \gamma_{n-r}\}$ is a basis for W. Clearly $\{\gamma_1 , \ldots , \gamma_{n-r}\}$ is linearly independent; we must prove that $L\{\gamma_1 , \ldots , \gamma_{n-r}\} = W$. Let $(c_1 , \ldots , c_n) \in W$; we shall show that $(c_1 , \ldots , c_n) = (-c_{r+1})\gamma_1 + \cdots + (-c_n)\gamma_{n-r}$, i.e.,

$$(c_1 , \ldots , c_n) + c_{r+1} \gamma_1 + \cdots + c_n \gamma_{n-r} = \mathbf{0} .$$

Let δ be the vector on the left-hand side of this equation; notice that each of the last $n - r$ terms of δ is 0, i.e., there are scalars t_1 , ... , t_r such that $\delta = (t_1 , \ldots , t_r , 0 , \ldots , 0)$. Now, W is a subspace of $\mathcal{R}_n$; so $\delta \in W$. Thus, by Lemma 2.4.1, $t_1 {}_1A + \cdots + t_r {}_rA = \mathbf{0}$. Recalling that $\{_1A , \ldots , _rA\}$ is linearly independent we see that $t_i = 0$, $i = 1 , \ldots , r$; i.e., $\delta = \mathbf{0}$. This proves that $(c_1 , \ldots , c_n) \in L\{\gamma_1 , \ldots , \gamma_{n-r}\}$; we conclude that $\{\gamma_1 , \ldots , \gamma_{n-r}\}$ is a basis for W. Thus dim $W = n - r$. Notice that we have implicitly assumed that $0 < r < n$. It remains to treat the cases in which $r = 0$ or $r = n$. Now, if $r = 0$ then $A = (0)$ and it follows that R_n is the solution set of (3); of course, dim $R_n = n$. Finally, assume that $r = n$; then $\{_1A , \ldots , _nA\}$ is a basis for R_n. Now, if the solution set of (3) has a nonzero member then there exist scalars c_1 , ... , c_n, not all 0, such that $c_1 {}_1A + \cdots + c_n {}_nA = \mathbf{0}$; of course, this means that $\{_1A , \ldots , _nA\}$ is linearly dependent. This contradiction proves that $W = \{\mathbf{0}\}$, so dim $W = 0$. This completes our proof of Theorem 2.4.2.

The proof of Theorem 2.4.2 is quite complicated; the following example illustrates the ideas involved in that proof.

Example 1: Find a basis for the subspace of vector solutions of the following homogeneous linear system:

(5)
$$\begin{cases} x_1 + 2x_2 - x_3 + 4x_4 = 0 \\ 2x_1 - x_2 + 3x_3 + 3x_4 = 0 \\ 4x_1 + x_2 + 3x_3 + 9x_4 = 0 \\ \quad\quad x_2 - x_3 + x_4 = 0 \\ 2x_1 + 3x_2 - x_3 + 7x_4 = 0 \end{cases}$$

Solution: The coefficient matrix of this linear system is

$$A = \begin{pmatrix} 1 & 2 & -1 & 4 \\ 2 & -1 & 3 & 3 \\ 4 & 1 & 3 & 9 \\ 0 & 1 & -1 & 1 \\ 2 & 3 & -1 & 7 \end{pmatrix} .$$

The column vectors of this matrix are $_1A = (1 , 2 , 4 , 0 , 2)$, $_2A = (2 , -1 , 1 , 1 , 3)$, $_3A = (-1 , 3 , 3 , -1 , -1)$, and $_4A = (4 , 3 , 9 , 1 , 7)$. The rank of the coefficient matrix is 2, since $\{_1A , _2A\}$ is linearly independent whereas

$_3A = {_1A} - {_2A}$ and $_4A = 2\,{_1A} + {_2A}$ (see Example 2, Section 2.2). Therefore, $\gamma_1 = (1, -1, -1, 0)$ and $\gamma_2 = (2, 1, 0, -1)$ are vector solutions of (5). Clearly, $\{\gamma_1, \gamma_2\}$ is linearly independent; indeed this set is a basis for W, the solution set of (5). To see this, let (c_1, c_2, c_3, c_4) be any vector solution of (5); consider the vector

$$(c_1, c_2, c_3, c_4) + c_3\,\gamma_1 + c_4\,\gamma_2 = (c_1 + c_3 + 2c_4, c_2 - c_3 + c_4, 0, 0) .$$

This vector is a vector solution of (5); so, by Lemma 2.4.1,

$$(c_1 + c_3 + 2c_4)\,{_1A} + (c_2 - c_3 + c_4)\,{_2A} = \mathbf{0} .$$

But $\{{_1A}, {_2A}\}$ is linearly independent; so $c_1 + c_3 + 2c_4 = 0$ and $c_2 - c_3 + c_4 = 0$. Hence,

$$(c_1, c_2, c_3, c_4) + c_3\,\gamma_1 + c_4\,\gamma_2 = \mathbf{0}$$

thus $(c_1, c_2, c_3, c_4) \in L\{\gamma_1, \gamma_2\}$. This proves that $\{(1, -1, -1, 0), (2, 1, 0, -1)\}$ is a basis for W. Notice that dim $W = 2$.

We now present some immediate consequences of our main result. We shall say that $\mathbf{0}$ is the *trivial* solution of any homogeneous linear system.

Corollary 2.4.1: A homogeneous linear system in n unknowns has a nontrivial solution if and only if the rank of its coefficient matrix is less than n.

Proof: Apply Theorem 2.4.2.

Corollary 2.4.2: A homogeneous linear system consisting of m equations in n unknowns, where $m < n$, possesses a nontrivial solution.

Proof: Consider a homogeneous linear system that consists of m equations in n unknowns, $m < n$. Now, the column vectors of its coefficient matrix are members of R_m; therefore, the dimension of the subspace spanned by these column vectors cannot exceed m. So, by Corollary 2.4.1, this homogeneous linear system possesses a nontrivial solution.

Now that we know how to characterize the vector solutions of any homogeneous linear system, let us turn to the more general problem of characterizing the vector solutions of a linear system. The idea is to solve the related homogeneous linear system and to find one vector solution of the given linear system. The following theorem displays the connection between the solution set of a linear system and the solution set of its related homogeneous linear system.

Theorem 2.4.3: Let τ be a vector solution of a linear system and let W be the subspace of vector solutions of the related homogeneous linear system. Then $\{\gamma + \tau \mid \gamma \in W\}$ is the solution set of the given linear system.

Proof: Consider the linear system (1) of Section 2.3. Let $\tau = (t_1, \ldots, t_n)$ be a vector solution of (1); so $t_1\,{_1A} + \cdots + t_n\,{_nA} = \beta$. Let $\gamma = (c_1, \ldots, c_n)$ be any vector solution of (3), the related homogeneous linear system; so $c_1 \, _1A + \cdots + c_n \, _nA = 0$. Clearly $\gamma + \tau$ is a vector solution of (1) since

$$(c_1 + t_1)_1A + \cdots + (c_n + t_n)_nA = (c_1 \, _1A + \cdots + c_n \, _nA) + (t_1 \, _1A + \cdots + t_n \, _nA)$$

$$= 0 + \beta = \beta \ .$$

Moreover each vector solution of (1) can be expressed as the sum of τ and a particular vector solution of (3). To see this, let α be any vector solution of (1); clearly $\alpha = \tau + (\alpha - \tau)$, It is easy to verify that $\alpha - \tau$ is a vector solution of (3). This completes our proof.

We have now proved that we can characterize the solution set of a linear system as follows.

    (a)   Obtain one vector solution of the given linear system.

    (b)   Obtain a basis for the solution set of the related homogeneous linear system.

There is a simple technique that yields the required information. Merely row-reduce the augmented matrix of the linear system. Of course, this yields a vector solution of the linear system. Moreover, by ignoring its final column we can read off a basis for the solution set of the related homogeneous linear system. Clearly, row-reducing the coefficient matrix yields a simpler homogeneous linear system possessing the same solution set as the related homogeneous linear system; so a basis for the solution set of the simpler homogeneous system is also a basis for the solution set of the given homogeneous system. The following example illustrates this technique.

Example 2:   Characterize the solution set of:

(6)
$$\begin{cases} x_1 + 2x_2 - x_3 + 4x_4 = 5 \\ 2x_1 - x_2 + 3x_3 + 3x_4 = 5 \\ 4x_1 + x_2 + 3x_3 + 9x_4 = 13 \\ x_2 - x_3 + x_4 = 1 \\ 2x_1 + 3x_2 - x_3 + 7x_4 = 9 \end{cases}$$

Solution: Row-reducing the augmented matrix of (6) we find that:

$$\begin{pmatrix} 1 & 2 & -1 & 4 & 5 \\ 2 & -1 & 3 & 3 & 5 \\ 4 & 1 & 3 & 9 & 13 \\ 0 & 1 & -1 & 1 & 1 \\ 2 & 3 & -1 & 7 & 9 \end{pmatrix} \sim \begin{pmatrix} 1 & 0 & 1 & 2 & 3 \\ 0 & 1 & -1 & 1 & 1 \\ 0 & 0 & 0 & 0 & 0 \\ 0 & 0 & 0 & 0 & 0 \\ 0 & 0 & 0 & 0 & 0 \end{pmatrix}.$$

From the reduced matrix, taking $x_3 = x_4 = 0$, we see that $x_1 = 3$ and $x_2 = 1$; so $(3, 1, 0, 0)$ is a vector solution of (6). Next, consider the matrix obtained from the reduced matrix by deleting its last column, namely

$$A = \begin{pmatrix} 1 & 0 & 1 & 2 \\ 0 & 1 & -1 & 1 \\ 0 & 0 & 0 & 0 \\ 0 & 0 & 0 & 0 \\ 0 & 0 & 0 & 0 \end{pmatrix}.$$

This is the coefficient matrix of a homogeneous linear system possessing the same solution set as does the homogeneous linear system associated with (6). We apply the algorithm contained in the proof of Theorem 2.4.2 to A. Clearly, $\{_1A\,,\,_2A\}$ is a basis for $L\{_1A\,,\,_2A\,,\,_3A\,,\,_4A\}$; moreover $_3A = {_1A} - {_2A}$ and $_4A = 2\,_1A + {_2A}$ (we read this information directly from the columns of A). Thus $\{(1\,,\,-1\,,\,-1\,,\,0)\,,\,(2\,,\,1\,,\,0\,,\,-1)\}$ is a basis for the solution set of our related homogeneous linear system. We conclude that $\{(3\,,\,1\,,\,0\,,\,0) + \gamma \mid \gamma \in W\}$ is the solution set of (6) where $W = L\{(1\,,\,-1\,,\,-1\,,\,0)\,,\,(2\,,\,1\,,\,0\,,\,-1)\}$.

Finally, we consider the following question: Under what circumstances does a linear system have a unique solution?

Theorem 2.4.4: A linear system which involves n unknowns has a unique solution if and only if the rank of both its coefficient matrix and augmented matrix is n.

Proof: In view of Theorem 2.3.1 it is necessary that the coefficient matrix and the augmented matrix have the same rank in order that the given linear system possesses a solution at all. Furthermore, we require that the related homogeneous linear system has a unique solution (namely the trivial solution $\mathbf{0}$) in order that the given linear system shall have just one solution. By Corollary 2.4.1 this means that the rank of its coefficient matrix is n. This establishes Theorem 2.4.4.

EXERCISES

1. Prove Theorem 2.4.1.

2. (a) Use Corollary 2.4.1 to show that the homogeneous linear system

$$\begin{cases} x_1 + 2x_2 - x_3 = 0 \\ 2x_1 - x_2 + x_3 = 0 \end{cases}$$

has a nontrivial solution.

   (b) Exhibit a nontrivial solution of this homogeneous linear system.
   (c) Exhibit a basis for the solution set of this system.

Characterize the solution set of each of the following linear systems.

3. $$\begin{cases} x_1 + x_2 - 2x_3 = 4 \\ 2x_1 + x_3 = 1 \\ 3x_1 + x_2 - x_3 = 5 \\ 2x_1 + 2x_2 - 2x_3 = 8 \end{cases}$$

4. $$\begin{cases} x_1 - 2x_2 + x_3 - x_4 = 1 \\ x_1 + x_2 - x_3 - x_4 = 0 \\ 3x_2 - 2x_3 = -1 \end{cases}$$

5.
$$\begin{cases} x_1 + x_2 - x_3 + 2x_4 + 3x_5 = 6 \\ 2x_1 \qquad + x_3 \qquad - x_5 = 2 \\ 3x_1 + x_2 \qquad - 4x_4 \qquad = 0 \\ 3x_1 + x_2 \qquad + 2x_4 + 2x_5 = 8 \\ 4x_1 + 2x_2 - x_3 - 2x_4 + 3x_5 = 6 \\ 5x_1 + x_2 + x_3 + 2x_4 + x_5 = 10 \end{cases}$$

6. Use Theorem 2.4.4 to show that the following linear system has a unique solution.

$$\begin{cases} x_1 + 2x_2 - x_3 + 3x_4 = 15 \\ 3x_1 - x_2 + 2x_3 + x_4 = -5 \\ 4x_1 + 2x_2 - 3x_3 + 5x_4 = 27 \\ 2x_1 + 7x_2 + 5x_3 - x_4 = 24 \end{cases}$$

7. Let $\alpha \cdot \gamma$ denote $\sum_{i=1}^{n} a_i c_i$ whenever $\alpha = (a_1, \ldots, a_n)$ and $\gamma = (c_1, \ldots, c_n)$. Let $(\beta_1, \ldots, \beta_n)$ be any ordered basis for R_n. Find all vectors $\zeta = (x_1, \ldots, x_n)$ such that $\beta_i \cdot \zeta = 0$, $i = 1, \ldots, n$. How many vectors have this property?

2.5 COMPUTING THE RANK OF A MATRIX

We now present a simple method of determining the rank of any $m \times n$ matrix, say A. Notice that A is the coefficient matrix of the homogeneous linear system represented by the vector equation

(6) $$x_1 \,_1A + \cdots + x_n \,_nA = 0.$$

Let rank $A = r$; then, by Theorem 2.4.2, $n - r$ is the dimension of $\{(x_1, \ldots, x_n) \mid x_1 \,_1A + \cdots + x_n \,_nA = 0\}$. Therefore, each homogeneous linear system equivalent to (6) (i.e., with the same solution set) has a coefficient matrix with rank r. It follows from this observation that our procedure for reducing a matrix does not affect its rank (i.e., the reduced matrix has the same rank as the given matrix). Recall that the matrix operations involved in reducing a matrix are the following:

(i) interchange two row vectors;
(ii) multiply a row vector by a nonzero scalar;
(iii) add one row vector to another row vector.

We emphasize that these operations do not affect rank because the corresponding homogeneous linear systems are equivalent. Of course, once we have reduced our matrix we can read off its rank.

Let us illustrate this idea.

Example 1: Compute the rank of

$$\begin{pmatrix} 2 & 1 & 0 & -1 & 3 \\ 1 & 2 & 1 & 2 & 0 \\ 0 & 3 & 1 & 1 & 1 \\ -1 & -5 & -3 & -7 & 3 \end{pmatrix}.$$

Solution:

$$
\begin{pmatrix}
2 & 1 & 0 & -1 & 3 \\
1 & 2 & 1 & 2 & 0 \\
0 & 3 & 1 & 1 & 1 \\
-1 & -5 & -3 & -7 & 3
\end{pmatrix}
\sim
\begin{pmatrix}
1 & 2 & 1 & 2 & 0 \\
0 & -3 & -2 & -5 & 3 \\
0 & 3 & 1 & 1 & 1 \\
0 & -3 & -2 & -5 & 3
\end{pmatrix}
$$

$$
\sim
\begin{pmatrix}
1 & 2 & 1 & 2 & 0 \\
0 & 3 & 1 & 1 & 1 \\
0 & 0 & -1 & -4 & 4 \\
0 & 0 & -1 & -4 & 4
\end{pmatrix}
\sim
\begin{pmatrix}
3 & 0 & 1 & 4 & -2 \\
0 & 3 & 0 & -3 & 5 \\
0 & 0 & -1 & -4 & 4 \\
0 & 0 & 0 & 0 & 0
\end{pmatrix}
$$

$$
\sim
\begin{pmatrix}
3 & 0 & 0 & 0 & 2 \\
0 & 3 & 0 & -3 & 5 \\
0 & 0 & -1 & -4 & 4 \\
0 & 0 & 0 & 0 & 0
\end{pmatrix}
\sim
\begin{pmatrix}
1 & 0 & 0 & 0 & \frac{2}{3} \\
0 & 1 & 0 & -1 & \frac{5}{3} \\
0 & 0 & 1 & 4 & -4 \\
0 & 0 & 0 & 0 & 0
\end{pmatrix}.
$$

We now compute the rank of the reduced matrix. Clearly, $\{\epsilon_1, \epsilon_2, \epsilon_3\}$ is linearly independent; furthermore, $(0, -1, 4, 0) = -\epsilon_2 + 4\epsilon_3$ and $(\frac{2}{3}, \frac{5}{3}, -4, 0) = \frac{2}{3}\epsilon_1 + \frac{5}{3}\epsilon_2 - 4\epsilon_3$. Thus, $\{\epsilon_1, \epsilon_2, \epsilon_3\}$ is a basis for the subspace spanned by the column vectors of the reduced matrix; so 3 is the rank of this matrix. We conclude that 3 is the rank of the given matrix.

Note: The matrix of Example 1 is the augmented matrix of the linear system

$$
\begin{cases}
2x_1 + x_2 \quad\quad\ - x_4 = 3 \\
x_1 + 2x_2 + x_3 + 2x_4 = 0 \\
\quad\quad 3x_2 + x_3 + x_4 = 1 \\
-x_1 - 5x_2 - 3x_3 - 7x_4 = 3
\end{cases}.
$$

Now, the coefficient matrix and the augmented matrix of this linear system have the same rank, namely 3; therefore, by Theorem 2.3.1, this system possesses at least one solution. In view of Theorem 2.4.4 we see that this linear system has more than one solution (hence, infinitely many solutions).

Here is an important result.

Lemma 2.5.1: Let A be an $n \times n$ matrix such that rank $A = n$. Then A can be row-reduced to I_n.

Proof: The goal of our row reduction process is to transform each column of the given matrix A into a column of the form $(0, \ldots, 0, 1, 0, \ldots, 0)$, which is represented by the n-vector ϵ_i for some i. Now, our reduction process comes to an end after treating the nth column of A, in which case the reduced matrix is I_n, or if after treating the jth column of A we find that each of the remaining columns of the reduced matrix has the form $(a_1, \ldots, a_j, 0, \ldots, 0)$. Thus, each column vector of the reduced matrix has this form. Therefore, each column vector of the reduced matrix is a linear combination of $\{\epsilon_1, \ldots, \epsilon_j\}$, a subset of R_n; hence, the rank of this matrix is at most j. We conclude that $j = n$. This completes our proof.

EXERCISES

Determine the rank of each of the following matrices.

1. $\begin{pmatrix} 1 & 2 & 3 & 1 \\ 3 & 1 & 2 & 0 \\ 0 & -1 & -2 & 1 \end{pmatrix}$

2. $\begin{pmatrix} -1 & 0 & 1 & 2 \\ 3 & 1 & 2 & -1 \\ 5 & 1 & 0 & -5 \end{pmatrix}$

3. $\begin{pmatrix} 1 & 1 & 2 & 1 \\ -2 & 2 & 5 & 4 \\ 4 & 0 & -1 & -2 \end{pmatrix}$

4. $\begin{pmatrix} -1 & 1 & 0 & 2 & 3 \\ 1 & 1 & -1 & -1 & 2 \\ 3 & 0 & -1 & 1 & -2 \\ 2 & -1 & 0 & 2 & -1 \end{pmatrix}$

5. $\begin{pmatrix} 2 & 0 & -1 & 3 & 2 & 1 \\ -1 & 1 & 0 & 1 & 3 & -2 \\ 3 & 1 & -2 & 5 & 7 & 0 \\ -5 & 1 & 2 & -3 & -1 & -4 \\ 1 & 3 & -2 & 7 & 13 & -4 \end{pmatrix}$

6. Does the linear system whose augmented matrix is the matrix of Exercise 1, possess a solution?

7. Does the linear system whose augmented matrix is the matrix of Exercise 5, possess a solution?

8. Let $\alpha = (a_1, a_2, \ldots, a_n)$ and $\beta = (b_1, b_2, \ldots, b_n)$ be any n-vectors; then α is said to be *orthogonal* to β if and only if $a_1 b_1 + a_2 b_2 + \cdots + a_n b_n = 0$.

   (a) Show that there is a nonzero vector $\xi = (x_1, x_2, x_3, x_4)$ such that ξ is orthogonal to each of the vectors $(1, 0, -1, 2), (2, 1, 3, -1)$ and $(3, 0, 1, 4)$.
   (b) Compute ξ.

2.6 RANK AND THE MAPPING DETERMINANT

The notion of the *rank* of a matrix can be characterized in terms of the matrices that can be constructed from the given matrix by deleting various rows and columns of the matrix. The resulting matrices are said to be *submatrices* of the given matrix. Actually, we are concerned primarily with the *square* submatrices of a given matrix. We say that a square matrix, say B, is *singular* if and only if $|B| = 0$, and we say that B is *nonsingular* if and only if $|B| \neq 0$.

Considering Definition 2.3.1 it is clear that only a *zero* matrix (i.e., a matrix whose entries are each 0) has rank zero. Accordingly, we concentrate on matrices with positive rank. We now present the main theorem of this section.

Theorem 2.6.1:   Let $r \in N$; a matrix, say A, has rank r if and only if

(*i*) A possesses a nonsingular $r \times r$ submatrix;
(*ii*)   If $t > r$ then each $t \times t$ submatrix of A is singular.

In order to prove this theorem we need to establish several preliminary results.

Theorem 2.6.2:   Let $n \in N$ and let A be any $n \times n$ matrix; then rank $A = n$ if and only if A is nonsingular.

Proof: There are two parts to our proof.

1.   Assume that rank $A = n$. Then A can be row-reduced to I_n (see Lemma 2.5.1). Now, each step in the reduction produces a matrix whose determinant is a nonzero multiple of $|A|$. Since $|I_n| \neq 0$, we conclude that $|A| \neq 0$; i.e., A is nonsingular.

2.   Assume that rank $A < n$. Then $\{_1A, \ldots, _nA\}$ is linearly dependent or this set does not have n members. So, by Definition 2.2.3, one of the column vectors of A is a linear combination of its other column vectors, or two column vectors of A are the same. Considering the properties of the mapping *det* we conclude that $|A| = 0$. This completes our proof.

We are now ready to prove half of Theorem 2.6.1.

Theorem 2.6.3:   Let A be any matrix with positive rank r; then

(*i*) A possesses a nonsingular $r \times r$ submatrix,
(*ii*)   If $t > r$ then each $t \times t$ submatrix of A is singular.

Proof: Let A be an $m \times n$ matrix. Let $\{_1A, \ldots, _rA\}$ be a basis for $L\{_iA \mid 1 \leq i \leq n\}$. Consider the $m \times r$ matrix B such that $_iB = {_iA}$, $i = 1, \ldots, r$; clearly, rank $B = r$. Now, our procedure for reducing a matrix does not affect rank (see Section 2.5); so B can be reduced to a matrix whose first r rows consist of 0's off the main diagonal and 1's on the main diagonal. Moreover, this reduced matrix can be obtained from B by using only r rows of B; so, the submatrix of B which consists of these r rows, has rank r. Notice that this submatrix of B is an $r \times r$ matrix. Thus, by Theorem 2.6.2, this submatrix is nonsingular; this proves that A possesses a nonsingular $r \times r$ submatrix. Finally, let $t > r$; we must prove that each $t \times t$ submatrix of A is singular. By assumption, any set of t column vectors of A, say $\{_1A, \ldots, _tA\}$, is linearly dependent or else it does not have t members. Consider the set of t-vectors obtained from $\{_1A, \ldots, _tA\}$ by deleting any $m - t$ rows of A; we point out that this set is also linearly dependent, or else it does not have t members. Hence, the rank of the corresponding $t \times t$ submatrix of A is less than t; so, by Theorem 2.6.2, this $t \times t$ submatrix of A is singular. We have established Theorem 2.6.3.

It is surprising, but true, that we can establish the remaining half of Theorem 2.6.1 by appealing to the half of this theorem that we have already established. Consider the following corollaries of Theorem 2.6.3.

Corollary 2.6.1: If A possesses a nonsingular $r \times r$ submatrix, then rank $A \geq r$.

Proof: If rank $A < r$, then each $r \times r$ submatrix of A is singular.

Corollary 2.6.2: Let $r \in N$ and suppose that each $t \times t$ submatrix of A is singular whenever $t > r$; then rank $A \leq r$.

Proof: Let rank $A = r_1$ and suppose that $r_1 > r$. Then, by Theorem 2.6.3, A possesses a nonsingular $r_1 \times r_1$ submatrix.

We now present the remaining half of Theorem 2.6.1, the converse of Theorem 2.6.3.

Theorem 2.6.4: A matrix A has positive rank r if

(*i*) A possesses a nonsingular $r \times r$ submatrix,
(*ii*)   If $t > r$ then each $t \times t$ submatrix of A is singular.

Proof: Let rank $A = r_1$. In view of Corollary 2.6.1 and the first assumption of the theorem, $r_1 \geq r$. Moreover, from Corollary 2.6.2 and the second assumption of the theorem, we see that $r_1 \leq r$. We conclude that $r_1 = r$. This completes our proof.

Of course, Theorems 2.6.3 and 2.6.4 together constitute a proof of Theorem 2.6.1; so we have established our main theorem.

Notice that Theorem 2.6.2 is a special case of Theorem 2.6.1. Using Theorem 2.6.2 we easily obtain a condition under which a linear system which consists of n equations in n unknowns has a unique solution.

Theorem 2.6.5: A linear system which consists of n equations in n unknowns has a unique solution if and only if its coefficient matrix is nonsingular.

Proof: Apply Theorems 2.4.4 and 2.6.2.

Next, we bring out an interesting consequence of our main theorem.

Theorem 2.6.6: Let A be any matrix; then A and A^t have the same rank.

Proof: First, we point out that each zero matrix has this property. Let rank $A = r$, where $r \in N$. By Theorem 2.6.1, A possesses a nonsingular $r \times r$ submatrix; moreover, each $s \times s$ submatrix of A, where $s > r$, is singular. Consider A^t. Since each square matrix and its transpose have the same determinant, it follows that A^t possesses a nonsingular $r \times r$ submatrix (namely, the transpose of any nonsingular $r \times r$ submatrix of A), moreover each $s \times s$ submatrix of A^t, where $s > r$, is singular. Thus, by Theorem 2.6.1, rank $A^t = r$. This establishes our result.

Noting that the column vectors of A^t are the row vectors of A, we obtain the following corollary to Theorem 2.6.6.

Corollary 2.6.3: The subspace spanned by the column vectors of a matrix A has the same dimension as the subspace spanned by the row vectors of A.

Proof: Let A by any $m \times n$ matrix. Now, rank $A = \dim L\{_1A , \ldots , _nA\}$ and rank $A^t = \dim L\{_1(A^t) , \ldots , _m (A^t)\} = \dim L\{A_1 , \ldots , A_m\}$. Thus, by Theorem 2.6.6, $\dim L\{_1A , \ldots , _nA\} = \dim L\{A_1 , \ldots , A_m\}$.

EXERCISES

1. List the submatrices of the matrix

$$\begin{pmatrix} 1 & 0 & 3 \\ 2 & -1 & 4 \end{pmatrix}.$$

2. By computing the determinant of the following matrix, show that this matrix has rank 4.

$$\begin{pmatrix} 1 & 0 & -1 & 2 \\ 2 & 1 & 2 & -1 \\ -2 & 2 & -1 & 3 \\ 3 & 4 & -1 & -2 \end{pmatrix}$$

3. Show that the following linear system has a unique solution for any choice of b_1, b_2, b_3 and b_4.

$$\begin{cases} x_1 \quad\quad - \; x_3 + 2x_4 = b_1 \\ 2x_1 + \; x_2 + 2x_3 - \; x_4 = b_2 \\ -2x_1 + 2x_2 - \; x_3 + 3x_4 = b_3 \\ 3x_1 + 4x_2 - \; x_3 - 2x_4 = b_4 \end{cases}$$

4. Given that $\{(a_1 , a_2 , a_3), (b_1 , b_2 , b_3), (c_1 , c_2 , c_3)\}$ has three members and is linearly independent, prove that $\{(a_1 , b_1 , c_1), (a_2 , b_2 , c_2), (a_3 , b_3 , c_3)\}$ has three members and is linearly independent.

5. Given that $\{(a_1 , a_2 , a_3), (b_1 , b_2 , b_3), (c_1 , c_2 , c_3)\}$ has three members and is linearly dependent, prove that $\{(a_1 , b_1 , c_1), (a_2 , b_2 , c_2), (a_3 , b_3 , c_3)\}$ is linearly dependent or does not have three members.

6. Given that $\{\alpha, \beta, \gamma\}$ is a linearly independent set of 3-vectors and has three members, prove that there is exactly one vector orthogonal to each of α, β and γ. Find this vector. (For a definition of *orthogonal* see Exercise 8, Section 2.5).

7. Given a linearly independent set of n-vectors, show that $\mathbf{0}$ is the only vector which is orthogonal to each of the given vectors.

3

MATRIX ALGEBRA

3.1 THE DOT PRODUCT

The purpose of this section is to investigate the properties of vectors that enable us to use vectors in geometry. First, we present the notion of the *dot product*.

Definition 3.1.1: Let $\alpha = (a_1, a_2, \ldots, a_n)$ and $\beta = (b_1, b_2, \ldots, b_n)$ be any n-vectors. Then by the *dot product* of α and β we mean the real number $a_1 b_1 + a_2 b_2 + \cdots + a_n b_n$. This scalar is denoted by $\alpha \cdot \beta$.

We point out that, for each natural number n, the dot product is a mapping of $R_n \times R_n$ into R. The following theorem brings out the basic properties of this mapping.

Theorem 3.1.1: Let $\{\alpha, \beta, \gamma\} \subset R_n$; and let $k \in R$; then

(i) $\alpha \cdot \beta = \beta \cdot \alpha$,
(ii) $\alpha \cdot (\beta + \gamma) = \alpha \cdot \beta + \alpha \cdot \gamma$,
(iii) $(k\alpha) \cdot \beta = k(\alpha \cdot \beta)$,
(iv) $\alpha \cdot \alpha > 0$ whenever $\alpha \neq \mathbf{0}$; $\mathbf{0} \cdot \mathbf{0} = 0$.

Proof: The details are straightforward and are left as an exercise.

This theorem is important because many properties of the dot product can be established algebraically on the basis of the properties exhibited in the theorem. In this way we avoid a detailed calculation based on Definition 3.1.1. Moreover, in Section 11.2 we generalize our dot product by introducing the concept of an *inner product;* an inner product is defined to be any mapping which possesses the properties listed in Theorem 3.1.1. Accordingly, it is good practice to apply Theorem 3.1.1 whenever possible, instead of the definition of our dot product.

Lemma 3.1.1: Let $\{\alpha, \beta_1, \ldots, \beta_t\} \subset R_n$; then $\alpha \cdot (\beta_1 + \cdots + \beta_t) = \alpha \cdot \beta_1 + \cdots + \alpha \cdot \beta_t$.

Proof: Use mathematical induction on t and apply Theorem 3.1.1 (*ii*).

Lemma 3.1.2: Let $\{\alpha, \beta_1, \ldots, \beta_t\} \subset R_n$ and let $\{k_1, \ldots, k_t\} \subset R$; then $\alpha \cdot (k_1 \beta_1 + \cdots + k_t \beta_t) = k_1(\alpha \cdot \beta_1) + \cdots + k_t(\alpha \cdot \beta_t)$.

Proof:

$$\alpha \cdot (k_1 \beta_1 + \cdots + k_t \beta_t) = \alpha \cdot (k_1 \beta_1) + \cdots + \alpha \cdot (k_t \beta_t) \qquad \text{by Lemma 3.1.1}$$
$$= (k_1 \beta_1) \cdot \alpha + \cdots + (k_t \beta_t) \cdot \alpha \qquad \text{by Theorem 3.1.1 (}i\text{)}$$
$$= k_1(\alpha \cdot \beta_1) + \cdots + k_t(\alpha \cdot \beta_t) \qquad \text{by Theorem 3.1.1 (}iii\text{) ,}$$
$$\text{and Theorem 3.1.1 (}i\text{).}$$

Lemma 3.1.3: If $\alpha \neq \mathbf{0}$, $\beta \neq \mathbf{0}$, and $\alpha \cdot \beta = 0$, then $\{\alpha, \beta\}$ is linearly independent.

Proof: Suppose that there are real numbers k_1 and k_2 such that $k_1 \alpha + k_2 \beta = \mathbf{0}$; then $(k_1 \alpha) \cdot \alpha + (k_2 \beta) \cdot \alpha = \mathbf{0} \cdot \alpha = 0$. Thus $k_1(\alpha \cdot \alpha) = 0$, so $k_1 = 0$. Similarly we see that $k_2 = 0$. Therefore $\{\alpha, \beta\}$ is linearly independent.

Theorem 3.1.2: Let $\beta_1, \beta_2, \ldots, \beta_m$ be nonzero n-vectors such that $\beta_i \cdot \beta_j = 0$ whenever $i \neq j$. Then $\{\beta_1, \beta_2, \ldots, \beta_m\}$ is linearly independent.

Proof: Apply the argument of Lemma 3.1.3.

It will soon be clear that the ideas of this section are slanted toward geometry. In Chapters 4 and 5 we develop a geometry which relies heavily on vectors. Consider the following concept.

Definition 3.1.2: Let α and β be any n-vectors; then we shall write $\alpha \perp \beta$ (read α is *orthogonal* to β) if and only if $\alpha \cdot \beta = 0$. Moreover, let $A \subset R_n$; then $\{\gamma \mid \gamma \perp \alpha \text{ whenever } \alpha \in A\}$ is called the *orthogonal complement* of A, and is denoted by $A^\perp$.

We point out that $\perp$ is a binary relation on R_n whenever $n \in N$; for example, $(5, -1, 2) \perp (2, 8, -1)$. Notice that $R_n^\perp = \{\mathbf{0}\}$.

Lemma 3.1.4: Let α and β be any n-vectors; than $\alpha \perp \beta$ if and only if $\beta \perp \alpha$.

Proof: Theorem 3.1.1 (*i*).

Theorem 3.1.3: Let $A \subset R_n$ and let $\beta \perp \alpha$ whenever $\alpha \in A$. Then $\beta \perp \gamma$ whenever $\gamma \in LA$.

Proof: Let $\gamma \in LA$; we can express γ in the form $\sum_{i=1}^{t} k_i \alpha_i$ where $\alpha_i \in A$ and $k_i \in R$, $i = 1, \ldots, t$. So, applying Lemma 3.1.2

$$\beta \cdot \gamma = \beta \cdot \sum_{i=1}^{t} k_i \alpha_i = \sum_{i=1}^{t} k_i(\beta \cdot \alpha_i) = 0 \ .$$

This completes our proof.

Theorem 3.1.4: Let $\{\alpha_1, \alpha_2, \ldots, \alpha_m\} \subset R_n$ where $1 \le m < n$. Then there is a nonzero n-vector which is orthogonal to each of the α's.

Proof: Consider the m vector equations $\alpha_i \cdot \zeta = 0$, $i = 1, 2, \ldots, m$. These equations constitute a homogeneous linear system which consists of m equations in n unknowns; the unknowns are the terms of ζ. Now $m < n$; so by Corollary 2.4.2, our linear system has a nontrivial solution. This establishes our result.

Example 1: Find a 4-vector orthogonal to each of $(1, 0, 2, -3)$, $(0, 1, -1, 3)$, and $(2, 0, 0, 2)$.

Solution: Now, (x_1, x_2, x_3, x_4) is a suitable vector if and only if

(1)
$$\begin{cases} x_1 + 2x_3 - 3x_4 = 0 \\ x_2 - x_3 + 3x_4 = 0 \\ 2x_1 + 2x_4 = 0 \end{cases} \cdot$$

We reduce the matrix of this homogeneous linear system.

$$\begin{pmatrix} 1 & 0 & 2 & -3 \\ 0 & 1 & -1 & 3 \\ 2 & 0 & 0 & 2 \end{pmatrix} \sim \begin{pmatrix} 1 & 0 & 2 & -3 \\ 0 & 1 & -1 & 3 \\ 0 & 0 & -4 & 8 \end{pmatrix}$$

$$\sim \begin{pmatrix} 1 & 0 & 2 & -3 \\ 0 & 1 & -1 & 3 \\ 0 & 0 & -1 & 2 \end{pmatrix} \sim \begin{pmatrix} 1 & 0 & 0 & 1 \\ 0 & 1 & 0 & 1 \\ 0 & 0 & -1 & 2 \end{pmatrix} \cdot$$

The rank of this matrix is 3; so, by Theorem 2.4.2, the dimension of the solution set of (1) is 1. Moreover, from the reduced matrix we see that the solution set of (1) is $\{k(-1, -1, 2, 1) \mid k \in R\}$. In particular, $(1, 1, -2, -1)$ is a member of this set; so $(1, 1, -2, -1)$ is orthogonal to each of the given vectors.

We can sharpen Theorem 3.1.4 as follows.

Theorem 3.1.5: Let W be any nontrivial subspace of $\mathfrak{R}_n$ such that dim $W = t$, and let $\{\alpha_1, \ldots, \alpha_m\}$ be a nonempty, linearly independent subset of W, where $m < t$. Then there is a nonzero member of W which is orthogonal to each of the α's.

Proof: Let $\{\gamma_1, \ldots, \gamma_t\}$ be any basis for W, and let $\beta = x_1\gamma_1 + \cdots + x_t\gamma_t$ be any member of W. We wish to choose $x_1, \ldots, x_t$ so that $\beta \ne 0$ and $\beta \perp \alpha_i$,

$i = 1, \ldots, m$. Consider the m equations $\beta \cdot \alpha_1 = 0, \ldots, \beta \cdot \alpha_m = 0$. Let us write out these equations in more detail. Using Theorem 3.1.1 we obtain:

(2)
$$\begin{cases} (\gamma_1 \cdot \alpha_1)x_1 + \cdots + (\gamma_t \cdot \alpha_1)x_t = 0 \\ \qquad\qquad\qquad \cdot \\ \qquad\qquad\qquad \cdot \\ \qquad\qquad\qquad \cdot \\ (\gamma_1 \cdot \alpha_m)x_1 + \cdots + (\gamma_t \cdot \alpha_m)x_t = 0 \end{cases}$$

We face a homogeneous linear system which consists of m equations in the t unknowns $x_1, \ldots, x_t$. By assumption $m < t$; so, by Corollary 2.4.2, (2) possesses a nontrivial solution, say $(k_1, \ldots, k_t)$. Since the k's are not all zero and since $\{\gamma_1, \ldots, \gamma_t\}$ is linearly independent, we see that $\beta \neq \mathbf{0}$. This establishes Theorem 3.1.5.

It is easy, now, to prove the following important theorem.

Theorem 3.1.6 (*Gram–Schmidt*): Let W be any nontrivial subspace of $\mathcal{R}_n$ such that dim $W = t$. Then there is a basis for W, say $\{\beta_1, \ldots, \beta_t\}$, such that $\beta_i \cdot \beta_j = 0$ whenever $i \neq j$.

Proof: We build up a suitable basis for W by applying Theorem 3.1.5 $t - 1$ times. Since $W \neq \{\mathbf{0}\}$, W possesses a nonzero member, say β_1. By Theorem 3.1.5, if $t > 1$ there is a nonzero member of W, say β_2, which is orthogonal to β_1. By Theorem 3.1.2, $\{\beta_1, \beta_2\}$ is linearly independent. So, if $t > 2$, by Theorem 3.1.5 there is a nonzero member of W, say β_3, which is orthogonal to β_1 and β_2. Again, if $t > 3$ then $\{\beta_1, \beta_2, \beta_3\}$ is a proper subset of a basis for W. So, by Theorem 3.1.5, there is a nonzero member of W, say β_4, which is orthogonal to β_1, β_2, and β_3. Continuing this process, we apply Theorem 3.1.5 a total of $t - 1$ times to obtain $\{\beta_1, \ldots, \beta_t\}$ where $\beta_i \cdot \beta_j = 0$ whenever $i \neq j$ and each β is a nonzero member of W. Applying Theorem 3.1.2 we conclude that $\{\beta_1, \ldots, \beta_t\}$ is a basis for W with the required properties. This completes our proof.

Note. A set of vectors is said to be *orthogonal* if any two of its members are orthogonal. Thus our result asserts that each subspace of $\mathcal{R}_n$, other than $\{\mathbf{0}\}$, possesses an orthogonal basis.

We now present an example which illustrates the Gram–Schmidt process; clearly, the process is almost as important as the theorem itself.

Example 2: Find an orthogonal basis for $W = L\{\alpha_1, \alpha_2, \alpha_3\}$ where $\alpha_1 = (1, 1, 0, 0, 0)$, $\alpha_2 = (0, 1, 1, 0, 0)$, and $\alpha_3 = (0, 0, 1, 1, 1)$.

Solution: By reducing the matrix

$$A = \begin{pmatrix} 1 & 0 & 0 \\ 1 & 1 & 0 \\ 0 & 1 & 1 \\ 0 & 0 & 1 \\ 0 & 0 & 1 \end{pmatrix}.$$

we readily verify that rank $A = 3$; so $\{\alpha_1 , \alpha_2 , \alpha_3\}$ is linearly independent. We apply the method of the proof of Theorem 3.1.5 to build up the required basis. Let $\beta_1 = \alpha_1$; we want a nonzero member of W, say β_2, orthogonal to β_1. Let $\beta_2 = k_1\alpha_1 + k_2\alpha_2 + k_3\alpha_3$; then we require that

$$k_1(\alpha_1 \cdot \beta_1) + k_2(\alpha_2 \cdot \beta_1) + k_3(\alpha_3 \cdot \beta_1) = 0 ,$$

i.e.,

$$2k_1 + k_2 = 0$$

Take $k_3 = 0$, $k_2 = -2$, and $k_1 = 1$. Thus

$$\beta_2 = \alpha_1 - 2\alpha_2 = (1 , -1 , -2 , 0 , 0) .$$

Next, we want a nonzero member of W, say β_3, orthogonal to β_1 and β_2. Let $\beta_3 = x_1 \alpha_1 + x_2 \alpha_2 + x_3 \alpha_3$; then

(3)
$$\begin{cases} x_1(\alpha_1 \cdot \beta_1) + x_2(\alpha_2 \cdot \beta_1) + x_3(\alpha_3 \cdot \beta_1) = 0 , \\ x_1(\alpha_1 \cdot \beta_2) + x_2(\alpha_2 \cdot \beta_2) + x_3(\alpha_3 \cdot \beta_2) = 0 \end{cases}$$

i.e.,

$$2x_1 + x_2 = 0 \quad \text{and} \quad -3x_2 - 2x_3 = 0 .$$

We now solve this homogeneous linear system:

$$\begin{pmatrix} 2 & 1 & 0 \\ 0 & -3 & -2 \end{pmatrix} \sim \begin{pmatrix} 6 & 0 & -2 \\ 0 & 3 & 2 \end{pmatrix} \sim \begin{pmatrix} 3 & 0 & -1 \\ 0 & 3 & 2 \end{pmatrix} .$$

The rank of this matrix is 2; so, by Theorem 2.4.2, the dimension of the solution set of (3) is 1. However, we want just one nonzero solution of (3); from the reduced matrix we see that $(1 , -2 , 3)$ is a solution of (3). Thus, we take $\beta_3 = \alpha_1 + (-2)\alpha_2 + 3\alpha_3 = (1 , -1 , 1 , 3 , 3)$. We conclude that $\{(1 , 1 , 0 , 0 , 0), (1 , -1 , -2 , 0 , 0) , (1 , -1 , 1 , 3 , 3)\}$ is an orthogonal basis for W.

EXERCISES

1. Prove Theorem 3.1.1.

2. Let α be any n-vector; prove that $0 \cdot \alpha = 0$. Present a direct proof based on Definition 3.1.1; also present an algebraic proof based on Theorem 3.1.1.

3. Prove Lemma 3.1.1.

4. Prove Theorem 3.1.2.

5. Show that there is exactly one vector, say $\zeta = (x_1 , x_2 , x_3)$, which is orthogonal to each of $(1 , 0 , 0), (0 , 1 , 0)$, and $(0 , 0 , 1)$. Determine ζ.

6. Find a nonzero member of R_4 which is orthogonal to each of $(2 , 1 , -1 , 0)$, $(1 , 0 , 2 , -1)$, and $(3 , 1 , -1 , 1)$.

7. Let γ be any n-vector. Prove that $\{\alpha \mid \alpha \perp \gamma)$ is a subspace of $\mathcal{R}_n$.

8. Let $\gamma_1, \gamma_2, \ldots , \gamma_t$ be any n-vectors. Prove that $\{\alpha \mid \alpha \perp \gamma_i , i = 1, 2, \ldots , t\}$ is a subspace of $\mathcal{R}_n$.

9. Let $\{\alpha_1, \alpha_2, \ldots, \alpha_m\}$ be a linearly independent subset of R_n with m members, where $m \leq n$. Prove that $\{\zeta \mid \zeta \perp \alpha_i, i = 1, 2, \ldots, m\}$ is a subspace of $\mathfrak{R}_n$ with dimension $n - m$.

10. Find an orthogonal basis for the subspace of $\mathfrak{R}_3$ which is spanned by $(2, -1, 0)$, $(3, 1, 1)$, and $(0, 5, 2)$.

11. Find an orthogonal basis for the subspace of $\mathfrak{R}_4$ spanned by $(1, 2, -1, 0)$, $(2, 0, 0, -1)$, and $(3, 1, 0, 1)$.

12. Let $A = L\{\alpha_1, \ldots, \alpha_m\}$ and let $A \subset R_n$. Prove that $\gamma \in A^\perp$ if and only if $\gamma \in \{\alpha_1, \ldots, \alpha_m\}^\perp$.

13. (a) Show that $A^\perp$ is a subspace of $\mathfrak{R}_n$ whenever A is a subspace of $\mathfrak{R}_n$. (b) Find a basis for $A^\perp$, where $A = L\{(1, 0, 2, 0, 3), (0, 1, 0, 1, 0)\}$.

14. A set of vectors, say $\{\alpha_1, \ldots, \alpha_t\}$, is said to be *orthonormal* if and only if $\{\alpha_1, \ldots, \alpha_t\}$ is orthogonal and $\alpha_i \cdot \alpha_i = 1$, $i = 1, \ldots, t$. Let W be any nontrivial subspace of $\mathfrak{R}_n$; prove that W possesses an orthonormal basis.

15. Let $(\beta_1, \ldots, \beta_n)$ be any ordered basis for R_n.

    (a) Prove that $\{(\beta_1 \cdot \beta_i, \ldots, \beta_n \cdot \beta_i) \mid 1 \leq i \leq n\}$ is linearly independent. *Hint:* Consider the homogeneous linear system $\beta_1 \cdot \zeta = 0, \ldots, \beta_n \cdot \zeta = 0$ in the unknown vector ζ.

    (b) Let $(k_1, \ldots, k_n) \in R_n$; prove that there is a unique vector γ such that $\beta_i \cdot \gamma = k_i, i = 1, \ldots, n$.

16. Let $(\beta_1, \ldots, \beta_n)$ be any ordered basis for R_n. Prove that $\{(\beta_1 \cdot \beta_i, \ldots, \beta_{n-1} \cdot \beta_i) \mid 1 \leq i \leq n\}$ is linearly dependent.

17. Let $\{\beta_1, \beta_2\}$ be a linearly independent subset of R_3 with two members. Prove that $\{(\beta_1 \cdot \beta_1, -\beta_2 \cdot \beta_1), (\beta_1 \cdot \beta_2, -\beta_2 \cdot \beta_2)\}$ is linearly independent.

3.2 LENGTH AND ANGLE

We now illustrate the significance of our dot product by developing some geometric ideas. Let α be any n-vector; so $\alpha = (a_1, \ldots, a_n)$. Consider the line-segment with endpoints $\mathbf{0}$ and α; intuitively, its length is $\sqrt{\sum_{i=1}^{n} a_i^2} = \sqrt{\alpha \cdot \alpha}$. Accordingly, we call this number the *length* (or *norm*) of α.

Definition 3.2.1: Let α be any n-vector; by the *length* of α we mean the real number $\sqrt{\alpha \cdot \alpha}$. This real number is denoted by $\|\alpha\|$.

For example, $\|(3, 4)\| = 5$, $\|(-1, 2, 0, -2)\| = 3$, and $\|\mathbf{0}\| = 0$. Remember the geometric significance of $\|\alpha\|$; namely, that $\|\alpha\|$ is the length of the line-segment with endpoints $\mathbf{0}$ and α. Generalizing, we point out that $\|\alpha - \beta\|$ is the length of the line-segment with endpoints α and β.

In view of Theorem 3.1.1 (iv) it is clear that each n-vector possesses a length. We now establish some properties of our concept.

Lemma 3.2.1: Let α be any n-vector. Then $\|\alpha\| > 0$ if $\alpha \neq 0$; moreover, $\|0\| = 0$.

Proof: Theorem 3.1.1 (iv).

Lemma 3.2.2: Let α be any n-vector and let $k \in R$. Then $\|k\alpha\| = |k|\,\|\alpha\|$.

Proof: Apply Definition 3.2.1. Here $|k|$ denotes the absolute value of k, not the determinant of the matrix (k).

Lemma 3.2.3: Let α be any nonzero n-vector; then $\alpha/\|\alpha\|$ is an n-vector whose length is 1.

Proof: Apply Lemma 3.2.2. By $\alpha/\|\alpha\|$ we mean $(1/\|\alpha\|)\alpha$.

Theorem 3.2.1: Let α and β be any n-vectors; then $\|\alpha + \beta\|^2 = \|\alpha\|^2 + \|\beta\|^2 + 2(\alpha \cdot \beta)$.

Proof: Apply Theorem 3.1.1; the details are straightforward and are left as an exercise.

Corollary 3.2.1: Let α and β be any n-vectors; then $\|\alpha - \beta\|^2 = \|\alpha\|^2 + \|\beta\|^2 - 2(\alpha \cdot \beta)$.

Proof: Note that $\alpha - \beta = \alpha + (-\beta)$.

The following result is the basis for the important Cauchy–Schwarz Inequality.

Lemma 3.2.4: Let α and β be any n-vectors whose length is 1; then $|\alpha \cdot \beta| \leq 1$.

Proof: Now,

$$0 \leq (\alpha + \beta) \cdot (\alpha + \beta) \qquad \text{by Theorem 3.1.1 } (iv)$$
$$= \|\alpha + \beta\|^2$$
$$= \|\alpha\|^2 + \|\beta\|^2 + 2(\alpha \cdot \beta) \qquad \text{by Theorem 3.2.1}$$
$$= 2 + 2(\alpha \cdot \beta) \qquad \text{by assumption .}$$

So $\alpha \cdot \beta \geq -1$. In the same manner, considering $\|\alpha - \beta\|^2$, we find that $\alpha \cdot \beta \leq 1$. Thus $|\alpha \cdot \beta| \leq 1$.

We are now in a position to establish the following fundamental result.

Theorem 3.2.2 (*Cauchy–Schwarz Inequality*): Let α and β be any n-vectors; then $|\alpha \cdot \beta| \leq \|\alpha\|\,\|\beta\|$.

Proof: If $\alpha = 0$ or $\beta = 0$, then $\alpha \cdot \beta = 0$ and $\|\alpha\|\,\|\beta\| = 0$. Assume, then, that $\alpha \neq 0$ and that $\beta \neq 0$. By Lemma 3.2.3, both $\alpha/\|\alpha\|$ and $\beta/\|\beta\|$ are n-vectors whose length is 1. So, by Lemma 3.2.4, $\left| \frac{\alpha}{\|\alpha\|} \cdot \frac{\beta}{\|\beta\|} \right| \leq 1$; hence, by Theorem 3.1.1 (*iii*), $\left| \frac{1}{\|\alpha\| \, \|\beta\|} (\alpha \cdot \beta) \right| \leq 1$, i.e., $\frac{1}{\|\alpha\| \, \|\beta\|} |\alpha \cdot \beta| \leq 1$, so $|\alpha \cdot \beta| \leq \|\alpha\| \, \|\beta\|$.

Here is the important Triangle Inequality.

Theorem 3.2.3 (*Triangle Inequality*): Let α and β be any *n*-vectors; then $\|\alpha + \beta\| \leq \|\alpha\| + \|\beta\|$.

Proof: Now,

$$
\begin{aligned}
\|\alpha + \beta\|^2 &= \|\alpha\|^2 + \|\beta\|^2 + 2(\alpha \cdot \beta) && \text{by Theorem 3.2.1} \\
&\leq \|\alpha\|^2 + \|\beta\|^2 + 2\|\alpha\| \, \|\beta\| && \text{by Theorem 3.2.2} \\
&= (\|\alpha\| + \|\beta\|)^2 \ .
\end{aligned}
$$

But $\|\gamma\| \geq 0$ whenever $\gamma \in R_n$; therefore $\|\alpha + \beta\| \leq \|\alpha\| + \|\beta\|$. This completes our proof.

There is one more geometric concept that we wish to consider in our algebraic setting, the notion of *angle*, more precisely, the notion of the angle between two vectors. Of course, the term *angle* conjures up the picture of two line-segments with a common endpoint. Let α and β be any *n*-vectors; consider the associated line-segments, one with endpoints **0** and α, and the other with endpoints **0** and β (see Figure 3.2.1). Now, when we consider the angle θ between two line-segments, we usually modify Figure 3.2.1 as follows. Notice that Figure 3.2.2 incorporates a small circular arc which has been labeled θ; we regard this as the arc of the unit circle with center at the common endpoint of our line-segments. We point out now that by the angle θ we mean the length of this arc! So, we have arithmeticized the angle concept. Although this is a satisfactory intuitive definition of angle, it is not adequate mathematically because of the technical problem of measuring a circular arc.

The following argument shows how we can overcome this problem. Referring to Figure 3.2.2, we propose to express $\cos \theta$ in terms of operations on α and β. This

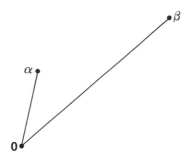

Figure 3.2.1

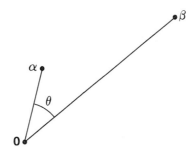

Figure 3.2.2

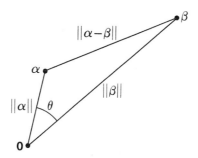

Figure 3.2.3

involves ideas of elementary trigonometry, and should be regarded merely as an intuitive justification for Definition 3.2.2. Consider the triangle with vertices $\mathbf{0}$, α, and β (see Figure 3.2.3). The lengths of the sides of this triangle are $\|\alpha\|$, $\|\beta\|$, and $\|\alpha - \beta\|$. So, by the Cosine Law for triangles (this is the intuitive part of our argument, since the Cosine Law involves the notion of angle)

$$\|\alpha - \beta\|^2 = \|\alpha\|^2 + \|\beta\|^2 - 2\|\alpha\| \, \|\beta\| \cos \theta \ .$$

Thus, by Corollary 3.2.1,

$$\|\alpha\|^2 + \|\beta\|^2 - 2\alpha \cdot \beta = \|\alpha\|^2 + \|\beta\|^2 - 2\|\alpha\| \, \|\beta\| \cos \theta$$

hence
$$\cos \theta = \frac{\alpha \cdot \beta}{\|\alpha\| \, \|\beta\|} \ .$$

Now, the function arccos is an inverse of the function cos; thus

$$\theta = \arccos \frac{\alpha \cdot \beta}{\|\alpha\| \, \|\beta\|} \ .$$

In a moment we discuss the functions cos and arccos; first we present our definition of *angle*.

Definition 3.2.2: Let α and β be any nonzero n-vectors; then the real number arccos $\dfrac{\alpha \cdot \beta}{\|\alpha\| \, \|\beta\|}$ is said to be the *angle* between α and β. This real number is denoted by angle(α , β).

Clearly, this definition is only as meaningful as our grasp of the function arccos. So, our task is to clarify this function. Remember that in this context a function is a set of ordered pairs of real numbers. To pin down arccos, or any function, we must announce its domain and we must show how to determine the number that the function associates with a given member of its domain (no matter which member of the domain is considered). Intuitively, arccos is an inverse of the function cos; of course, we are not entitled, here, to assume a knowledge of this function. Still, it is useful to clarify the relationship between cos and arccos. In Figure 3.2.4 we exhibit the graph of cos. Restricting cos to the interval $[0 , \pi]$ we obtain the function whose graph is displayed in Figure 3.2.5. (We mention that $[a , b]$ denotes $\{t \mid a \leq t \leq b\}$ and that (a , b) denotes $\{t \mid a < t < b\}$; if $a < b$ then $[a , b]$ is called a *closed interval* and (a , b) an *open interval*. Now, the inverse of a one-one function is obtained by reversing the terms of each member of the function. Accordingly, the graph of our inverse can be obtained mechanically from the graph of this one-one function by turning the graph paper through a right angle counter-clockwise and then putting it face down. If the graph paper is transparent you are

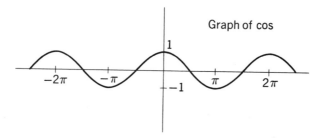

Figure 3.2.4

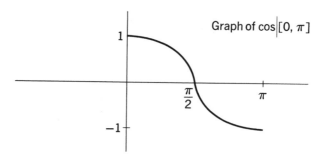

Figure 3.2.5

now looking at the graph of the inverse! Applying this procedure to the graph displayed in Figure 3.2.5, we obtain the graph of arccos (see Figure 3.2.6).

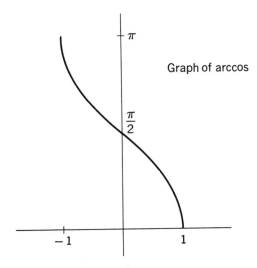

Figure 3.2.6

We must now face up to the task of defining arccos without using cos. First we announce that the closed interval $[-1, 1]$ is the domain of arccos. Next, we must define arccos t whenever $t \in [-1, 1]$. The endpoints of this interval offer no problem; we define arccos $-1 = \pi$ and we define arccos $1 = 0$. Finally, let $t \in (-1, 1)$; then we define

$$\arccos t = \pi/2 - \int_0^t (1 - x^2)^{-\frac{1}{2}} .$$

Here we are using calculus; notice that $\int_0^t (1 - x^2)^{-\frac{1}{2}}$ can be approximated to any desired accuracy by applying Simpson's Rule. For example,

$$\arccos .1 = \pi/2 - \int_0^{.1} (1 - x^2)^{-\frac{1}{2}}$$

$$\approx 1.5708 - \frac{.1}{6} [1 + 4(1 - .0025)^{-\frac{1}{2}} + (1 - .01)^{-\frac{1}{2}}]$$

$$\approx 1.5708 - \frac{.1}{6} [1 + 4(1 + .00125) + (1 + .005)] \qquad \text{by the Binomial Theorem}$$

$$= 1.5708 - .601/6$$

$$\approx 1.4706 .$$

Here is a short table for arccos which was produced by an automatic digital computer; a more extensive table is provided at the back of this book.

ARCCOS

t	.00	.01	.02	.03	.04	.05	.06	.07	.08	.09
−1.0	3.1416	3.0001	2.9413	2.8960	2.8578	2.8240	2.7934	2.7652	2.7389	2.7141
−0.9	2.6906	2.6681	2.6467	2.6260	2.6061	2.5868	2.5681	2.5499	2.5322	2.5149
−0.8	2.4981	2.4816	2.4655	2.4496	2.4341	2.4189	2.4039	2.3891	2.3746	2.3603
−0.7	2.3462	2.3323	2.3186	2.3050	2.2916	2.2784	2.2653	2.2523	2.2395	2.2269
−0.6	2.2143	2.2019	2.1895	2.1773	2.1652	2.1532	2.1412	2.1294	2.1176	2.1060
−0.5	2.0944	2.0829	2.0715	2.0601	2.0488	2.0376	2.0264	2.0153	2.0042	1.9933
−0.4	1.9823	1.9714	1.9606	1.9498	1.9391	1.9284	1.9177	1.9071	1.8965	1.8860
−0.3	1.8755	1.8650	1.8546	1.8442	1.8338	1.8235	1.8132	1.8029	1.7926	1.7824
−0.2	1.7722	1.7620	1.7518	1.7416	1.7315	1.7214	1.7113	1.7012	1.6911	1.6810
−0.1	1.6710	1.6609	1.6509	1.6409	1.6308	1.6208	1.6108	1.6008	1.5908	1.5808
−0.0	1.5708	1.5608	1.5508	1.5408	1.5308	1.5208	1.5108	1.5007	1.4907	1.4807
0.1	1.4706	1.4606	1.4505	1.4404	1.4303	1.4202	1.4101	1.4000	1.3898	1.3796
0.2	1.3694	1.3592	1.3490	1.3387	1.3284	1.3181	1.3078	1.2974	1.2870	1.2766
0.3	1.2661	1.2556	1.2451	1.2345	1.2239	1.2132	1.2025	1.1918	1.1810	1.1702
0.4	1.1593	1.1483	1.1374	1.1263	1.1152	1.1040	1.0928	1.0815	1.0701	1.0587
0.5	1.0472	1.0356	1.0239	1.0122	1.0004	0.9884	0.9764	0.9643	0.9521	0.9397
0.6	0.9273	0.9147	0.9021	0.8892	0.8763	0.8632	0.8500	0.8366	0.8230	0.8093
0.7	0.7954	0.7813	0.7670	0.7525	0.7377	0.7227	0.7075	0.6920	0.6761	0.6600
0.8	0.6435	0.6266	0.6094	0.5917	0.5735	0.5548	0.5355	0.5156	0.4949	0.4735
0.9	0.4510	0.4275	0.4027	0.3764	0.3482	0.3176	0.2838	0.2456	0.2003	0.1415

Having pinned down our function arccos, we have succeeded in defining *angle,* since Definition 3.2.2 is now meaningful. We now illustrate this definition. Let $\alpha = (1, 0, 0)$ and let $\beta = (0, 1, 0)$; then angle$(\alpha, \beta) = $ arccos $0 = \pi/2$. Again, let $\alpha = (\sqrt{8}, 0, 2, -2)$ and let $\beta = (0, 0, -1, 0)$; then angle $(\alpha, \beta) = $ arccos $-2/4 = $ arccos $-.5 \approx 2.0944$.

Since $\{t \mid -1 \leq t \leq 1\}$ is the domain of arccos, we must verify that $-1 \leq \dfrac{\alpha \cdot \beta}{\|\alpha\| \, \|\beta\|} \leq 1$ whenever α and β are nonzero *n*-vectors. Of course, this follows from the Cauchy–Schwarz Inequality.

We now display some properties of our notion of *angle;* the proofs are straightforward and are left as exercises.

Lemma 3.2.5: Let α and β be any nonzero *n*-vectors; then

- (*i*) $\alpha \perp \beta$ if and only if angle$(\alpha, \beta) = \pi/2$,
- (*ii*) angle$(\alpha, \beta) = $ angle(β, α),
- (*iii*) angle$(\alpha, \alpha) = 0$,
- (*iv*) angle$(\alpha, k\alpha) = 0$ whenever $k > 0$,
- (*v*) angle$(\alpha, -\alpha) = \pi$,
- (*vi*) angle$(\alpha, k\alpha) = \pi$ whenever $k < 0$.

To round off our discussion of arccos we present a short table for cos; again, a more extensive table is provided at the back of the book. We mention that $\cos(-t) = \cos t$ whenever $t \in R$.

cos

t	.0	.1	.2	.3	.4	.5	.6	.7	.8	.9
0	1.0000	0.9950	0.9801	0.9553	0.9211	0.8776	0.8253	0.7648	0.6967	0.6216
1	0.5403	0.4536	0.3624	0.2675	0.1700	0.0707	-0.0292	-0.1288	-0.2272	-0.3233
2	-0.4161	-0.5048	-0.5885	-0.6663	-0.7374	-0.8011	-0.8569	-0.9041	-0.9422	-0.9710
3	-0.9900	-0.9991	-0.9983	-0.9875	-0.9668	-0.9365	-0.8968	-0.8481	-0.7910	-0.7259
4	-0.6536	-0.5748	-0.4903	-0.4008	-0.3073	-0.2108	-0.1122	-0.0124	0.0875	0.1865
5	0.2837	0.3780	0.4685	0.5544	0.6347	0.7087	0.7756	0.8347	0.8855	0.9275
6	0.9602	0.9833	0.9965	0.9999	0.9932	0.9766	0.9502	0.9144	0.8694	0.8157
7	0.7539	0.6845	0.6084	0.5261	0.4385	0.3466	0.2513	0.1534	0.0540	-0.0460
8	-0.1455	-0.2435	-0.3392	-0.4314	-0.5193	-0.6020	-0.6787	-0.7486	-0.8111	-0.8654
9	-0.9111	-0.9477	-0.9748	-0.9922	-0.9997	-0.9972	-0.9847	-0.9624	-0.9304	-0.8892
10	-0.8391	-0.7806	-0.7143	-0.6408	-0.5610	-0.4755	-0.3853	-0.2913	-0.1943	-0.0954
11	0.0044	0.1042	0.2030	0.2997	0.3935	0.4833	0.5683	0.6476	0.7204	0.7861
12	0.8439	0.8932	0.9336	0.9647	0.9862	0.9978	0.9994	0.9911	0.9728	0.9449
13	0.9074	0.8610	0.8059	0.7427	0.6722	0.5949	0.5117	0.4234	0.3308	0.2349
14	0.1367	0.0372	-0.0628	-0.1621	-0.2598	-0.3549	-0.4465	-0.5336	-0.6154	-0.6910
15	-0.7597	-0.8208	-0.8737	-0.9179	-0.9530	-0.9785	-0.9942	-1.0000	-0.9958	-0.9816
16	-0.9577	-0.9241	-0.8814	-0.8298	-0.7699	-0.7024	-0.6278	-0.5470	-0.4607	-0.3698
17	-0.2752	-0.1778	-0.0787	0.0212	0.1209	0.2194	0.3157	0.4089	0.4980	0.5820
18	0.6603	0.7320	0.7964	0.8528	0.9006	0.9395	0.9690	0.9888	0.9988	0.9987
19	0.9887	0.9688	0.9392	0.9003	0.8523	0.7958	0.7314	0.6596	0.5813	0.4972
20	0.4081	0.3149	0.2186	0.1201	0.0204	-0.0796	-0.1787	-0.2760	-0.3706	-0.4615
21	-0.5477	-0.6285	-0.7030	-0.7705	-0.8303	-0.8818	-0.9245	-0.9579	-0.9818	-0.9958
22	-1.0000	-0.9941	-0.9783	-0.9527	-0.9176	-0.8733	-0.8203	-0.7591	-0.6903	-0.6147
23	-0.5328	-0.4457	-0.3541	-0.2590	-0.1612	-0.0619	0.0380	0.1376	0.2358	0.3317
24	0.4242	0.5125	0.5956	0.6729	0.7433	0.8064	0.8614	0.9078	0.9452	0.9730
25	0.9912	0.9995	0.9977	0.9860	0.9645	0.9333	0.8928	0.8434	0.7855	0.7198
26	0.6469	0.5676	0.4825	0.3927	0.2989	0.2021	0.1034	0.0035	-0.0963	-0.1952
27	-0.2921	-0.3862	-0.4763	-0.5617	-0.6415	-0.7149	-0.7811	-0.8396	-0.8896	-0.9308
28	-0.9626	-0.9848	-0.9972	-0.9997	-0.9921	-0.9746	-0.9474	-0.9108	-0.8650	-0.8106
29	-0.7481	-0.6781	-0.6013	-0.5185	-0.4306	-0.3383	-0.2427	-0.1446	-0.0451	0.0548

EXERCISES

1. (a) Show, intuitively, that $\|\alpha\|$ is the length of the line-segment with endpoints α and $(0\,,\,0)$, whenever $\alpha \in R_2$.

   (b) Show, intuitively, that $\|\alpha - \beta\|$ is the length of the line-segment with endpoints α and β, whenever $\{\alpha\,,\,\beta\} \subset R_2$ and $\alpha \neq \beta$.

2. Let $\alpha = (1\,,\,2\,,\,2)$ and let $\beta = (1\,,\,0\,,\,0)$.

   (a) Compute $\|\alpha + \beta\|$.
   (b) Compute $\|\alpha - \beta\|$.
   (c) Compute $\alpha \cdot \beta$.
   (d) Compute $\|\alpha\|\,\|\beta\|$.
   (e) Compute $\|\alpha\| + \|\beta\|$.

3. Prove Lemma 3.2.1.

4. Prove Lemma 3.2.2.

5. Prove Lemma 3.2.3.

6. Prove Theorem 3.2.1.

7. Prove Corollary 3.2.1.

8. Let $\alpha = (a_1\,,\,\ldots\,,\,a_n)$ and let $\beta = (b_1\,,\,\ldots\,,\,b_n)$. Prove the Cauchy–Schwarz Inequality by observing that $\sum_{i=1}^{n} (xa_i + b_i)^2 \geq 0$ whenever $x \in R$; expand the left-hand side and consider its discriminant.

9. Prove that $|\alpha \cdot \beta| = \|\alpha\|\,\|\beta\|$ if $\alpha = \mathbf{0}$ or $\beta \in L\{\alpha\}$.

10. Prove that $\|\alpha + \beta\| = \|\alpha\| + \|\beta\|$ if $\alpha = \mathbf{0}$ or there is a non-negative real number k such that $\beta = k\alpha$.

11. Use Simpson's Rule to compute arccos .01.

12. Let $\alpha = (-1\,,\,2\,,\,2)$ and let $\beta = (1\,,\,0\,,\,0)$; compute angle $(\alpha\,,\,\beta)$.

13. Compute angle$((3\,,\,4)\,,\,(-1\,,\,2))$.

14. Prove that $-1 \leq \dfrac{\alpha \cdot \beta}{\|\alpha\|\,\|\beta\|} \leq 1$ whenever α and β are nonzero n-vectors.

15. Prove Lemma 3.2.5.

3.3 MATRIX ALGEBRA

In order to develop a useful algebra of matrices we now introduce suitable operations on matrices; namely, addition, multiplication by a real number (which is called *scalar* multiplication), and matrix multiplication. To add matrices we add corresponding row vectors. To multiply a matrix by a scalar we multiply each row vector of the matrix by the scalar. To multiply matrices A and B we form the matrix whose ith row vector is the linear combination of the row vectors of B obtained by using the corresponding terms of A_i as scalars; accordingly, we require that A have exactly as many columns as B has rows.

Definition 3.3.1: Let A and B be any $m \times n$ matrices; then $A + B = C$ where $C_i = A_i + B_i, i = 1, \ldots, m$.

Definition 3.3.2: Let A be any $m \times n$ matrix and let k be any scalar; then $kA = D$ where $D_i = kA_i, i = 1, \ldots, m$.

Definition 3.3.3: Let $A = (a_{ij})$ be any $r \times n$ matrix and let B be any $n \times s$ matrix; then $A \cdot B = E$ where $E_i = a_{i1} B_1 + \cdots + a_{in} B_n, i = 1, \ldots, r$.

We point out that the dot for matrix multiplication is sometimes omitted. Let us illustrate these definitions.

$$\begin{pmatrix} 1 & 4 \\ 2 & 5 \\ 3 & 6 \end{pmatrix} + \begin{pmatrix} 2 & 0 \\ 1 & 3 \\ -2 & 4 \end{pmatrix} = \begin{pmatrix} 3 & 4 \\ 3 & 8 \\ 1 & 10 \end{pmatrix} .$$

$$3 \begin{pmatrix} 1 & 0 & 2 \\ 3 & -2 & -3 \end{pmatrix} = \begin{pmatrix} 3 & 0 & 6 \\ 9 & -6 & -9 \end{pmatrix} .$$

$$\begin{pmatrix} 1 & 2 & -1 & 3 \\ -2 & 3 & -3 & 5 \end{pmatrix} \begin{pmatrix} 4 & -1 & 5 \\ 2 & 1 & 0 \\ 1 & 3 & 1 \\ 0 & 2 & -2 \end{pmatrix} = \begin{pmatrix} 7 & 4 & -2 \\ -5 & 6 & -23 \end{pmatrix} .$$

In connection with the preceding example we point out that the first row vector of the product is the following linear combination of the row vectors of its second factor:

$$1(4, -1, 5) + 2(2, 1, 0) + -1(1, 3, 1) + 3(0, 2, -2)$$

$$= (4, -1, 5) + (4, 2, 0) + (-1, -3, -1) + (0, 6, -6)$$

$$= (7, 4, -2) .$$

Matrix multiplication can also be characterized in terms of the *dot product* of Section 3.1. It is easy to verify that, for each i and j, the entry in the ith row and jth column of AB is the dot product $A_i \cdot {}_jB$.

Lemma 3.3.1: Let A be any $r \times n$ matrix and let B be any $n \times s$ matrix; then $AB = (A_i \cdot {}_jB)$, an $r \times s$ matrix.

We mention that Lemma 3.3.1 can be formulated as follows: $(a_{ij})(b_{ij}) = (\sum_{k=1}^{n} a_{ik} b_{kj})$ whenever (a_{ij}) has n columns and (b_{ij}) has n rows.

In a moment we will present several useful methods of characterizing matrix multiplication. In this connection we need the following theorem, which asserts that the transpose of a product is the product of the transposes in reverse order.

Theorem 3.3.1: Let A and B be any matrices such that AB exists; then $(AB)^t = B^t A^t$.

Proof: By Lemma 3.3.1 $AB = (A_i \cdot {}_j B)$, so $(AB)^t = (A_j \cdot {}_i B)$. Again by Lemma 3.3.1, $B^t A^t = ([B^t]_i \cdot {}_j[A^t]) = ({}_i B \cdot A_j) = (A_j \cdot {}_i B)$.

We are now in a position to prove that the jth column vector of AB is the linear combination of the column vectors of A obtained by using the corresponding terms of ${}_j B$ as scalars.

Lemma 3.3.2: Let A be any $r \times n$ matrix and let $B = (b_{ij})$ be any $n \times s$ matrix; then ${}_j(AB) = b_{1j}\,({}_1 A) + \cdots + b_{nj}\,({}_n A), j = 1, \ldots, s$.

Proof: Now,

$$
{}_j(AB) = (B^t\, A^t)_j \qquad\qquad \text{by Theorem 3.3.1}
$$

$$
= b_{1j}\,(A^t)_1 + \cdots + b_{nj}\,(A^t)_n \qquad \text{by Definition 3.3.3}
$$

$$
= b_{1j}\,({}_1 A) + \cdots + b_{nj}\,({}_n A)\ .
$$

There are several more lemmas that interest us. Before considering them we must clarify one point, namely the relation between an n-vector $(a_1, \ldots, a_n)$ and the corresponding $1 \times n$ matrix $(a_1 \ \ \ldots \ \ a_n)$. Let us not fall into the error of identifying these objects; after all, the matrix $(a_1 \ldots a_n)$ can be regarded as an ordered 1-tuple whose one and only term is the n-vector $(a_1, \ldots, a_n)$. Certainly, we do not identify $\{t\}$ with t; so, we must agree that $(a_1 \ldots a_n) \neq (a_1, \ldots, a_n)$. Nonetheless, it is useful to adopt the following convention; we interpret an n-vector which appears in a matrix context as a $1 \times n$ matrix. Similarly, we interpret a $1 \times n$ matrix as an n-vector if the matrix appears in a vector context. This is simply and purely a notational agreement; i.e., we propose to simplify our notation by agreeing to suppress a symbol that transforms an n-vector into the corresponding $1 \times n$ matrix, and to suppress a symbol that transforms a $1 \times n$ matrix into the corresponding n-vector.

Let us prove that each row vector of a matrix product can be expressed as a matrix product.

Lemma 3.3.3: Let A and B be matrices such that AB exists; then $(AB)_i = A_i \cdot B$, a matrix product, for each i.

Proof: Applying our convention, we interpret A_i as a matrix with one row whenever A_i appears in a matrix context; in particular, $A_i \cdot B$ is a matrix product. Now, Lemma 3.3.1 simplifies in the case of a matrix product whose first factor has just one row, as follows. Let α be any $1 \times n$ matrix and let B be any $n \times s$ matrix; then the jth entry of αB is $\alpha \cdot {}_j B$, a dot product. Returning to our lemma, we see that the jth entry of $A_i \cdot B$ is $A_i \cdot {}_jB$. By Lemma 3.3.1, $A_i \cdot {}_jB$ is the jth entry of $(AB)_i$, for each j. This proves that $(AB)_i = A_i \cdot B$.

Let us prove that each column vector of a matrix product can be expressed as a matrix product.

Lemma 3.3.4: Let A and B be matrices such that AB exists; then ${}_j(AB) = {}_jB \cdot A^t$, a matrix product, for each j.

Proof: Now,

$$ {}_j(AB) = (B^t \, A^t)_j \qquad \text{by Theorem 3.3.1} $$

$$ = (B^t)_j \cdot A^t \qquad \text{by Lemma 3.3.3} $$

$$ = ({}_jB)A^t. $$

The preceding methods of characterizing the row and column vectors of AB are useful in developing the algebraic properties of matrix multiplication. In Lemma 3.3.5 we present a valuable identity concerning dot products. There, we need the notion of a *matrix with multipliers*, which we now present. Let $B = (b_{ij})$ be any $m \times n$ matrix, let $\alpha = (a_1, \ldots, a_m)$, and let $\gamma = (c_1, \ldots, c_n)$. Let us agree that the following expression, which we call a *matrix with multipliers*,

$$
\begin{array}{cc}
& \begin{array}{ccc} c_1 & \cdots & c_n \end{array} \\
\begin{array}{c} a_1 \\ \cdot \\ \cdot \\ \cdot \\ a_m \end{array} &
\left(\begin{array}{ccc} b_{11} & \cdots & b_{1n} \\ \cdot & & \\ \cdot & & \\ \cdot & & \\ b_{m1} & \cdots & b_{mn} \end{array} \right)
\end{array}
$$

denotes the scalar obtained by multiplying each entry of B by its row and column headings, and summing. For example, the matrix with multipliers

$$
\begin{array}{cc}
& \begin{array}{cccc} 4 & 5 & -1 & 2 \end{array} \\
\begin{array}{c} 3 \\ -1 \end{array} &
\left(\begin{array}{cccc} 2 & -1 & 3 & 5 \\ 4 & 0 & -7 & 6 \end{array} \right)
\end{array}
$$

denotes -5. In view of the distributive law we can obtain our sum by taking subtotals according to columns or rows. Taking subtotals by columns means that we first multiply each entry of a column by the corresponding row heading, and then we multiply their sum by the column heading; finally, we total the subtotals for each column. Taking subtotals by rows means that we first multiply each entry of a row by the corresponding column heading, and then we multiply their sum by the row heading; finally, we total the subtotals for each row. The point is that these operations can be represented by dot products. Taking subtotals by columns yields

$$ \left[(3, -1) \begin{pmatrix} 2 & -1 & 3 & 5 \\ 4 & 0 & -7 & 6 \end{pmatrix} \right] \cdot (4, 5, -1, 2). $$

Taking subtotals by rows yields

$$(3,\,-1)\cdot\left[(4,\,5,\,-1,\,2)\begin{pmatrix}2 & -1 & 3 & 5\\4 & 0 & -7 & 6\end{pmatrix}^{t}\right].$$

So, a matrix with multipliers expresses the value of a dot product, indeed of the two dot products built up from the matrix and its multipliers in the manner of this example. We conclude that these dot products are the same.

We now consider the general situation.

Lemma 3.3.5: Let $\alpha \in R_m$, $\gamma \in R_n$, and let B be any $m \times n$ matrix. Then $(\alpha B)\cdot\gamma = \alpha\cdot(\gamma B^t)$.

Proof: Let $\alpha = (a_1,\,\ldots,\,a_m)$, let $\gamma = (c_1,\,\ldots,\,c_n)$, and let $B = (b_{ij})$.

Taking subtotals by columns we see that

$$
\begin{array}{c}
\begin{array}{ccc} c_1 & \cdots & c_n \end{array}\\
\begin{array}{c} a_1 \\ \cdot \\ \cdot \\ \cdot \\ a_m \end{array}
\begin{pmatrix} b_{11} & \cdots & b_{1n} \\ \cdot & & \\ & \cdot & \\ & & \cdot \\ b_{m1} & \cdots & b_{mn} \end{pmatrix} = (\alpha B)\cdot\gamma\ .
\end{array}
$$

Taking subtotals by rows we see that

$$
\begin{array}{c}
\begin{array}{ccc} c_1 & \cdots & c_n \end{array}\\
\begin{array}{c} a_1 \\ \cdot \\ \cdot \\ \cdot \\ a_m \end{array}
\begin{pmatrix} b_{11} & \cdots & b_{1n} \\ \cdot & & \\ & \cdot & \\ & & \cdot \\ b_{m1} & \cdots & b_{mn} \end{pmatrix} = \alpha\cdot(\gamma B^t)\ .
\end{array}
$$

We conclude that $(\alpha B)\cdot\gamma = \alpha\cdot(\gamma B^t)$.

Notice that Lemma 3.3.5 amounts to a special case of the associative law for matrix multiplication, which we now state.

Lemma 3.3.6: Let $\alpha \in R_m$, $\gamma \in R_n$, and let B be any $m \times n$ matrix. Then $(\alpha B)\gamma^t = \alpha(B\gamma^t)$.

Proof: The point is that $(\alpha B)\cdot\gamma$ is the entry of the 1×1 matrix $(\alpha B)\gamma^t$; whereas $\alpha\cdot(B\gamma^t)^t = \alpha\cdot(\gamma B^t)$ is the entry of the 1×1 matrix $\alpha(B\gamma^t)$. So, by Lemma 3.3.5, $(\alpha B)\gamma^t = \alpha(B\gamma^t)$.

Next, we prove that matrix multiplication is associative.

Theorem 3.3.2: Let A be any $r \times s$ matrix, let B be any $s \times t$ matrix, and let C be any $t \times u$ matrix. Then $A(BC) = (AB)C$.

First Proof: Here, the idea is to prove that $A(BC)$ and $(AB)C$ have the same row vectors. By Lemma 3.3.3, the ith row vector of $A(BC)$ is $A_i \cdot (BC)$, and by Lemma 3.3.4, the jth column vector of $A_i \cdot (BC)$ is $_j(BC) \cdot (A_i)^t = (_jC \cdot B^t) \cdot (A_i)^t$, a matrix product. Similarly, the ith row vector of $(AB)C$ is $(A_i \cdot B) \cdot C$ whose jth column vector is $_jC \cdot (A_i \cdot B)^t = _jC \cdot (B^t \cdot [A_i]^t)$, a matrix product. But $(_jC \cdot B^t) \cdot (A_i)^t = _jC \cdot (B^t \cdot [A_i]^t)$ by Lemma 3.3.6. We conclude that $A(BC)$ and $(AB)C$ have the same row vectors; thus $A(BC) = (AB)C$.

Second Proof: This time we use Lemmas 3.3.1 and 3.3.5 to prove that $A(BC)$ and $(AB)C$ have the same entries. Let $A(BC) = (d_{ij})$ and let $(AB)C = (e_{ij})$. Then

$$d_{ij} = A_i \cdot {}_j(BC) = A_i \cdot (_jC \cdot B^t)$$

and

$$e_{ij} = (AB)_i \cdot {}_jC = (A_i \cdot B) \cdot {}_jC = A_i \cdot (_jC \cdot B^t) = d_{ij}.$$

Therefore, $A(BC) = (AB)C$.

Since vector addition is commutative and associative, it follows that matrix addition is commutative and associative. However, matrix multiplication is not commutative; i.e., there exist matrices A and B such that $AB \neq BA$. For example,

$$\begin{pmatrix} 2 & 3 \\ 1 & 4 \end{pmatrix}\begin{pmatrix} -1 & 4 \\ 5 & 3 \end{pmatrix} = \begin{pmatrix} 13 & 17 \\ 19 & 16 \end{pmatrix} \quad \text{whereas} \quad \begin{pmatrix} -1 & 4 \\ 5 & 3 \end{pmatrix}\begin{pmatrix} 2 & 3 \\ 1 & 4 \end{pmatrix} = \begin{pmatrix} 2 & 13 \\ 13 & 27 \end{pmatrix}.$$

Luckily, matrix multiplication distributes over addition from either side. This is a very useful fact. We now present our distributive laws.

Theorem 3.3.3 (*Distributive Law*): Let A be any $r \times s$ matrix and let B and C be any $s \times t$ matrices. Then $A(B + C) = AB + AC$.

Proof: Apply Lemma 3.3.1 and Theorem 3.!.1.

Theorem 3.3.4 (*Distributive Law*): Let A and B be any $r \times s$ matrices and let C be any $s \times t$ matrix. Then $(A + B)C = AC + BC$.

Proof: Apply Lemma 3.3.1 and Theorem 3.1.1. Alternatively, use Theorem 3.3.3 and Theorem 3.3.1.

Finally, we establish that the determinant of a product of $n \times n$ matrices is the product of their determinants.

Theorem 3.3.5: Let A and B be any $n \times n$ matrices; then $|AB| = |A| \, |B|$.

Proof: Let $A = (a_{ij})$; then

$$|AB| = \det \left(\sum_{i=1}^{n} a_{1j} B_j, \ldots, \sum_{j=1}^{n} a_{nj} B_j \right)$$

$$= \sum_{\mu \in M_n} \det (a_{1,\mu(1)} B_{\mu(1)}, \ldots, a_{n,\mu(n)} B_{\mu(n)}) \qquad \text{by Lemma 1.4.6}$$

$$= \sum_{\Pi \in P_n} \det (a_{1,\Pi(1)} B_{\Pi(1)}, \ldots, a_{n,\Pi(n)} B_{\Pi(n)}) \qquad \text{by Corollary 1.4.1}$$

$$= \sum_{\Pi \in P_n} a_{1,\Pi(1)} \times \cdots \times a_{n,\Pi(n)} \times \det (B_{\Pi(1)}, \ldots, B_{\Pi(n)}) \quad \text{by Theorem 1.4.2}$$

$$= \sum_{\Pi \in P_n} a_{1,\Pi(1)} \times \cdots \times a_{n,\Pi(n)} \times \operatorname{sgn} \Pi \times |B| \qquad \text{by Lemma 1.6.7}$$

$$= |A||B| . \qquad \text{by Theorem 1.6.3}$$

This completes our proof.

EXERCISES

1. Prove Lemma 3.3.1.

2. Compute

$$\begin{pmatrix} 1 & -2 & 4 \\ 0 & 3 & 5 \end{pmatrix} \begin{pmatrix} 2 & 4 & 0 \\ -1 & 1 & 1 \\ 3 & 5 & 2 \end{pmatrix}$$

in three different ways.

3. Compute $(AB)_2$ given that

$$A = \begin{pmatrix} 2 & -1 \\ 1 & 2 \\ 4 & 0 \\ 3 & 1 \end{pmatrix} \quad \text{and} \quad B = \begin{pmatrix} 3 & 4 & 7 \\ -2 & 5 & 3 \end{pmatrix} .$$

4. (a) Prove that $\epsilon_i \cdot A = A_i$ whenever this matrix product exists.
   (b) Prove that $A \cdot \epsilon_j{}^t = {}_jA$ whenever this matrix product exists.
   (c) Simplify the matrix product $\epsilon_i \cdot A \cdot \epsilon_j{}^t$.
   (d) Simplify the matrix product $\epsilon_i \cdot A \cdot B \cdot \epsilon_j{}^t$.

5. Prove Theorem 3.3.3.

6. Prove Theorem 3.3.4.

7. Simplify the matrix product $(\epsilon_i + \epsilon_j)A$.

8. Let B be the matrix obtained from I_n by interchanging its ith and jth row vectors, and let A be any $n \times n$ matrix. Prove that BA is the matrix obtained from A by interchanging its ith and jth row vectors.

9. Let C be the matrix obtained from I_n by multiplying its ith row vector by a scalar k, and let A be any $n \times n$ matrix. Prove that CA is the matrix obtained from A by multiplying its ith row vector by k.

10. Let D be the matrix obtained from I_n by adding its ith row vector to its jth row vector, and let A be any $n \times n$ matrix. Prove that DA is the matrix obtained from A by replacing A_j by $A_i + A_j$.

11. Use the result contained in Exercise 8 to characterize the matrix obtained from A by interchanging its ith and jth column vectors.

12. Use the result contained in Exercise 9 to characterize the matrix obtained from A by multiplying its ith column vector by a scalar k.

13. Use the result contained in Exercise 10 to characterize the matrix obtained from A by replacing $_jA$ by $_iA + _jA$.

3.4   INVERSES

Next, let $n \in N$ and consider the $n \times n$ matrix diag $(1 , \ldots , 1)$ which we have agreed to denote by I_n. The following lemma, which states that I_n is a multiplicative identity, is easy to prove.

Lemma 3.4.1:   Let $n \in N$ and let A be any $n \times n$ matrix; then $AI_n = I_nA = A$.

Proof: Apply Definition 3.3.3 and Lemma 3.3.2.

By an *inverse* of an $n \times n$ matrix A we mean any $n \times n$ matrix B such that $AB = I_n$. Notice that if $a \neq 0$ then $(1/a)$ is an inverse of the 1×1 matrix (a). It is easy to see that certain square matrices do not have inverses; indeed, if $|A| = 0$ then A does not have an inverse.

Lemma 3.4.2:   No singular matrix possesses an inverse.

Proof: Let $n \in N$ and let A be any singular $n \times n$ matrix; i.e., $|A| = 0$. Now, suppose that B is an inverse of A; then $AB = I_n$. Therefore, by Theorem 3.3.5, $|A||B| = |I_n| = 1$. But $|A| = 0$; so $|A||B| = 0$. This contradiction establishes our result.

In a moment we present a method of obtaining an inverse of a square matrix, provided the matrix has an inverse, which makes use of the *adjoint* matrix.

Definition 3.4.1:   Let $n > 1$ and let $A = (a_{ij})$ be any $n \times n$ matrix; then $(A_{ij})^t$ is said to be the *adjoint* matrix of (a_{ij}), and is denoted by *adj* A.

For example,

$$\text{adj} \begin{pmatrix} 1 & 3 \\ 2 & 4 \end{pmatrix} = \begin{pmatrix} 4 & -2 \\ -3 & 1 \end{pmatrix}^t = \begin{pmatrix} 4 & -3 \\ -2 & 1 \end{pmatrix} \quad \text{and}$$

$$\text{adj} \begin{pmatrix} 2 & 1 & 0 \\ 3 & -2 & 1 \\ 4 & 0 & -1 \end{pmatrix} = \begin{pmatrix} 2 & 7 & 8 \\ 1 & -2 & 4 \\ 1 & -2 & -7 \end{pmatrix}^t = \begin{pmatrix} 2 & 1 & 1 \\ 7 & -2 & -2 \\ 8 & 4 & -7 \end{pmatrix}.$$

Our method is based on the following result.

Lemma 3.4.3: Let $n > 1$ and let A be any $n \times n$ matrix. Then $A \text{ adj } A = |A|I_n$.

Proof: Let $A = (a_{ij})$; then $\text{adj } A = (A_{ji})$. Now, by Lemma 3.3.3,

$$(A \cdot \text{adj } A)_i = A_i \cdot \text{adj } A = \left(\sum_{t=1}^{n} a_{it} A_{1t}, \ldots, \sum_{t=1}^{n} a_{it} A_{nt} \right).$$

But $$\sum_{t=1}^{n} a_{it} A_{jt} = \begin{cases} 0 & \text{if } j \neq i \quad \text{(by Theorem 1.6.2)} \\ |A| & \text{if } j = i \quad \text{(by Theorem 1.4.5)} \end{cases}.$$

So $(A \cdot \text{adj } A)_i = |A|\epsilon_i$; therefore, $A \cdot \text{adj } A = \text{diag} (|A|, \ldots, |A|) = |A|I_n$.

We now present our main result.

Theorem 3.4.1: Let $n > 1$ and let A be any $n \times n$ nonsingular matrix. Then $\frac{1}{|A|}\text{adj } A$ is an inverse of A.

Proof: Now, $A\left(\frac{1}{|A|}\text{adj } A \right) = \frac{1}{|A|}(A \cdot \text{adj } A) = \frac{1}{|A|}(|A|I_n)$ by Lemma 3.4.3

$$= I_n.$$

Thus $\frac{1}{|A|}\text{adj } A$ is an inverse of A.

Theorem 3.4.1 is important largely for its theoretical significance (e.g., see Theorem 3.4.2 and the proof of the Cayley–Hamilton Theorem). It also possesses computational value; for example, this result enables us to compute inverses of 2×2 matrices effortlessly. Also, it can be used to compute inverses, where $n > 2$, in conjunction with an efficient technique for computing adjoints. However, in Section 3.5, we present a very effective method of computing inverses which is based on another approach. To bring out the theoretical value of Theorem 3.4.1, we point out that this result together with Lemma 3.4.2 provides us with a necessary and sufficient condition for the *existence* of an inverse of a square matrix.

Theorem 3.4.2: A square matrix A has an inverse if and only if A is non-singular.

Let us illustrate our main theorem, Theorem 3.4.1.

Example 1: Determine an inverse of $\begin{pmatrix} 1 & 3 \\ -1 & 2 \end{pmatrix}$.

Solution:

Let $A = \begin{pmatrix} 1 & 3 \\ -1 & 2 \end{pmatrix}$; now, $|A| = 5$ and adj $A = \begin{pmatrix} 2 & 1 \\ -3 & 1 \end{pmatrix}^t = \begin{pmatrix} 2 & -3 \\ 1 & 1 \end{pmatrix}$.

Therefore, by Theorem 3.4.1, $\frac{1}{5}\begin{pmatrix} 2 & -3 \\ 1 & 1 \end{pmatrix}$ is an inverse of A. Checking,

we see that

$$\begin{pmatrix} 1 & 3 \\ -1 & 2 \end{pmatrix}\begin{pmatrix} 2/5 & -3/5 \\ 1/5 & 1/5 \end{pmatrix} = \begin{pmatrix} 1 & 0 \\ 0 & 1 \end{pmatrix}.$$

Many useful properties of inverses are freely available once we establish the kind of algebraic system that we face. In Section 6.2 we present the group concept; there we see that the algebraic system $(G, \cdot, I_n)$, where G is the set of all nonsingular $n \times n$ matrices and $\cdot$ denotes matrix multiplication restricted to G, is a group. It is easy to check that the group postulates are true for this algebraic system (see Definition 6.2.1); in particular, it follows from Theorem 3.3.5 that $\cdot$ is a binary operation on G and that inverses are nonsingular. Looking ahead, we now utilize certain facts about groups. Alternatively, a proof of each of the following theorems can be obtained mechanically from the proof of the corresponding result of Section 6.2; it is merely a matter of formulating the general proofs of Section 6.2 in the language of this section. These observations illustrate the power of the abstract approach of Chapter 6.

Theorem 3.4.3: Each nonsingular $n \times n$ matrix possesses a unique inverse.

Proof: This is true for any group (see Theorem 6.2.4).

In view of this result we are entitled to speak of *the* inverse of a nonsingular square matrix. Let A be any nonsingular square matrix; let us agree to denote the inverse of A by writing A^{-1}. The following theorem asserts that if $B = A^{-1}$ then $A = B^{-1}$; in particular, it follows that $(A^{-1})^{-1} = A$.

Theorem 3.4.4: Let A and B be nonsingular $n \times n$ matrices such that $AB = I_n$; then $BA = I_n$.

Proof: This is true for any group. However, to illustrate the observation that precedes Theorem 3.4.3, we present the proof of Lemma 6.2.2 in the language of matrices. Let $AB = I_n$. In view of Theorem 3.3.5, $|B| \neq 0$; so B has an inverse, say C. Now,

$$BA = (BA)I_n \qquad \text{by Lemma 3.4.1}$$
$$= (BA)(BC) \qquad \text{since } C = B^{-1}$$
$$= ((BA)B)C \qquad \text{by Theorem 3.3.2}$$
$$= (B(AB))C \qquad \text{by Theorem 3.3.2}$$
$$= (BI_n)C \qquad \text{since } AB = I_n$$
$$= BC \qquad \text{by Lemma 3.4.1}$$
$$= I_n \ .$$

Theorem 3.4.5: Let A and B be any nonsingular $n \times n$ matrices; then $(AB)^{-1} = B^{-1}A^{-1}$.

Proof: This is true for any group (see Lemma 6.2.6).

Here is an interesting relation between our unary operations *transpose* and *inverse*. This result depends primarily on Theorem 3.3.1.

Corollary 3.4.1: Let A be any nonsingular $n \times n$ matrix; then $(A^t)^{-1} = (A^{-1})^t$.

Proof: By Theorem 3.4.4, $A^{-1}A = I_n$; so, by Theorem 3.3.1,

$$A^t(A^{-1})^t = (I_n)^t = I_n$$

thus $(A^t)^{-1} = (A^{-1})^t$.

Using this result and Theorem 3.4.1 we can characterize $(A^t)^{-1}$.

Corollary 3.4.2: Let A be any nonsingular matrix; then $(A^t)^{-1} = \dfrac{1}{|A|}(A_{ij})$.

Proof: $(A^t)^{-1} = (A^{-1})^t = \left[\dfrac{1}{|A|}(A_{ij})^t\right]^t = \dfrac{1}{|A|}(A_{ij})$.

EXERCISES

1. Prove Lemma 3.4.1.

2. Prove that $AB = I_n$ if and only if $BA = I_n$.

3. Compute the adjoint matrix of each of the following.

   (a) $\begin{pmatrix} 2 & 1 \\ -1 & 3 \end{pmatrix}$

   (b) $\begin{pmatrix} -3 & 5 \\ 2 & 4 \end{pmatrix}$

   (c) $\begin{pmatrix} 2 & 1 & 0 \\ 0 & 2 & 1 \\ 1 & -1 & 4 \end{pmatrix}$

   (d) $\begin{pmatrix} 3 & 1 & 2 \\ 2 & 0 & 1 \\ 0 & 0 & 0 \end{pmatrix}$

(e) $\begin{pmatrix} 1 & 2 & 3 & -2 \\ 0 & 1 & 2 & 3 \\ -1 & -2 & 0 & -1 \\ 2 & 1 & -1 & 1 \end{pmatrix}$
(f) $\begin{pmatrix} 1 & -1 & 2 & 1 \\ 2 & 0 & 1 & -2 \\ 1 & 3 & 4 & 2 \\ 0 & 1 & 5 & -1 \end{pmatrix}$

4. Exhibit the inverse of each nonsingular matrix of Exercise 3.

5. Find a matrix X such that $\begin{pmatrix} 2 & 1 \\ -1 & 3 \end{pmatrix} X = \begin{pmatrix} 4 & 1 \\ 1 & 2 \end{pmatrix}$.

6. Find a matrix X such that

$$\begin{pmatrix} 1 & -1 & 2 & 1 \\ 2 & 0 & 1 & -2 \\ 1 & 3 & 4 & 2 \\ 0 & 1 & 5 & -1 \end{pmatrix} X = \begin{pmatrix} 2 & 0 & 1 & 2 \\ 0 & 1 & 0 & 3 \\ -1 & 1 & -1 & 1 \\ 1 & 2 & 1 & 2 \end{pmatrix}.$$

7. Find a matrix X such that

$$\begin{pmatrix} 1 & -1 & 2 & 1 \\ 2 & 0 & 1 & -2 \\ 1 & 3 & 4 & 2 \\ 0 & 1 & 5 & -1 \end{pmatrix} X = \begin{pmatrix} 2 \\ 0 \\ -1 \\ 1 \end{pmatrix}.$$

8. Let $n > 1$, let A be any nonsingular $n \times n$ matrix, and let A_{ij} be the cofactor of (i,j) in A. Prove that:

   (a) $|A_{ij}| = |A|^{n-1}$,
   (b) $|\text{adj } A| = |A|^{n-1}$.

9. Use the result of Exercise 8 to compute $|B|$ where

$$B = \text{adj}\begin{pmatrix} 1 & 2 & 3 & -2 \\ 0 & 1 & 2 & 3 \\ -1 & -2 & 0 & -1 \\ 2 & 1 & -1 & 1 \end{pmatrix}.$$

10. A matrix, say B, is said to be *symmetric* if and only if $B^t = B$. Prove that $A \cdot A^t$ is symmetric whenever A is a matrix.

11. (a) Let A and B be any $m \times n$ matrices, show that $(A + B)^t = A^t + B^t$.
    (b) Prove that $A + A^t$ is symmetric whenever A is a square matrix.

12. Prove Theorem 3.4.2.

13. Prove Theorem 3.4.3 without referring to groups.

14. Prove that the inverse of a nonsingular matrix is also nonsingular.

15. Prove Theorem 3.4.5 without referring to groups.

16. We define the *trace* of a square matrix as follows. Let $A = (a_{ij})$ be any $n \times n$ matrix; then trace $A = \sum_{i=1}^{n} a_{ii}$, the sum of its diagonal entries.

(a) Show that trace $(A + B)$ = trace A + trace B whenever A and B are $n \times n$ matrices.

(b) Prove that trace (AB) = trace (BA) whenever A and B are $n \times n$ matrices. *Hint:* Use mathematical induction over n.

(c) Prove that $AB - BA \neq I_n$ whenever A and B are $n \times n$ matrices.

17. We define *similar* matrices as follows. Let A and B be any $n \times n$ matrices; then B is said to be *similar* to A if and only if there is a nonsingular matrix P such that $B = PAP^{-1}$.

(a) Prove that similar matrices have the same trace.

(b) Prove that similar matrices have the same rank.

18. Let A and B be matrices such that AB exists.

(a) Prove that rank $AB \leq$ rank A.

(b) Prove that rank $AB \leq$ rank B.

(c) Assuming that A is $n \times n$ and that B is nonsingular, prove that rank AB = rank BA = rank A.

3.5 ELEMENTARY MATRICES; MIXED MATRICES

In Section 3.4 we presented a method of computing the inverse of a nonsingular $n \times n$ matrix by considering its adjoint matrix. This method is terribly inefficient since it involves computing the determinant of n^2, $n - 1 \times n - 1$ matrices, and the determinant of one $n \times n$ matrix. However, in Chapter 4 we develop a technique that enables us to compute adjoints with relative ease. We propose, now, to present a very efficient method of calculating inverses which is based on another approach. The key idea is that each nonsingular $n \times n$ matrix can be reduced to I_n by a sequence of permitted row operations; we have discussed this idea, in a more general setting, in Section 2.5. Recall that there are exactly three permitted row operations:

     (*i*) interchange two row vectors;
     (*ii*) multiply a row vector by a nonzero scalar;
     (*iii*) add one row vector to another row vector.

Here, we propose to pin down these operations by expressing the result of carrying out an operation as a matrix product whose right-hand factor is the given matrix. A suitable left-hand factor can be characterized very simply. Let A be any nonsingular $n \times n$ matrix. We obtain the required left-hand factor by performing the operation in question on I_n. For example, let B be the matrix obtained from I_n by interchanging its ith and jth row vectors. We claim that BA is the matrix obtained from A by interchanging its ith and jth row vectors. To see this, we apply Lemma 3.3.3. Now, $(BA)_i = B_i \cdot A = \epsilon_j \cdot A = A_j$ and $(BA)_j = B_j \cdot A = \epsilon_i \cdot A = A_i$; whereas $(BA)_m = B_m \cdot A = \epsilon_m \cdot A = A_m$ if $m \neq i$ and $m \neq j$. Thus BA is the matrix obtained from A by interchanging its ith and jth row vectors. Similarly, it is easy to verify our statement that CA is the matrix obtained from A by multiplying its ith row vector by k, a nonzero scalar, where C is the matrix obtained from I_n by multiplying its ith row vector by k. It remains to verify that DA is the matrix obtained from A by replacing A_j by $A_i + A_j$, where $i \neq j$ and D is the matrix obtained from I_n by adding its ith row vector to its jth row vector. By Lemma 3.3.3 and Theorem 3.3.4

$$(DA)_j = D_j \cdot A = (\epsilon_i + \epsilon_j) \cdot A = \epsilon_i \cdot A + \epsilon_j \cdot A = A_i + A_j$$

whereas if $m \neq j$ then $(DA)_m = D_m \cdot A = \epsilon_m \cdot A = A_m$. So DA is the matrix obtained from A by replacing A_j by $A_i + A_j$. Each matrix obtained from I_n by applying a permitted row operation is said to be an *elementary* matrix.

We have now demonstrated that each permitted row operation can be carried out by premultiplying by an appropriate elementary matrix. Let A be any $n \times n$ nonsingular matrix; now, there is a finite sequence of permitted row operations that transforms A into I_n. In view of the associative law for matrix multiplication, there are corresponding elementary matrices $E_1, \ldots, E_s$ such that $(E_s \ldots E_1)A = I_n$. Applying Theorem 3.4.4 we conclude that A^{-1} is the matrix product $E_s \ldots E_1$.

At first sight, it appears that we must keep track of each row operation involved in reducing A, and form the product of the corresponding elementary matrices. Fortunately, we can simplify our technique by noting that $E_s \ldots E_1 = (E_s \ldots E_1)I_n$. Reversing the preceding argument, it follows that the right-hand side of this equation is the matrix obtained by applying the corresponding row operations to I_n. In short, we obtain A^{-1} by simultaneously row reducing A and I_n so that A is transformed into I_n. The matrix obtained from I_n is the inverse of A. An effective way of applying the same row operations to A and I_n is to place A and I_n side by side. Consider the following examples.

Example 1:　Determine $\begin{pmatrix} 1 & 3 \\ -1 & 2 \end{pmatrix}^{-1}$.

Solution:

$$\begin{pmatrix} 1 & 3 & 1 & 0 \\ -1 & 2 & 0 & 1 \end{pmatrix} \sim \begin{pmatrix} 1 & 3 & 1 & 0 \\ 0 & 5 & 1 & 1 \end{pmatrix} \sim \begin{pmatrix} 1 & 3 & 1 & 0 \\ 0 & 1 & 1/5 & 1/5 \end{pmatrix} \sim \begin{pmatrix} 1 & 0 & 2/5 & -3/5 \\ 0 & 1 & 1/5 & 1/5 \end{pmatrix}$$

Thus　　　　　　　　　$\begin{pmatrix} 1 & 3 \\ -1 & 2 \end{pmatrix}^{-1} = \begin{pmatrix} 2/5 & -3/5 \\ 1/5 & 1/5 \end{pmatrix}$.

Example 2:　Determine $\begin{pmatrix} 1 & 0 & -1 & 0 \\ 2 & 0 & 0 & 3 \\ 0 & 1 & 1 & 0 \\ 0 & 2 & 0 & 0 \end{pmatrix}^{-1}$.

Solution:

$$
\begin{pmatrix}
1 & 0 & -1 & 0 & 1 & 0 & 0 & 0 \\
2 & 0 & 0 & 3 & 0 & 1 & 0 & 0 \\
0 & 1 & 1 & 0 & 0 & 0 & 1 & 0 \\
0 & 2 & 0 & 0 & 0 & 0 & 0 & 1
\end{pmatrix}
\sim
\begin{pmatrix}
1 & 0 & -1 & 0 & 1 & 0 & 0 & 0 \\
0 & 0 & 2 & 3 & -2 & 1 & 0 & 0 \\
0 & 1 & 1 & 0 & 0 & 0 & 1 & 0 \\
0 & 1 & 0 & 0 & 0 & 0 & 0 & 1/2
\end{pmatrix}
\sim
$$

$$
\begin{pmatrix}
1 & 0 & -1 & 0 & 1 & 0 & 0 & 0 \\
0 & 1 & 0 & 0 & 0 & 0 & 0 & 1/2 \\
0 & 0 & 1 & 0 & 0 & 0 & 1 & -1/2 \\
0 & 0 & 0 & 3 & -2 & 1 & -2 & 1
\end{pmatrix}
$$

$$
\sim
\begin{pmatrix}
1 & 0 & 0 & 0 & 1 & 0 & 1 & -1/2 \\
0 & 1 & 0 & 0 & 0 & 0 & 0 & 1/2 \\
0 & 0 & 1 & 0 & 0 & 0 & 1 & -1/2 \\
0 & 0 & 0 & 1 & -2/3 & 1/3 & -2/3 & 1/3
\end{pmatrix}.
$$

Therefore
$$
\begin{pmatrix}
1 & 0 & -1 & 0 \\
2 & 0 & 0 & 3 \\
0 & 1 & 1 & 0 \\
0 & 2 & 0 & 0
\end{pmatrix}^{-1}
=
\begin{pmatrix}
1 & 0 & 1 & -1/2 \\
0 & 0 & 0 & 1/2 \\
0 & 0 & 1 & -1/2 \\
-2/3 & 1/3 & -2/3 & 1/3
\end{pmatrix}.
$$

Our method of computing A^{-1}, which we have now illustrated, has been reached by a rather lengthy and patchy development; in particular, the idea of forming an $n \times 2n$ matrix so as to operate on A and I_n simultaneously, is pure opportunism. We propose, now, to develop our method from a more basic viewpoint which brings out the fundamental reason for considering an $n \times 2n$ matrix. Let A be any nonsingular $n \times n$ matrix; now, X is the inverse of A if and only if $AX = I_n$. Thus, we must solve the matrix equation $AX = I_n$ for the unknown $n \times n$ matrix X. Here, the key idea is to regard the row vectors of X as the unknowns, not the entries of X. Let $A = (a_{ij})$; in view of Definition 3.3.3 we obtain the following n conditions on the row vectors of X:

(1)
$$
\sum_{i=1}^{n} a_{1i} X_i = \epsilon_1, \ldots, \sum_{i=1}^{n} a_{ni} X_i = \epsilon_n .
$$

This is a linear system involving n equations in n unknowns $X_1, \ldots, X_n$. We emphasize that the unknowns of this linear system are n-vectors. We can solve this linear system by applying the method of Section 1.2. Clearly, A is the coefficient matrix of the system. Here, the augmented matrix is the matrix obtained by adjoining the vectors on the right-hand sides of the equations of (1), as our $n + 1$st column. So, our augmented matrix is a *mixed* matrix, i.e., a matrix whose entries are scalars or vectors. Notice that the operations involved in reducing the augmented matrix are vector operations, either vector addition or scalar multiplication; of course, there is also the usual operation of interchanging rows. But $b\alpha + c\alpha = (b + c)\alpha$ and $b(c\alpha) = (bc)\alpha$ whenever b and c are scalars and α is a vector; so, in the case of the first n columns of the augmented matrix, these vector operations can be treated as corresponding field operations. Since A is nonsingular a suitable sequence of row operations produces an equivalent linear system represented by the $n \times n + 1$ mixed matrix

$$\begin{pmatrix} 1 & 0 & \cdots & 0 & \alpha_1 \\ & \cdot & & & \\ & \cdot & & & \\ & \cdot & & & \\ 0 & 0 & \cdots & 1 & \alpha_n \end{pmatrix}.$$

Thus $X_1 = \alpha_1, \ldots, X_n = \alpha_n$. We conclude that A^{-1} is the matrix whose ith row vector is α_i, $i = 1, \ldots, n$. We point out that each vector that appears in our mixed matrix is an n-vector; so we can regard our mixed matrix as an ordinary $n \times 2n$ matrix.

Next, let us consider the more general problem of solving a matrix equation of the form $AX = B$ for the unknown matrix X. This problem can be handled effectively by our method. The idea is to treat the row vectors of X as the unknowns and to set up a linear system in these unknowns. Reducing the augmented matrix of this linear system, we are led to an equivalent linear system whose solution set is visible. The following examples illustrate our procedure.

Example 3:   Solve $\begin{pmatrix} 1 & 0 & 3 & 4 \\ 2 & -1 & 0 & 2 \\ -1 & 3 & 12 & 11 \end{pmatrix} X = \begin{pmatrix} 2 & 5 \\ 0 & -1 \\ 4 & 4 \end{pmatrix}.$

Solution: First, we observe that X must be a 4×2 matrix. Clearly, X satisfies the given matrix equation if and only if its row vectors satisfy the following linear system:

$$\begin{cases} X_1 \quad\quad\; + \; 3X_3 + \; 4X_4 = (2, \, 5) \\ 2X_1 - \; X_2 \quad\quad\;\; + \; 2X_4 = (0, \, -1) \\ -X_1 + 3X_2 + 12X_3 + 11X_4 = (4, \, 4) \end{cases}.$$

We now reduce the mixed matrix that represents this linear system (alternatively, we can work with the corresponding 3×6 matrix).

$$\begin{pmatrix} 1 & 0 & 3 & 4 & (2, \, 5) \\ 2 & -1 & 0 & 2 & (0, \, -1) \\ -1 & 3 & 12 & 11 & (4, \, 4) \end{pmatrix} \sim \begin{pmatrix} 1 & 0 & 3 & 4 & (2, \, 5) \\ 0 & -1 & -6 & -6 & (-4, \, -11) \\ 0 & 1 & 5 & 5 & (2, \, 3) \end{pmatrix}$$

$$\sim \begin{pmatrix} 1 & 0 & 3 & 4 & (2, \, 5) \\ 0 & -1 & -6 & -6 & (-4, \, -11) \\ 0 & 0 & -1 & -1 & (-2, \, -8) \end{pmatrix} \sim \begin{pmatrix} 1 & 0 & 0 & 1 & (-4, \, -19) \\ 0 & 1 & 0 & 0 & (-8, \, -37) \\ 0 & 0 & 1 & 1 & (2, \, 8) \end{pmatrix}$$

Therefore, $X_1 + X_4 = (-4, \, -19)$, $X_2 = (-8, \, -37)$, and $X_3 + X_4 = (2, \, 8)$. We conclude that the given matrix equation has infinitely many solutions; the row vectors of a solution X can be expressed in terms of X_4 as follows: $X_1 = (-4, \, -19)$

$-X_4$, $X_2 = (-8, -37)$, and $X_3 = (2, 8) - X_4$. In particular, taking $X_4 = (0, 0)$, we see that

$$\begin{pmatrix} -4 & -19 \\ -8 & -37 \\ 2 & 8 \\ 0 & 0 \end{pmatrix}$$

is a solution of the given matrix equation.

Our next example shows that our method works even if the matrix equation involved has no solution.

Example 4:   Solve $\begin{pmatrix} 1 & 2 \\ 2 & 5 \\ 1 & 0 \end{pmatrix} X = \begin{pmatrix} 1 & 0 \\ 2 & 1 \\ 0 & -1 \end{pmatrix}$.

Solution: A matrix X satisfies the given equation if and only if:

$$\begin{cases} X_1 + 2X_2 = (1, 0) \\ 2X_1 + 5X_2 = (2, 1) \\ X_1 \quad\quad = (0, -1) \end{cases}$$

We now reduce the mixed matrix that represents this linear system:

$$\begin{pmatrix} 1 & 2 & (1, 0) \\ 2 & 5 & (2, 1) \\ 1 & 0 & (0, -1) \end{pmatrix} \sim \begin{pmatrix} 1 & 2 & (1, 0) \\ 0 & 1 & (0, 1) \\ 0 & -2 & (-1, -1) \end{pmatrix} \sim \begin{pmatrix} 1 & 0 & (1, -2) \\ 0 & 1 & (0, 1) \\ 0 & 0 & (-1, 1) \end{pmatrix}.$$

Thus, $X_1 = (1, -2)$, $X_2 = (0, 1)$, and $\mathbf{0} = (-1, 1)$. Since this linear system does not possess a solution, we conclude that the given matrix equation is not solvable.

Of course, our methods can be applied to a matrix equation of the form $XA = B$, where X is the unknown matrix. We can take the column vectors of X as the unknowns and set up a linear system, or we can observe that $XA = B$ if and only if $A^t X^t = B^t$, and solve the latter equation for X^t.

In Section 2.3 we saw that a linear system can be represented by a single *vector* equation. We now point out that a linear system can be represented by a single *matrix* equation. To be explicit, the linear system

(1)
$$\begin{cases} a_{11}\, x_1 + \cdots + a_{1n}\, x_n = b_1 \\ \quad\quad\quad \cdot \\ \quad\quad\quad \cdot \\ \quad\quad\quad \cdot \\ a_{m1}\, x_1 + \cdots + a_{mn}\, x_n = b_m \end{cases}$$

is represented by the vector equation

(2)
$$x_{1\,1}A + \cdots + x_{n\,n}A = \beta$$

where A is the coefficient matrix of (1) and $\beta = (b_1, \cdots, b_m)$.

Moreover, (1) is represented by the matrix equation

(3) $$X A^t = \beta$$

where $X = (x_1, \ldots, x_n)$ is the unknown. Recall that we have agreed to interpret any $1 \times n$ matrix as an n-vector, and vice versa. Applying Lemma 3.3.1 to the left-hand side of (3), we see at once that (3) is a compact way of writing (1). So (1) and (3) have the same solution set. Of course, (1) is also represented by the matrix equation

(4) $$AY = \beta^t$$

where $Y = (x_1, \ldots, x_n)^t$ is the unknown.

EXERCISES

Compute the inverse of each of the following matrices, or show that it does not possess an inverse.

1. $\begin{pmatrix} 2 & 1 & 0 \\ 0 & 2 & 1 \\ 1 & -1 & 4 \end{pmatrix}$

2. $\begin{pmatrix} 1 & 0 & 2 \\ -2 & 3 & 1 \\ 0 & 3 & 5 \end{pmatrix}$

3. $\begin{pmatrix} 1 & 2 & 3 & -2 \\ 0 & 1 & 2 & 3 \\ -1 & -2 & 0 & -1 \\ 2 & 1 & -1 & 1 \end{pmatrix}$

4. $\begin{pmatrix} 1 & -2 & -1 & 1 \\ 1 & 1 & 0 & 0 \\ 0 & 4 & 2 & -1 \\ 0 & 2 & 1 & -1 \end{pmatrix}$

5. $\begin{pmatrix} 1 & 0 & 0 & -1 \\ -1 & 1 & 0 & 1 \\ -2 & 2 & -1 & 1 \\ 0 & 0 & 1 & 2 \end{pmatrix}$

6. $\begin{pmatrix} -1 & 2 & 0 & 3 & 1 \\ 1 & 0 & 3 & -2 & 2 \\ 2 & 0 & 0 & -4 & -2 \\ 0 & 1 & 0 & 2 & -3 \\ 0 & -1 & 2 & 1 & 1 \end{pmatrix}$

7. $\begin{pmatrix} 1 & 0 & 2 & 1 & 3 & 5 \\ 0 & 1 & 2 & -1 & 0 & 1 \\ -2 & 0 & -1 & -2 & 0 & -6 \\ 1 & 1 & 0 & 0 & -1 & 2 \\ 3 & -1 & -2 & 0 & -5 & -9 \\ 0 & 0 & -1 & 2 & -2 & 3 \end{pmatrix}$

Solve each of the following matrix equations.

8. $\begin{pmatrix} 4 & 1 \\ -3 & -1 \end{pmatrix} X = \begin{pmatrix} -1 \\ 4 \end{pmatrix}$.

9. $\begin{pmatrix} 1 & 1 \\ 2 & 1 \end{pmatrix} X = \begin{pmatrix} 2 & -1 & 5 & 6 \\ 3 & 4 & 7 & 0 \end{pmatrix}$.

10. $\begin{pmatrix} 1 & 0 & 1 \\ 2 & -1 & 1 \\ 0 & 1 & 2 \end{pmatrix} X = \begin{pmatrix} -2 & 0 & 3 & 1 \\ 4 & -1 & 2 & 5 \\ -3 & 1 & 0 & 0 \end{pmatrix}.$

11. $\begin{pmatrix} 1 & 1 & 0 & 2 \\ -2 & 0 & 1 & 0 \end{pmatrix} X = \begin{pmatrix} 2 \\ 5 \end{pmatrix}.$

12. $\begin{pmatrix} 1 & 1 & 0 & 2 \\ -2 & 0 & 1 & 0 \end{pmatrix} X = \begin{pmatrix} 4 & 6 \\ -5 & -2 \end{pmatrix}.$

13. $\begin{pmatrix} 1 & 3 & 0 & 2 \\ 0 & 2 & -1 & 3 \end{pmatrix} X = \begin{pmatrix} 4 & 4 \\ 7 & 4 \end{pmatrix}.$

14. $X \begin{pmatrix} 1 & 0 & 3 \\ 2 & -1 & 5 \end{pmatrix} = \begin{pmatrix} 4 & -1 & 11 \\ -1 & 0 & -3 \\ 5 & -1 & 14 \end{pmatrix}.$

15. $X \begin{pmatrix} 2 & -1 & 0 & 0 \\ 1 & -3 & 1 & -1 \end{pmatrix} = \begin{pmatrix} 5 & 0 & -1 & 1 \\ 1 & -3 & 1 & -1 \end{pmatrix}.$

16. $X \begin{pmatrix} 3 & 0 & 1 & 2 \\ 1 & -2 & 0 & 4 \end{pmatrix} = \begin{pmatrix} 8 & -4 & 2 & 12 \\ -2 & -2 & -1 & 2 \\ 3 & 0 & 1 & 2 \end{pmatrix}.$

4

LINES

4.1 THREE-DIMENSIONAL EUCLIDEAN SPACE

Anyone who has been exposed to geometry as developed in the classical manner of Euclid, is aware that it is possible to study geometry without knowing what a *point* or a *line* is. It is enough to know that points and lines have certain properties; Euclid called these fundamental properties the *postulates* (axioms) of geometry.

We are not going to follow Euclid's approach here. Instead we carefully define, or construct, each geometric entity as we meet it. To this purpose we draw on the mathematical objects and concepts associated with the vector space $\Re_3$. Of course, knowing just what each geometric entity is, enables us to establish their basic properties. So, our approach permits us to prove Euclid's postulates.

Let us give a name to the mathematical system that we are about to construct. We shall call it *three-dimensional Euclidean space* and we denote it by E_3. This mathematical system involves four concepts: points, lines, planes, distance between points. Thus, E_3 is a 4-tuple. Points are easy to define: each member of R_3 is said to be a *point*. So α is a point of E_3 if and only if $\alpha \in R_3$. Intuitively, points are zero-dimensional, lines are one-dimensional, and planes are two-dimensional. To emphasize this idea and to exploit our work on vector spaces, we define lines and planes as the translations of one-dimensional and two-dimensional subspaces of $\Re_3$, in the following sense.

Definition 4.1.1: Let α be any point; then $\{\alpha + \gamma \mid \gamma \in W\}$ is said to be a *line* if and only if W is a one-dimensional subspace of $\Re_3$, whereas $\{\alpha + \gamma \mid \gamma \in W\}$ is said to be a *plane* if and only if W is a two-dimensional subspace of $\Re_3$.

Notice that $\{0\}$ is the only zero-dimensional subspace of $\mathcal{R}_3$; so $\{\alpha + \gamma \mid \gamma \in W\} = \{\alpha\}$ whenever W is a zero-dimensional subspace of $\mathcal{R}_3$. In this weak sense, a point α is a translation of a zero-dimensional subspace (we must distinguish between $\{\alpha\}$ and α).

Next, we define *distance* between points: we say that $\|\alpha - \beta\|$ is the distance between α and β whenever $\{\alpha, \beta\} \subset R_3$.

Let us illustrate these ideas.

Example 1:   Let $W = L\{(0, 3, -1)\}$; then $\{(1, 2, 0) + \gamma \mid \gamma \in W\}$ is a line.

Example 2:   Let $W = L\{(0, 3, -1), (2, 0, 1)\}$;   then $\{(1, 2, 0) + \gamma \mid \gamma \in W\}$ is a plane.

Example 3: $\{(1, 2, 0) + t(0, 3, -1) \mid t \in R\}$ is a line, namely the line of Example 1.

Example 4: $\{(1, 2, 0) + s(0, 3, -1) + t(2, 0, 1) \mid \{s, t\} \subset R\}$ is a plane, namely the plane of Example 2.

Example 5:   The distance between the points $(1, 2, -4)$ and $(3, -1, 2)$ is $\|(1, 2, -4) - (3, -1, 2)\| = \|(-2, 3, -6)\| = (4 + 9 + 36)^{\frac{1}{2}} = 7$.

The lines $L\{\epsilon_1\}$, $L\{\epsilon_2\}$, and $L\{\epsilon_3\}$ are important from the geometric viewpoint, as we might suspect from the fact that ϵ_1, ϵ_2, and ϵ_3 are significant algebraically. We are going to see more about this in Section 4.3. Notice that $L\{\epsilon_1\} \cap L\{\epsilon_2\} \cap L\{\epsilon_3\} = \{0\}$.

Later, we shall see that there is a unique plane that contains two given lines whose intersection is a point (see Theorem 5.2.5). The plane that contains $L\{\epsilon_1\}$ and $L\{\epsilon_2\}$ is called the XY-plane; the plane that contains $L\{\epsilon_2\}$ and $L\{\epsilon_3\}$ is called the YZ-plane; the plane that contains $L\{\epsilon_3\}$ and $L\{\epsilon_1\}$ is called the ZX-plane. To bring out the geometric importance of these planes we mention that $|a|$ is the distance between (a, b, c) and the YZ-plane, that $|b|$ is the distance between (a, b, c) and the ZY-plane, and that $|c|$ is the distance between (a, b, c) and the XY-plane (see Theorem 5.4.2). Of course, we have not yet defined the notion of the distance between a point and a plane; our intention here is merely to illustrate the geometric significance of these planes.

Here are some more examples.

Example 6:   Find the points on the line $\{(1, 0, 0) + t(1, 2, 3) \mid t \in R\}$ at a distance of $4\sqrt{14}$ from $(3, 4, 6)$.

Solution: Let α be a point on the given line at a distance of $4\sqrt{14}$ from $(3, 4, 6)$. Then there is a real number t such that

$$\alpha = (1, 0, 0) + t(1, 2, 3) = (1 + t, 2t, 3t)$$

and
$$\|\alpha - (3, 4, 6)\| = 4\sqrt{14}$$

Thus $(t - 2)^2 + (2t - 4)^2 + (3t - 6)^2 = 224$; i.e., $t^2 - 4t - 12 = 0$, so $t = 6$ or $t = -2$. Therefore, the required points are $(7, 12, 18)$ and $(-1, -4, -6)$. Checking, we readily verify that these points are at a distance of $4\sqrt{14}$ from $(3, 4, 6)$.

Example 7: Find a line L such that $(1, 0, 2) \in L$ and $(2, -1, 0) \in L$.

Solution: Let $\alpha = (1, 0, 2)$ and let $\beta = (2, -1, 0)$. Now, $\{\alpha + t(\beta - \alpha) \mid t \in R\}$ is a line since $L\{\beta - \alpha\}$ is a one-dimensional subspace of $\mathcal{R}_3$. Clearly α and β are members of this line (take t to be 0 and 1 in turn). Thus the line $\{(1, 0, 2) + t(1, -1, -2) \mid t \in R\}$ has the required properties.

Example 8: Characterize the set of all points equidistant from $(1, 0, 0)$ and $(-1, 0, 0)$.

Solution: Let $\mathcal{P}$ be the required set of points; then $(a, b, c) \in \mathcal{P}$ if and only if $\|(a - 1, b, c)\| = \|(a + 1, b, c)\|$, i.e., $(a, b, c) \in \mathcal{P}$ if and only if $(a - 1)^2 + b^2 + c^2 = (a + 1)^2 + b^2 + c^2$, i.e., $(a, b, c) \in \mathcal{P}$ if and only if $a = 0$. Thus $\mathcal{P} = \{(0, b, c) \mid b \in R \text{ and } c \in R\} = \{0 + s\epsilon_2 + t\epsilon_3 \mid \{s, t\} \subset R\}$. So $\mathcal{P}$ is a plane. We point out that $\mathcal{P}$ is the YZ-plane since $L\{\epsilon_2\} \subset \mathcal{P}$ and $L\{\epsilon_3\} \subset \mathcal{P}$.

Example 9: Characterize the set of all points equidistant from $(2, -3, 1)$ and $(-1, 1, 3)$.

Solution: Let $\mathcal{P}$ be the required set of points; then $(a, b, c) \in \mathcal{P}$ if and only if $\|(a - 2, b + 3, c - 1)\| = \|(a + 1, b - 1, c - 3)\|$, i.e., $(a, b, c) \in \mathcal{P}$ if and only if $-6a + 8b + 4c + 3 = 0$. Thus $\mathcal{P} = \{(a, b, c) \mid -6a + 8b + 4c = -3\}$. We point out that $\mathcal{P} = \{(\frac{1}{2}, 0, 0) + \gamma \mid \gamma \in W\}$ where $W = L\{(2, 0, 3), (0, -1, 2)\}$; so $\mathcal{P}$ is a plane.

We say that E_3 is three-dimensional because the vector space $\mathcal{R}_3$ involved in the construction of E_3 is three-dimensional. It is just as easy to discuss n-dimensional Euclidean space E_n where $n \geq 2$. This mathematical system is constructed from the vector space $\mathcal{R}_n$. Here, each member of R_n is said to be a *point*. Lines and planes are defined to be translations of one-dimensional and two-dimensional subspaces of $\mathcal{R}_n$, in the same sense as for E_3. Thus, let $\alpha \in R_n$; then $\{\alpha + \gamma \mid \gamma \in W\}$ is said to be a *line* if and only if W is a one-dimensional subspace of $\mathcal{R}_n$, whereas this set is said to be a *plane* if and only if W is a two-dimensional subspace of $\mathcal{R}_n$. Distance between points is defined just as for E_3: so $\|\alpha - \beta\|$ is the distance between α and β whenever $\{\alpha, \beta\} \subset R_n$. Finally, we present the notion of a *hyperplane*. Let α and β be distinct points of E_n; then the set of all points equidistant from α and β is said to be a *hyperplane*. For $n = 3$ each hyperplane is a plane and each plane is a hyperplane; for $n = 2$ each hyperplane is a line and each line is a hyperplane.

EXERCISES

1. Find the distance between the points $(2, -1, 3)$ and $(-4, 1, 5)$.

2. Show that $(1, 5, -2)$ is equidistant from $(3, 7, 0)$ and $(-1, 3, -4)$.

3. Find a point which is equidistant from $(2, -4, 6)$ and $(8, 0, 4)$.

4. Show that $\{(a, 0, 0) \mid a \in R\}$ is a line.

5. Show that $\{(0, a, 0) \mid a \in R\}$ is a line.

6. Show that $\{(0, 0, a) \mid a \in R\}$ is a line.

7. Show that $\{(3 - a, 2, 1) \mid a \in R\}$ is a line.

8. Show that $\{(-t, 1 + t, 2t) \mid t \in R\}$ is a line.

9. Find a line L such that $(2, -1, 3) \in L$ and $(4, 0, 1) \in L$.

10. Characterize the set of all points equidistant from $(0, 1, 0)$ and $(0, -1, 0)$. Show that this plane is the ZX-plane.

11. Characterize the set of all points equidistant from $(0, 0, 1)$ and $(0, 0, -1)$. Show that this plane is the XY-plane.

12. Characterize the set of all points equidistant from $(3, 0, -1)$ and $(5, 4, 1)$. Is $(-1, 2, 4)$ a member of this set?

13. (a) Prove that each line of $\mathcal{R}_2$ is a hyperplane.
    (b) Prove that each hyperplane of $\mathcal{R}_2$ is a line.

14. (a) Prove that each plane of $\mathcal{R}_3$ is a hyperplane.
    (b) Prove that each hyperplane of $\mathcal{R}_3$ is a plane.

15. In E_4 find a line L such that $(2, 0, 1, 1) \in L$ and $(0, 1, 1, 1) \in L$. Is $(2, 2, 3, 3)$ a member of L?

16. In E_4 find a plane through $(0, 0, 0, 0)$, $(1, 0, 0, 1)$, and $(1, 1, 0, 0)$. Is $(2, 3, 1, 2)$ a member of this plane?

17. Let $\alpha \in R_3$ and let β a nonzero 3-vector.

    (a) Show that $\{\alpha + t\beta \mid t \in R\}$ is a line.
    (b) Prove that $\{\alpha + t(k\beta) \mid t \in R\}$ is a line whenever $k \neq 0$.

4.2 THE LINE THROUGH TWO POINTS

One of Euclid's postulates for geometry is this: "There is exactly one line through two points." When we say that a line is through (or passes through) a point, we mean that the point is a member of the line. (Similarly, when we say that a plane passes through a point we mean that the point is a member of the plane.) Now, each line is characterized by a one-dimensional subspace of $\mathcal{R}_3$, say W, and a point α. Clearly, α is a member of the line; we now observe that we obtain the same line if we replace α by any member of the line.

Lemma 4.2.1: Let $L = \{\alpha + \gamma \mid \gamma \in W\}$ be a line, where $\alpha \in R_3$ and W is a one-dimensional subspace of $\mathcal{R}_3$. Let $\alpha_1 \in L$; then $L = \{\alpha_1 + \gamma \mid \gamma \in W\}$.

Proof: Let $A = \{\alpha_1 + \gamma \mid \gamma \in W\}$. By assumption, there is a member of W, say γ_1, such that $\alpha_1 = \alpha + \gamma_1$. Consider any member of A, say $\alpha_1 + \gamma$; now

$$\alpha_1 + \gamma = (\alpha + \gamma_1) + \gamma = \alpha + (\gamma_1 + \gamma) \ .$$

But $\gamma_1 + \gamma \in W$ since W is a subspace; so, $\alpha_1 + \gamma \in L$. This proves that $A \subset L$. Now, $\alpha = \alpha_1 + (-1)\gamma_1$, so $\alpha \in A$; thus, by the first part of this proof, $L \subset A$. We conclude that $L = A$.

Theorem 4.2.1: Let $L_1 = \{\alpha_1 + \gamma \mid \gamma \in W_1\}$ and $L_2 = \{\alpha_2 + \gamma \mid \gamma \in W_2\}$ be any lines, where $\{\alpha_1, \alpha_2\} \subset R_3$ and W_1 and W_2 are one-dimensional subspaces of $\mathcal{R}_3$. Then $L_1 = L_2$ if and only if $W_1 = W_2$ and $\alpha_1 \in L_2$.

Proof: Our proof has two parts.

1.   Assume that $W_1 = W_2$ and that $\alpha_1 \in L_2$. Then $L_1 = \{\alpha_2 + \gamma \mid \gamma \in W_1\} = \{\alpha_2 + \gamma \mid \gamma \in W_2\} = L_2$.

2.   Assume that $L_1 = L_2$. Then $\alpha_1 \in L_2$. Let $W_1 = L\{\beta\}$; so $\alpha_1 + \beta \in L_1$, thus $\alpha_1 + \beta \in L_2$. But $L_2 = \{\alpha_1 + \gamma \mid \gamma \in W_2\}$ by Lemma 4.2.1; therefore, $\beta \in W_2$. Clearly, $\{\beta\}$ is a basis for W_2. We conclude that $W_2 = L\{\beta\} = W_1$.

Now, let us see about Euclid's postulate. First, we present a method of characterizing a line through two points.

Lemma 4.2.2: Let α_1 and α_2 be distinct points; then $\{\alpha_1 + t(\alpha_2 - \alpha_1) \mid t \in R\}$ is a line through α_1 and α_2.

Proof: $L\{\alpha_2 - \alpha_1\}$ is a one-dimensional subspace of $\mathcal{R}_3$. Clearly, α_1 and α_2 are members of the given set.

We now present Euclid's postulate.

Theorem 4.2.2: There is a unique line through two points.

Proof: Let α_1 and α_2 be distinct points. By Lemma 4.2.2 there is at least one line through these points. We wish to prove that $\{\alpha_1 + t(\alpha_2 - \alpha_1) \mid t \in R\}$ is the only line through α_1 and α_2. Let $L = \{\alpha + \gamma \mid \gamma \in W\}$ be any line through α_1 and α_2, where W is a one-dimensional subspace of $\mathcal{R}_3$ and α is a point. By Lemma 4.2.1, $L = \{\alpha_1 + \gamma \mid \gamma \in W\}$. Moreover, $\alpha_2 \in L$; so $\alpha_2 - \alpha_1 \in W$. Therefore $\{\alpha_2 - \alpha_1\}$ is a basis for W. We conclude that $L = \{\alpha_1 + t(\alpha_2 - \alpha_1) \mid t \in R\}$. This completes our proof.

We now present some examples.

Example 1: Find the line through $(3, 0, -2)$ and $(4, -1, -1)$.

Solution: By Theorem 4.2.2 and Lemma 4.2.2 the required line is $\{(3, 0, -2) + t(1, -1, 1) \mid t \in R\}$.

Example 2: Is the point $(2, 0, 1)$ on the line through $(7, -3, 4)$ and $(1, 2, 5)$?

Solution: The line through $(7, -3, 4)$ and $(1, 2, 5)$ is $\{(7, -3, 4) + t(-6, 5, 1) \mid t \in R\}$. Now, $(2, 0, 1)$ is on this line if and only if there is a real number t such that $(2, 0, 1) = (7, -3, 4) + t(-6, 5, 1)$; i.e.,

$$2 = 7 - 6t, 0 = -3 + 5t, 1 = 4 + t .$$

Since this linear system has no solution, we conclude that $(2, 0, 1)$ is not on the given line.

Here is a useful result.

Theorem 4.2.3: If α, β, and γ are points on one line, then $\det(\alpha, \beta, \gamma) = 0$.

Proof: By Corollary 1.4.1, $\det(\alpha, \beta, \gamma) = 0$ if the given points are not distinct. Accordingly, let us assume that $\alpha \neq \beta$. Then $L = \{\alpha + t(\beta - \alpha) \mid t \in R\}$ is the unique line through α and β. By assumption, $\gamma \in L$; so there is a scalar t such that $\gamma = \alpha + t(\beta - \alpha) = (1 - t)\alpha + t\beta$. Thus

$$\det(\alpha, \beta, \gamma) = \det(\alpha, \beta, (1 - t)\alpha + t\beta)$$

$$= \det(\alpha, \beta, \mathbf{0}) \qquad \text{by Theorem 1.4.4 (applied twice)}$$

$$= 0 .$$

It is customary to say that three or more points are *collinear* if and only if the points are members of one line. Notice that Theorem 4.2.3 can be formulated as follows.

Corollary 4.2.1: If $\det(\alpha, \beta, \gamma) \neq 0$ then α, β, and γ are *not* collinear.

It is tempting to formulate the following conjecture.

CONJECTURE: Points α, β, and γ are collinear if and only if $\det(\alpha, \beta, \gamma) = 0$.

However, it is easy to disprove this conjecture by presenting a counterexample.

As we have seen, we can characterize lines as follows: L is a line if and only if there are points α and β, $\beta \neq \mathbf{0}$, such that $L = \{\alpha + t\beta \mid t \in R\}$. Notice that the one-dimensional subspace W associated with L is spanned by β; i.e., $W = L\{\beta\}$. Indeed, just as we can replace α by any member of L, so we can replace β by any nonzero member of W. The fact is that each basis for W has exactly one member, so each nonzero member of W spans W.

EXERCISES

1. Find the line through $(2, -3, 1)$ and $(1, 0, 5)$.

2. Find the line through $(0, 2, -3)$ and $(0, 1, 1)$.

3. Is the point $(-1, 2, 8)$ on the line through $(1, 0, 2)$ and $(2, -1, -1)$?

4. Is the point $(7, -1, 3)$ on the line through $(1, 2, 0)$ and $(3, 1, 1)$?

5. Is the point $(6, 2, 2)$ on the line through $(0, 1, -5)$ and $(2, 0, -2)$?

6. Do the lines $\{(1, 0, 0) + t(-1, 2, 1) \mid t \in R\}$ and $\{(2, -1, 3) + t(1, 0, 2) \mid t \in R\}$ intersect?

7. Do the lines $\{(3, -2, 1) + t(1, -1, 1) \mid t \in R\}$ and $\{(0, -1, -3) + t(2, 0, 3) \mid t \in R\}$ intersect?

8. Show that the line through $(1, 0, 2)$ and $(2, -1, 4)$ intersects the line through $(2, 1, 3)$ and $(6, -7, 13)$.

9. Do the lines $\{(2t, 0, 3 - t) \mid t \in R\}$ and $\{(4 + 2t, 3 - t, t - 5) \mid t \in R\}$ intersect?

10. Do the lines $\{(t, 2 - t, 4 + 3t) \mid t \in R\}$ and $\{(1 + t, 3 - 2t, 1 + 6t) \mid t \in R\}$ intersect?

11. Show that the lines $\{(1 - t, t + 1, t + 2) \mid t \in R\}$ and $\{(3t, 1 - t, 2 + 3t) \mid t \in R\}$ do not intersect.

12. Let $L_1 = \{\alpha_1 + \gamma \mid \gamma \in W_1\}$ and let $L_2 = \{\alpha_2 + \gamma \mid \gamma \in W_2\}$ be any lines. Prove that $L_1 = L_2$ if and only if $W_1 = W_2$ and $L_1 \cap L_2 \neq \emptyset$.

13. Let $\{\alpha + t\beta \mid t \in R\}$ be any line; what is the geometric significance of the parameter t? *Hint:* assume that $\|\beta\| = 1$; consider the distance between α and $\alpha + t_1\beta$.

14. Show that the conjecture of the text is false.

15. Use Theorem 4.2.1 to show that the points $(2, 5, -1)$, $(0, 3, 1)$, and $(1, 2, -1)$ are *not* collinear. *Hint:* Compare the subspaces involved in the line through $(2, 5, -1)$ and $(0, 3, 1)$, and the line through $(0, 3, 1)$ and $(1, 2, -1)$. Show that these points are not collinear by applying Corollary 4.2.1.

16. Prove Theorem 4.2.3 by considering the 3×3 matrix whose column vectors are α, β, and γ; show that the rank of this matrix is less than 3.

4.3   DIRECTION AND DIRECTED LINES

Intuitively, a line in space points out exactly two directions. Consider any line, say $L = \{\alpha + \gamma \mid \gamma \in W\}$ where W is a one-dimensional subspace of $\mathcal{R}_3$ and $\alpha \in R_3$. As we have mentioned earlier, α is a member of L (indeed, we can replace α

by any member of L); but what is the function of W here? Well, W enables us to associate two directions with L, as follows. First, we must partition $W - \{0\}$ into two disjoint subsets. Choose any nonzero member of W, say β; then

$$W - \{0\} = \{k\beta \mid k > 0\} \cup \{k\beta \mid k < 0\} .$$

Moreover, we obtain these subsets of $W - \{0\}$ no matter which nonzero member of W we choose for β. Let us agree to call $\{k\beta \mid k > 0\}$ and $\{k\beta \mid k < 0\}$ the *directions of* L. For example, the directions of the line $\{t(1, 2, -1) \mid t \in R\}$ are $\{k(1, 2, -1) \mid k > 0\}$ and $\{k(1, 2, -1) \mid k < 0\}$.

We have talked about a direction of a line; let us adopt a more fundamental viewpoint and consider the notion of *direction* itself. To this purpose we now introduce an equivalence relation on $R_3 - \{0\}$. The idea is to regard nonzero 3-vectors β_1 and β_2 as equivalent if and only if they are members of the same direction of a line; in this case we shall write $\beta_1 \equiv \beta_2$.

Definition 4.3.1: Let β_1 and β_2 be any nonzero 3-vectors; then $\beta_1 \equiv \beta_2$ if and only if there is a positive real number k such that $\beta_2 = k\beta_1$.

For example, $(1, 2, -1) \equiv (5, 10, -5)$; whereas $(1, 2, -1)$ and $(-1, -2, 1)$ are not equivalent.

Lemma 4.3.1: $\equiv$ is an equivalence relation on $R_3 - \{0\}$.

Proof: Show that $\equiv$ is reflexive, symmetric, and transitive.

We denote an equivalence class $\{\alpha \mid \alpha \equiv \beta\}$, where $\beta \in R_3 - \{0\}$, by writing $[\beta]$. For example, $(2, 0, -4) \in [(1, 0, -2)]$; indeed $[(1, 0, -2)] = \{t(1, 0, -2) \mid t > 0\}$. Recall that if E is an equivalence relation on a set S, then the set of all equivalence classes of E is a *partition* of S, i.e., S is the union of these equivalence classes and no two equivalence classes have a common member. So, in the case of our equivalence relation $\equiv$ the resulting equivalence classes form a partition of $R_3 - \{0\}$. In particular, $[\beta_1] = [\beta_2]$ if and only if $\beta_1 \equiv \beta_2$, whenever β_1 and β_2 are nonzero 3-vectors.

We now present our notion of *direction*.

Definition 4.3.2: Let β be any nonzero 3-vector; then $[\beta]$ is said to be a *direction*.

For example, $\{k(3, 0, -4) \mid k > 0\}$ is a direction.

The following lemma, which is easy to prove, relates the two ideas of *direction* and *direction of a line*.

Lemma 4.3.2: Let $L = \{\alpha + \gamma \mid \gamma \in W\}$ be any line; then $[\beta]$ is a direction of L if and only if $\beta \in W - \{0\}$.

Clearly, *direction* is our basic idea. A direction is available to a given line L

if and only if the direction is a subset of the subspace W associated with L. The two directions available to L are called the directions of L. In this sense, then, the subspace W associated with a line L provides L with two possible directions. This is the geometric interpretation of W.

Let us examine our position. Two directions can be associated with a particular line (namely, the directions of the line). Notice this: once we seize on a specific direction of a line and agree to associate it with the line, we have in fact *directed* the line. The possibility of being directed belongs to each line; the fact of possessing a specific direction belongs only to a directed line.

It is easy to represent a directed line by a precise mathematical object. A directed line is an ordered pair whose first term is a line and whose second term is a direction of the line. For example, let $L = \{\alpha + t\beta \mid t \in R\}$ be a line; then $(L, [\beta])$ is a directed line and $(L, [-\beta])$ is a directed line. Notice that $(L, [\beta]) \neq (L, [-\beta])$; whereas $(L, [\beta]) = (L, [k\beta])$ whenever $k > 0$. To simplify our notation we write (L, β) in place of $(L, [\beta])$; this is a bracket-omitting convention. Of course, $(L, \beta_1) = (L, \beta_2)$ if and only if $\beta_1 \equiv \beta_2$.

Next, we introduce the notion of the *angle* between directed lines.

Definition 4.3.3:   Let (L_1, β_1) and (L_2, β_2) be any directed lines; then arccos $\dfrac{\beta_1 \cdot \beta_2}{\|\beta_1\| \ \|\beta_2\|}$ is said to be the *angle* between these directed lines.

This means that the angle between (L_1, β_1) and (L_2, β_2) is the angle between the vectors β_1 and β_2. We point out that this definition of *angle* does not require that the lines L_1 and L_2 possess a common point.

Notice that the angle between (L_1, β_1) and (L_2, β_2) does not depend upon which members of the equivalence classes are used. This is so because $\dfrac{(s\beta_1) \cdot (t\beta_2)}{\|s\beta_1\| \ \|t\beta_2\|} = \dfrac{\beta_1 \cdot \beta_2}{\|\beta_1\| \ \|\beta_2\|}$ whenever $s > 0$ and $t > 0$.

Before illustrating Definition 4.3.3 we mention that there is a simple way of characterizing a directed line. Let us agree that by *the line directed from α_1 to α_2,* where $\alpha_1 \neq \alpha_2$, we mean the directed line (L, β) where L is the line through α_1 and α_2, and $\beta = \alpha_2 - \alpha_1$.

Example 1:   Find the angle between the line directed from $(-1, 0, 2)$ to $(2, 1, 1)$, and the line directed from $(3, -1, 2)$ to $(0, 0, 0)$.

Solution: Our directed lines are $(L_1, (3, 1, -1))$ and $(L_2, (-3, 1, -2))$.

The angle between these directed lines is

$$\text{arccos} \frac{(3, 1, -1) \cdot (-3, 1, -2)}{\|(3, 1, -1)\| \ \|(-3, 1, -2)\|} =$$

$$\text{arccos} \frac{-6.}{\sqrt{11} \ \sqrt{14}} \approx \text{arccos} \ -.4835 \approx 2.075 \ .$$

We mentioned earlier that the lines $L\{\epsilon_1\}$, $L\{\epsilon_2\}$, and $L\{\epsilon_3\}$ have geometric significance. To see this, consider the directed lines $X = (L\{\epsilon_1\}$, $\epsilon_1)$, $Y = (L\{\epsilon_2\}$, $\epsilon_2)$, and $Z = (L\{\epsilon_3\}$, $\epsilon_3)$. Now, let $(L$, $\beta)$ be any directed line and take $\beta = (l$, m , $n)$ such that $\|\beta\| = 1$. Clearly

$$\text{arccos } l \text{ is the angle between } (L , \beta) \text{ and } X ,$$
$$\text{arccos } m \text{ is the angle between } (L , \beta) \text{ and } Y ,$$
$$\text{arccos } n \text{ is the angle between } (L , \beta) \text{ and } Z .$$

These angles are said to be the *direction angles* of $(L$, $\beta)$. The cosines of the direction angles are said to be the *direction cosines* of $(L$, $\beta)$. Thus, the direction cosines of $(L$, $\beta)$ are the terms of β, provided that $\|\beta\| = 1$. Of course, this observation reflects the geometric significance of the *direction* of a directed line.

For example, the direction cosines of X are the terms of ϵ_1; the direction angles of X are arccos 1, arccos 0, and arccos 0, i.e., 0, $\pi/2$, $\pi/2$.

Example 2: Determine the direction angles of $(L\{\epsilon_1\}, -\epsilon_1)$.

Solution: Now, $\| -\epsilon_1\| = 1$; so the required angles are arccos -1, arccos 0, and arccos 0; i.e., π, $\pi/2$, $\pi/2$.

Example 3: Determine the direction cosines of $(L$, $\beta)$ where $\beta = (0$, $\sqrt{3}$, 1) and $L = L\{\beta\}$.

Solution: Here, $\|\beta\| = 2$; so we consider $(L$, $\beta/2)$. The required direction cosines are the terms of $\beta/2$, namely 0, $\sqrt{3}/2$, $1/2$.

Example 4: Determine the direction cosines of the line directed from (1 , 3 , 2) to (4 , -1 , 0).

Solution: Our directed line is $(L$, $\beta)$ where $\beta = (3$, -4 , $-2)$. Now, $\|\beta\| = \sqrt{29}$; so, the direction cosines of $(L$, $\beta)$ are the terms of $(3/\sqrt{29}, -4/\sqrt{29}, -2/\sqrt{29})$.

One of the most significant of Euclid's postulates is the famous postulate of *parallel lines:* "Given any line and any point not on the line, there is exactly one line through the given point which is parallel to the given line." To establish this proposition we must first define the term *parallel.* We talk about directed lines, rather than lines.

Definition 4.3.4: Directed lines $(L_1$, $\beta_1)$ and $(L_2$, $\beta_2)$ are said to be *parallel* if and only if $\beta_1 \equiv \beta_2$.

Thus, directed lines are parallel if and only if they possess the same direction. Let us establish Euclid's postulate.

Theorem 4.3.1: Let $(L$, $\beta)$ be any directed line and suppose that $\alpha \notin L$; then there is exactly one directed line parallel to $(L$, $\beta)$, say $(L_1$, $\beta)$, such that $\alpha \in L_1$.

Proof: Let $\alpha_1 \in L$; then $L = \{\alpha_1 + t\beta \mid t \in R\}$. Let $L_1 = \{\alpha + t\beta \mid t \in R\}$; clearly, (L_1 , β) is parallel to (L , β) and $\alpha \in L_1$. Let us show that there is no other directed line through α which is parallel to (L , β). Suppose that (L_2 , β) is parallel to (L , β) and that $\alpha \in L_2$. Then, by Lemma 4.2.1, $L_2 = \{\alpha + t\beta \mid t \in R\} = L_1$. This completes our proof.

We find it convenient to use the term *parallel* in connection with lines as well as directed lines. Thus, we say that lines L_1 and L_2 are *parallel* if and only if they involve the same subspace. For example, $\{\epsilon_1 + t(2 , -1 , 1) \mid t \in R\}$ and $\{(3 , 2 , 5) + t(-4 , 2 , -2) \mid t \in R\}$ are parallel.

EXERCISES

1. Determine the angle between the line directed from $(1 , 0 , -1)$ to $(2 , 1 , 3)$, and the line directed from $(2 , 2 , 1)$ to $(0 , 1 , -1)$.

2. Determine the angle between the line directed from $(-1 , 1 , 1)$ to $(1 , 0 , 0)$, and the line directed from $(0 , 0 , 0)$ to $(1 , -1 , -1)$.

3. Compute the angle between the directed lines (L_1 , β) and $(L_2 , -\beta)$.

4. Find the direction cosines of the line directed from $(2 , -1 , -2)$ to $(1 , 0 , 0)$.

5. Find the angle between the directed lines Y and Z.

6. Find the angle between $(L\{\epsilon_1\} , -\epsilon_1)$ and $(L\{\epsilon_3\} , -\epsilon_3)$.

7. Show that two directed lines are parallel if and only if the angle between them is zero.

8. Two lines, say $\{\alpha_1 + t\beta_1 \mid t \in R\}$ and $\{\alpha_2 + t\beta_2 \mid t \in R\}$, are said to be *perpendicular* (or *orthogonal*) if and only if $\beta_1 \perp \beta_2$. Show that any two of $L\{\epsilon_1\}, L\{\epsilon_2\}, L\{\epsilon_3\}$ are perpendicular.

9. Are the lines $\{t(1 , 2 , -1) \mid t \in R\}$ and $\{(1 , 0 , 1) + t(2 , -1 , 0) \mid t \in R\}$ perpendicular?

10. Find a line which is perpendicular to $\{(2 , -1 , 1) + t(1 , 0 , 1) \mid t \in R\}$.

11. Find a line through $(1 , 0 , 2)$ which is perpendicular to $\{(0 , 0 , 1) + t(2 , -1 , 0) \mid t \in R\}$.

4.4 DIRECTED DISTANCE

Let (L , β) be any directed line and let $\alpha \in L$; then $L = \{\alpha + t\beta \mid t \in R\}$. We can refine the geometric significance of the parameter t by introducing the notion of the *directed* distance from a point of L to a point of L. Let $\alpha_1 \in L$ and let $\alpha_2 \in L$; then we say that $\|\alpha_2 - \alpha_1\|$ is the directed distance from α_1 to α_2 in case $\alpha_2 - \alpha_1 \equiv \beta$; otherwise we say that $-\|\alpha_2 - \alpha_1\|$ is the directed distance from α_1 to α_2. So the directed distance from one point of a directed line to another point of the directed line depends upon the direction of the directed line.

Example 1: Determine the directed distance from $(2, -1, 1)$ to $(3, 0, 1)$ along the directed line (L, β) where $L = \{(1, -2, 1) + t(1, 1, 0) \mid t \in R\}$ and $\beta = (-1, -1, 0)$.

Solution: Here $(3, 0, 1) - (2, -1, 1) = (1, 1, 0)$, which is not equivalent to $(-1, -1, 0)$. Therefore, the directed distance from $(2, -1, 1)$ to $(3, 0, 1)$ is $-\|(1, 1, 0)\|$, namely $-\sqrt{2}$.

Let us consider the geometric significance of the parameter t for the line $\{\alpha + t\beta \mid t \in R\} = L$. Assume that $\|\beta\| = 1$, and consider the directed line (L, β). We claim that if t_1 is the value of the parameter that produces α_1, where $\alpha_1 \in L$, then t_1 is the directed distance from α to α_1 along the directed line (L, β). By assumption $\alpha_1 = \alpha + t_1\beta$; therefore, $\alpha_1 - \alpha = t_1\beta$, so $\|\alpha_1 - \alpha\| = |t_1| \, \|\beta\| = |t_1|$. There are two cases, as follows.

1. If $t_1 > 0$ then $\alpha_1 - \alpha \equiv \beta$, so the directed distance from α to α_1 is $\|\alpha_1 - \alpha\| = t_1$.

2. If $t_1 < 0$ then $\alpha_1 - \alpha$ is not equivalent to β, so the directed distance from α to α_1 is $-\|\alpha_1 - \alpha\| = -|t_1| = t_1$. In either case t_1, the value of the parameter, is the directed distance from α to α_1 along the directed line. Let us state this result as a theorem.

Theorem 4.4.1: Let $L = \{\alpha + t\beta \mid t \in R\}$, where $\|\beta\| = 1$, and let $\alpha_1 = \alpha + t_1\beta$. Then t_1 is the directed distance from α to α_1 along the directed line (L, β).

We can use this result to determine the point that subdivides a given line-segment into parts whose lengths satisfy a given ratio. Now, a *line-segment* can be defined as follows.

Definition 4.4.1: Let α_1 and α_2 be distinct points; then $\{\alpha_1 + t(\alpha_2 - \alpha_1) \mid t \in [0, 1]\}$ is said to be a *line-segment;* the points α_1 and α_2 are called its *endpoints.*

Notice that each line-segment is a subset of a line; indeed, $\{\alpha + t\beta \mid t \in [0, 1]\}$ is a line-segment with endpoints α and $\alpha + \beta$.

Example 2: $\{(2, 0, 1) + t\epsilon_1 \mid t \in [0, 1]\}$ is a line-segment with endpoints $(2, 0, 1)$ and $(3, 0, 1)$.

We now illustrate this application of Theorem 4.4.1.

Example 3: Find the midpoint of the line-segment with endpoints $(2, 3, -1)$ and $(5, -1, -1)$.

Solution: Consider the line directed from $(2, 3, -1)$ to $(5, -1, -1)$; namely (L, β) where $L = \{(2, 3, -1) + t\beta \mid t \in R\}$ and $\beta = .2(3, -4, 0)$. Clearly, 5 is the directed distance from $(2, 3, -1)$ to $(5, -1, -1)$; thus, 2.5 is the directed distance from $(2, 3, -1)$ to the midpoint of the given line-segment. Therefore, by Theorem 4.4.1, the required point is

$$(2, 3, -1) + 2.5\beta = (2, 3, -1) + .5(3, -4, 0) = (3.5, 1, -1) .$$

EXERCISES

1. Consider the line directed from $\mathbf{0}$ to $(1, 2, -2)$.

   (a) Find the directed distance from $(2, 4, -4)$ to $(3, 6, -6)$.
   (b) Find the directed distance from $(-1, -2, 2)$ to $(-2, -4, 4)$.
   (c) Find the directed distance from $\mathbf{0}$ to $(-1, -2, 2)$.
   (d) Find the midpoint of the line-segment with endpoints $(2, 4, -4)$ and $(4, 8, -8)$.

2. Find the midpoint of the line-segment with endpoints $(0, 1, 2)$ and $(-3, 4, 1)$.

3. Find the point on the line directed from $(0, 1, 2)$ to $(4, -3, -10)$ whose directed distance from $(1, 0, -1)$ is -3.

4. (a) Show that $t \in [0, 1]$ if and only if $1 - t \in [0, 1]$.
   (b) Let $\alpha \neq \beta$; prove that $\{s\alpha + (1 - s)\beta \mid s \in [0, 1]\}$ is the line-segment with endpoints α and β.

5. A linear combination of a set of vectors is said to be *convex* provided that the scalars involved total 1 and each scalar is a member of $[0, 1]$. More precisely, $\sum_{i=1}^{m} a_i\alpha_i$ is a convex combination of $\{\alpha_1, \ldots, \alpha_m\}$, a set with m members, if and only if $\sum_{i=1}^{m} a_i = 1$ and $a_i \in [0, 1]$ for each i.

   (a) Let α and β be the endpoints of a line-segment in E_3; show that this line-segment is the set of all convex combinations of $\{\alpha, \beta\}$.
   (b) Let α, β, and γ be the vertices of a triangle in E_3; prove that the boundary and interior of this triangle is the set of all convex combinations of $\{\alpha, \beta, \gamma\}$.

6. Notice that the notion of a line-segment generalizes to any dimension; indeed, Definition 4.4.1 applies unchanged for E_n, $n \in N$. Working in E_n prove the following:

   (a) The line-segment with endpoints α and β is the set of all convex combinations of $\{\alpha, \beta\}$.
   (b) The boundary and interior of the triangle with vertices α, β, and γ is the set of all convex combinations of $\{\alpha, \beta, \gamma\}$.

4.5 PERPENDICULAR LINES; THE VECTOR PRODUCT

We begin with a definition.

Definition 4.5.1: Let $\{\alpha_1 + t\beta_1 \mid t \in R\}$ and $\{\alpha_2 + t\beta_2 \mid t \in R\}$ be any lines; then these lines are said to be *perpendicular* (or *orthogonal*) if and only if $\beta_1 \perp \beta_2$.

Example 1: Find the line through $(1, -1, 0)$ which is perpendicular to lines with directions $[(1, 5, -2)]$ and $[(2, -7, 3)]$.

Solution: Let $[(l, m, n)]$ be a direction of the required line. Then

$$\begin{cases} l + 5m - 2n = 0 \\ 2l - 7m + 3n = 0 \end{cases}.$$

This linear system is represented by

$$\begin{pmatrix} 1 & 5 & -2 \\ 2 & -7 & 3 \end{pmatrix} \sim \begin{pmatrix} 1 & 5 & -2 \\ 0 & -17 & 7 \end{pmatrix} \sim \begin{pmatrix} 17 & 0 & 1 \\ 0 & -17 & 7 \end{pmatrix}.$$

So one solution of our linear system is $n = 17, m = 7, l = -1$. This means that $[(-1, 7, 17)]$ is a direction of the required line. Hence, our line is

$$\{(1, -1, 0) + t(-1, 7, 17) \mid t \in R\}.$$

The problem of Example 1 occurs frequently; therefore it is worthwhile to develop a formula for a vector orthogonal to two nonzero vectors. Such a formula is contained in the following lemma.

Lemma 4.5.1: Let $\{\alpha, \beta\} \subset R_3$, let M be a 3×3 matrix such that $M_2 = \alpha$ and $M_3 = \beta$, and let γ be the 3-vector whose terms are the cofactors of $(1, 1)$, $(1, 2)$, and $(1, 3)$ in M. Then γ is orthogonal to both α and β.

Proof: Let $M_1 = \alpha$; then $\alpha \cdot \gamma = |M| = 0$. Let $M_1 = \beta$; then $\beta \cdot \gamma = |M| = 0$.

Example 2: Find a line perpendicular to the lines $\{(2 - t, 3t, 2) \mid t \in R\}$ and $\{(5t, 1 + 2t, t) \mid t \in R\}$.

Solution: We must find a vector orthogonal to both $(-1, 3, 0)$ and $(5, 2, 1)$. To apply Lemma 4.5.1 we compute the cofactors of $(1, 1)$, $(1, 2)$, and $(1, 3)$ for

$$\begin{pmatrix} -1 & 3 & 0 \\ 5 & 2 & 1 \end{pmatrix}$$

a 3×3 matrix whose first row is blank. Now, $\begin{vmatrix} 3 & 0 \\ 2 & 1 \end{vmatrix} = 3, \begin{vmatrix} 0 & -1 \\ 1 & 5 \end{vmatrix} = 1$, and $\begin{vmatrix} -1 & 3 \\ 5 & 2 \end{vmatrix} = -17$; so, by Lemma 4.5.1, $(3, 1, -17)$ is orthogonal to both $(-1, 3, 0)$ and $(5, 2, 1)$. Thus $\{t(3, 1, -17) \mid t \in R\}$ is perpendicular to the given lines.

The following result functions as an *existence* theorem.

Theorem 4.5.1: Let $\{\gamma_1, \gamma_2\}$ be any linearly independent subset of R_3 where $\gamma_1 \neq \gamma_2$; then $\{\alpha \mid \alpha \perp \gamma_1 \text{ and } \alpha \perp \gamma_2\}$ is a one-dimensional subspace of $\mathcal{R}_3$.

Proof: Let $\gamma_1 = (l_1, m_1, n_1)$ and let $\gamma_2 = (l_2, m_2, n_2)$. Now, $\alpha = (l, m, n)$ is orthogonal to both γ_1 and γ_2 if and only if

(1)
$$\begin{cases} l_1 l + m_1 m + n_1 n = 0 \\ l_2 l + m_2 m + n_2 n = 0 \end{cases}.$$

The coefficient matrix of this homogeneous linear system is $\begin{pmatrix} l_1 & m_1 & n_1 \\ l_2 & m_2 & n_2 \end{pmatrix}$, the matrix whose row vectors are γ_1 and γ_2. The rank of this matrix is the dimension of the subspace spanned by its row vectors (see Corollary 2.6.3). By assumption, $L\{\gamma_1, \gamma_2\}$ is two-dimensional; so, the above matrix has rank 2. Thus, by Theorem 2.4.2, the subspace of all vector solutions of (1) is one-dimensional. This establishes our theorem.

Considering this result, we see that if we are given two nonparallel lines, we can determine a nonzero vector β such that each line perpendicular to both given lines involves the subspace $L\{\beta\}$.

Example 3: Characterize the lines which are perpendicular to $\{(2 - 3t, 7, 2t) \mid t \in R\}$ and $\{(-t, 3 + 5t, 1 + 3t) \mid t \in R\}$.

Solution: First, we must find a nonzero vector orthogonal to $(-3, 0, 2)$ and $(-1, 5, 3)$. Applying Lemma 4.5.1 to the 3×3 matrix

$$\begin{pmatrix} & & \\ -3 & 0 & 2 \\ -1 & 5 & 3 \end{pmatrix}$$

whose first row has been left blank, we see that the vector $(-10, 7, -15)$ has the required property. In view of Theorem 4.5.1, we conclude that each line perpendicular to the given lines is constructed from the subspace $W = L\{(-10, 7, -15)\}$; i.e., let $\alpha \in R_3$, then $\{\alpha + \gamma \mid \gamma \in W\}$ is perpendicular to the given lines.

Example 4: Find the line through the point $(2, -3, 4)$ which is perpendicular to the lines $\{(2 - 3t, 7, 2t) \mid t \in R\}$ and $\{(-t, 3 + 5t, 1 + 3t) \mid t \in R\}$.

Solution: Considering the result of Example 3 we see that the required line is $\{(2, -3, 4) + t(-10, 7, -15) \mid t \in R\}$.

The operation involved in determining a vector which is orthogonal to two given vectors can be formalized as a binary operation on R_3; this operation is called the *vector product* or *cross product* and is denoted by $\times$ (read *cross*).

Definition 4.5.2: Let $\alpha = (a_1, a_2, a_3)$ and $\beta = (b_1, b_2, b_3)$ be any 3-vectors; then $\alpha \times \beta = (a_2 b_3 - a_3 b_2, a_3 b_1 - a_1 b_3, a_1 b_2 - a_2 b_1)$.

For example, $(2, 0, 1) \times (-1, 2, -2) = (-2, 3, 4)$. The following algebraic properties of the vector product are easy to establish.

Lemma 4.5.2: Let α and β be any 3-vectors; then $\alpha \times \beta = -(\beta \times \alpha) = (-\beta) \times \alpha$.

Lemma 4.5.3: Let α and β be any 3-vectors, and let $k \in R$; then $(k\alpha) \times \beta = k(\alpha \times \beta)$.

Lemma 4.5.4: Let α, β, and γ be any 3-vectors; then $\alpha \times (\beta + \gamma) = \alpha \times \beta + \alpha \times \gamma$.

We must emphasize one point: the vector product is a binary operation on R_3 only. Unlike vector addition or scalar multiplication, this operation does not generalize to subspaces of higher dimension. However, if we regard $\times$ as a mapping (e.g. think of the mapping det) we find that $\times$ in fact can be generalized. Recall that the basic property of $\alpha \times \beta$ is that this vector is orthogonal to both α and β. Let $n > 1$ and let $(\alpha_2, \ldots, \alpha_n)$ be any ordered $(n - 1)$ tuple of n-vectors. We follow the construction of Lemma 4.5.1; let M be an $n \times n$ matrix such that $M_i = \alpha_i$, $i = 2, \ldots, n$, and let γ be the n-vector whose terms are the cofactors of $(1, 1), \ldots, (1, n)$ in M. Considering the proof of Lemma 4.5.1, it is easy to see that γ is orthogonal to α_i, $i = 2, \ldots, n$. Let us denote γ by $\times(\alpha_2, \ldots, \alpha_n)$, read the *cross product* of $\alpha_2, \ldots, \alpha_n$. So, we have generalized our mapping. Notice that we have generalized "down" as well as "up"; i.e., $\times$ associates a 2-vector with each 2-vector, in particular, $\times(a, b) = (b, -a)$.

Let us illustrate our generalized cross product.

Example 5: $\times((1, 2, 0, -1), (2, -1, 1, 1), (-1, 2, 2, 1)) = (2, 6, -12, 14)$. The terms of this vector are

$$\begin{vmatrix} 2 & 0 & -1 \\ -1 & 1 & 1 \\ 2 & 2 & 1 \end{vmatrix}, \quad -\begin{vmatrix} 1 & 0 & -1 \\ 2 & 1 & 1 \\ -1 & 2 & 1 \end{vmatrix}, \quad \begin{vmatrix} 1 & 2 & -1 \\ 2 & -1 & 1 \\ -1 & 2 & 1 \end{vmatrix}, \text{ and } -\begin{vmatrix} 1 & 2 & 0 \\ 2 & -1 & 1 \\ -1 & 2 & 2 \end{vmatrix}, \text{ respectively.}$$

The calculations involved in the preceding problem are laborious; we are now about to develop a more efficient technique for computing a cross product. First, we must establish the following facts about the cross product. The proofs of these lemmas follow from corresponding properties of det (see Section 1.4) and are left as exercises. By a *transposition* of $\{1, \ldots, n\}$ we mean a permutation of $\{1, \ldots, n\}$ that interchanges two members of this set, and does not affect its remaining members.

Lemma 4.5.5: Let $\alpha_1, \ldots, \alpha_n$ be any $(n + 1)$-vectors and let Π be any transposition of $\{1, \ldots, n\}$. Then $\times(\alpha_{\Pi(1)}, \ldots, \alpha_{\Pi(n)}) = -\times(\alpha_1, \ldots, \alpha_n)$.

Lemma 4.5.6: Let $\alpha_1, \ldots, \alpha_n$ be any $(n + 1)$-vectors and let k be any scalar. Then $\times(\alpha_1, \ldots, k\alpha_r, \ldots, \alpha_n) = k \times(\alpha_1, \ldots, \alpha_r, \ldots, \alpha_n)$.

Lemma 4.5.7: Let $\alpha_1, \ldots, \alpha_n$ be any $(n+1)$-vectors and let r and s be distinct members of $\{1, \ldots, n\}$. Then

$$\times(\alpha_1, \ldots, \underbrace{\alpha_r + \alpha_s}_{r\text{th term}}, \ldots, \alpha_n) = \times(\alpha_1, \ldots, \alpha_r, \ldots, \alpha_n).$$

The impact of these lemmas is that we can use our row-reduction procedure to compute a cross product. The idea is to row-reduce the matrix whose row vectors are the vectors involved in the cross product, keeping track of any scalar multiplications and any row interchanges. Applying the preceding lemmas we see that the cross product of the row vectors of the reduced matrix is related to the original cross product. We now illustrate this technique by reworking Example 5.

Second Solution to Example 5:

$$\begin{pmatrix} 1 & 2 & 0 & -1 \\ 2 & -1 & 1 & 1 \\ -1 & 2 & 2 & 1 \end{pmatrix} \sim \begin{pmatrix} 1 & 2 & 0 & -1 \\ 0 & -5 & 1 & 3 \\ 0 & 4 & 2 & 0 \end{pmatrix} \sim \begin{pmatrix} 1 & 2 & 0 & -1 \\ 0 & -1 & 3 & 3 \\ 0 & 4 & 2 & 0 \end{pmatrix}$$

$$\sim \begin{pmatrix} 1 & 0 & 6 & 5 \\ 0 & -1 & 3 & 3 \\ 0 & 0 & 14 & 12 \end{pmatrix} \sim \begin{pmatrix} 1 & 0 & 0 & -1/7 \\ 0 & -1 & 0 & \cdot & 3/7 \\ 0 & 0 & 14 & 12 \end{pmatrix}.$$

Thus $\quad \times((1, 2, 0, -1), (2, -1, 1, 1), (-1, 2, 2, 1))$

$$= \times((1, 0, 0, -1/7), (0, -1, 0, 3/7), (0, 0, 14, 12))$$

$$= (2, 6, -12, 14) .$$

Of course, we can find all vectors that are orthogonal to given vectors by setting up a homogeneous linear system and row-reducing its coefficient matrix. As we have seen, it is useful to have a formula that displays explicitly, not implicitly, a suitable vector. Now, **0** is orthogonal to given vectors; so our problem is to find a nonzero vector which is orthogonal to given vectors. Can we be sure that our cross product associates a nonzero vector with given vectors? Consider the following theorem.

Theorem 4.5.2: Let $\alpha_2, \ldots, \alpha_n$ be distinct n-vectors. Then $\times(\alpha_2, \ldots, \alpha_n) = \mathbf{0}$ if and only if $\{\alpha_2, \ldots, \alpha_n\}$ is linearly dependent.

Proof: There are two parts to our proof.

1. Assume that $\{\alpha_2, \ldots, \alpha_n\}$ is linearly dependent. Let M be the $n - 1 \times n$ matrix such that $M_i = \alpha_{i+1}, i = 1, \ldots, n - 1$, and let A be any submatrix of M obtained by deleting one column vector of M. Clearly, the row vectors of A are linearly dependent; so $|A| = 0$. Thus, $\times(\alpha_2, \ldots, \alpha_n) = \mathbf{0}$.

2. Assume that $\times(\alpha_2, \ldots, \alpha_n) = \mathbf{0}$. If $\{\alpha_2, \ldots, \alpha_n\}$ is linearly independent, then choose α_1 so that $\{\alpha_1, \ldots, \alpha_n\}$ is a basis for R_n. But $\det(\alpha_1, \ldots, \alpha_n) = \alpha_1 \cdot \times(\alpha_2, \ldots, \alpha_n) = \alpha_1 \cdot \mathbf{0} = 0$, whereas n is the rank of the matrix with row vectors $\alpha_1, \ldots, \alpha_n$, so this matrix is nonsingular. This contradiction proves that $\{\alpha_2, \ldots, \alpha_n\}$ is linearly dependent.

In the preceding proof we have already used the following fact which displays an intimate relation between the mappings $\times$ and det.

Lemma 4.5.8: Let $\alpha_1, \ldots, \alpha_n$ be any n-vectors; then $\det(\alpha_1, \ldots, \alpha_n) = \alpha_1 \cdot \times(\alpha_2, \ldots, \alpha_n)$.

Proof: Apply Lemma 1.4.4.

Of course, the value of Theorem 4.5.2 is that it assures us that $\times(\alpha_2, \ldots, \alpha_n)$ is a nonzero vector orthogonal to α_i, $i = 2, \ldots, n$, if $\{\alpha_2, \ldots, \alpha_n\}$ has $n - 1$ members and is linearly independent.

Example 6: Find a nonzero vector orthogonal to each of $(1, 2, 0, -1)$, $(2, -1, 1, 1)$, and $(-1, 2, 2, 1)$.

Solution: First, we observe that $\{(1, 2, 0, -1), (2, -1, 1, 1), (-1, 2, 2, 1)\}$ is linearly independent. So, by Theorem 4.5.2,

$$\times((1, 2, 0, -1), (2, -1, 1, 1), (-1, 2, 2, 1))$$

is a nonzero vector orthogonal to each of the given vectors. By Example 5, $\times((1, 2, 0, -1), (2, -1, 1, 1), (-1, 2, 2, 1)) = (2, 6, -12, 14)$.

Here is another property of $\times$ of obvious computational value.

Lemma 4.5.9: Let $\alpha_1, \ldots, \alpha_n, \beta$ be any $(n + 1)$-vectors and let $r \in \{1, \ldots, n\}$. Then

$$\times(\alpha_1, \ldots, \alpha_r + \beta, \ldots, \alpha_n) =$$

$$\times(\alpha_1, \ldots, \alpha_r, \ldots, \alpha_n) + \times(\alpha_1, \ldots, \underbrace{\beta}_{r\text{th term}}, \ldots, \alpha_n) .$$

Finally, we mention that $\times$ enables us to exhibit the column vectors (and the row vectors) of A^{-1} whenever A is a nonsingular, square matrix.

EXERCISES

1. Are the lines $\{(1 + t, t, 2t) \mid t \in R\}$ and $\{(2 - t, 3, 4 + t/2) \mid t \in R\}$ perpendicular?

2. Find a line which is perpendicular to both lines of Exercise 1.

3. Find a line perpendicular to the lines $\{(t, -t, 3t) \mid t \in R\}$ and $\{(2 + 3t, 1 - t, 5) \mid t \in R\}$.

4. Characterize the lines which are perpendicular to the lines $\{(5, 2, 4) + t(-3, 1, 7) \mid t \in R\}$ and $\{(0, 1, -2) + t(2, 3, 0) \mid t \in R\}$.

5. Find the line through the point $(2, 5, -1)$ which is perpendicular to the lines $\{(5, 2, 4) + t(-3, 1, 7) \mid t \in R\}$ and $\{(0, 1, -2) + t(2, 3, 0) \mid t \in R\}$.

6. Find the line through $(1, -3, 2)$ which is perpendicular to $\{t(1, 2, 3) \mid t \in R\}$ and $\{(-3, 4, 1) + t(2, -1, 1) \mid t \in R\}$.

7. Let A be any $n \times n$ matrix. Prove that $(A_{11}, A_{12}, \ldots, A_{1n}) \perp A_i, i = 2, 3, \ldots, n$. where for each j, A_{1j} is the cofactor of $(1, j)$ in the matrix A.

8. Find a nonzero vector orthogonal to each of $(2, 1, 6, 0), (1, -2, 0, 2),$ $(-3, 0, 1, 4)$.

9. Find a nonzero vector orthogonal to each of $(3, 0, 0, 1, -2),$ $(2, 1, 4, 0, -1), (1, 0, -1, 0, 1), (2, 1, 0, 0, 0)$.

10. Let $\{\gamma_1, \gamma_2, \ldots, \gamma_{n-1}\}$ be any linearly independent subset of R_n with $n - 1$ members. Prove that $\{\alpha \mid \alpha \perp \gamma_i, i = 1, 2, \ldots, n - 1\}$ is a one-dimensional subspace of $\Re_n$.

11. Let $\gamma_1, \gamma_2, \ldots, \gamma_n$ be mutually orthogonal, unit vectors and let A be the $n \times n$ matrix such that $A_i = \gamma_i, i = 1, \ldots, n$. Prove that $|A|^2 = 1$.

12. Let L be any line in 3-dimensional space; show that $\{\alpha - \beta \mid \alpha \in L$ and $\beta \in L\}$ is a subspace of $\Re_3$. Compute the dimension of this subspace.

13. Prove Lemma 4.5.2.

14. Prove Lemma 4.5.3.

15. Prove Lemma 4.5.4.

16. Let $i = (1, 0, 0), j = (0, 1, 0), k = (0, 0, 1)$.

    (a) Prove that $i \times i = j \times j = k \times k = 0$.
    (b) Prove that $i \times j = k$.
    (c) Prove that $j \times k = i$.
    (d) Prove that $k \times i = j$.

17. Let α and β be any 3-vectors. Prove that:

    (a) $\|\alpha \times \beta\|^2 = \|\alpha\|^2\|\beta\|^2 - [\alpha \cdot \beta]^2$,
    (b) $\|\alpha \times \beta\| = \|\alpha\| \|\beta\| \sin \theta$, where $\theta = $ angle (α, β).

18. Let α and β be distinct 3-vectors; prove that $\{\alpha, \beta\}$ is linearly dependent if and only if $\alpha \times \beta = 0$.

19. Find 3-vectors α, β and γ such that $\alpha \times (\beta \times \gamma) \neq (\alpha \times \beta) \times \gamma$.

20. Let $\alpha, \beta,$ and γ be any 3-vectors. Prove that

$$\alpha \times (\beta \times \gamma) = (\alpha \cdot \gamma)\beta - (\alpha \cdot \beta)\gamma.$$

21. Let $\alpha = (a, b, c)$ and $\beta = (l, m, n)$ be unit vectors, and let $\theta = $ angle(α, β). Prove that

$$\begin{vmatrix} a & b \\ l & m \end{vmatrix}^2 + \begin{vmatrix} b & c \\ m & n \end{vmatrix}^2 + \begin{vmatrix} c & a \\ n & l \end{vmatrix}^2 = \sin^2\theta.$$

22. Let (a, b, c) and (l, m, n) be unit, orthogonal vectors. Prove that

$$\begin{vmatrix} a & b \\ l & m \end{vmatrix}^2 + \begin{vmatrix} b & c \\ m & n \end{vmatrix}^2 + \begin{vmatrix} c & a \\ n & l \end{vmatrix}^2 = 1.$$

23. (a) Prove Lemma 4.5.5.
    (b) Prove Lemma 4.5.6.
    (c) Prove Lemma 4.5.7.

24. Let $\alpha_1, \ldots, \alpha_n$ be any $(n+1)$-vectors.

    (a) Prove that $\times(\alpha_1, \ldots, \alpha_n) = \mathbf{0}$ if $\alpha_i = \mathbf{0}$
    (b) Prove that $\times(\alpha_1, \ldots, \alpha_n) = \mathbf{0}$ if $\alpha_r = \alpha_s$ where $r \neq s$.

25. Let α, β, and γ be 4-vectors. Simplify:

    (a) $\times(\alpha, \alpha, \alpha)$;
    (b) $\times(\alpha, 2\beta, \alpha + \beta)$;
    (c) $\times(\alpha, \beta, \beta + \gamma)$;
    (d) $\times(\alpha + \beta, \beta + \gamma, \gamma + \alpha)$;
    (e) $\times(\alpha, \beta, \alpha + \beta + \gamma)$.

26. (a) Prove that $\times(\epsilon_2, \ldots, \epsilon_n) = \epsilon_1$.
    (b) Prove that $\times(k_2\epsilon_2, \ldots, k_n\epsilon_n) = (k_2 \ldots k_n)\epsilon_1$.

27. Prove Lemma 4.5.9.

5

PLANES

5.1 PLANES AND HYPERPLANES

So far we have discussed the concepts of *point*, *line*, and *direction* in E_3, three-dimensional Euclidean space, and ideas related to the *distance* concept such as directed distance, Now. we have defined a plane as a translation of a two-dimensional subspace of $\Re_3$, and we have defined a hyperplane as the set of all points equidistant from two points. To illustrate the importance of the *distance* concept we propose to demonstrate that a subset of R_3 is a plane if and only if it is a hyperplane.

First, we must establish certain facts.

Lemma 5.1.1: Let $W = L\{\beta_1, \beta_2\}$ be any two-dimensional subspace of $\Re_3$ and let β be any nonzero vector orthogonal to both β_1 and β_2. Then $W = \{\gamma \mid \beta \cdot \gamma = 0\}$.

Proof: Consider the homogeneous linear system

(1) $$\beta \cdot \gamma = 0$$

which consists of one equation in three unknowns (the unknowns are the terms of γ). Now, the coefficient matrix of (1) is the 1×3 matrix β, whose rank is 1. Thus, by Theorem 2.4.2, $\{\gamma \mid \beta \cdot \gamma = 0\}$ is a two-dimensional subspace of $\Re_3$. Clearly, β_1 and β_2 are vector solutions of (1); so $\{\beta_1, \beta_2\}$ is a basis for $\{\gamma \mid \beta \cdot \gamma = 0\}$. We conclude that $\{\gamma \mid \beta \cdot \gamma = 0\} = L\{\beta_1, \beta_2\} = W$.

Using this result we easily establish an important method of characterizing planes.

Theorem 5.1.1: Let $\mathcal{P} = \{\alpha + \gamma \mid \gamma \in W\}$ be any plane where $\alpha \in R_3$ and $W = L\{\beta_1, \beta_2\}$ is a two-dimensional subspace of $\mathcal{R}_3$. Let β be any nonzero vector orthogonal to both β_1 and β_2; then $\mathcal{P} = \{\gamma \mid \beta \cdot (\gamma - \alpha) = 0\}$.

Proof: By Lemma 5.1.1, $W = \{\gamma \mid \beta \cdot \gamma = 0\}$; so

$$\mathcal{P} = \{\alpha + \gamma \mid \beta \cdot \gamma = 0\} = \{\zeta \mid \beta \cdot (\zeta - \alpha) = 0\} = \{\gamma \mid \beta \cdot (\gamma - \alpha) = 0\} \ .$$

We wish to show that any set such as $\{\gamma \mid \beta \cdot (\gamma - \alpha) = 0\}$ is a plane provided $\{\alpha, \beta\} \subset R_3$ and $\beta \neq 0$. We can demonstrate this by applying Theorem 5.1.1 itself.

Corollary 5.1.1: Let $\{\alpha, \beta\} \subset R_3$ where $\beta \neq 0$; then $\{\gamma \mid \beta \cdot (\gamma - \alpha) = 0\}$ is a plane.

Proof: Now, $W = \{\gamma \mid \beta \cdot \gamma = 0\}$ is a two-dimensional subspace of $\mathcal{R}_3$; thus $\mathcal{P} = \{\alpha + \gamma \mid \gamma \in W\}$ is a plane. By construction β is orthogonal to each member of W; so, by Theorem 5.1.1, $\mathcal{P} = \{\gamma \mid \beta \cdot (\gamma - \alpha) = 0\}$.

We turn now to hyperplanes.

Lemma 5.1.2: Each plane is a hyperplane.

Proof: Let $\mathcal{P} = \{\gamma \mid \beta \cdot (\gamma - \alpha) = 0\}$ be any plane (so $\beta \neq 0$). We must find distinct points γ_1 and γ_2 such that $\mathcal{P}$ is the set of all points equidistant from γ_1 and γ_2. Take $\gamma_1 = \alpha + \beta$ and $\gamma_2 = \alpha - \beta$, and let $\mathcal{K} = \{\zeta \mid \|\zeta - \gamma_1\| = \|\zeta - \gamma_2\|\}$. Now

$$\gamma \in \mathcal{K} \Leftrightarrow \|\gamma - (\alpha + \beta)\| = \|\gamma - (\alpha - \beta)\|$$

$$\Leftrightarrow \|(\gamma - \alpha) - \beta\| = \|(\gamma - \alpha) + \beta\| \quad \text{by vector algebra}$$

$$\Leftrightarrow \sqrt{\|\gamma - \alpha\|^2 + \|\beta\|^2 - 2(\gamma - \alpha) \cdot \beta} = \sqrt{\|\gamma - \alpha\|^2 + \|\beta\|^2 + 2(\gamma - \alpha) \cdot \beta}$$
$$\text{by Corollary 3.2.1 and Theorem 3.2.1}$$

$$\Leftrightarrow (\gamma - \alpha) \cdot \beta = 0 \ .$$

Thus $\gamma \in \mathcal{K}$ if and only if $\gamma \in \mathcal{P}$; we conclude that $\mathcal{P} = \mathcal{K}$, so each plane is a hyperplane. Notice our use of $\Leftrightarrow$ as an abbreviation for "if and only if."

Lemma 5.1.3: Each hyperplane is a plane.

Proof: Let $\mathcal{K} = \{\gamma \mid \|\gamma - \gamma_1\| = \|\gamma - \gamma_2\|\}$ be any hyperplane; let $\alpha = \frac{1}{2}(\gamma_1 + \gamma_2)$ and let $\beta = \frac{1}{2}(\gamma_1 - \gamma_2)$. Notice that $\beta \neq 0$. Consider the plane $\mathcal{P} = \{\gamma \mid \beta \cdot (\gamma - \alpha) = 0\}$. By the proof of Lemma 5.1.2, $\mathcal{P} = \mathcal{K}$. We conclude that each hyperplane is a plane.

These lemmas establish our main result.

Theorem 5.1.2: Let $A \subset R_3$; then A is a plane if and only if A is a hyperplane.

The following result is obvious and useful.

Lemma 5.1.4: Let $\mathcal{P} = \{\gamma \mid \beta \cdot (\gamma - \alpha) = 0\}$ be any plane, let $\alpha_1 \in \mathcal{P}$, and let β_1 be any nonzero member of $L\{\beta\}$. Then $\mathcal{P} = \{\gamma \mid \beta_1 \cdot (\gamma - \alpha_1) = 0\}$.

Proof: By Theorem 5.1.1, $\mathcal{P} = \{\gamma \mid \beta_1 \cdot (\gamma - \alpha) = 0\}$. Now $\alpha_1 \in \mathcal{P}$; so $\beta_1 \cdot (\alpha_1 - \alpha) = 0$, thus $\beta_1 \cdot \alpha_1 = \beta_1 \cdot \alpha$. Thus

$$\mathcal{P} = \{\gamma \mid \beta_1 \cdot \gamma = \beta_1 \cdot \alpha\} = \{\gamma \mid \beta_1 \cdot \gamma = \beta_1 \cdot \alpha_1\} = \{\gamma \mid \beta_1 \cdot (\gamma - \alpha_1) = 0\}$$

EXERCISES

1. Let $\mathcal{P} = \{(2, 0, 3) + \gamma \mid \gamma \in W\}$ where $W = L\{\epsilon_1, \epsilon_2\}$.
   (a) Express $\mathcal{P}$ in the form $\{\gamma \mid \beta \cdot (\gamma - \alpha) = 0\}$.
   (b) Express $\mathcal{P}$ in the form $\{\gamma \mid \|\gamma - \gamma_1\| = \|\gamma - \gamma_2\|\}$.

2. Let $\mathcal{P} = \{(-1, 4, 1) + \gamma \mid \gamma \in W\}$ where $W = L\{(2, 3, 0), (1, 0, -1)\}$.
   (a) Express $\mathcal{P}$ in the form $\{\gamma \mid \beta \cdot (\gamma - \alpha) = 0\}$.
   (b) Express $\mathcal{P}$ in the form $\{\gamma \mid \|\gamma - \gamma_1\| = \|\gamma - \gamma_2\|\}$.

3. Determine the set of all points equidistant from $(5, 1, -2)$ and $(1, -3, 2)$.

4. Determine the set of all points equidistant from $(-1, 0, 1)$ and $(2, 1, 0)$.

5. Find a point of intersection of the line $\{t(1, 2, 3) \mid t \in R\}$ and the plane $\{\gamma \mid \gamma \cdot (2, -1, 3) = 18\}$.

6. Find a point of intersection of the line through $(0, -1, 2)$ and $(2, 3, 1)$, and the plane $\{\gamma \mid \gamma \cdot (1, 1, -2) = 10\}$.

7. Find a point of intersection of the line through $(1, -2, 1)$ and $(2, 0, 1)$, and the plane $\{(x, y, z) \mid 2x - y + z = 5\}$.

8. Exhibit a line and a plane which do not intersect.

9. Find a plane which contains the line $\{(2, 0, 0) + t(-1, 3, 0) \mid t \in R\}$ and the point $(1, 2, -2)$.

10. Show that $\{(1, 0, -8) + t(1, 5, 7) \mid t \in R\} \subset \{\gamma \mid \gamma \cdot (2, 1, -1) = 10\}$.

11. Find a basis for $\{\gamma \mid \gamma \cdot (2, -3, 5) = 0\}$.

12. Let $\mathcal{P} = \{\gamma \mid \gamma \cdot (5, 2, -1) = 3\}$.
    (a) Show that $W = \{\gamma - (0, 0, -3) \mid \gamma \in \mathcal{P}\}$ is a subspace of $\mathcal{R}_3$.
    (b) Find a basis for W.

5.2 NORMAL TO A PLANE

In this section we discuss the notion of a *normal* to a plane. We need certain facts. First, let us prove that the line through two members of a plane is a subset of that plane.

Lemma 5.2.1: Let $\mathcal{P}$ be any plane and let $\{\gamma_1, \gamma_2\} \subset \mathcal{P}$, $\gamma_1 \neq \gamma_2$. Then the line through γ_1 and γ_2 is a subset of $\mathcal{P}$.

Proof: Let $\mathcal{P} = \{\gamma \mid \beta \cdot (\gamma - \alpha) = 0\}$ be any plane and let γ_1 and γ_2 be distinct members of $\mathcal{P}$. By assumption, $\beta \cdot (\gamma_1 - \alpha) = 0$ and $\beta \cdot (\gamma_2 - \alpha) = 0$; so $\beta \cdot \gamma_1 = \beta \cdot \gamma_2$. Next, consider any member of the line through γ_1 and γ_2, say $\gamma_1 + t(\gamma_2 - \gamma_1)$. Now,

$$\beta \cdot (\gamma_1 + t(\gamma_2 - \gamma_1)) - \alpha) = \beta \cdot (\gamma_1 - \alpha) + t\beta \cdot (\gamma_2 - \gamma_1)$$
$$= t\beta \cdot (\gamma_2 - \gamma_1)$$
$$= 0$$

since $\beta \cdot \gamma_1 = \beta \cdot \gamma_2$. We conclude that $\{\gamma_1 + t(\gamma_2 - \gamma_1) \mid t \in R\} \subset \mathcal{P}$.

We are interested in knowing whether a particular line is contained in a particular plane. Here is a test that provides an answer.

Theorem 5.2.1: Let $\mathcal{P} = \{\gamma \mid \beta \cdot (\gamma - \alpha) = 0\}$ be any plane and let $L = \{\alpha_1 + t\beta_1 \mid t \in R\}$ be any line. Then $L \subset \mathcal{P}$ if and only if $\beta \cdot \beta_1 = 0$ and $\alpha_1 \in \mathcal{P}$.

Proof: There are two parts to our proof.

1. Assume that $L \subset \mathcal{P}$. Now, $\alpha_1 \in L$, so $\mathcal{P} = \{\gamma \mid \beta \cdot (\gamma - \alpha_1) = 0\}$ by Lemma 5.1.4. By assumption, $\alpha_1 + \beta_1 \in \mathcal{P}$; so $\beta \cdot (\alpha_1 + \beta_1 - \alpha_1) = 0$, i.e., $\beta \cdot \beta_1 = 0$.
2. Assume that $\beta \cdot \beta_1 = 0$ and that $\alpha_1 \in \mathcal{P}$. Then $\mathcal{P} = \{\gamma \mid \beta \cdot (\gamma - \alpha_1) = 0\}$. But $\beta \cdot (\alpha_1 + \beta_1 - \alpha_1) = \beta \cdot \beta_1 = 0$; so $\alpha_1 + \beta_1 \in \mathcal{P}$. Now, L is the line through α_1 and $\alpha_1 + \beta_1$; therefore, by Lemma 5.2.1, $\{\alpha_1 + t\beta_1 \mid t \in R\} \subset \mathcal{P}$.

In view of Theorem 5.2.1 there is a line which is perpendicular to each line contained in the plane $\mathcal{P} = \{\gamma \mid \beta \cdot (\gamma - \alpha) = 0\}$; namely any line with direction $[\beta]$. Accordingly, we introduce the notion of a *normal* to a plane.

Definition 5.2.1: Any line which is perpendicular to each line contained in a plane $\mathcal{P}$ is said to be a *normal* to $\mathcal{P}$.

Example 1: The line $\{t(1, 2, -1) \mid t \in R\}$ is a normal to the plane $\{\gamma \mid (1, 2, -1) \cdot (\gamma - (2, 0, 0)) = 0\}$.

Let us formalize the comment that precedes Definition 5.2.1.

Theorem 5.2.2: Let $\mathcal{P} = \{\gamma \mid \beta \cdot (\gamma - \alpha) = 0\}$ be any plane; then each line with directions $[\beta]$ and $[-\beta]$ is a normal to $\mathcal{P}$. Moreover, $\mathcal{P}$ has no other normals.

Example 2: Find a plane $\mathcal{P}$ such that $(5, 1, -2) \in \mathcal{P}$ and the line $\{(0, 1, 2) + t(1, 2, -1) \mid t \in R\}$ is a normal to $\mathcal{P}$.

Solution: By Theorem 5.2.2 the required plane is $\{\gamma \mid (1, 2, -1) \cdot ((\gamma - (5, 1, -2)) = 0\}$, namely $\{\gamma \mid (1, 2, -1) \cdot \gamma = 9\}$.

We have seen that it is very useful to characterize a plane $\mathcal{P}$ in terms of a nonzero vector and a point, as follows: $\mathcal{P} = \{\gamma \mid \beta \cdot (\gamma - \alpha) = 0\}$. The geometric significance of the parameters α and β is now clear: $\alpha \in \mathcal{P}$ and $[\beta]$ is a direction of a normal to $\mathcal{P}$. Notice that $\beta \cdot \alpha$ is a scalar; so planes can also be characterized as follows.

Theorem 5.2.3: Let $\beta \neq 0$ and let $d \in R$; then $\{\gamma \mid \beta \cdot \gamma = d\}$ is a plane. Moreover, each plane can be characterized in this form.

Proof: It is easy to find a 3-vector α such that $\beta \cdot \alpha = d$ [e.g., if $\beta = (b_1, b_2, b_3)$ and if $b_1 \neq 0$, take $\alpha = (d/b_1, 0, 0)$]. Now,

$$\{\gamma \mid \beta \cdot \gamma = d\} = \{\gamma \mid \beta \cdot \gamma = \beta \cdot \alpha\} = \{\gamma \mid \beta \cdot (\gamma - \alpha) = 0\}$$

which is a plane. Moreover, let $\mathcal{P}$ by any plane; then there is a nonzero vector β_1 and a vector α_1 such that $\mathcal{P} = \{\gamma \mid \beta_1 \cdot (\gamma - \alpha_1) = 0\}$. Let $\beta_1 \cdot \alpha_1 = d_1$; then $\mathcal{P} = \{\gamma \mid \beta_1 \cdot \gamma = d_1\}$.

Example 3: Find a plane through $(1, 2, 3)$, $(2, 0, 5)$, and $(8, 4, 21)$.

Solution 1: Suppose that there is a plane through the given points; let it be $\{\gamma \mid \beta \cdot \gamma = d\}$.   Then

$$(2) \qquad \beta \cdot (1, 2, 3) = d, \quad \beta \cdot (2, 0, 5) = d, \quad \beta \cdot (8, 4, 21) = d$$

Now, (2) is a homogeneous linear system in four unknowns, d and the terms of β. To solve this system we use matrices. Now,

$$\begin{pmatrix} 1 & 2 & 3 & -1 \\ 2 & 0 & 5 & -1 \\ 8 & 4 & 21 & -1 \end{pmatrix} \sim \begin{pmatrix} 1 & 2 & 3 & -1 \\ 0 & -4 & -1 & 1 \\ 0 & 4 & 1 & 3 \end{pmatrix} \sim \begin{pmatrix} 2 & 0 & 5 & -1 \\ 0 & -4 & -1 & 1 \\ 0 & 0 & 0 & 4 \end{pmatrix}.$$

Thus $d = 0$. Let $\beta = (l, m, n)$; then $l = -5n/2$ and $m = -n/4$. Taking $n = -4$, we see that $l = 10$ and $m = 1$. So $(10, 1, -4)$ is a vector solution of (2). Notice that each solution of (2) is a scalar multiple of $(10, 1, -4)$. We conclude that $\{\gamma \mid (10, 1, -4) \cdot \gamma = 0\}$ is the only plane that contains the given points. Checking, we easily verify that the given points are members of this plane.

We now present another solution of Example 3 which makes more use of geometry.

Solution 2: If there is a plane through the given points then it is $\{\gamma \mid \beta \cdot (\gamma - (1, 2, 3)) = 0\}$ where $[\beta]$ is a direction of a normal to the required plane. Let us determine β. The line through $(1, 2, 3)$ and $(2, 0, 5)$ has direction $[(-1, 2, -2)]$, and the line through $(1, 2, 3)$ and $(8, 4, 21)$ has direction $[(7, 2, 18)]$. Therefore, $\beta \perp (-1, 2, -2)$ and $\beta \perp (7, 2, 18)$. Recall that the vector product of two 3-vectors is orthogonal to both vectors. Now, $(-1, 2, -2) \times (7, 2, 18) = (40, 4, -16)$; so we take $\beta = (10, 1, -4)$. Hence, if there is a plane through the given points, it is $\{\gamma \mid (10, 1, -4)\cdot(\gamma - (1, 2, 3)) = 0\}$; i.e., $\{\gamma \mid (10, 1, -4)\cdot\gamma = 0\}$. Checking, we see that the given points are on this plane.

We now establish a *unique-existence* theorem for problems of the type illustrated in Example 3.

Theorem 5.2.4: There is a unique plane through points α_1, α_2, and α_3 if and only if these points are not collinear.

Proof: There are two parts to our proof.

1. Assume that α_1, α_2, and α_3 are not collinear. First, we prove that there is at most one plane through these points, say $\mathcal{P}$. By assumption, $\alpha_1 \neq \alpha_2$; therefore there is a unique line through α_1 and α_2, namely $\{\alpha_1 + t(\alpha_2 - \alpha_1) \mid t \in R\}$. By assumption, α_3 is not on this line; so $\alpha_3 - \alpha_1 \notin L\{\alpha_2 - \alpha_1\}$. It follows that $\{\alpha_2 - \alpha_1, \alpha_3 - \alpha_1\}$ has two members and is linearly independent. Thus, the 2×3 matrix whose row vectors are $\alpha_2 - \alpha_1$ and $\alpha_3 - \alpha_1$ has rank 2. Applying Theorem 2.4.2 we see that the solution set of the homogeneous linear system

$$(3) \qquad (\alpha_2 - \alpha_1)\cdot\beta = 0 , \quad (\alpha_3 - \alpha_1)\cdot\beta = 0$$

is a one-dimensional subspace of $\mathcal{R}_3$. Let β be any nonzero vector solution of (3); then each normal to $\mathcal{P}$ has directions $[\beta]$ and $[-\beta]$. This means that $\{\gamma \mid \beta\cdot(\gamma - \alpha_1) = 0\}$ is the only plane through α_1, α_2, and α_3. Let us verify that this plane contains the given points. Clearly $\beta\cdot(\alpha_1 - \alpha_1) = 0$, $\beta\cdot(\alpha_2 - \alpha_1) = 0$, and $\beta\cdot(\alpha_3 - \alpha_1) = 0$. This proves that there is a unique plane through α_1, α_2, and α_3.

2. Assume that α_1, α_2, and α_3 are collinear. Let α_4 be a point such that α_1, α_2, and α_4 are not collinear. By the first part of this proof there is a plane through α_1, α_2, and α_4, say $\mathcal{P}_1$. Now, α_3 is on the line through α_1 and α_2; so $\alpha_3 \in \mathcal{P}_1$. By choosing a point α_5 which is not a member of $\mathcal{P}_1$, and repeating our argument, we readily find another plane through α_1, α_2, and α_3. This establishes our theorem.

Here is another *unique-existence* theorem.

Theorem 5.2.5: Suppose that $\alpha \notin L$, where L is a line and α is a point. Then there is a unique plane that contains L and α.

Proof: Let α_1 and α_2 be two points on the given line. Then α, α_1, and α_2 are not collinear. So, by Theorem 5.2.4, there is a unique plane $\mathcal{P}$ through these points. Since $\mathcal{P}$ contains α_1 and α_2, $\mathcal{P}$ contains the line through α_1 and α_2, namely L. This establishes our result.

We now illustrate Theorem 5.2.5.

Example 4: Find the plane that contains the line $\{(1, 0, 3) + t(-1, 2, 1) \mid t \in R\}$ and the point $(2, 2, 2)$.

Solution: Notice that $(2, 2, 2)$ is not a member of the given line; therefore, by Theorem 5.2.5, there is a nonzero vector β such that the plane $\mathcal{P} = \{\gamma \mid \beta \cdot (\gamma - (2, 2, 2)) = 0\}$ contains the given line. Let us determine β. Now, $\beta \cdot (-1, 2, 1) = 0$. Moreover, $\mathcal{P}$ contains the line through $(1, 0, 3)$ and $(2, 2, 2)$; thus $\beta \cdot (1, 2, -1) = 0$. But $(-1, 2, 1) \times (1, 2, -1) = (-4, 0, -4)$; so $[(1, 0, 1)]$ is a direction of a normal to our plane. Thus, our plane is $\{\gamma \mid (1, 0, 1) \cdot (\gamma - (2, 2, 2)) = 0\}$; i.e., $\{\gamma \mid (1, 0, 1) \cdot \gamma = 4\}$.

EXERCISES

1. Find a normal to $\{\gamma \mid \gamma \cdot (2, -1, 1) = 3\}$.

2. Find a normal to $\{\gamma \mid \gamma \cdot (3, 1, 2) = -5\}$.

3. Find a normal to $\{(x, y, z) \mid 2x - 3z = 6\}$.

4. Find a normal to $\{\gamma \mid \|\gamma - (2, 0, 1)\| = \|\gamma - (3, 2, 4)\|\}$.

5. (a) Find a direction of a normal to the plane through the points $(2, -1, 0)$, $(3, 4, 1)$, and $(4, 5, 0)$.
    (b) Find the plane through $(2, -1, 0)$, $(3, 4, 1)$, and $(4, 5, 0)$.

6. Find a plane $\mathcal{P}$ such that $\mathbf{0} \in \mathcal{P}$ and the line $\{(2, 0, 0) + t(1, 0, 1) \mid t \in R\}$ is a normal to $\mathcal{P}$.

7. Find a plane $\mathcal{P}$ such that $(2, 2, 0) \in \mathcal{P}$ and the line $\{t(1, 1, 0) \mid t \in R\}$ is a normal to $\mathcal{P}$.

8. Prove Theorem 5.2.2.

9. Find the plane through ϵ_1, ϵ_2, and ϵ_3.

10. Find the plane through $(0, 1, 1)$, $(1, 0, 1)$, and $(1, 1, 0)$.

11. Find the plane through $(2, -1, 4)$, $(5, 2, -3)$, and $(3, 4, 2)$.

12. Find two planes through $(2, -2, 1)$, $(1, 2, 4)$, and $(5, -14, -8)$.

13. Find the plane that contains $\{(0, 1, 1) + t(1, 1, 0) \mid t \in R\}$ and $(1, 2, 2)$.

14. Find the plane that contains $\{(1, 0, 0) + t(-2, 0, 3) \mid t \in R\}$ and $(3, 0, 1)$.

15. Exhibit two planes that contain $\{(1, 1, 0) + t(0, 0, 1) \mid t \in R\}$ and $(1, 1, 1)$.

5.3 INTERSECTION OF PLANES

Let $\mathcal{P}_1$ and $\mathcal{P}_2$ be any planes; we propose to show that $\mathcal{P}_1 \cap \mathcal{P}_2$ is either a plane, a line, or the empty set. The key concept is the notion of *parallel* planes.

Definition 5.3.1: Planes $\mathcal{P}_1$ and $\mathcal{P}_2$ are said to be *parallel* if and only if they possess a common normal.

For example, the planes $\{\gamma \mid (2, 0, 3)\cdot\gamma = 0\}$ and $\{\gamma \mid (2, 0, 3)\cdot\gamma = 5\}$ are parallel. Each plane is parallel to itself.

In view of Theorem 5.2.2 we easily establish the following fact.

Theorem 5.3.1: Let $\mathcal{P}_1 = \{\gamma \mid \beta_1\cdot\gamma = d_1\}$ and $\mathcal{P}_2 = \{\gamma \mid \beta_2\cdot\gamma = d_2\}$ be any planes. Then $\mathcal{P}_1$ and $\mathcal{P}_2$ are parallel if and only if $\beta_2 \in L\{\beta_1\}$.

Corollary 5.3.1: $\mathcal{P}_1$ and $\mathcal{P}_2$ are parallel planes if and only if there is a nonzero vector β and scalars d_1 and d_2 such that $\mathcal{P}_1 = \{\gamma \mid \beta\cdot\gamma = d_1\}$ and $\mathcal{P}_2 = \{\gamma \mid \beta\cdot\gamma = d_2\}$.

Proof: Apply Lemma 5.1.4.

Now that we have pinned down our notion of parallel planes, let us see how this helps us analyze $\mathcal{P}_1 \cap \mathcal{P}_2$, where $\mathcal{P}_1$ and $\mathcal{P}_2$ are planes. First, we show that parallel planes are either identical or do not have any common member. Of course, this brings out the intuitive content of our concept.

Theorem 5.3.2: Let $\mathcal{P}_1$ and $\mathcal{P}_2$ be parallel planes. Then either $\mathcal{P}_1 \cap \mathcal{P}_2 = \varnothing$ or $\mathcal{P}_1 = \mathcal{P}_2$.

Proof: Suppose that $\mathcal{P}_1 \cap \mathcal{P}_2 \neq \varnothing$; i.e., suppose that there is a point α such that $\alpha \in \mathcal{P}_1$ and $\alpha \in \mathcal{P}_2$. Let $[\beta]$ and $[-\beta]$ be the directions of a common normal to $\mathcal{P}_1$ and $\mathcal{P}_2$. Then, by Lemma 5.1.4, $\mathcal{P}_1 = \{\gamma \mid \beta\cdot(\gamma - \alpha) = 0\}$ and $\mathcal{P}_2 = \{\gamma \mid \beta\cdot(\gamma - \alpha) = 0\}$. So $\mathcal{P}_1 = \mathcal{P}_2$.

We have now analyzed $\mathcal{P}_1 \cap \mathcal{P}_2$ for the case of parallel planes. If the parallel planes are distinct, then $\mathcal{P}_1 \cap \mathcal{P}_2 = \varnothing$; if the parallel planes are the same, then $\mathcal{P}_1 \cap \mathcal{P}_2 = \mathcal{P}_1 = \mathcal{P}_2$. We now turn to nonparallel planes, our main result.

Theorem 5.3.3: Let $\mathcal{P}_1$ and $\mathcal{P}_2$ be any nonparallel planes. Then $\mathcal{P}_1 \cap \mathcal{P}_2$ is a line.

Proof: Let $\mathcal{P}_1 = \{\gamma \mid \beta_1\cdot\gamma = d_1\}$ and let $\mathcal{P}_2 = \{\gamma \mid \beta_2\cdot\gamma = d_2\}$ be nonparallel planes. Then $\beta_2 \notin L\{\beta_1\}$. The key to our result is the observation that $\mathcal{P}_1 \cap \mathcal{P}_2$ is the solution set of the linear system

$$(4) \qquad\qquad \beta_1\cdot\gamma = d_1, \quad \beta_2\cdot\gamma = d_2$$

which consists of two equations in three unknowns, the terms of γ. Recall from Section 2.4 that we can solve (4) by considering the related homogeneous linear system

$$(5) \qquad\qquad \beta_1\cdot\gamma = 0, \quad \beta_2\cdot\gamma = 0 \ .$$

Now, the row vectors of the coefficient matrix of (5) are β_1 and β_2; so 2 is the rank of this matrix. Let W be the solution set of (5); recall that W is a subspace of $\mathcal{R}_3$.

By Theorem 2.4.2, dim $W = 1$. Now, consider (4); 2 is the rank of its coefficient matrix, so 2 is the rank of its augmented matrix. Thus, by Theorem 2.3.1, (4) has a solution, say α. We conclude from Theorem 2.4.3 that the solution set of (4) is $\{\alpha + \gamma \mid \gamma \in W\}$. So $\mathcal{P}_1 \cap \mathcal{P}_2 = \{\alpha + \gamma \mid \gamma \in W\}$, a line. This establishes Theorem 5.3.3.

Next, we develop a technique for determining the line of intersection of specific nonparallel planes. Of course, it is enough to determine two points that are on both planes. The calculations are a trifle simpler, however, if we determine one point on both planes and a direction of their line of intersection. The idea is to row-reduce the augmented matrix of (4); it is easy to read off two vector solutions of (4), or one vector solution of (4) and one vector solution of (5) (the latter is found by considering the appropriate 3×3 submatrix of the reduced matrix). We now illustrate these ideas.

Example 1: Find the intersection of the planes $\{\gamma \mid (1 , -2 , 3){\cdot}\gamma = 3\}$ and $\{\gamma \mid (2 , 3 , -1){\cdot}\gamma = -1\}$.

Solution: The matrix that gives us a point on both planes also gives us a direction of the line of intersection of the planes:

$$\begin{pmatrix} 1 & -2 & 3 & 3 \\ 2 & 3 & -1 & -1 \end{pmatrix} \sim \begin{pmatrix} 1 & -2 & 3 & 3 \\ 0 & 7 & -7 & -7 \end{pmatrix} \sim \begin{pmatrix} 1 & 0 & 1 & 1 \\ 0 & 1 & -1 & -1 \end{pmatrix}.$$

From the last matrix we can read off the coordinates of a point on both planes; also, we can read off a direction of the line of intersection of the planes. Let a point of intersection be $(a , b , 0)$; then $a = 1$ and $b = -1$. Thus, the point $(1 , -1 , 0)$ is on both planes. Let $[(l_0 , m_0 , n_0)]$ be a direction of the line of intersection of the given planes; considering only the first three columns of our matrix, we see that

$$l_0 + n_0 = 0 \quad \text{and} \quad m_0 - n_0 = 0 .$$

Take $n_0 = -1$; then $l_0 = 1$ and $m_0 = -1$. Thus $[(1 , -1 , -1)]$ is a direction of our line. Hence, the line of intersection of the given planes is $\{(1 , -1 , 0) + t(1 , -1 , -1) \mid t \in R\}$. Checking, we see that this line is a subset of both planes.

The result of this section is interesting for an unexpected reason; it provides us with an alternative method of characterizing a line; namely, as the intersection of two nonparallel planes. Given a line, it is a simple matter to find one plane which contains the line; merely choose a point which is not on the given line. A second plane containing the given line is easily found by choosing a point which is not on the first plane.

Example 2: Express the line $L = \{(4 , -5 , 2) + t(2 , -3 , 1) \mid t \in R\}$ as the intersection of two planes.

Solution: Notice that $(0, 0, 0) \notin L$. The plane through L and this point contains lines with directions $[(2, -3, 1)]$ and $[(4, -5, 2)]$. Now, $(2, -3, 1) \times (4, -5, 2) = (-1, 0, 2)$; so each normal to our plane has direction $[(-1, 0, 2)]$. Thus $L \subset \{\gamma \mid (-1, 0, 2) \cdot \gamma = 0\}$. Next, observe that $(1, 0, 0) \notin \{\gamma \mid (-1, 0, 2) \cdot \gamma = 0\}$; so we shall determine the plane through $(1, 0, 0)$ and L. This plane contains two lines which possess directions $[(2, -3, 1)]$ and $[(3, -5, 2)]$. Now, $(2, -3, 1) \times (3, -5, 2) = (-1, -1, -1)$; so each normal to our plane has direction $[(1, 1, 1)]$. Thus $L \subset \{\gamma \mid (1, 1, 1) \cdot \gamma = 1\}$. We conclude that $L = \{\gamma \mid (1, 0, -2) \cdot \gamma = 0\} \cap \{\gamma \mid (1, 1, 1) \cdot \gamma = 1\}$. We point out that $L = \{\gamma \mid (1, 0, -2) \cdot \gamma = 0 \text{ and } (1, 1, 1) \cdot \gamma = 1\}$.

EXERCISES

1. Show that the planes $\{\gamma \mid (2, -1, 3) \cdot \gamma = 2\}$ and $\{\gamma \mid (-6, 3, -9) \cdot \gamma = 3\}$ are parallel.

2. Show that the plane through $(2, 3, 0), (-1, 1, 2)$, and $(1, 3, 3)$ is parallel to $\{\gamma \mid (12, -5, 4) \cdot \gamma = 3\}$.

3. Prove Theorem 5.3.1.

4. Prove Corollary 5.3.1.

5. Let $\{\gamma \mid (l_1, m_1, n_1) \cdot \gamma = d_1\}$ and $\{\gamma \mid (l_2, m_2, n_2) \cdot \gamma = d_2\}$ be nonparallel planes, and let $l_1 \neq 0$. Prove that $l_2 m_1 \neq l_1 m_2$ or $l_2 n_1 \neq l_1 n_2$.

6. Given that $n_2 l_1 = n_1 l_2$, $n_2 m_1 = n_1 m_2$, and that $n_1 \neq 0$, prove that $(l_2, m_2, n_2) \in L\{(l_1, m_1, n_1)\}$.

7. Let $\{\gamma \mid (l_1, m_1, n_1) \cdot \gamma = d_1\}$ and $\{\gamma \mid (l_2, m_2, n_2) \cdot \gamma = d_2\}$ be nonparallel planes, and let $m_1 \neq 0$. Prove that $m_2 n_1 \neq m_1 n_2$ or $m_2 l_1 \neq m_1 l_2$.

8. Let $\{\gamma \mid (l_1, m_1, n_1) \cdot \gamma = d_1\}$ and $\{\gamma \mid (l_2, m_2, n_2) \cdot \gamma = d_2\}$ be nonparallel planes, and let $n_1 \neq 0$. Prove that $n_2 l_1 \neq n_1 l_2$ or $n_2 m_1 \neq n_1 m_2$.

9. Simplify $\{\gamma \mid (1, -2, 0) \cdot \gamma = 2\} \cap \{\gamma \mid (2, 1, -1) \cdot \gamma = 4\}$.

10. Simplify $\{\gamma \mid (3, 1, 1) \cdot \gamma = 0\} \cap \{\gamma \mid (2, 2, -1) \cdot \gamma = 5\}$.

11. Simplify $\{(x, y, z) \mid x = z\} \cap \{(x, y, z) \mid y = z\}$.

12. Simplify $\{(x, y, z) \mid x = z\} \cap \{(x, y, z) \mid y = -z\}$.

13. Express the line $\{(0, 1, 2) + t(1, 1, 1) \mid t \in R\}$ as the intersection of two planes.

14. Express the line $\{(1, 2, 1) + t(-2, 0, 1) \mid t \in R\}$ as the intersection of two planes.

5.4   DISTANCE BETWEEN A POINT AND A PLANE

We have seen that $\mathcal{P} = \{\gamma \mid \beta \cdot \gamma = d\}$ is a plane provided that $\beta \neq \mathbf{0}$. The vector β possesses geometric significance since each line with directions $[\beta]$ and $[-\beta]$ is a normal to $\mathcal{P}$. The scalar d also has geometric significance. Let $\|\beta\| = 1$ and consider the directed line (L, β) where $L = \{t\beta \mid t \in R\}$. Let α_1 be the point of intersection of L and $\mathcal{P}$; i.e., $L \cap \mathcal{P} = \{\alpha_1\}$. Then d is the directed distance from $\mathbf{0}$ to α_1 along (L, β). Notice that L is a normal to $\mathcal{P}$; intuitively, $|d|$ is the distance between $\mathbf{0}$ and $\mathcal{P}$.

To back up our remarks we present two facts.

Lemma 5.4.1:   Let $\|\beta\| = 1$ and let $L = \{t\beta \mid t \in R\}$. Then d is the directed distance from $\mathbf{0}$ to $d\beta$ along (L, β).

Proof: Apply Theorem 4.4.1.

Lemma 5.4.2:   Let $\|\beta\| = 1$; then $d\beta \in \{\gamma \mid \beta \cdot \gamma = d\}$.

We now present the notion of the distance between a point and a plane.

Definition 5.4.1:   The distance between a plane $\mathcal{P}$ and a point α is said to be $\|\gamma - \alpha\|$ where γ is the point of intersection of $\mathcal{P}$ and the normal to $\mathcal{P}$ through α.

The following theorem illustrates this concept.

Theorem 5.4.1:   Let $\|\beta\| = 1$; then $|d|$ is the distance between $\mathbf{0}$ and the plane $\mathcal{P} = \{\gamma \mid \beta \cdot \gamma = d\}$.

Proof: If $\mathbf{0} \in \mathcal{P}$ then $d = 0$ and the distance between $\mathbf{0}$ and $\mathcal{P}$ is also 0. Assume, then, that $\mathbf{0} \notin \mathcal{P}$. Now, there is a unique normal to $\mathcal{P}$ through $\mathbf{0}$, namely $\{t\beta \mid t \in R\}$. This line intersects $\mathcal{P}$ at the point $d\beta$. So, the distance between $\mathbf{0}$ and $\mathcal{P}$ is $\|d\beta - \mathbf{0}\| = \|d\beta\| = |d|$.

Example 1:   Compute the distance between $\mathbf{0}$ and $\{\gamma \mid (5, -2, 3) \cdot \gamma = -4\}$.

Solution: The given plane is $\left\{\gamma \mid \dfrac{\gamma}{\sqrt{38}} \cdot (5, -2, 3) = -4/\sqrt{38}\right\}$. Therefore, by Theorem 5.4.1, $4/\sqrt{38}$ is the required distance.

We now generalize Theorem 5.4.1.

Theorem 5.4.2:   Let $\|\beta\| = 1$; then $|\beta \cdot \alpha - d|$ is the distance between the point α and the plane $\mathcal{P} = \{\gamma \mid \beta \cdot \gamma = d\}$.

Proof: If $\alpha \in \mathcal{P}$ then $\beta \cdot \alpha = d$, so $|\beta \cdot \alpha - d| = 0$; in this case the distance between α and $\mathcal{P}$ is also 0. Assume, then, that $\alpha \notin \mathcal{P}$. Notice that $\{\alpha + t\beta \mid t \in R\}$ is the normal to $\mathcal{P}$ through α. Let t_0 be the scalar such that $\alpha + t_0\beta \in \mathcal{P}$; so $\beta \cdot (\alpha + t_0\beta) = d$, hence $\beta \cdot \alpha + t_0 = d$, thus $t_0 = d - \beta \cdot \alpha$. Clearly, $|t_0|$ is the distance between α and $\alpha + t_0\beta$; so $|\beta \cdot \alpha - d|$ is the distance between α and $\mathcal{P}$.

Corollary 5.4.1: $\dfrac{|\beta \cdot \alpha - d|}{\|\beta\|}$ is the distance between the point α and the plane $\{\gamma \mid \beta \cdot \gamma = d\}$.

Proof: Apply Theorem 5.4.2.

Example 2: Compute the distance between $(2, -1, 3)$ and $\{\gamma \mid (4, 2, -3) \cdot \gamma = 5\}$.

Solution: By Corollary 5.4.1 the required distance is

$$\frac{|(4, 2, -3) \cdot (2, -1, 3) - 5|}{\|(4, 2, -3)\|} = 8/\sqrt{29} \ .$$

Next, we introduce the notion of the distance between parallel planes.

Definition 5.4.2: The *distance* between a plane and itself is said to be zero; the *distance* between distinct parallel planes is said to be the distance between two points, one on each plane, such that the line through the points is a normal to both planes.

Intuitively, the distance between the points of intersection of a normal to distinct parallel planes, with these planes, is independent of the normal involved (i.e., we obtain the same distance no matter which normal is used). It is a nice exercise in vector algebra to establish this fact rigorously. In this connection, the proof of the following theorem is helpful.

Theorem 5.4.3: Let $\|\beta\| = 1$; then $|d_2 - d_1|$ is the distance between $\mathcal{P}_1 = \{\gamma \mid \beta \cdot \gamma = d_1\}$ and $\mathcal{P}_2 = \{\gamma \mid \beta \cdot \gamma = d_2\}$.

Proof: If $\mathcal{P}_1 = \mathcal{P}_2$ then $d_1 = d_2$, so $|d_2 - d_1| = 0$. Assume that $\mathcal{P}_1 \neq \mathcal{P}_2$. Notice that $L = \{t\beta \mid t \in R\}$ is a normal to both planes. Moreover, $d_1\beta \in \mathcal{P}_1$ and $d_2\beta \in \mathcal{P}_2$. Thus, the distance between $\mathcal{P}_1$ and $\mathcal{P}_2$ is

$$\|d_2\beta - d_1\beta\| = \|(d_2 - d_1)\beta\| = |d_2 - d_1| \, \|\beta\| = |d_2 - d_1| \, .$$

Example 3: Compute the distance between $\{\gamma \mid (2, 1, -4) \cdot \gamma = 5\}$ and $\{\gamma \mid (-6, -3, 12) \cdot \gamma = 6\}$.

Solution: Let $\beta = \dfrac{1}{\sqrt{21}}(2, 1, -4)$; then the given planes are $\{\gamma \mid \beta \cdot \gamma = 5/\sqrt{21}\}$ and $\{\gamma \mid \beta \cdot \gamma = -2/\sqrt{21}\}$. So, by Theorem 5.4.3, the required distance is $|5/\sqrt{21} + 2/\sqrt{21}| = 7/\sqrt{21} = \sqrt{21}/3$.

Finally, we present the idea of the *directed* distance from a plane $\mathcal{P}$ to a point α along a directed normal to $\mathcal{P}$.

Definition 5.4.3: Let $\mathcal{P} = \{\gamma \mid \beta \cdot \gamma = d\}$ be a plane, let $\alpha \in R_3$, and let L be a normal to $\mathcal{P}$ through α. The *directed distance* from $\mathcal{P}$ to α along (L, β) is said to be the directed distance from γ to α along (L, β) where $\gamma \in \mathcal{P} \cap L$.

Before illustrating this concept we work out an efficient method of computing the directed distance from a plane to a point.

Theorem 5.4.4: Let $\|\beta\| = 1$ and let $L = \{\alpha + t\beta \mid t \in R\}$; the directed distance from $\mathcal{P} = \{\gamma \mid \beta\cdot\gamma = d\}$ to α along (L , β) is $\beta\cdot\alpha - d$.

Proof: Considering the proof of Theorem 5.4.2, we see that the directed distance from $\mathcal{P}$ to α along (L , β) is $\beta\cdot\alpha - d$.

Corollary 5.4.2: Let $L = \{\alpha + t\beta \mid t \in R\}$. The directed distance from $\mathcal{P} = \{\gamma \mid \beta\cdot\gamma = d\}$ to α along (L , β) is $\dfrac{\beta\cdot\alpha - d}{\|\beta\|}$.

Proof: By Theorem 5.4.4 the directed distance from $\{\gamma \mid (\beta/\|\beta\|)\cdot\gamma = d/\|\beta\|\}$ to α along (L , β) is $(\beta/\|\beta\|)\cdot\alpha - d/\|\beta\| = \dfrac{\beta\cdot\alpha - d}{\|\beta\|}$.

Here is one more example.

Example 4: Determine the directed distance from $\{\gamma \mid \epsilon_1\cdot(\gamma - \alpha_0) = 0\}$ to α along $(\{\alpha + t\epsilon_1 \mid t \in R\}, \epsilon_1)$.

Solution: By Corollary 5.4.2 the directed distance is $\epsilon_1\cdot(\alpha - \alpha_0)$, which is the first term of $\alpha - \alpha_0$.

EXERCISES

1. Prove Lemma 5.4.1.

2. Prove Lemma 5.4.2.

3. Compute the distance between $\mathbf{0}$ and $\left\{\gamma \mid \dfrac{1}{\sqrt{2}}(1 , 0 , -1)\cdot\gamma = 2\right\}$.

4. Compute the distance between $\mathbf{0}$ and $\{\gamma \mid (2 , 1 , -3)\cdot\gamma = -5\}$.

5. Prove Corollary 5.4.1.

6. Compute the distance between $(1 , -2 , 0)$ and $\{\gamma \mid (1 , 1 , 1)\cdot\gamma = 2\}$.

7. Compute the distance between $(2 , 3 , -2)$ and $\{\gamma \mid (1 , -2 , 1)\cdot\gamma = -5\}$.

8. Prove that the distance between the points of intersection of a normal to distinct parallel planes with these planes, is independent of the normal involved.

9. Compute the distance between $\{\gamma \mid (2, 3, -1)\cdot\gamma = 2\}$ and $\{\gamma \mid (6, 9, -3)\cdot\gamma = -1\}$.

10. Compute the distance between $\{\gamma \mid (1, 1, -2)\cdot\gamma = 3\}$ and $\{\gamma \mid (5, 5, -10)\cdot\gamma = 3\}$.

11. Compute the distance between $\{\gamma \mid (-1, 0, 2)\cdot\gamma = -3\}$ and $\{\gamma \mid (1, 0, -2)\cdot\gamma = 0\}$.

12. Compute the distance between $\{\gamma \mid (2, -2, 1)\cdot\gamma = -4\}$ and $\{\gamma \mid (6, -6, 3)\cdot\gamma = 2\}$.

13. Prove Theorem 5.4.4.

14. Compute the directed distance from $\{\gamma \mid (1, 2, 0)\cdot\gamma = 5\}$ to $(2, -1, 3)$ along $(L, (1, 2, 0))$, where $L = \{(2, -1, 3) + t(1, 2, 0) \mid t \in R\}$.

15. Determine the directed distance from $\{\gamma \mid \epsilon_2\cdot(\gamma - \alpha_0) = 0\}$ to α along (L, ϵ_2), where $L = \{\alpha + t\epsilon_2 \mid t \in R\}$.

16. Determine the directed distance from $\{\gamma \mid \epsilon_3\cdot(\gamma - \alpha_0) = 0\}$ to α along (L, ϵ_3), where $L = \{\alpha + t\epsilon_3 \mid t \in R\}$.

6

MODERN ALGEBRA

6.1 ALGEBRAIC SYSTEMS

In Chapters 4 and 5 we have developed the geometry of vectors; here, and in Chapter 7, we come to grips with the algebra of vectors. We have worked out in detail the algebra of n-tuples and the algebra of matrices. You may have noticed that these mathematical systems possess many common algebraic properties; moreover, other important mathematical systems share these properties (see Chapters 8 and 9). Obviously, it is inefficient to work out the properties of each mathematical system individually; much better to establish once and for all that each mathematical system of a specified type possesses certain definite algebraic properties.

In this chapter we study mathematical systems of a simple type called *algebraic systems*. For example, any mathematical system that consists only of some operations on a set is called an algebraic system; of course, the set involved is also part of the algebraic system. We use a tuple to display the components of an algebraic system. By convention the set involved is displayed as the first term of the tuple; this set is said to be the *basic* set or the *supporting* set of the algebraic system because each term of the algebraic system is constructed from it. Thus, $(N, +)$ and $(I, +, \cdot)$ are algebraic systems; here N is the set of all natural numbers and I is the set of all integers.

Now, in Chapter 1 we learned how to add vectors, so $+$ is a binary operation on R_n; thus $(R_n, +)$ is an algebraic system. We are familiar with the properties of $(R_n, +)$; in particular, recall that $+$ is associative on R_n. Any algebraic system which involves just one binary operation is said to be a *semigroup* provided that the operation is associative; i.e., $(S, \circ)$ is a *semigroup* provided that $\circ$ is a binary operation on S and is associative on S. Thus, the one postulate for a semigroup $(S, \circ)$ is the following statement.

SEMIGROUP POSTULATE: $x \circ (y \circ z) = (x \circ v) \circ z$ whenever $\{x, y, z\} \subset S$.

We have already observed that $(R_n, +)$ is a semigroup whenever n is a natural number. Here are some more examples.

Example 1: $(N, +)$ is a semigroup.

Example 2: $(N, \cdot)$ is a semigroup.

Example 3: $(I, +)$ is a semigroup.

Example 4: $(I, \cdot)$ is a semigroup.

Example 5: $(\{a, b\}, \circ)$ is a semigroup where $\circ$ is the binary operation on $\{a, b\}$ such that $a \circ a = a \circ b = b \circ a = a$ and $b \circ b = b$.

Example 6: $(\mathcal{P}S, \doteq)$ is a semigroup where S is a set, $\mathcal{P}S$ is the set of all subsets of S, and $\doteq$ is the *symmetric difference* operation on $\mathcal{P}S$, i.e., $A \doteq B = \{t \mid t \in A$ or else $t \in B\}$ whenever $\{A, B\} \subset \mathcal{P}S$. Let us take a closer look at this example now, because we shall use it throughout this chapter to illustrate various ideas. Now, $\mathcal{P}S$ (called the *power* set of S) is the set of all subsets of S; thus $\mathcal{P}\{1, 2\} = \{\varnothing, \{1\}, \{2\}, \{1, 2\}\}$ and $\mathcal{P}\{1, 2, 3\} = \{\varnothing, \{1\}, \{2\}, \{3\}, \{1, 2\}, \{1, 3\}, \{2, 3\}, \{1, 2, 3\}\}$. We are mainly interested in the *symmetric difference* operation; notice that $\{2, 3\} \doteq \{1\} = \{1, 2, 3\}, \{2, 3\} \doteq \{2\} = \{3\}, \{2, 3\} \doteq \varnothing = \{2, 3\}$. Let S be any set; we must prove that $A \doteq (B \doteq C) = (A \doteq B) \doteq C$ whenever $A, B,$ and C are subsets of S. This can be achieved as follows. First establish the connection between $\doteq$ and $-$ (the *difference* operation), where $A - B = \{t \mid t \in A$ and $t \notin B\} = A \cap B'$; namely prove that $A \doteq B = (A - B) \cup (B - A)$. Next, show that

$$A - (B \doteq C) = (A \cap B \cap C) \cup (A \cap B' \cap C')$$

and

$$(A \doteq B) - C = (A \cap B' \cap C') \cup (A' \cap B \cap C') \ .$$

The associative law for $\doteq$ can now be established. The details are left as an exercise.

So far we have considered algebraic systems that involve operations only. We mention that a mathematical system that involves relations as well as operations is also called an algebraic system. Thus $(N, +, \cdot, <)$ is called an algebraic system where $<$ is the *less than* relation on the natural numbers. Moreover, it is sometimes convenient to display certain members of the supporting set of an algebraic system; thus, if $(S, +)$ is an algebraic system and a is a member of S that we regard as important, we form the tuple $(S, +, a)$ and call this an algebraic system also. To illustrate, 1 is an important natural number, so we call $(N, +, \cdot, <, 1)$ an algebraic system, indeed this algebraic system is usually called the *natural number system*. Similarly, the system of integers $(I, +, \cdot, <, 0, 1)$, which displays two integers, is an algebraic system. Notice that we distinguish between a set of numbers and a number system.

However, in this chapter we confine our attention mainly to algebraic systems that do not involve relations; i.e., we concentrate on operations. We want to pin down this important mathematical concept and to simplify our method of representing an operation; in fact, our goal is to represent an operation, or relation, by a set. As usual, let S_n be the set of all n-tuples whose terms are members of S. Now, by an n-ary operation on S we mean a mapping of S_n into S, whereas an n-ary relation on S is a subset of S_n. We are involved primarily with unary and binary operations. Notice that a unary operation on S is a mapping of S into S, i.e., a rule that associates a member of S with each member of S; a binary operation on S is a mapping of $S \times S$ into S, i.e., a rule that associates a member of S with each member of S_2. These mappings are usually represented by sets; a unary operation is represented by a set of pairs, and a binary operation is represented by a set of triples. The idea is to form the pair whose first term is the member of S or S_2 involved, and whose second term is the member of S associated with the first term by the mapping [we point out that the pair $((a, b), c)$ is identified with the triple (a, b, c)]. For example, consider the unary operation on $\{1, 2, 3\}$ that associates 2 with 1, 3 with 2, and 1 with 3. This mapping is represented by $\{(1, 2), (2, 3), (3, 1)\}$. The binary operation on $\{1, 2\}$ that associates 1 with both $(1, 1)$ and $(2, 2)$, and associates 2 with both $(1, 2)$ and $(2, 1)$, is represented by $\{(1, 1, 1), (2, 2, 1), (1, 2, 2), (2, 1, 2)\}$.

A table can be used to exhibit a binary operation on a finite set. To illustrate the idea consider $\{1, 2, 3\}$. Now, the first step toward exhibiting a particular binary operation on $\{1, 2, 3\}$ is to form $\{1, 2, 3\} \times \{1, 2, 3\}$; next, we must associate a member of $\{1, 2, 3\}$ with each member of the preceding set, i.e., we must fill in the blanks in

(1) $\{(1, 1,), (1, 2,), (1, 3,), (2, 1,), (2, 2,),$

$(2, 3,), (3, 1,), (3, 2,), (3, 3,)\}$.

This can be achieved efficiently by constructing the following table

	1	2	3
1			
2			
3			

which represents the first step of our construction. Here, we agree that the entries of the first column represent a first term of a member of (1), whereas the entries of the first row represent a second term of a member of (1). The remaining step, i.e., filling in the blanks that appear in (1), is carried out by filling in the main body of the above table. For example, the binary operation $\circ = \{(1, 1, 2), (1, 2, 1), (1, 3, 1), (2, 1, 1), (2, 2, 3), (2, 3, 3), (3, 1, 1), (3, 2, 3), (3, 3, 2)\}$ is represented by the table

$\circ$	1	2	3
1	2	1	1
2	1	3	3
3	1	3	2

A table is much more than a device to represent a binary operation with minimum effort. In fact, we can sometimes read directly from a table useful algebraic properties of the binary operation involved. The point is that a table displays the objects associated with each ordered pair; so, the eye can detect at a glance properties of the operation that are obscured by its standard representation as a set. For example, if the main body of the table is symmetric (i.e., the ith row and the ith column are identical for each i) then we know that the operation is *commutative*, i.e., the blanks in $(x, y, \ )$ and $(y, x, \ )$ are filled with the same object whenever x and y are members of the set involved.

Throughout this chapter we use the various number systems of mathematics to illustrate and motivate our algebraic concepts. Moreover, we sometimes consider an algebraic system which is obtained from a number system by deleting some of its terms. For example, deleting the third, fourth, and fifth terms of the natural number system $(N, +, \cdot, <, 1)$ we obtain the algebraic system $(N, +)$. Similarly, the algebraic systems $(I, +)$, $(I, +, 0)$, $(I, +, \cdot, 0)$, and $(I, +, \cdot, 0, 1)$ are each obtained from the system of integers by deleting terms. We refer to these algebraic systems later.

Of course, there are many ways of obtaining an algebraic system from a given algebraic system. For example, we can adjoin more terms instead of deleting terms; we can replace the basic set by one of its nonempty subsets (altering the operations and relations of the algebraic system accordingly); we can replace the basic set by one of its supersets (altering its remaining terms suitably).

Now that we have been introduced to algebraic systems let us see about increasing our knowledge of these important mathematical objects. We begin by classifying algebraic systems. Examining a particular algebraic system objectively, we observe that it is an m-tuple, where m is a specific natural number, that certain of its terms are operations, of various order, on its basic set, other terms are relations of various order, and still other terms are members of the basic set. So, we can classify algebraic systems, in the first instance, according to their type; this is a completely objective description which takes into account the physical makeup of the algebraic system. Next, we subclassify algebraic systems of the same type according to their algebraic properties. What does this mean? Consider a family of algebraic systems, all of the same type, and consider certain statements that are meaningful for the algebraic systems of the family; i.e., each statement is either true or false for a particular algebraic system. We now select for our subclass each algebraic system of the family for which each of the given statements is true. In short, we can use a set of statements to gather together all algebraic systems of the same type for which the given statements are true.

We have already used this idea when we presented the notion of a semigroup. There, the type of algebraic system under consideration is exemplified by $(S, \circ)$ where $\circ$ is a binary operation on S. Moreover, there is just one statement that selects for us a subclass of the family of all algebraic systems of this type, namely the statement asserting that $\circ$ is associative. The statements that characterize the subclass involved are said to be the *postulates* for the subclass.

It is possible to obtain a semigroup from a given semigroup by manipulating the terms of its binary operation in the following manner. We use this result in Chapter 9 (see Theorem 9.3.3).

Theorem 6.1.1: Let $(S, \circ)$ be any semigroup and let $+$ be the binary operation on S such that $x + y = y \circ x$ whenever $(x, y) \in S_2$. Then $(S, +)$ is a semigroup.

Proof: We must prove that $+$ is associative on S. Let $\{x, y, z\} \subset S$; now

$$x + (y + z) = (y + z) \circ x$$

$$= (z \circ y) \circ x$$

$$= z \circ (y \circ x) \qquad \text{since } \circ \text{ is associative on } S$$

$$= (y \circ x) + z$$

$$= (x + y) + z .$$

This establishes our theorem.

EXERCISES

1. (a) Simplify $\{2, 3\} \div \{3\}$.
   (b) Simplify $\{3, 4\} \div \{1, 2\}$.
   (c) Simplify $\{3, 4\} \div \{1, 2, 3\}$.
   (d) Show that $A \div B = A \cup B$ if $A \cap B = \varnothing$.
   (e) Show that $A \div B = A - B$ if $B \subset A$.
   (f) Show that $A \div \varnothing = A$ whenever A is a set.
   (g) Show that $A \div B = B \div A$ whenever A and B are sets.
   (h) Let $A \subset S$; find a subset of S, say B, such that $A \div B = \varnothing$.

2. Let A, B, and C be any subsets of S; prove each of the following.

   (a) $A \div B = (A - B) \cup (B - A)$.
   (b) $A - (B \div C) = (A \cap B \cap C) \cup (A \cap B' \cap C')$.
   (c) $A \div (B - C) = (A \cap B' \cap C') \cup (A' \cap B \cap C')$.
   (d) $A \div (B \div C) = (A \div B) \div C$.
   (e) $A \cap (B \div C) = (A \cap B) \div (A \cap C)$.

3. Is $(\mathcal{P}S, -)$ a semigroup, where $-$ is the *difference* operation on $\mathcal{P}S$?

4. (a) Is $\{(t, t^2) \mid t \in I\}$ a unary operation on I?
   (b) Is $\{(t, t^2) \mid t \in I\}$ a binary relation on I?
   (c) Is $\{(t, \sqrt{t}) \mid t \in I\}$ a unary operation on I?
   (d) Is $\{(a, b, ab^2) \mid \{a, b\} \subset R\}$ a binary operation on R, the set of all real numbers?
   (e) Is $\{(a, b, a/b) \mid \{a, b\} \subset R\}$ a binary operation on R, the set of all real numbers?

5. Let S be any nonempty set and let M be the set of all mappings of S into S. Let $\circ$ be the binary operation on M defined as follows: $\mu \circ \nu$ associates $\mu(\nu(t))$ with t whenever $t \in S$.

(a)   Prove that $(M, \circ)$ is a semigroup.
(b)   Prove that $(M, +)$ is a semigroup, where $+$ is the binary operation on M such that $\mu + \nu = \nu \circ \mu$ whenever $\{\mu, \nu\} \subset M$.

6.2 GROUPS

The main goal of this chapter is to develop the notions of *group*, *ring*, and *field*. We use the "building-block" approach; i.e., we characterize each of these concepts in terms of preceding concepts. This way the postulates for each theory are easily absorbed. We now present the notion of a *group*; this is a very significant mathematical concept and is fundamental to the rest of this book. Carrying out our basic philosophy, we define groups in terms of semigroups.

Definition 6.2.1:   A 3-tuple $(G, \circ, e)$ is said to be a *group* if and only if:

(*i*) $(G, \circ)$ is a semigroup;
(*ii*) $x \circ e = x$ whenever $x \in G$;
(*iii*)   Given any member of G, say x, there is a member of G, say y, such that $x \circ y = e$.

Expanding (*i*) we obtain the following theorem which exhibits the group postulates.

Theorem 6.2.1:   An algebraic system, say $(G, \circ, e)$ where $\circ$ is a binary operation on G and $e \in G$, is a group if and only if:

(*i*) $x \circ (y \circ z) = (x \circ y) \circ z$ whenever $\{x, y, z\} \subset G$;
(*ii*) $x \circ e = x$ whenever $x \in G$.
(*iii*)   Given any member of G, say x, there is a member of G, say y, such that $x \circ y = e$.

In words, an algebraic system $(G, \circ, e)$ is a group if and only if $\circ$ is associative, e is a right identity, and each member of G possesses a right inverse with respect to e.

We now illustrate this concept.

Example 1: $(I, +, 0)$ is a group where this algebraic system is obtained from the system of integers by deleting terms.

Example 2: $(R_n, +, \mathbf{0})$ is a group whenever $n \in N$ (see Section 1.1).

Example 3: $(\mathscr{P}S, \doteq, \varnothing)$ is a group whenever S is a set. Here $\mathscr{P}S$ denotes the set of all subsets of S, and $\doteq$ is the operation of *symmetric difference* (see Example 6 of Section 6.1).

Example 4: $(M, +, (0))$ is a group where M is the set of all $m \times n$ matrices, $+$ is matrix addition, and (0) is the $m \times n$ matrix each of whose entries is 0 (see Section 3.3).

Example 5: $(G, \cdot, I_n)$ is a group where G is the set of all nonsingular $n \times n$ matrices, and $\cdot$ is matrix multiplication restricted to G (see Section 3.4).

The propositions (*i*), (*ii*), and (*iii*) listed under Theorem 6.2.1 are called the *group postulates*. Carrying out the axiomatic method, we now establish the truth for any group of certain other propositions. This is important for the following reason. We study many groups throughout this book; by establishing the basic facts about any group here and now, we are justified in applying these facts to any particular group when we meet it. Of course, we must be able to recognize a group at sight; but this is merely a matter of applying Definition 6.2.1. Let $(G, \circ, e)$ be any group; the following statements refer to this algebraic system.

Lemma 6.2.1: $e \circ e = e$.

Proof: Now, $(G, \circ, e)$ is a group; therefore $x \circ e = x$ whenever $x \in G$. But $e \in G$; so $e \circ e = e$. This establishes our result.

Next, we prove that each *right* inverse of x with respect to e is also a *left* inverse of x with respect to e.

Lemma 6.2.2: If x and y are members of G such that $x \circ y = e$, then $y \circ x = e$.

Proof: Previously, we demonstrated that the group of Example 5 has this property (see Theorem 3.4.4). We now show that each group has this property. Let $x \circ y = e$. By Theorem 6.2.1 (*iii*) there is a member of G, say c, such that $y \circ c = e$. Now,

$$
\begin{aligned}
y \circ x &= (y \circ x) \circ e && \text{by Theorem 6.2.1 (\textit{ii})} \\
&= (y \circ x) \circ (y \circ c) && \text{since } y \circ c = e \\
&= [(y \circ x) \circ y] \circ c && \text{by Theorem 6.2.1 (\textit{i})} \\
&= [y \circ (x \circ y)] \circ c && \text{by Theorem 6.2.1 (\textit{i})} \\
&= (y \circ e) \circ c && \text{since } x \circ y = e \\
&= y \circ c && \text{by Theorem 6.2.1 (\textit{ii})} \\
&= e \, .
\end{aligned}
$$

This establishes our theorem.

Next, we show that each member of G possesses a *left* inverse with respect to e.

Corollary 6.2.1: Given any member of G, say x, there is a member of G, say y, such that $y \circ x = e$.

Proof: Consider Lemma 6.2.2 and Theorem 6.2.1 (*iii*).

We now establish a *cancellation* law.

Theorem 6.2.2: $x = y$ whenever $x \circ z = y \circ z$.

Proof: Suppose that x, y, and z are members of G such that $x \circ z = y \circ z$. By Theorem 6.2.1 (*iii*), there is a member of G, say a, such that $z \circ a = e$. Therefore, $(x \circ z) \circ a = (y \circ z) \circ a$ since $x \circ z = y \circ z$. Now,

$$(x \circ z) \circ a = x \circ (z \circ a) \qquad \text{by Theorem 6.2.1 (i)}$$

$$= x \circ e \qquad \text{since } z \circ a = e$$

$$= x \qquad \text{by Theorem 6.2.1 (ii)}$$

Moreover, $(y \circ z) \circ a = y \circ (z \circ a) \qquad \text{by Theorem 6.2.1 (i)}$

$$= y \circ e \qquad \text{since } z \circ a = e$$

$$= y \qquad \text{by Theorem 6.2.1 (ii) .}$$

Hence, $x = y$. This establishes our theorem.

Let us prove that e is a *left* identity

Lemma 6.2.3: $e \circ x = x$ whenever $x \in G$.

Proof: Let $x \in G$; by Theorem 6.2.1 (*iii*), there is a member of G, say a, such that $x \circ a = e$. Therefore,

$$e \circ x = (x \circ a) \circ x = x \circ (a \circ x) \qquad \text{by Theorem 6.2.1 (i)}$$

$$= x \circ e \qquad \text{by Lemma 6.2.2}$$

$$= x \qquad \text{by Theorem 6.2.1 (ii) .}$$

This establishes our result.

Here is another *cancellation* law.

Theorem 6.2.3: $x = y$ whenever $z \circ x = z \circ y$.

Proof: The proof is similar to the proof of Theorem 6.2.2; use Corollary 6.2.1 in place of Theorem 6.2.1 (*iii*), and use Lemma 6.2.3 in place of Theorem 6.2.1 (*ii*).

We now prove that each member of the basic set of a group possesses a *unique* right inverse.

Theorem 6.2.4: Give any member of G, say x, there is a unique member of G, say y, such that $x \circ y = e$.

Proof: Suppose $x \in G$; we know that x possesses a right inverse; assume that x possesses two right inverses, say a and b. Then $x \circ a = x \circ b = e$.

By Theorem 6.2.1 (i), $b \circ (x \circ a) = (b \circ x) \circ a$. Now,

$$b \circ (x \circ a) = b \circ e = b \qquad \text{by Theorem 6.2.1 } (ii) \text{ .}$$

Moreover, $\qquad (b \circ x) \circ a = e \circ a \qquad \text{by Lemma 6.2.2}$

$$= a \qquad \text{by Lemma 6.2.3 .}$$

Hence, $a = b$. This contradiction establishes our theorem.

Corollary 6.2.2: Given any member of G, say x, there is a unique member of G, say y, such that $x \circ y = y \circ x = e$.

Proof: Apply Lemma 6.2.2.

Since each member of G has a unique inverse we may speak of *the* inverse of a member of G. It is useful to introduce a unary operation on G which associates the inverse of x with x whenever $x \in G$. In case the group operation is denoted by $\circ$ or $\cdot$, the inverse of x is denoted by x^{-1} or by $1/x$; whereas, in case the group operation is denoted by $+$, the inverse of x is denoted by $-x$.

It turns out that a group possesses just one *right* identity, and just one *left* identity.

Lemma 6.2.4: Each group possesses exactly one right identity and exactly one left identity.

Proof: Let $(G, \circ, e)$ be any group. Certainly, e is a right identity. Suppose that a is also a right identity, where $a \in G$. Then $x \circ a = x$ whenever $x \in G$; in particular, $e \circ a = e$. Therefore, by Lemma 6.2.2, $a \circ e = e$. But $a \circ e = a$ by Theorem 6.2.1 (ii). We conclude that $a = e$. Similarly, it is easy to prove that e is the one and only left identity of $(G, \circ, e)$.

Now, by an *identity* of $(G, \circ, e)$ we shall mean a member of G which is both a *right* identity and a *left* identity. Our proof of Lemma 6.2.4 has disclosed that e is the one and only identity of $(G, \circ, e)$. This result is worth stating.

Theorem 6.2.5: Each group $(G, \circ, e)$ possesses exactly one identity, namely its third term e.

In view of Theorem 6.2.5, we may speak of *the* identity of a group. In case the binary operation of a group is denoted by $+$, it is convenient to denote the identity of the group by 0. Accordingly, let $(G, +, 0)$ be any group. The following theorems refer to this algebraic system, and are easily established. Remember that $-x$ denotes the unique inverse of x, so $x + (-x) = 0$ whenever $x \in G$.

Lemma 6.2.5: $-(-x) = x$ whenever $x \in G$.

Lemma 6.2.6: $-(x + y) = -y + -x$ whenever $\{x, y\} \subset G$.

It is a simple matter, now, to define the binary operation of *subtraction*. This operation associates $x + (-y)$ with the ordered pair (x, y), and is usually denoted by $-$. Of course, it is possible to confuse *subtraction* with the unary operation *inverse of;* however, it is generally clear from the context whether a unary operation or a binary operation has been mentioned.

Definition 6.2.2: $x - y = x + (-y)$ whenever $\{x, y\} \subset G$.

Example 6: Let us illustrate those operations. Consider the group $(\{0, 1, 2\}, +, 0)$ where $+$ is given by the following table.

$+$	0	1	2
0	0	1	2
1	1	2	0
2	2	0	1

Here, the unary operation *inverse of* is as follows:

$$- = \{(0, 0), (1, 2), (2, 1)\} .$$

Whereas, the binary operation *subtraction* has the following table:

$-$	0	1	2
0	0	2	1
1	1	0	2
2	2	1	0

Note: To verify that the algebraic system of Example 6 is a group, follow the pattern of the solution to Exercise 13 (a) on page 323.

We now list a few obvious facts about subtraction, concerning any group $(G, +, 0)$; the following statements are easy to prove.

Lemma 6.2.7: $x - x = 0$ whenever $x \in G$.

Lemma 6.2.8: $x - 0 = x$ whenever $x \in G$.

Lemma 6.2.9: $(x + y) - y = x$ whenever $\{x, y\} \subset G$.

Lemma 6.2.10: $-(x - y) = y - x$ whenever $\{x, y\} \subset G$.

Next, we present the important notion of an *abelian* group.

Definition 6.2.3: A group, say $(G, \circ, e)$, is said to be *abelian* (or *commutative*) if and only if $x \circ y = y \circ x$ whenever $\{x, y\} \subset G$.

The groups of Examples 1 to 4 are abelian, the group of Example 5 is not abelian, the group of Example 6 is abelian.

Here is a useful mapping of $I \times G$ into G, where I is the set of integers and G is the basic set of a group $(G, +, 0)$. In the following, na denotes the member of G associate with (n, a) by this mapping, whenever $n \in I$ and $a \in G$.

Definition 6.2.4:   Let $n \in I$ and let $a \in G$; then

$$na = \begin{cases} a + \cdots + a \ (n \ a\text{'s}) & \text{if } n > 0 \\ 0 & \text{if } n = 0 \\ -a + \cdots + -a \ (|n| \ -a\text{'s}) & \text{if } n < 0 \end{cases}$$

If the group operation is denoted by $\cdot$ or $\circ$, then the mapping of Definition 6.2.4 is expressed in multiplicative notation as follows:

$$a^n = \begin{cases} a \ldots a \ (n \ a\text{'s}) & \text{if } n > 0 \\ e & \text{if } n = 0 \\ 1/a \ldots 1/a \ (|n| \ 1/a\text{'s}) & \text{if } n < 0 \end{cases}$$

where e is the group identity.

Example 7:   Consider the group $(\{a, b\}, +, a)$, where $+ = \{(a, a, a), (a, b, b), (b, a, b), (b, b, a)\}$. Here,

$$2b = b + b = a$$
$$3b = b + b + b = b$$
$$-3b = (-b) + (-b) + (-b) = b + b + b = b \qquad \text{since } -b = b$$
$$-3a = (-a) + (-a) + (-a) = a + a + a = a \qquad \text{since } -a = a \ .$$

Here are some properties of this mapping that are easy to prove. Again, the following statements refer to any group $(G, +, 0)$.

Lemma 6.2.11:   Let $a \in G$ and let $\{m, n\} \subset I$; then $ma + na = (m + n)a$

Note: We point out that the first $+$ refers to the group operation, whereas the second $+$ denotes the operation of addition in the system of integers.

Lemma 6.2.12:   Let $a \in G$ and let $\{m, n\} \subset I$; then $ma + na = na + ma$

Lemma 6.2.13:   Let $a \in G$ and let $\{m, n\} \subset I$; then $m(na) = (mn)a$.

Lemma 6.2.14:   Let $a \in G$ and let $n \in I$; then $(-n)a = -(na)$.

It is wise at this stage to indicate the value of our mapping. Consider any group, say $(G, +, 0)$, and let $a \in G$. We are interested in constructing a group from $(G, +, 0)$ by choosing a subset of G, say G' where $a \in G'$, and restricting $+$ to G'. Any group obtained in this way is said to be a *subgroup* of $(G, +, 0)$.

Since $a \in G'$ it follows that $\{na|n \in I\} \subset G'$. Indeed, let $G' = \{na|n \in I\}$; we point out that $(G', +', 0)$ is a group where $+'$ is the operation on G' obtained by restricting $+$ to G', i.e., $x +' y = x + y$ whenever $\{x, y\} \subset G'$. To see this, notice that the first two group postulates are automatically satisfied; moreover, by Lemma 6.2.14, each member of $\{na|n \in I\}$ possesses a right inverse. We conclude that $(G', +', 0)$ is a group. Moreover, in view of Lemma 6.2.12,

$$x +' y = y +' x \quad \text{whenever} \quad \{x, y\} \subset G'.$$

So $(G', +', 0)$ is an abelian group. We have proved that each group possesses a commutative subgroup.

EXERCISES

1. Show that the algebraic system $(\{0, 1\}, +, 0)$ is a group, where $+$ is given by the following table.

+	0	1
0	0	1
1	1	0

2. Show that the algebraic system $(\{0, 1, 2\}, +, 0)$ is a group, where $+$ is given by the following table.

+	0	1	2
0	0	1	2
1	1	2	0
2	2	0	1

3. Show that each of the following algebraic systems is a group:

    (a) The algebraic system of Example 2.
    (b) The algebraic system of Example 3.
    (c) The algebraic system of Example 5.

4. Prove Corollary 6.2.1.

5. Prove Theorem 6.2.3.

6. Prove Corollary 6.2.2.

7. Given that $(G, \circ, e)$ is a group, prove that e is its only *left* identity.

8. Let $(G, +, 0)$ be any group.

    (a) Prove that given any members of G, say x and z, there is exactly one member of G, say y, such that $x + y = z$.
    (b) Prove that given any members of G, say y and z, there is exactly one member of G, say x, such that $x + y = z$.

9. Prove Lemma 6.2.5.

10. Prove Lemma 6.2.6.

11. A group $(G, +, 0)$ is said to have *characteristic* 2 if $x + x = 0$ whenever $x \in G$. Prove that each group of characteristic 2 is abelian.

12. (a) Prove Lemma 6.2.7.
    (b) Prove Lemma 6.2.8.
    (c) Prove Lemma 6.2.9.
    (d) Prove Lemma 6.2.10.

13. Let $\mathcal{G} = (\{0, 1, 2, 3\}, +, 0)$ where the table for $+$ is

+	0	1	2	3
0	0	1	2	3
1	1	2	3	0
2	2	3	0	1
3	3	0	1	2

   (a) Show that $\mathcal{G}$ is an abelian group.
   (b) Present the table for the binary operation *subtraction*.

14. Let $\mathcal{G} = (\{0, 1, 2, 3\}, +, 0)$ where the table for $+$ is

+	0	1	2	3
0	0	1	2	3
1	1	0	3	2
2	2	3	0	1
3	3	2	1	0

   (a) Show that $\mathcal{G}$ is an abelian group.
   (b) Present the table for the binary operation *subtraction*.

15. Let $(G, +, 0)$ be any group.

   (a) Prove that $x - (y - z) = (x + z) - y$ whenever $\{x, y, z\} \subset G$.
   (b) Prove that $x + (y - z) = (x + y) - z$ whenever $\{x, y, z\} \subset G$.
   (c) Prove that $x - (y + z) = (x - z) - y$ whenever $\{x, y, z\} \subset G$.

16. (a) Prove Lemma 6.2.11.
    (b) Prove Lemma 6.2.12.
    (c) Prove Lemma 6.2.13.
    (d) Prove Lemma 6.2.14.

17. Let $(G, \circ, e)$ and $(G', \circ', e')$ be groups such that $G' \subset G$ and $\circ' \subset \circ$; then $(G', \circ', e')$ is said to be a *subgroup* of $(G, \circ, e)$. Prove that $e' = e$.

18. Given that $(G, +, 0)$ is a group, that $G' \subset G$, and that $+' \subset +$, prove that $(G', +', 0)$ is a subgroup of $(G, +, 0)$ if and only if:

   (*i*) $+'$ is a binary operation on G';
   (*ii*) $-x \in G'$ whenever $x \in G'$.

6.3 RINGS

We now make use of groups and semigroups to characterize more complex algebraic systems called *rings*. Mathematicians talk about the ring of integers, a ring of matrices (see Section 3.3), or a ring of polynomials. In Section 8.2 we discuss a ring of polynomials, and in Section 9.3 we meet a ring of linear operators. Clearly, the notion of a ring is most important; consider the following definition.

Definition 6.3.1: A 4-tuple $(B, +, \cdot, 0)$ is said to be a *ring* if and only if:

(*i*) $(B, +, 0)$ is an abelian group;
(*ii*) $(B, \cdot)$ is a semigroup;
(*iii*) $x \cdot (y + z) = x \cdot y + x \cdot z$ whenever $\{x, y, z\} \subset B$;
(*iv*) $(y + z) \cdot x = y \cdot x + z \cdot x$ whenever $\{x, y, z\} \subset B$.

Propositions (*iii*) and (*iv*) are called *distributive* laws.

Expanding conditions (*i*) and (*ii*), of the Definition, we obtain the following theorem which exhibits the ring postulates in more detail.

Theorem 6.3.1: An algebraic system, say $(B, +, \cdot, 0)$ where $+$ and $\cdot$ are binary operations on B and $0 \in B$, is a ring if and only if:

(*i*) $x + (y + z) = (x + y) + z$ whenever $\{x, y, z\} \subset B$;
(*ii*) $x + 0 = x$ whenever $x \in B$;
(*iii*) Given any member of B, say x, there is a member of B, say y, such that $x + y = 0$;
(*iv*) $x + y = y + x$ whenever $\{x, y\} \subset B$;
(*v*) $x \cdot (y \cdot z) = (x \cdot y) \cdot z$ whenever $\{x, y, z\} \subset B$;
(*vi*) $x \cdot (y + z) = x \cdot y + x \cdot z$ whenever $\{x, y, z\} \subset B$;
(*vii*) $(y + z) \cdot x = y \cdot x + z \cdot x$ whenever $\{x, y, z\} \subset B$.

For example, the 4-tuple $(I, +, \cdot, 0)$ is a ring where I is the set of all integers, and $+$ and $\cdot$ denote addition and multiplication. Let S be any set; then the algebraic system $(\wp S, \doteq, \cap, \varnothing)$ is a ring; this is easy to see in view of the properties of *symmetric difference* and *intersection*.

Example 1: As another example of a ring we present the algebraic system $(\{0, 1, 2, 3\}, +, \cdot, 0)$ where the binary operations $+$ and $\cdot$ are given by the following table.

+	0	1	2	3		$\cdot$	0	1	2	3
0	0	1	2	3		0	0	0	0	0
1	1	2	3	0		1	0	1	2	3
2	2	3	0	1		2	0	2	0	2
3	3	0	1	2		3	0	3	2	1

It is easy to verify that $(\{0, 1, 2, 3\}, +, 0)$ is an abelian group (see the solution to Exercise 13 (*a*) in Section 6.2). The remaining ring postulates are easily established by observing that $\cdot$ can be expressed as follows. If x is any member of $\{0, 1, 2, 3\}$, then $0 \cdot x = 0$, $1 \cdot x = x$, $2 \cdot x = x + x$, and $3 \cdot x = (x + x) + x$; in short, $n \cdot x = nx$ whenever $n \in \{0, 1, 2, 3\}$ (here, we are using the mapping of Definition 6.2.4). These statements are easily verified by examining the tables for $+$ and $\cdot$. Moreover, from the table for $\cdot$ we see that $\cdot$ is commutative. We can now establish the distributive laws. Clearly, it is enough to demonstrate one distributive law of Theorem 6.3.1, say (vi). Thus; we must show that $n(y + z) = ny + nz$ whenever $\{n, y, z\} \subset \{0, 1, 2, 3\}$. Considering the significance of the expression nx (see Definition 6.2.4) and bearing in mind that $+$ is associative and commutative, we readily establish this distributive law. Finally, we point out that the associative law for $\cdot$ can be verified by a similar argument, as follows. The idea is to show that $n(x \cdot y) = (nx) \cdot y$ whenever $\{n, x, y\} \subset \{0, 1, 2, 3\}$. Certainly, $n = 0$ and $n = 1$ offer no problem. Let $n = 2$; now

$$2(x \cdot y) = x \cdot y + x \cdot y = (x + x) \cdot y \qquad \text{by a distributive law}$$

$$= (2x) \cdot y \ .$$

Finally, we consider $n = 3$;

$$3(x \cdot y) = x \cdot y + x \cdot y + x \cdot y = (x + x + x) \cdot y \qquad \text{by a distributive law}$$

$$= (3x) \cdot y \ .$$

This establishes that $\cdot$ is associative and completes our demonstration that the algebraic system $(\{0, 1, 2, 3\}, +, \cdot, 0)$ is a ring.

We now establish several theorems about rings. Let $(B, +, \cdot, 0)$ be any ring; the following two theorems refer to this algebraic system.

Theorem 6.3.2: $0 \cdot x = 0$ whenever $x \in B$.

Proof: Let $x \in B$; then

$$0 \cdot x = (0 + 0) \cdot x \qquad \text{since } 0 + 0 = 0$$

$$= 0 \cdot x + 0 \cdot x \qquad \text{by Definition 6.3.1 } (iv) \ .$$

Let y be the inverse of $0 \cdot x$ (i.e., $y = -(0 \cdot x)$); then

$$0 \cdot x + y = (0 \cdot x + 0 \cdot x) + y$$

and it follows from (i) of the Definition that $0 = 0 \cdot x$. This establishes our result.

Theorem 6.3.3: $-(x \cdot y) = (-x) \cdot y$ whenever $\{x, y\} \subset B$.

Proof: Let x and y be any members of B. Now,

$$x \cdot y + (-x) \cdot y = (x + -x) \cdot y \qquad \text{by Definition 6.3.1 } (iv)$$

$$= 0 \cdot y \qquad \text{since } -x \text{ is the inverse of } x$$

$$= 0 \qquad \text{by Theorem 6.3.2.}$$

We conclude that $(-x) \cdot y$ is the inverse of $x \cdot y$. This establishes Theorem 6.3.3.

Next, let $(B, +, \cdot, 0)$ be a ring and let e be a member of B such that $x \cdot e = x$ and $e \cdot x = x$ whenever $x \in B$. Then e is said to be an *identity;* moreover, the algebraic system $(B, +, \cdot, 0)$ is said to be a *ring with identity*. We present some examples in a moment; first, let us establish one fact in this connection.

Theorem 6.3.4: Each ring has at most one identity.

Proof: Let e_1 and e_2 be identities of a ring $(B, +, \cdot, 0)$. Then $x \cdot e_1 = e_1 \cdot x = x$ and $x \cdot e_2 = e_2 \cdot x = x$ whenever $x \in B$. In particular, $e_2 \cdot e_1 = e_2$ and $e_2 \cdot e_1 = e_1$; thus $e_1 = e_2$.

Some rings have the property that the second binary operation of the algebraic system is commutative; e.g., the ring of integers $(I, +, \cdot, 0)$ has this property. Rings of this sort are said to be *commutative*. Let us illustrate these ideas. The algebraic system $(\mathscr{P}S, \dot{-}, \cap, \varnothing)$ is a commutative ring with identity; here the identity is S. Considering the ring $(\{0, 1, 2, 3\}, +, \cdot, 0)$ of Example 1, we see that this ring is commutative and has an identity, namely 1. Moreover, the algebraic system $(I, +, \cdot, 0)$ is a commutative ring with identity.

In case a ring possesses an identity, say 1, we may find it convenient to exhibit 1 as a term of the ring; thus, we say that the 5-tuple $(B, +, \cdot, 0, 1)$ is a *ring with identity* if and only if $(B, +, \cdot, 0)$ is a ring with identity 1. For example, $(I, +, \cdot, 0, 1)$ is a commutative ring with identity.

Next, we present the concept of an *integral domain*. The idea is to seize on certain properties of the system of integers. We have already observed that $(I, +, \cdot, 0, 1)$ is a commutative ring with identity. We now point out that this algebraic system has the following property. Let $\{x, y\} \subset I$ and suppose that $x \cdot y = 0$; then $x = 0$ or $y = 0$. That is, if a product of integers is zero, then at least one of the factors is zero. Mathematicians describe this by saying that 0 has no *proper* divisors, which means that $x \cdot y = 0$ only if $x = 0$ or $y = 0$.

We now define the term *integral domain*.

Definition 6.3.2: A 5-tuple $(B, +, \cdot, 0, 1)$ is said to be an *integral domain* if and only if:

(*i*) $(B, +, \cdot, 0, 1)$ is a commutative ring with identity;
(*ii*) 0 has no proper divisors;
(*iii*) $0 \neq 1$.

Thus, an integral domain is a commutative ring with identity, say 1, such that $1 \neq 0$ and 0 has no proper divisors. We shall not be rigorous about displaying the identity of an integral domain; the main idea is that a ring is called an *integral domain* provided it is commutative, possesses an identity different from 0, and provided 0 has no proper divisors.

Of course, the main example of an integral domain is the ring of integers $(I, +, \cdot, 0)$. Here is another example of an integral domain: the algebraic system

$(\{0, 1\}, +, \cdot, 0, 1)$ where $+$ and $\cdot$ are the binary operations on $\{0, 1\}$ given by the following tables.

$+$	0	1
0	0	1
1	1	0

$\cdot$	0	1
0	0	0
1	0	1

We point out that $(\{0, 1, 2, 3\}, +, \cdot, 0)$, the ring of Example 1, is a commutative ring with identity. However, it is not an integral domain since $2 \cdot 2 = 0$; i.e., 2 is a proper divisor of 0. Moreover, $(\mathcal{P}\{1, 2\}, \doteq, \cap, \varnothing)$ is also a commutative ring with identity, and is not an integral domain; here, $\{1\} \cap \{2\} = \varnothing$, so $\{1\}$ and $\{2\}$ are proper divisors of $\varnothing$.

Let us establish one theorem about integral domains, a cancellation law for multiplication.

Theorem 6.3.5: Let $(B, +, \cdot, 0, 1)$ be any integral domain, and let x, y, and z be members of B such that $z \neq 0$ and $x \cdot z = y \cdot z$; then $x = y$.

Proof: We are given that $x \cdot z = y \cdot z$ and that $z \neq 0$. Now, by Theorem 6.3.3, $(-y) \cdot z$ is the inverse of $y \cdot z$; so

$$x \cdot z + (-y) \cdot z = y \cdot z + (-y) \cdot z = (y + (-y)) \cdot z = 0 \cdot z = 0 .$$

Thus, by Theorem 6.3.1, (vii), $(x - y) \cdot z = 0$. But $z \neq 0$ by assumption; so $x - y = 0$. We conclude that $x = y$. This establishes Theorem 6.3.5.

EXERCISES

1. Prove Theorem 6.3.1.

2. Prove that $(\mathcal{P}S, \doteq, \cap, \varnothing)$ is a ring whenever S is a set.

3. (a) Exhibit the tables for the binary operations of the ring $(\mathcal{P}S, \doteq, \cap, \varnothing)$ where $S = \{a, b\}$.
   (b) Exhibit the tables for the binary operations of the ring $(\mathcal{P}S, \doteq, \cap, \varnothing)$ where $S = \{a, b, c\}$.

4. Show that the algebraic system $(\{0, 1, 2, 3\}, +, \cdot, 0)$ of the text is a ring without using the mapping of Definition 6.2.4.

5. Let $(B, +, \cdot, 0)$ be any ring; prove that $x \cdot 0 = 0$ whenever $x \in B$.

6. Let $(B, +, \cdot, 0)$ be any ring; prove that $x \cdot (-y)$ is the additive inverse of $x \cdot y$ whenever $\{x, y\} \subset B$.

7. Let $(B, +, \cdot, 0, e)$ be a ring with identity.

   (a) Prove that $(-e) \cdot x$ is the additive inverse of x whenever $x \in B$.
   (b) Prove that $(-e) \cdot (-e) = e$.
   (c) Prove that $(-x) \cdot (-y) = x \cdot y$ whenever $\{x, y\} \subset B$.

8. (a) Exhibit a ring whose basic set has exactly five members.
    (b) Is the ring of part (*a*) also an integral domain?

9. Show that the algebraic system ($\{0\}$, $\{(0, 0, 0)\}$, $\{(0, 0, 0)\}$, 0, 0) is a commutative ring with identity, and possesses no proper divisors of 0.

10. Let *B* be the set of all mappings of *R* into *R*. Define the binary operations $+$ and $\cdot$ as follows: $f + g = \{(a, b) \mid b = f(a) + g(a)\}$ whenever $\{f, g\} \subset B$, and $f \cdot g = \{(a, b) \mid b = f(a)g(a)\}$ whenever $\{f, g\} \subset B$. Let 0 denote $\{(a, 0) \mid a \in R\}$.

    (a) Show that $(B, +, \cdot, 0)$ is a commutative ring.
    (b) Show that $(B, +, \cdot, 0)$ has an identity.
    (c) Show that $(B, +, \cdot, 0)$ is *not* an integral domain.

11. Let $k \in N$ and let $\circledB = (\{0, 1, \ldots, k - 1\}, +, \cdot, 0)$ where $+$ and $\cdot$ are the binary operations on $\{0, 1, \ldots, k - 1\}$ obtained by adding modulo k and multiplying modulo k, respectively.

    (a) Show that $\circledB$ is a commutative ring with identity.
    (b) Prove that $\circledB$ is an integral domain if and only if k is prime.

12. (a) Consider the set B of all mappings of *R* into *R*, and define $+$ and 0 as in Exercise 10. Let $\circ$ be the binary operation on *B* defined as follows: $f \circ g = \{(a, b) \mid b = f(g(a))\}$ whenever $\{f, g\} \subset B$. Show that the algebraic system $(B, +, \circ, 0)$ satisfies postulates (*i*), (*ii*), and (*iv*) of Definition 6.3.1, and does *not* satisfy postulate (*iii*) of that definition.
    (b) Exhibit an algebraic system which satisfies postulates (*i*), (*ii*), and (*iii*) of Definition 6.3.1, and does *not* satisfy postulate (*iv*).

13. Find the fallacy in the following argument. "Let $(B, +, 0, 1)$ be any integral domain and let $x \neq 0$. By the cancellation law for multiplication (Theorem 6.3.5), $y \cdot x \neq z \cdot x$ whenever $y \neq z$; therefore, $\{z \cdot x \mid z \in B\}$ has exactly as many members as *B*. But $\{z \cdot x \mid z \in B\} \subset B$; hence $\{z \cdot x \mid z \in B\} = B$. In particular, $1 \in \{z \cdot x \mid z \in B\}$. We conclude that given any nonzero member of *B*, say *x*, there is a member of *B*, say *y*, such that $x \cdot y = 1$."

14. Let $(B, +, \cdot, 0, 1)$ be any integral domain such that *B* has a finite number of members. Prove that given any nonzero member of *B*, say *x*, there is a member of *B*, say *y*, such that $x \cdot y = 1$.

15. Let $(B, +, \cdot, 0, 1)$ be any integral domain and let *a* be any nonzero member of *B*. By the *characteristic* of *a* we mean the smallest natural number *k* such that $0 = a + \cdots + a$ (*k* *a*'s), i.e., $0 = ka$. In case $ka \neq 0$ whenever $k \in N$, then we say that the characteristic of *a* is zero.

    (a) Prove that all nonzero members of *B* have the same characteristic. *Hint:* Consider the characteristic of 1.
    (b) Let *k* be the characteristic of 1. Prove that *k* is prime if $k \neq 0$.

16. Exhibit a ring which is *not* commutative.

17. Exhibit a ring which has no identity.

6.4 FIELDS

Before continuing our development of the basic structures of algebra, let us take a general look at the ideas that we have discussed so far. We have talked about semigroups, groups, rings, and integral domains. Looking back, perhaps we can appreciate that there is an underlying principle which has guided this algebraic development. Indeed, the number systems of mathematics constitute the key to our work. Mathematicians like to think of the number systems as flowing from the natural number system. Thus, starting with the natural number system $(N, +, \cdot, <, 1)$ we construct in turn the system of integers $(I, +, \cdot, <, 0, 1)$, the rational number system $(Rt, +, \cdot, <, 0, 1)$, the real number system $(R, +, \cdot, <, 0, 1)$, and the complex number system $(C, +, \cdot, 0, 1)$. So, the well known number systems of mathematics are based on the natural number system.

Now, let us see about the connection with our work. We introduced the notion of a *semigroup* in order to understand the algebraic systems $(N, +)$ and $(N, \cdot)$ obtained from the natural number system $(N, +, \cdot, <, 1)$. We introduced the notion of a *group* in order to understand the algebraic system $(I, +, 0)$ obtained from the system of integers. We introduced *rings* and *integral domains* in order to understand the algebraic systems $(I, +, \cdot, 0)$ and $(I, +, \cdot, 0, 1)$. In short, the work of this chapter is aimed at clarifying the algebraic properties of number systems.

We are ready, now, for the next step in our algebraic development. Consider the rational number system $(Rt, +, \cdot, <, 0, 1)$. It is well known that $(Rt, +, \cdot, 0, 1)$ is an integral domain (you have certainly used the integral domain postulates when calculating with rational numbers); moreover, each nonzero rational number possesses a multiplicative inverse. This is the algebraic property that distinguishes the rational number system from the system of integers. We now present the notion of a *field*.

Definition 6.4.1: A 5-tuple $(F, +, \cdot, 0, 1)$ is said to be a *field* if and only if:

(*i*) $(F, +, \cdot, 0, 1)$ is an integral domain;
(*ii*) Each nonzero member of F possesses a multiplicative inverse.

For example, $(R, +, \cdot, 0, 1)$ is a field, where this algebraic system is obtained from the real number system by deleting $<$.

Also, the algebraic system $(\{0, 1\}, +, \cdot, 0, 1)$ is a field, where the binary operations $+$ and $\cdot$ are given by the following tables.

+	0	1
0	0	1
1	1	0

·	0	1
0	0	0
1	0	1

Moreover, $(\{0, 1, 2\}, +, \cdot, 0, 1)$ is a field, where $+$ and $\cdot$ are given by the following tables.

$+$	0	1	2
0	0	1	2
1	1	2	0
2	2	0	1

$\cdot$	0	1	2
0	0	0	0
1	0	1	2
2	0	2	1

Since there are ten postulates for an integral domain, we see that there are eleven postulates for a field. However, it is easy to show that the integral domain postulate "0 has no proper divisors" follows from the other field postulates. Thus, we obtain the following theorem, which displays the necessary field postulates in detail.

Theorem 6.4.1: An algebraic system, say $(F, +, \cdot, 0, 1)$ where $+$ and $\cdot$ are binary operations on F and $\{0, 1\} \subset F$, is a field if and only if:

(i) $x + (y + z) = (x + y) + z$ whenever $\{x, y, z\} \subset F$.

(ii) $x + 0 = x$ whenever $x \in F$.

(iii) Given any member of F, say x, there is a member of F, say y, such that $x + y = 0$.

(iv) $x + y = y + x$ whenever $\{x, y\} \subset F$.

(v) $x \cdot (y \cdot z) = (x \cdot y) \cdot z$ whenever $\{x, y, z\} \subset F$.

(vi) $x \cdot 1 = x$ whenever $x \in F$.

(vii) Given any nonzero member of F, say x, there is a member of F, say y, such that $x \cdot y = 1$.

(viii) $x \cdot y = y \cdot x$ whenever $\{x, y\} \subset F$.

(ix) $x \cdot (y + z) = x \cdot y + x \cdot z$ whenever $\{x, y, z\} \subset F$.

(x) $0 \neq 1$.

Notice that Theorem 6.4.1 (vii) asserts that each nonzero member of F has a multiplicative inverse. It is a common fallacy to deduce from (vii) that 0 does not have a multiplicative inverse. However, using Theorem 6.3.2, we can settle this matter. Now, each field is a ring; so $0 \cdot x = 0$ whenever $x \in F$. We conclude that there is no member of F, say y, such that $0 \cdot y = 1$ (recall that $0 \neq 1$ by (x)). Of course, this means that in a field we cannot divide by 0. Notice that dividing b by a is achieved by multiplying b by $a^{-1} = 1/a$, the multiplicative inverse of a. It is customary to denote $b \cdot a^{-1}$ by writing b/a.

Now that the concept of a field has been clarified, let us show that the complex number system is a field. It is well known that the complex number system can be constructed from the real number system as follows. First, we must define the complex numbers themselves; we say that each ordered pair of real numbers is a complex number. Let C denote the set of all complex numbers; then $C = R \times R$. Next, we define $+$ and $\cdot$, binary operations of addition and multiplication. Let (a_1, b_1) and (a_2, b_2) be any complex numbers; then $(a_1, b_1) + (a_2, b_2)$ is defined to be $(a_1 + a_2, b_1 + b_2)$ and $(a_1, b_1) \cdot (a_2, b_2)$ is defined to be $(a_1 a_2 - b_1 b_2, a_1 b_2 + a_2 b_1)$. At first sight these definitions are mysterious. Actually, they arise directly from our intuitive ideas about complex numbers. We regard a complex number as possessing a *real* part and an *imaginary* part. Now, the first term a of the complex number (a, b) represents its real part, and the second term b of this ordered pair represents the imaginary part of this complex number. Moreover, the complex number of our intuition with real part a and imaginary part b, is ordinarily represented by $a + bi$ where i denotes the complex number whose square is -1, i.e., $i \cdot i = -1$. Consider the complex number $(0, 1)$ of our formal system. Under our definition of multiplication $(0, 1) \cdot (0, 1) = (-1, 0)$ the complex number with real part -1 and imaginary part 0. Accordingly, the ordered pair $(0, 1)$ represents the complex number i of our intuition.

Now we are in a position to clarify the binary operations that we introduced above. Consider addition. We have just verified that our formal object (a, b) corresponds to the complex number $a + bi$ of our intuition. But the sum of complex numbers $a_1 + b_1 i$ and $a_2 + b_2 i$ is found by adding their real parts, and adding their imaginary parts. This is precisely the content of our definition of $+$. Next, consider multiplication. Let $a_1 + b_1 i$ and $a_2 + b_2 i$ be any complex numbers of our intuition. Their product is found by carrying out a straightforward multiplication and assuming that $i^2 = -1$. So their product is $a_1 a_2 - b_1 b_2 + (a_1 b_2 + a_2 b_1)i$; so the real part of the product is $a_1 a_2 - b_1 b_2$ and the imaginary part is $a_1 b_2 + a_2 b_1$. Thus, our formal definition of multiplication agrees with our intuitive ideas.

Next, let 0 denote $(0, 0)$ and let 1 denote $(1, 0)$; consider the algebraic system $\mathcal{C} = (C, +, \cdot, 0, 1)$ which is called the *complex number field*. We claim that $\mathcal{C}$ is a field; the details are easy and are left as an exercise. Notice that if $(a, b) \neq 0$, then $(a, b) \cdot (c, d) = 1$ where $c = \dfrac{a}{a^2 + b^2}$ and $d = \dfrac{-b}{a^2 + b^2}$.

The key to our construction of $\mathcal{C}$ is the equation $x^2 = -1$. Indeed, our purpose in developing the complex number system is to obtain a number system in which this equation can be solved. Accordingly, we take our numbers to be ordered pairs of real numbers (remember, we are working in the context of the real number system); in particular, we want $(0, 1) = i$ to be a solution of our equation. This means that multiplication must be defined so that $i \cdot i = -1$. Permitting our intuition to guide us, we are easily led to suitable definitions of multiplication and addition. In fact, the procedure works; i.e., we obtain a field in which the equation $x^2 = -1$ possesses a root.

In a similar fashion we can construct a field from the rational number field $(Rt, +, \cdot, 0, 1)$ by considering the equation $x^2 = 2$. Now, there is no rational number whose square is 2; so this equation has no solution in the rational number field. Our goal is to construct a number field, an extension of the rational number field, in which $x^2 = 2$ has a solution. Again, our numbers are ordered pairs of rational numbers, say (a, b). Here (a, b) represents the real number $a + b\sqrt{2}$; so $(0, 1)$ represents $\sqrt{2}$. For simplicity, let α denote $(0, 1)$. As before, α is to be a solution of the given equation, so $\alpha \cdot \alpha = 2$. This observation enables us to define addition and multiplication on our number-set $Rt \times Rt$, bearing in mind that (a, b) represents $a + b\sqrt{2}$. We are led to the following definitions:

$$(a_1, b_1) + (a_2, b_2) = (a_1 + a_2, b_1 + b_2),$$

$$(a_1, b_1) \cdot (a_2, b_2) = (a_1 a_2 + 2b_1 b_2, a_1 b_2 + a_2 b_1)$$

whenever (a_1, b_1) and (a_2, b_2) are ordered pairs of rational numbers.

Again, let 0 denote $(0 , 0)$, and let 1 denote $(1 , 0)$. Then the algebraic system $(Rt \times Rt , + , \cdot , 0 , 1)$ is an extension of the rational number field in which the equation $x^2 = 2$ possesses a root. Moreover, this number system is a field. Notice that if $(a , b) \neq 0$, then $(a , b) \cdot (c , d) = 1$ where $c = \dfrac{a}{a^2 - 2b^2}$ and $d = \dfrac{-b}{a^2 - 2b^2}$.

EXERCISES

1. Show that the algebraic system $(\{0 , 1 , 2 , 3 , 4\} , + , \cdot , 0 , 1)$ is a field, where $+$ and $\cdot$ represent addition modulo 5 and multiplication modulo 5, respectively.

2. Prove Theorem 6.4.1.

3. Prove that the algebraic system $(\{0 , 1 , \ldots , k - 1\} , + , \cdot , 0 , 1)$ is a field if and only if k is prime, where $+$ and $\cdot$ represent addition modulo k and multiplication modulo k, respectively.

4. Is $(\{0\} , \{(0 , 0 , 0)\} , \{(0 , 0 , 0)\} , 0 , 0)$ a field?

5. Let $(F , + , \cdot , 0 , 1)$ be any field and let $\{x , y\} \subset F$ where $x \neq 0$; prove that there is exactly one member of F, say z, such that $x \cdot z = y$.

6. Verify that the complex number system $\mathcal{C} = (C , + , \cdot , 0 , 1)$ is a field.

7. Verify that $(Rt \times Rt , + , \cdot , 0 , 1)$ is a field, where 0 denotes $(0 , 0)$, 1 denotes $(1 , 0)$, and $+$ and $\cdot$ are binary operations on $Rt \times Rt$ such that $(a_1 , b_1) + (a_2 , b_2) = (a_1 + a_2 , b_1 + b_2)$ and $(a_1 , b_1) \cdot (a_2 , b_2) = (a_1 a_2 + 2b_1 b_2 , a_1 b_2 + a_2 b_1)$ whenever (a_1 , b_1) and (a_2 , b_2) are ordered pairs of rational numbers.

8. Show that $(Rt \times Rt , + , \cdot , 0 , 1)$ is a field, where 0 denotes $(0 , 0)$, 1 denotes $(1 , 0)$, and $+$ and $\cdot$ are binary operations on $Rt \times Rt$ such that $(a_1 , b_1) + (a_2 , b_2) = (a_1 + a_2 , b_1 + b_2)$ and $(a_1 , b_1) \cdot (a_2 , b_2) = (a_1 a_2 + 3b_1 b_2 , a_1 b_2 + a_2 b_1)$ whenever (a_1 , b_1) and (a_2 , b_2) are ordered pairs of rational numbers.

9. Let $\mathcal{F} = (F , + , \cdot , 0 , 1)$ be any field; then $\mathcal{F}$ is said to have *characteristic* k if k is the smallest natural number such that $k1 = 0$. In case $k1 \neq 0$ whenever $k \in N$, then we say that $\mathcal{F}$ has characteristic zero.

   (a) Determine the characteristic of the field of Exercise 1.
   (b) Determine the characteristic of the field of Exercise 3.
   (c) Determine the characteristic of the rational number field.

10. Exhibit a field of characteristic two whose basic set has exactly two members.

11. Exhibit a field of characteristic two whose basic set has exactly four members.

12. Let $\mathcal{F}$ be a field of characteristic k, $k \neq 0$; prove that k is prime.

13. Let $\mathfrak{F}$ be a field whose basic set is finite. Prove that the characteristic of $\mathfrak{F}$ is *not* zero.

14. Let $\mathfrak{F}$ be a field whose basic set is infinite. Is it necessarily the case that $\mathfrak{F}$ has characteristic zero?

6.5　ISOMORPHIC ALGEBRAIC SYSTEMS

In this section we introduce the important notion of two algebraic systems that are essentially the same, i.e., have the property that one of the algebraic systems can be obtained from the other by applying a suitable one-one mapping to it. The technical term used in this connection is the word *isomorphic*. Before formalizing this important concept we must clarify what we mean by applying a mapping to an algebraic system.

Let S be the supporting set of an algebraic system $\mathcal{S} = (A_1 , \ldots , A_m)$ and let μ be a mapping of $S = A_1$ into some set; then $\mu\mathcal{S} = (\mu(A_1) , \ldots , \mu(A_m))$, the algebraic system obtained by applying μ to each term of $\mathcal{S}$. Recall that $\mu(A) = \{\mu(x) \mid x \in A\}$ whenever A is a set. In short, $\mu\mathcal{S}$ is the algebraic system obtained from $\mathcal{S}$ by replacing each occurrence in $\mathcal{S}$ of a member of S by its image under μ. For example, let $\mathcal{S} = (\{0 , 1\} , \circ , 0)$ where $\circ = \{(0 , 0 , 0), (0 , 1 , 1), (1 , 0 , 1), (1 , 1 , 0)\}$, and let μ be the mapping of $\{0 , 1\}$ onto $\{a , b\}$ such that $\mu(0) = a$ and $\mu(1) = b$. Then

$$\mu\mathcal{S} = (\{a , b\} , + , a)$$

where $+ = \{(a , a , a) , (a , b , b) , (b , a , b) , (b , b , a)\}$.

Here is our definition.

Definition 6.5.1: An algebraic system $\mathcal{S}$ is said to be *isomorphic* to an algebraic system $\mathfrak{J}$ (in symbols, $\mathcal{S} \cong \mathfrak{J}$) if and only if there is a one-one mapping of the supporting set of $\mathcal{S}$ onto the supporting set of $\mathfrak{J}$, say μ, such that $\mu\mathcal{S} = \mathfrak{J}$. The mapping μ is said to be an *isomorphism* of $\mathcal{S}$ onto $\mathfrak{J}$.

For example, $(\{0 , 1\} , \circ , 0) \cong (\{a , b\} , + , a)$ where $\circ$ and $+$ are the binary operations given above; the isomorphism involved is the mapping $\mu = \{(0 , a) , (1 , b)\}$.

Our definition of isomorphic algebraic systems relies on the fact that an algebraic system is constructed from its supporting set S in the sense that each of its terms is a subset of S_n, for some n, or is a member of S. Thus, it makes sense to apply a mapping μ to each term of the algebraic system, not merely its supporting set.

Clearly $\cong$ is a binary relation on algebraic systems. It is easy to prove that this is an equivalence relation on the class of all algebraic systems. For this reason, we regard isomorphic algebraic systems as equal from the algebraic viewpoint. In this connection the vital point is that isomorphic algebraic systems differ only as to the *names* of members of their respective basic sets; otherwise, isomorphic algebraic systems are identical.

On occasion in Section 6.4 we have mentioned that an algebraic system is an *extension* of another algebraic system. Let us clarify this term.

Definition 6.5.2: An algebraic system $\mathfrak{I}$ is said to be an *extension* of an algebraic system $\mathcal{S}$ if and only if $\mathcal{S}$ is isomorphic to a subsystem of $\mathfrak{I}$.

The following result about fields of characteristic zero is most important. A field, say $(F, +, \cdot, 0, 1)$, is said to have *characteristic zero* if and only if $n1 \neq 0$ whenever $n \in N$. Notice that the rational, real, and complex number fields have characteristic zero.

Theorem 6.5.1: Each field of characteristic zero is an extension of the rational number field $(Rt, +, \cdot, 0, 1)$.

Proof: We establish our theorem by using the construction that produces the rational number system from the system of integers. Let $\mathfrak{F} = (F, +', \cdot', 0', 1')$ be any field of characteristic zero. We need a suitable mapping of Rt into F. Our mapping is constructed in two stages. The idea is to classify rational numbers into integers and nonintegers; of course, the *integers* are members of Rt of the form $n1$, where $n \in I$. We now define μ as follows: Let $\mu(n1) = n1'$ whenever $n \in I$; so we have defined the image under μ of each integer member of Rt. Next, we observe that each rational number r is represented uniquely by (a, b), an ordered pair of relatively prime integers with positive second term, in the sense that $r = a \cdot b^{-1}$. Then $\mu(r)$ is defined to be $\mu(a) \cdot [\mu(b)]^{-1}$. It follows from this definition of μ that μ is one-one, $\mu(x + y) = \mu(x) +' \mu(y)$, and $\mu(x \cdot y) = \mu(x) \cdot' \mu(y)$ whenever $\{x, y\} \subset Rt$. We conclude that μ is an isomorphism of $(Rt, +, \cdot, 0, 1)$ into a subsystem of $\mathfrak{F}$.

EXERCISES

1. Compute $\mu(\{0, 1, 2\}, \{(0, 1), (0, 2), (1, 2)\})$ where $\mu(0) = a$, $\mu(1) = b$, and $\mu(2) = c$.

2. Let $\mathcal{S} = (\{0, 1, 2\}, +, 0)$ where $+$ is given by the following table:

$+$	0	1	2
0	0	1	2
1	1	2	0
2	2	0	1

Compute $\mu\mathcal{S}$ where $\mu(0) = 1$, $\mu(1) = 2$, and $\mu(2) = 0$.

3. Let $s = (\{0, 1\}, \circ, 0)$ and let $\mathfrak{I} = (\{0, 1\}, +, 1)$ where $\circ$ and $+$ are given by the following table:

$$
\begin{array}{c|cc}
\circ & 0 & 1 \\
\hline
0 & 0 & 1 \\
1 & 1 & 0
\end{array}
\qquad \text{and} \qquad
\begin{array}{c|cc}
+ & 0 & 1 \\
\hline
0 & 1 & 0 \\
1 & 0 & 1
\end{array} \ .
$$

(a) Show that $s \cong \mathfrak{I}$.
(b) Exhibit an isomorphism of s onto $\mathfrak{I}$.

4. Let μ be an isomorphism of $s = (S, +, R)$ onto $\mathfrak{I} = (T, \circ, R')$ where $+$ is a binary operation on S and R is a binary relation on S.

(a) Prove that $\mu(x + y) = \mu(x) \circ \mu(y)$ whenever $\{x, y\} \subset S$.
(b) Prove that $x \, R \, y$ if and only if $\mu(x) R' \mu(y)$.

5. An algebraic system is said to have n elements if and only if its supporting set has n elements. Algebraic systems are said to be *distinct* if and only if no two of them are isomorphic.

(a) List the distinct two-element groups.
(b) List the distinct three-element groups.
(c) List the distinct four-element groups.
(d) List the distinct two-element semigroups.

7

VECTOR SPACES

7.1 VECTOR SPACES

In Section 1.1 we mentioned, rather mysteriously, that n-tuples form a vector space. At last we are in a position to clarify that statement. First, we point out that a vector space is a mathematical system which involves three mathematical objects, a field, an abelian group, and a mapping. Now, in Section 1.1 we were working with the real number field, the abelian group $(R_n, +, 0)$, and a mapping of $R \times R_n$ into R_n called scalar multiplication. There we established four algebraic properties of scalar multiplication, given by Lemmas 1.1.5 to 1.1.8. We shall use these properties to generalize the mathematical system of Section 1.1. Thus, a mathematical system $(\mathcal{F}, \mathcal{V}, \circ)$, where $\mathcal{F}$ is a field, $\mathcal{V}$ is an abelian group, and $\circ$ is a mapping of $F \times V$ into V, is called a *vector space* provided that $\circ$, the group operation, and the field operations possess the algebraic properties described in Lemmas 1.1.5 to 1.1.8. Here is our formal definition.

Definition 7.1.1: Let $\mathcal{F} = (F, +, \cdot, 0, 1)$ be a field, let $\mathcal{V} = (V, +, 0)$ be an abelian group, and let $\circ$ be a mapping of $F \times V$ into V. Then the 3-tuple $(\mathcal{F}, \mathcal{V}, \circ)$ is said to be a *vector space* if and only if:

(i) $a \circ (\beta + \gamma) = (a \circ \beta) + (a \circ \gamma)$ whenever $a \in F$ and $\{\beta, \gamma\} \subset V$;
(ii) $(a + b) \circ \gamma = (a \circ \gamma) + (b \circ \gamma)$ whenever $\{a, b\} \subset F$ and $\gamma \in V$;
(iii) $(a \cdot b) \circ \gamma = a \circ (b \circ \gamma)$ whenever $\{a, b\} \subset F$ and $\gamma \in V$;
(iv) $1 \circ \gamma = \gamma$ whenever $\gamma \in V$.

The abelian group $\mathcal{V} = (V, +, 0)$ is the main component of a vector space $(\mathcal{F}, \mathcal{V}, \circ)$. The field $\mathcal{F}$ usually provides the raw material from which the abelian

149

group $\mathcal{V}$ is constructed. Primarily, it is $\mathcal{V}$ that interests us. As we mentioned in Section 1.1, the members of V are called *vectors* and the members of F are called *scalars*. We continue our practice of denoting vectors by Greek letters and scalars by Latin letters. Throughout this chapter we continue to use heavy type for the vector $\mathbf{0}$ (the identity of the group) and light type for the scalar 0 (the additive identity of the field). We have already adopted the convention of suppressing the symbol $\circ$ for scalar multiplication. For the sake of clarity, however, throughout most of this section we exhibit this symbol; thereafter we freely suppress it. Since the symbol for multiplication is also suppressed, this means that we must rely on the context to distinguish between scalar multiplication and field multiplication.

We now present some examples.

Example 1: Let $\mathcal{R} = (R, +, \cdot, 0, 1)$, the real number field, let $\mathcal{G} = (R_n, +, \mathbf{0})$ the algebraic system considered in Section 1.1, and let $\circ$ be the scalar multiplication introduced in Section 1.1. In view of Lemmas 1.1.1–1.1.4, $\mathcal{G}$ is an abelian group; moreover, by Lemmas 1.1.5–1.1.8, $\circ$, $+$, and the field operations are related as required. So $(\mathcal{R}, \mathcal{G}, \circ)$ is a vector space. This vector space is denoted by $\mathcal{R}_n$.

The construction involved in Example 1 can be extended to any field.

Example 2: Let $\mathcal{F} = (F, +, \cdot, 0, 1)$ be a field, let $F_n = \underbrace{F \times \cdots \times F}_{n\ F\text{'s}}$, and let $+, \circ$, and $\mathbf{0}$ be defined as in Example 1. It is easy to verify that $\mathcal{G} = (F_n, +, \mathbf{0})$ is an abelian group and that $(\mathcal{F}, \mathcal{G}, \circ)$ is a vector space. If $\mathcal{F}$ is the complex number field $\mathcal{C}$, the resulting vector space is denoted by $\mathcal{C}_n$.

Example 3: Let $\mathcal{F} = (F, +, \cdot, 0, 1)$ be any field, let M be the set of all mappings of $\{0, 1\}$ into F, let $f + g = \{(0, f(0) + g(0)), (1, f(1) + g(1))\}$ whenever $\{f, g\} \subset M$, let $\mathbf{0} = \{(0, 0), (1, 0)\}$, and let $k \circ f = \{(0, kf(0)), (1, kf(1))\}$ whenever $k \in F$ and $f \in M$. It is easy to verify that $\mathfrak{M} = (M, +, \mathbf{0})$ is an abelian group and that $(\mathcal{F}, \mathfrak{M}, \circ)$ is a vector space.

Example 4: Let $\mathcal{F} = (F, +, \cdot, 0, 1)$ be a field and let M be the set of all mappings of F into F. Let $f + g = \{(t, f(t) + g(t)) \mid t \in F\}$ whenever $\{f, g\} \subset M$, let $\mathbf{0} = \{(t, 0) \mid t \in F\}$, and let $k \circ f = \{(t, kf(t)) \mid t \in F\}$ whenever $k \in F$ and $f \in M$. It is easy to verify that $\mathfrak{M} = (M, +, \mathbf{0})$ is an abelian group and that $(\mathcal{F}, \mathfrak{M}, \circ)$ is a vector space.

Example 5: Let $\mathcal{R}$ be the real number field, let C be the set of all continuous functions with domain $[0, 1]$, let $+$ be the usual addition of functions, let $\mathbf{0} = \{(t, 0) \mid t \in [0, 1]\}$, and let $k \circ f = \{(t, kf(t)) \mid t \in [0, 1]\}$ whenever $k \in R$ and $f \in C$. It is easy to verify that $\mathcal{C} = (C, +, \mathbf{0})$ is an abelian group and that $(\mathcal{R}, \mathcal{C}, \circ)$ is a vector space.

It is instructive to interpret Example 5 geometrically.

Example 6: The graph of a continuous function is a curve (of a special sort) so let C be the set of all curves between the ordinates at 0 and 1. We know how to *add* curves (merely apply the analytic definition of Example 5); so we obtain $+$, a binary operation on C. The null vector $\mathbf{0}$ is the line-segment $[0, 1]$. Finally, we need a method of associating a curve with a real number k and a given curve; of course, we know how to multiply a curve by a real number (merely apply the analytic definition of Example 5); so we obtain $\circ$ the required scalar multiplication. Notice that this mathematical system is a vector space; here vectors are curves and scalars are real numbers.

Example 7: In our work with linear systems we have *added* equations and we have *multiplied* equations by scalars. We point out that this is another example of a vector space. Let $\Re$ be the real number field and let E be the set of all linear equations in n unknowns $x_1, \ldots, x_n$ with real coefficients. The sum of two equations is found by adding corresponding coefficients, and the product of an equation by a real number k is obtained by multiplying each coefficient by k. Here $\mathbf{0}$ denotes the equation whose coefficients are all zero. We leave it as an exercise to verify that $\mathcal{E} = (E, +, \mathbf{0})$ is an abelian group and that $(\Re, \mathcal{E}, \circ)$ is a vector space.

Example 8: Let M be the set of all $m \times n$ matrices with real entries, let $+$ be the binary operation on M defined in Definition 3.3.1, let (0) be the $m \times n$ matrix each of whose entries is 0, and let $\circ$ be the scalar multiplication described in Definition 3.3.2. It is easy to verify that $\mathfrak{M} = (M, +, (0))$ is an abelian group and that $(\Re, \mathfrak{M}, \circ)$ is a vector space.

We must emphasize that the term "vector space" is a tag that can be applied to certain mathematical systems. We have presented various mathematical systems that in fact are vector spaces. Let us now exhibit some algebraic properties that are possessed by all vector spaces. Our goal is to develop the algebra of vector spaces. Let $(\mathfrak{F}, \mathcal{V}, \circ)$ be any vector space where $\mathfrak{F} = (F, +, \cdot, 0, 1)$ and $\mathcal{V} = (V, +, \mathbf{0})$; the following statements refer to this mathematical system.

Lemma 7.1.1: $0 \circ \alpha = \mathbf{0}$ whenever $\alpha \in V$.

Proof: Let $\alpha \in V$; now

$$0 \circ \alpha = (0 + 0) \circ \alpha \qquad \text{since } \mathfrak{F} \text{ is a field}$$

$$= 0 \circ \alpha + 0 \circ \alpha \qquad \text{by } (ii) .$$

But $0 \circ \alpha \in V$; adding its inverse to both sides of the preceding equation and recalling that $\mathcal{V}$ is a group, we readily verify that $0 \circ \alpha$ is the identity of $\mathcal{V}$, i.e., $0 \circ \alpha = \mathbf{0}$.

Lemma 7.1.2: Let $\alpha \in V$; then $(-1) \circ \alpha$ is the inverse of α.

Proof: We must prove that $\alpha + (-1) \circ \alpha = \mathbf{0}$ whenever $\alpha \in V$. Now,

$$\alpha + (-1) \circ \alpha = 1 \circ \alpha + (-1) \circ \alpha \qquad \text{by } (iv)$$
$$= (1 + -1) \circ \alpha \qquad \text{by } (ii)$$
$$= 0 \circ \alpha$$
$$= \mathbf{0} \qquad \text{by Lemma 7.1.1}$$

This completes our proof.

Lemma 7.1.3: $a \circ \mathbf{0} = \mathbf{0}$ whenever $a \in F$.

Proof: Observe that $\mathbf{0} = \mathbf{0} + \mathbf{0}$ and apply (i); the details are left as an exercise.

The following result should be considered carefully.

Lemma 7.1.4: Let $a \circ \beta = \gamma$ where $a \neq 0$; then $\beta = a^{-1} \circ \gamma$.

Proof: Since $a \neq 0$, a possesses a unique multiplicative inverse which we have agreed to denote by a^{-1} or by $1/a$. Now,

$$\gamma = a \circ \beta$$

so
$$a^{-1} \circ \gamma = a^{-1} \circ (a \circ \beta)$$
$$= (a^{-1} \cdot a) \circ \beta \qquad \text{by } (iii)$$
$$= 1 \circ \beta$$
$$= \beta \qquad \text{by } (iv).$$

This establishes our lemma.

Next, we point out that postulates (i), (ii), and (iii) can be generalized as follows.

Lemma 7.1.5: Let $k \in F$ and let $\alpha_1, \ldots, \alpha_n$ be any vectors, not necessarily distinct; then $k \circ (\alpha_1 + \cdots + \alpha_n) = k \circ \alpha_1 + \cdots + k \circ \alpha_n$.

Proof: Use mathematical induction.

Lemma 7.1.6: Let $k_1, \ldots, k_n$ be any scalars, not necessarily distinct, and let $\alpha \in V$; then $(k_1 + \cdots + k_n) \circ \alpha = k_1 \circ \alpha + \cdots + k_n \circ \alpha$.

Proof: Use mathematical induction.

Lemma 7.1.7: Let $k_1, \ldots, k_n$ be any scalars, not necessarily distinct, and let $\alpha \in V$; then $(k_1 \cdot k_2 \cdot \ldots \cdot k_n) \circ \alpha = k_1 \circ (k_2 \circ (\ldots \circ (k_n \circ \alpha) \ldots))$.

Proof: Use mathematical induction.

The following lemma, a generalization of Lemma 7.1.4, is needed to establish our Test for Linear Dependence.

Lemma 7.1.8: Let $a \neq 0$ and let $a \circ \beta = k_1 \circ \gamma_1 + \cdots + k_n \circ \gamma_n$; then $\beta = (k_1/a) \circ \gamma_1 + \cdots + (k_n/a) \circ \gamma_n$.

Proof: Now,

$$
\begin{aligned}
\beta &= a^{-1} \circ (k_1 \circ \gamma_1 + \cdots + k_n \circ \gamma_n) && \text{by Lemma 7.1.4} \\
&= a^{-1} \circ (k_1 \circ \gamma_1) + \cdots + a^{-1} \circ (k_n \circ \gamma_n) && \text{by Lemma 7.1.5} \\
&= (a^{-1} \cdot k_1) \circ \gamma_1 + \cdots + (a^{-1} \cdot k_n) \circ \gamma_n && \text{by } (iii) \\
&= (k_1/a) \circ \gamma_1 + \cdots + (k_n/a) \circ \gamma_n \ .
\end{aligned}
$$

Our plan, now, is to generalize the concepts introduced in Sections 2.1 and 2.2. We begin with the notion of a *subspace*. Notice that we talk about a subspace of a vector space, rather than a subspace of a set.

Definition 7.1.2: Let $V = (\mathfrak{F}, \mathcal{V}, \circ)$ be a vector space where $\mathfrak{F} = (F, +, \cdot, 0, 1)$ and $\mathcal{V} = (V, +, \mathbf{0})$. Then W is said to be a *subspace of* V if and only if:

    (*i*) W is a nonempty subset of V;

    (*ii*) $\alpha + \beta \in W$ whenever $\{\alpha, \beta\} \subset W$;

    (*iii*) $k \circ \alpha \in W$ whenever $\alpha \in W$ and $k \in F$.

By restricting the operations and mappings of V to one of its subspaces W, we obtain a mathematical system that has the same form as V. First, W grows into $\mathcal{W} = (W, + \mid W \times W, \mathbf{0})$, a subsystem of $\mathcal{V}$, the group of V. Next, restricting $\circ$ to $F \times W$, we obtain $(\mathfrak{F}, \mathcal{W}, \circ \mid F \times W)$, a *subsystem of* V. The fact is that $\mathcal{W}$ is a subgroup of $\mathcal{V}$; this follows from the assumption that W is a nonempty set of vectors which is closed under the group operation and under scalar multiplication. Let us illustrate this idea.

Example 9: Clearly, $W = \{(a, b, 0) \mid \{a, b\} \subset R\}$ is a subspace of $\mathcal{R}_3$. Now, the group of this vector space is $(R_3, +, \mathbf{0})$; so $\mathcal{W} = (W, +', \mathbf{0})$ where $+' = + \mid W \times W$, i.e., $(a, b, 0) +' (c, d, 0) = (a + c, b + d, 0)$ whenever $\{(a, b, 0), (c, d, 0)\} \subset W$. Moreover, W is closed under scalar multiplication, so $(-1)\alpha \in W$ whenever $\alpha \in W$; but $(-1)\alpha$ is the inverse of α, thus each member of W possesses an inverse in W. Also, $0\alpha = \mathbf{0}$, so the group identity is a member of W. Notice that $+'$ is associative and commutative on W because $+' \subset +$ and $+$ is associative and commutative on R, a superset of W. So $\mathcal{W}$ is an abelian group. Finally, we point out that $(\mathcal{R}, \mathcal{W}, \circ \mid R \times W)$ is a vector space. So, the subspace W leads us to another vector space via the abelian group $\mathcal{W}$.

We now formalize our notion of a *subsystem* of a vector space.

Definition 7.1.3: Let W be a subspace of a vector space $V = (\mathfrak{F}, \mathcal{V}, \circ)$ and let $\mathcal{W} = (W, + \mid W \times W, \mathbf{0})$. Then $(\mathfrak{F}, \mathcal{W}, \circ \mid F \times W)$ is said to be the *subsystem* of V corresponding to W.

The point is that each subsystem of a vector space obtained in this way, is itself a vector space.

Theorem 7.1.1: Each subsystem of a vector space that corresponds to a subspace, is itself a vector space.

Proof: Let $(\mathfrak{F}, \mathcal{W}, \circ \mid F \times W)$ be the subsystem of a vector space $(\mathfrak{F}, \mathcal{V}, \circ)$ corresponding to a subspace W of this vector space. It is easy to verify that $(W, + \mid W \times W, \mathbf{0})$ is an abelian group and that the remaining conditions of Definition 7.1.1 are satisfied. The details are left as an exercise.

As we have already illustrated, this result is valuable because it enables us to construct a vector space from a given vector space by merely considering one of its subspaces. Here is another example. Let S be the solution set of the homogeneous linear system

$$a_{11}\, x_1 + \cdots + a_{1n}\, x_n = 0 , \ldots, a_{m1}\, x_1 + \cdots + a_{mn}\, x_n = 0 .$$

We have already verified that S is a subspace of the vector space $\mathfrak{R}_n$ (see Section 2.4); so S leads us to another vector space via the abelian group $(S, + \mid S \times S, \mathbf{0})$.

In Section 2.1 we showed that the problem of determining the smallest subspace of $\mathfrak{R}_n$ that contains given vectors, led us to the notion of a *linear combination*. In turn, this led to the concept of a *spanning* subset of a subspace, and to the question of whether the spanning subset is redundant. So we formulated our concepts of *linearly dependent* and *linearly independent* sets. In Section 2.2 we sharpened these ideas and presented appropriate definitions. We point out that these ideas apply equally well in the more general setting of this section. For convenience, we now repeat the definitions of Section 2.2. Throughout the remainder of this section we deal with a vector space $V = (\mathfrak{F}, \mathcal{V}, \circ)$ where $\mathfrak{F} = (F, +, \cdot, 0, 1)$ and $\mathcal{V} = (V, +, \mathbf{0})$; this agreement permits us to abbreviate our definitions and theorems.

Definition 7.1.4: Let $A \subset V$ and let $\gamma \in V$; then γ is said to be a *linear combination* of A if and only if there is a natural number s, a subset of A with s members, say $\{\alpha_1, \ldots, \alpha_s\}$, and corresponding scalars $k_1, \ldots, k_s$ not necessarily distinct, such that $\gamma = k_1\, \alpha_1 + \cdots + k_s\, \alpha_s$.

Definition 7.1.5: Let $A \subset V$; then LA denotes the set of all linear combinations of A. We shall say that A *spans* LA, or that LA is *spanned* by A.

Definition 7.1.6: Let $A \subset V$; then A is said to be *linearly dependent* if and only if $\mathbf{0} \in A$ or there is a member of A, say γ such that $\gamma \in L(A - \{\gamma\})$.

Definition 7.1.7: Let $A \subset V$; then A is said to be *linearly independent* if and only if A is not linearly dependent.

TEST FOR LINEAR DEPENDENCE: Let $A = \{\alpha_1, \ldots, \alpha_m\}$ be a subset of V with m members, where $m \in N$. Then A is linearly dependent if and only if there are scalars $k_1, \ldots, k_m$, not all zero, such that $k_1\, \alpha_1 + \cdots + k_m\, \alpha_m = \mathbf{0}$.

Proof: See the proof given in Section 2.1; in the first part use Lemma 7.1.2, in the second part use Lemma 7.1.8.

TEST FOR LINEAR DEPENDENCE OF INFINITE SETS: An infinite subset of V, say A, is linearly dependent if and only if A possesses a finite, linearly dependent subset.

Proof: See the proof given in Section 2.2.

We now generalize the concepts of *basis* and *dimension*.

Definition 7.1.8: Let W be a subspace of V and let $B \subset W$; then B is said to be a *basis* for W if and only if:

(*i*) $W = LB$.
(*ii*) B is linearly independent.

As before, we call $\{0\}$ the *trivial* subspace of a vector space.

Definition 7.1.9: The *dimension* of a nontrivial subspace W is the largest natural number t such that W possesses a basis with t members; if there is no such natural number then W is said to have *infinite* dimension. The dimension of $\{0\}$ is 0.

It is convenient to extend the notions of *basis* and *dimension* in the following way.

Definition 7.1.10: We say that B is a *basis* for $\mathbf{V}$ if and only if B is a basis for V. We say that t is the *dimension* of $\mathbf{V}$ if and only if t is the dimension of V.

Notice our use of symbols. The set of vectors of a vector space is denoted by V; the abelian group involved is denoted by $\mho$; the vector space itself is denoted by $\mathbf{V}$.

EXERCISES

1. Let $\mathfrak{F} = (F, +, \cdot, 0, 1)$ be any field and let $\mho = (F, +, 0)$.

    (a)   Show that $\mho$ is an abelian group.
    (b)   Show that $(\mathfrak{F}, \mho, \cdot)$ is a vector space.
    (c)   Find a basis for $(\mathfrak{F}, \mho, \cdot)$.
    (d)   Determine the dimension of $(\mathfrak{F}, \mho, \cdot)$.

2. (a)   Let $\mathfrak{F} = (F, +, \cdot, 0, 1)$ be any field and let $n \in N$. Show that $(\mathfrak{F}, \mho, \circ)$ is a vector space where V is the set of all mappings of $\{1, 2, \ldots, n\}$ into F, $f + g = \{(t, f(t) + g(t)) \mid t \in \{1, \ldots, n\}\}$ whenever $\{f, g\} \subset V$, $0 = \{(t, 0) \mid t \in \{1, \ldots, n\}\}$, and $c \circ f = \{(t, c \cdot f(t)) \mid t \in \{1, \ldots, n\}\}$ whenever $c \in F$ and $f \in V$.

    (b)   Exhibit n linearly independent vectors of the vector space of part (a).

3. Let $\mathcal{R} = (R, +, \cdot, 0, 1)$ be the real number field, let $(C, +, \cdot, 0, 1)$ be the complex number field, let $\mathcal{V} = (C, +, 0)$, and let $k \circ (a, b) = (k \cdot a, k \cdot b)$ whenever $(a, b) \in C$ and $k \in R$.

    (a) Show that $\mathcal{V}$ is an abelian group.
    (b) Show that $V = (\mathcal{R}, \mathcal{V}, \circ)$ is a vector space.
    (c) Exhibit a basis for V.
    (d) Determine the dimension of V.

4. Prove Lemma 7.1.3.

5. Prove that $(-a) \circ \gamma$ is the inverse of $a \circ \gamma$ whenever a is a scalar and γ is a vector.

6. Prove Lemma 7.1.5.

7. Given that k is a nonzero scalar and that α is a vector, prove that $k \circ \alpha = \mathbf{0}$ if and only if $\alpha = \mathbf{0}$.

8. Prove Lemma 7.1.6.

9. Prove Lemma 7.1.7.

10. Show that each of the following is a vector space:

    (a) The mathematical system of Example 2.
    (b) The mathematical system of Example 3.
    (c) The mathematical system of Example 4.
    (d) The mathematical system of Example 5.
    (e) The mathematical system of Example 6.
    (f) The mathematical system of Example 7.
    (g) The mathematical system of Example 8.

11. Prove Theorem 7.1.1.

12. Given that $\{\alpha_1, \ldots, \alpha_i\}$ is linearly independent and that $k \neq 0$, prove that $\{k\alpha_1, \ldots, k\alpha_i\}$ is linearly independent.

13. Prove the TEST FOR LINEAR DEPENDENCE.

14. Given that A is linearly independent and that $A \cup \{\beta\}$ is linearly dependent, prove that $\beta \in LA$.

15. Let B be a basis for a vector space; show that no proper subset of B is a basis for that vector space.

16. Let $(\mathcal{F}, \mathcal{V}, \circ)$ and $(\mathcal{F}, \mathcal{V}', \circ')$ be vector spaces where $\mathcal{V} = (V, +, \mathbf{0})$ and $\mathcal{V}' = (V', +', \mathbf{0}')$. Let $\mathcal{G} = (V \times V', \oplus, (\mathbf{0}, \mathbf{0}'))$ where $\oplus$ is defined as follows: $(\alpha, \alpha') \oplus (\beta, \beta') = (\alpha + \beta, \alpha' +' \beta')$ whenever $\{\alpha, \beta\} \subset V$ and $\{\alpha', \beta'\} \subset V'$. Let $\circ''$ be the mapping of $F \times (V \times V')$ into $V \times V'$ such that $k \circ'' (\alpha, \alpha') = (k \circ \alpha, k \circ' \alpha')$ whenever $k \in F$, $\alpha \in V$, and $\alpha' \in V'$.

    (a) Show that $\mathcal{G}$ is an abelian group.
    (b) Show that $(\mathcal{F}, \mathcal{G}, \circ'')$ is a vector space.

17. Let $\mathfrak{F} = (F, +, \cdot, 0, 1)$ be any field, let $\mathfrak{V} = (V, +, \mathbf{0})$ be any abelian group, and let $\circ$ be the mapping of $F \times V$ into V such that $a \circ \beta = \mathbf{0}$ whenever $a \in F$ and $\beta \in V$. Given that $(\mathfrak{F}, \mathfrak{V}, \circ)$ is a vector space, what can you deduce about $\mathfrak{V}$?

18. Let $\mathfrak{F} = (F, +, \cdot, 0, 1)$ be any field, let $\mathfrak{V} = (V, +, \mathbf{0})$ be any abelian group, and let $\circ$ be the mapping of $F \times V$ into V such that $a \circ \beta = \beta$ whenever $a \in F$ and $\beta \in V$. Given that $(\mathfrak{F}, \mathfrak{V}, \circ)$ is a vector space, what can you deduce about $\mathfrak{V}$?

7.2 STEINITZ REPLACEMENT THEOREM

In Section 2.2 we quoted certain facts about $\mathfrak{R}_n$ and mentioned that they would be established in Section 7.2; these facts are consequences of the Steinitz Replacement Theorem which we consider presently. We begin by observing that the first two lemmas of Section 2.2 apply to any vector space. As an abbreviating device let us agree that the statements of this section refer to a vector space $\mathbf{V} = (\mathfrak{F}, \mathfrak{V}, \circ)$ where $\mathfrak{F} = (F, +, \cdot, 0, 1)$ and $\mathfrak{V} = (V, +, \mathbf{0})$.

Lemma 7.2.1: Let A and B be subsets of V such that $A \subset B$; then $LA \subset LB$.

Proof: See the proof of Lemma 2.2.1.

Lemma 7.2.2: Let $A \subset V$ and let $\gamma \in LA$; then $L(A \cup \{\gamma\}) = LA$.

Proof: See the proof of Lemma 2.2.2.

Our plan is to establish a special case of the Steinitz Replacement Theorem, namely Theorem 7.2.1; the fact is that the Steinitz Replacement Theorem can be proven by applying Theorem 7.2.1 over and over. First, we need to prove that if β is a nonzero linear combination of A, a set of vectors, then there is a member of A which is a linear combination of β and the other members of A.

Lemma 7.2.3: Let $\beta \in LA$ where $\beta \neq \mathbf{0}$; then there is a member of A, say α, such that $\alpha \in L((A - \{\alpha\}) \cup \{\beta\})$.

Proof: We are given that $\beta \in LA$; so there are members of A, say $\alpha_1, \ldots, \alpha_m$, and scalars $t_1, \ldots, t_m$ such that

(1) $$\beta = t_1 \alpha_1 + \cdots + t_m \alpha_m .$$

Now, $\beta \neq \mathbf{0}$; so at least one of the scalars $t_1, \ldots, t_m$ is nonzero. Let $t_i \neq 0$; rewriting (1) so that α_i stands alone, we see that α_i is a linear combination of β and the other α's, i.e., $\alpha_i \in L((A - \{\alpha_i\}) \cup \{\beta\})$.

This proof does more than establish the lemma; it shows how to find a suitable α. The point is that any member of A that actually appears in (1) (in the sense that its scalar multiplier is not 0) is suitable. This simple fact is the key to this section; here is an example.

Example 1: Let $A = \{\epsilon_1, \epsilon_2, \epsilon_3, \epsilon_4\}$ and let $\beta = (2, 0, 0, -1)$. Now, $\beta = 2\epsilon_1 + (-1)\epsilon_4$; thus $\epsilon_1 = \frac{1}{2}\beta + \frac{1}{2}\epsilon_4$. So ϵ_1 is a linear combination of β and the other members of A; i.e., $\epsilon_1 \in L\{\beta, \epsilon_2, \epsilon_3, \epsilon_4\}$. Of course, ϵ_4 has this property also, i.e., $\epsilon_4 \in L\{\beta, \epsilon_1, \epsilon_2, \epsilon_3\}$, but neither ϵ_2 nor ϵ_3 has this property.

We now present our special case of the Steinitz Replacement Theorem.

Theorem 7.2.1 (*Exchange Theorem*): Let $A \subset V$, let β be any nonzero member of LA, and let α be a member of A such that $\alpha \in LC$ where $C = (A - \{\alpha\}) \cup \{\beta\}$. Then $LC = LA$ and C is linearly independent if A is linearly independent.

Proof: By Lemma 7.2.3 α exists as required. We prove that $LC = LA$ by applying Lemma 7.2.2 twice. Now, $\beta \in LA$ so $LA = L(A \cup \{\beta\})$; also, $\alpha \in LC$ so $LC = L(C \cup \{\alpha\}) = L(A \cup \{\beta\}) = LA$. Next, let A be linearly independent and assume that C is linearly dependent. Notice that $\beta \notin A$ (otherwise $C \subset A$; so C is linearly independent). Consider our assumption that C is linearly dependent. Clearly, $0 \notin C$. So, by Definition 7.1.6, $\beta \in L(A - \{\alpha\})$ or there is a member of $C - \{\beta\}$, say γ, such that $\gamma \in L(C - \{\gamma\})$. If the latter, then γ has the form

$$k\beta + (t_1\alpha_1 + \cdots + t_m\alpha_m)$$

where $\alpha_i \in C - \{\beta, \gamma\}$, $i = 1, \ldots, m$. Notice that $k \neq 0$ (otherwise A is linearly dependent). It follows that $\beta \in L(A - \{\alpha\})$. So, in either case, $\beta \in L(A - \{\alpha\})$; thus, by Lemma 7.2.2,

$$LC = L((A - \{\alpha\}) \cup \{\beta\}) = L(A - \{\alpha\}).$$

Therefore $\alpha \in L(A - \{\alpha\})$; we conclude that A is linearly dependent. This contradiction establishes the second part of our theorem.

Before going on to our generalization of Theorem 7.2.1 we mention that this theorem is useful in its own right. Remember that we are interested in characterizing an infinite subspace W by means of a subset of W that spans W. The value of Theorem 7.2.1 is that it permits us to operate on a set A that spans W, replacing a member of A by a nonzero member of W. We now illustrate this idea.

Example 2: Extend $\{(2, 0, 0, -1), (1, 3, -1, 0)\}$ to a basis for $\mathcal{R}_4$.

Solution: Clearly $\{\epsilon_1, \epsilon_2, \epsilon_3, \epsilon_4\}$ is a basis for $\mathcal{R}_4$. By Example 1, $\epsilon_1 \in L\{(2, 0, 0, -1), \epsilon_2, \epsilon_3, \epsilon_4\}$; so, by Theorem 7.2.1,

$$L\{(2, 0, 0, -1), \epsilon_2, \epsilon_3, \epsilon_4\} = L\{\epsilon_1, \epsilon_2, \epsilon_3, \epsilon_4\} = R_4$$

and $B = \{(2, 0, 0, -1), \epsilon_2, \epsilon_3, \epsilon_4\}$ is linearly independent. Thus B is a basis for $\mathcal{R}_4$. Next, we express $(1, 3, -1, 0)$ as a linear combination of B:

$$(1, 3, -1, 0) = \frac{1}{2}(2, 0, 0, -1) + 3\epsilon_2 + (-1)\epsilon_3 + \frac{1}{2}\epsilon_4 .$$

Since ϵ_2 actually appears (i.e., its scalar multiplier is not 0) it follows from Theorem 7.2.1 that we can replace the basis vector ϵ_2 by $(1 , 3 , -1 , 0)$, i.e., $L\{(2, 0, 0, -1)$, $(1, 3, -1, 0)$, ϵ_3, $\epsilon_4\} = LB = R_4$ and $\{(2, 0, 0, -1), (1, 3, -1, 0), \epsilon_3, \epsilon_4\}$ is linearly independent. So, this set is a basis for $\mathcal{R}_4$.

Here is the Steinitz Replacement Theorem; notice that it is a generalization of Theorem 7.2.1 and that its proof relies on Theorem 7.2.1.

Steinitz Replacement Theorem: Let $A \subset V$ and let B be any finite, linearly independent subset of LA. There is a subset of A equinumerous with B, say A_1, such that $L((A - A_1) \cup B) = LA$; moreover $(A - A_1) \cup B$ is linearly independent if A is linearly independent.

Proof: Let $B = \{\beta_1 , \ldots , \beta_m\}$ be a linearly independent subset of LA with m members. Our idea is to apply Theorem 7.2.1 repeatedly using a member of B as the β of the theorem, and using the set produced at the preceding step as the A of the theorem, until B is exhausted. There are two problems that we must face. First, we must show that at each stage β_i is a linear combination of the set C_{i-1} produced at the preceding stage; secondly, we must show that when we apply Theorem 7.2.1 to C_{i-1} and β_{i-1}, the member of C_{i-1} which is replaced by β_i is a member of A, more specifically is not one of the β's treated at an earlier stage. Actually, it is quite easy to dispose of these points; to see this, we carry through the first two stages, treating β_1 and β_2.

1.   Treat β_1. By Theorem 7.2.1 there is a member of A, say α_1, that we can replace by β_1 in the sense that $LC_1 = LA$ where $C_1 = (A - \{\alpha_1\}) \cup \{\beta_1\}$. Moreover, by Theorem 7.2.1, C_1 is linearly independent if A is linearly independent. Here there are no problems. Notice that $LC_1 = LA$ and $B \subset LA$; so $B \subset LC_1$.

2.   Treat β_2. Here we show how we handle the two difficulties mentioned earlier. Now $B \subset LC_1$; so $\beta_2 \in LC_1$. This takes care of our first difficulty (remember that we wish to apply Theorem 7.2.1 to C_1 and β_2). By Theorem 7.2.1 there is a member of C_1, say α, such that $LC_2 = LC_1$ where $C_2 = (C_1 - \{\alpha\}) \cup \{\beta_2\}$. We must show that $\alpha \neq \beta_1$. This is quite easy! Now, $\beta_2 \in LC_1$; so

$$(2) \qquad\qquad \beta_2 = t_1\beta_1 + t_2\alpha_2 + \cdots + t_s\alpha_s$$

where $\alpha_i \in C_1 - \{\alpha_1 , \beta_1\}$, $i = 2, \ldots , s$. By the proof of Lemma 7.2.3 we can take for α any member of C_1 that actually appears on the right-hand side of (2). If β_1 is the only vector that appears there (i.e., $t_i = 0$ if $i > 1$) then $\{\beta_1 , \beta_2\}$ is linearly dependent and it follows that B is linearly dependent. We conclude that a member of $C_1 - B$, say α_2, actually appears in the right-hand side of (2), i.e., $t_2 \neq 0$. Therefore we can use α_2 as the α of Theorem 7.2.1. So $LC_2 = LC_1 = LA$ where $C_2 = (C_1 - \{\alpha_2\}) \cup \{\beta_2\} = (A - \{\alpha_1, \alpha_2\}) \cup \{\beta_1 , \beta_2\}$. Moreover C_2 is linearly independent if C_1 is linearly independent; thus C_2 is linearly independent if A is linearly independent.

It is clear, now, that we can repeat step 2, treating each remaining member of B in turn. Since B is finite our construction will come to an end. We conclude that there is a subset of A with m members, say $A_1 = \{\alpha_1 , \ldots , \alpha_m\}$, such that $LC = LA$

where $C = (A - A_1) \cup B$; moreover C is linearly independent if A is linearly independent. This completes our proof of the Steinitz Replacement Theorem.

Our proof relies on the assumption that B is *finite*. We mention that the Steinitz Replacement Theorem can be generalized by dropping this condition. A proof of this statement requires some fairly sophisticated mathematics and is beyond the scope of this book. Notice that the Steinitz Replacement Theorem is an *existence* theorem; it asserts the existence of a subset of A which possesses certain properties. This is of considerable theoretical value, as we shall shortly discover. It is a separate problem, however, to *exhibit* a suitable subset of A, even though we know one exists.

The Steinitz Replacement Theorem is a fertile source of facts concerning the notion of a basis for a subspace of V.

Corollary 7.2.1:   Let W be a subspace of V that possesses a basis with t members, where $t \in N$. Then each basis for W has t members.

Proof: Let B_1 be a basis for W with t members and let B_2 be another basis for W. Let us assume that these bases are not equinumerous; so one of B_1 or B_2 has more members than the other. Take the larger basis as the B of the Steinitz Replacement Theorem, and the other basis as the A of this theorem. So, there exists a subset of the smaller basis which is equinumerous with the larger basis! Clearly this is impossible (since one of these sets is finite). We conclude that B_1 and B_2 are equinumerous.

Note: If the larger basis is infinite replace it by one of its finite subsets that has more members than the other basis; recall that each subset of a linearly independent set is also linearly independent.

Corollary 7.2.2:   Let W be a subspace of V that possesses a basis with t members, where $t \in N$. Then each linearly independent subset of W with t members is a basis for W.

Proof: Let A be a basis for W with t members and let B be any linearly independent subset of W with t members. There is just one subset of A equinumerous with B, namely A itself. So, by the Steinitz Replacement Theorem, $LB = LA = W$. We conclude that B is a basis for W.

Corollary 7.2.3:   Let $A \subset V$ and let B be a subset of LA with more members than A. Then B is linearly dependent.

Proof: Assume that B is linearly independent. Let B_1 be any finite subset of B with more members than A (we introduce B_1 to cover the possibility that B is infinite); clearly B_1 is linearly independent. Thus, by the Steinitz Replacement Theorem, there is a subset of A equinumerous with B_1. This is impossible; so we conclude that the assumption of our proof is false. Thus, B is linearly dependent.

We shall now prove that each subspace, except $\{0\}$, of a finite-dimensional vector space possesses a basis. Remember that $\{0\}$ is called the trivial subspace of a vector space.

Theorem 7.2.2: Each nontrivial subspace of a finite-dimensional vector space possesses a basis.

Proof: Consider any vector space of dimension n, where $n \in N$, and let W be any nontrivial subspace of this vector space. By assumption, W possesses a nonzero member, say α_1. Clearly, $L\{\alpha_1\} \subset W$. If $L\{\alpha_1\} = W$ then $\{\alpha_1\}$ is a basis for W. Otherwise, choose any member of $W - L\{\alpha_1\}$, say α_2. It is easy to see that $\{\alpha_1, \alpha_2\}$ is linearly independent and that $L\{\alpha_1, \alpha_2\} \subset W$. If $L\{\alpha_1, \alpha_2\} = W$ then $\{\alpha_1, \alpha_2\}$ is a basis for W. Otherwise, we repeat our argument and choose any member of $W - L\{\alpha_1, \alpha_2\}$, say α_3. Again, $\{\alpha_1, \alpha_2, \alpha_3\}$ is linearly independent and $L\{\alpha_1, \alpha_2, \alpha_3\} \subset W$. If $L\{\alpha_1, \alpha_2, \alpha_3\} = W$ we have completed our construction; otherwise, we continue. By Corollary 7.2.3 each linearly independent subset of W has at most n members; therefore our construction requires at most n steps. So, there is a natural number t, where $t \leq n$, such that $L\{\alpha_1, \ldots, \alpha_t\} = W$ and $\{\alpha_1, \ldots, \alpha_t\}$ is linearly independent. This completes our proof.

We mention that Lemma 2.2.7 can be generalized to any vector space.

Lemma 7.2.4: Let W_1 and W_2 be finite-dimensional subspaces of a vector space such that $W_1 \subset W_2$. Then $W_1 = W_2$ if and only if dim $W_1 =$ dim W_2.

Proof: See the proof of Lemma 2.2.7.

Throughout this book we have denoted the real number field by $\mathfrak{R}$ and the complex number field by $\mathfrak{C}$. Let us agree to call a vector space $(\mathfrak{R}, \mathfrak{V}, \circ)$ a *real* vector space, and to call a vector space $(\mathfrak{C}, \mathfrak{V}, \circ)$ a *complex* vector space.

The following theorem states that each finite-dimensional, real vector space is isomorphic to a vector space of Section 1.1.

Theorem 7.2.3: Let $(\mathfrak{R}, \mathfrak{V}, \circ)$ be a real, n-dimensional vector space, where $n \in N$. Then $(\mathfrak{R}, \mathfrak{V}, \circ) \cong \mathfrak{R}_n$.

Proof: By assumption, $(\mathfrak{R}, \mathfrak{V}, \circ)$ possesses a basis with n members, say $\{\alpha_1, \ldots, \alpha_n\}$. Consider the n-tuple $(\alpha_1, \ldots, \alpha_n)$ which we shall call an *ordered* basis for our vector space. To establish our theorem we must exhibit a suitable mapping μ of V onto R_n. Let $\gamma \in V$; by assumption, there is an n-tuple of scalars $(t_1, \ldots, t_n)$ such that $\gamma = \sum_{i=1}^{n} t_i \alpha_i$. We shall use the n-tuple $(t_1, \ldots, t_n)$ to define our mapping μ; indeed, we take $\mu(\gamma) = (t_1, \ldots, t_n)$. It is easy to prove that μ is actually a one-one mapping of V onto R_n, and that the vector space $\mathfrak{R}_n$ is the image of $(\mathfrak{R}, \mathfrak{V}, \circ)$ under μ. The details are left as an exercise.

EXERCISES

1. Let $(\mathfrak{F}, \mathcal{V}, \circ)$ be any vector space, let $W = LA$ where A is a subset of V with three members, and let B be a linearly independent subset of W with two members. Without using the Steinitz Replacement Theorem, prove that there is a member of A, say α, such that $W = L(B \cup \{\alpha\})$.

2. Let $(\mathfrak{F}, \mathcal{V}, \circ)$ be any vector space where $\mathfrak{F} = (F, +, \cdot, 0, 1)$ and $\mathcal{V} = (V, +, \mathbf{0})$. Let $A \subset V$, let $\beta \in LA$, and let α be a member of A such that $\beta \notin L(A - \{\alpha\})$. Prove that $L((A - \{\alpha\}) \cup \{\beta\}) = LA$.

3. Extend $\{(0, 2, 3, -1), (1, 0, 1, 0)\}$ to a basis for $\mathcal{R}_4$.

4. Extend $\{(3, 0, -1, 0, 2), (2, 3, 0, -1, 0)\}$ to a basis for $\mathcal{R}_5$.

5. Prove Lemma 7.2.4.

6. Complete the proof of Theorem 7.2.3.

7. Let $(\mathfrak{F}, \mathcal{V}, \circ)$ be any vector space where $\mathcal{V} = (V, +, \mathbf{0})$, and let T be any mapping of V into V such that $T(k\alpha + \beta) = kT(\alpha) + T(\beta)$ whenever $\{\alpha, \beta\} \subset V$ and k is a scalar.

   (a) Prove that $T(\mathbf{0}) = \mathbf{0}$.
   (b) Prove that $T(\alpha + \beta) = T(\alpha) + T(\beta)$ whenever $\{\alpha, \beta\} \subset V$.
   (c) Prove that $T(k\alpha) = kT(\alpha)$ whenever $\alpha \in V$ and k is a scalar.
   (d) Prove that $\{\gamma \mid T(\gamma) = \mathbf{0}\}$ is a subspace of $(\mathfrak{F}, \mathcal{V}, \circ)$.

8. Let $\mathbf{V} = (\mathfrak{F}, \mathcal{V}, \circ)$ be any vector space and let W_1 and W_2 be finite-dimensional subspaces of $\mathbf{V}$.

   (a) Show that $W_1 \cap W_2$ is a subspace of $\mathbf{V}$.
   (b) Show that $\{\alpha_1 + \alpha_2 \mid \alpha_1 \in W_1 \text{ and } \alpha_2 \in W_2\}$ is a subspace of $\mathbf{V}$.
   (c) Let A be a basis for $W_1 \cap W_2$, let $A \cup B$ be a basis for W_1, and let $A \cup C$ be a basis for W_2. Prove that $A \cup B \cup C$ is a basis for the subspace of part (b).
   (d) Express the dimension of the subspace of part (b) in terms of the dimensions of W_1, W_2, and $W_1 \cap W_2$.

   Note: The subspace of part (b) is called the *sum* of W_1 and W_2, and is denoted by $W_1 + W_2$.

7.3 CHANGE OF BASIS

Here, we concentrate on the role of a basis in reducing vectors to tuples. For simplicity, we consider only finite-dimensional subspaces. Now, the vectors of an n-dimensional subspace W may not be n-tuples; nonetheless, it is possible to associate an n-tuple of scalars with each member of W. The idea is to choose a basis for W, say $\{\alpha_1, \ldots, \alpha_n\}$; next, we *order* this set, so obtaining an *ordered basis*, say $(\alpha_1, \ldots, \alpha_n)$ (of course, there are $n!$ ordered bases arising from $\{\alpha_1, \ldots, \alpha_n\}$). As we shall see in this section, it is important that we distinguish between the basis and an ordered basis constructed from it. Now, each member of W is a linear combination of $\{\alpha_1, \ldots, \alpha_n\}$; let us show that the scalars involved in a linear combination are unique.

Theorem 7.3.1: Let $(\alpha_1, \ldots, \alpha_n)$ be any ordered basis for W, and let $\gamma \in W$; then there is a unique n-vector $(k_1, \ldots, k_n)$ such that $\gamma = k_1 \alpha_1 + \cdots + k_n \alpha_n$.

Proof: By assumption there exists an ordered n-tuple of real numbers, say $(k_1, \ldots, k_n)$, such that $\gamma = k_1 \alpha_1 + \cdots + k_n \alpha_n$. Suppose that there is another member of R_n, say $(t_1, \ldots, t_n)$, such that $\gamma = t_1 \alpha_1 + \cdots + t_n \alpha_n$; then $k_1 \alpha_1 + \cdots + k_n \alpha_n = t_1 \alpha_1 + \cdots + t_n \alpha_n$, so $(k_1 - t_1)\alpha_1 + \cdots + (k_n - t_n)\alpha_n = \mathbf{0}$. But $\{\alpha_1, \ldots, \alpha_n\}$ is linearly independent; therefore $k_1 - t_1 = 0, \ldots, k_n - t_n = 0$. This establishes our theorem.

In one sense, an ordered basis imposes a coordinate system on the subspace involved. In n-dimensional geometry a coordinate system is used to associate a member of R_n with each point of the geometry (we avoided this step by *defining* points to be n-tuples); just so, an ordered basis associates an n-tuple of scalars with each member of the subspace, indeed the terms of the n-tuple associated with a vector γ are sometimes called the *coordinates* of γ with respect to the ordered basis. The n-tuple associated with γ is said to be the *matrix* of γ with respect to the ordered basis.

Example 1: Consider $\{(a_1, a_2, a_3, 0) \mid (a_1, a_2, a_3) \in R_3\}$, a subspace of R_4. Clearly $((1, 0, 0, 0), (0, 1, 0, 0), (0, 0, 1, 0))$, is an ordered basis for this subspace. Thus, if γ is a member of our subspace and $\gamma = (a_1, a_2, a_3, 0)$, then $\gamma = a_1(1, 0, 0, 0) + a_2(0, 1, 0, 0) + a_3(0, 0, 1, 0)$. Therefore, the 3-tuple (a_1, a_2, a_3) is the matrix of $(a_1, a_2, a_3, 0)$ with respect to the given ordered basis.

Let us formalize this important concept.

Definition 7.3.1: Let $\mathcal{B} = (\beta_1, \ldots, \beta_n)$ be an ordered basis for a subspace W, and let $\gamma \in W$. Then $(k_1, \ldots, k_n)$ is said to be the *matrix of γ with respect to $\mathcal{B}$* if and only if $\gamma = \sum_{i=1}^{n} k_i \beta_i$. The matrix of γ with respect to $\mathcal{B}$ is denoted by $[\gamma]_{\mathcal{B}}$.

Consider the following example.

Example 2: Let $W = L\{(2, 0, -1), (1, 2, 0)\}$; clearly $\mathcal{B} = ((2, 0, -1), (1, 2, 0))$ is an ordered basis for W. Now, $(8, 4, -3) \in W$; indeed

$$(8, 4, -3) = 3(2, 0, -1) + 2(1, 2, 0) .$$

So $[(8, 4, -3)]_{\mathcal{B}} = (3, 2)$. Similarly, $(1, -14, -4) \in W$ since

$$(1, -14, -4) = 4(2, 0, -1) + -7(1, 2, 0) .$$

So $[(1, -14, -4)]_{\mathcal{B}} = (4, -7)$.

Here are two obvious properties of our concept.

Lemma 7.3.1: Let $\mathfrak{B}$ be any ordered basis for a finite-dimensional subspace W, and let $\{\alpha, \gamma\} \subset W$; then $[\alpha + \gamma]_\mathfrak{B} = [\alpha]_\mathfrak{B} + [\gamma]_\mathfrak{B}$.

Lemma 7.3.2: Let $\mathfrak{B}$ be any ordered basis for a finite-dimensional subspace W, let $\alpha \in W$, and let k be any scalar. Then $[k\alpha]_\mathfrak{B} = k\,[\alpha]_\mathfrak{B}$.

Using these lemmas and mathematical induction we easily establish the following useful fact.

Lemma 7.3.3: Let $\mathfrak{B}$ be any ordered basis for a finite-dimensional subspace W, let $\gamma_i \in W$, and let k_i be a scalar, $i = 1, \ldots, s$. Then $[k_1 \gamma_1 + \cdots + k_s \gamma_s]_\mathfrak{B} = k_1 [\gamma_1]_\mathfrak{B} + \cdots + k_s [\gamma_s]_\mathfrak{B}$.

The main goal of this section is to determine the relationship between $[\gamma]_\mathfrak{a}$ and $[\gamma]_\mathfrak{B}$ where $\mathfrak{a}$ and $\mathfrak{B}$ are ordered bases for the subspace W involved and $\gamma \in W$. In other words, we want to find out what happens to the matrix of a vector when the ordered basis involved is changed.

Theorem 7.3.2: Let $\mathfrak{a}$ and $\mathfrak{B} = (\beta_1, \ldots, \beta_n)$ be ordered bases for an n-dimensional subspace W, and let M be the $n \times n$ matrix whose ith row vector is $[\beta_i]_\mathfrak{a}$, $i = 1, \ldots, n$. Then $[\gamma]_\mathfrak{a} = [\gamma]_\mathfrak{B} M$ whenever $\gamma \in W$.

Proof: Let $\gamma \in W$ and let $[\gamma]_\mathfrak{B} = (b_1, \ldots, b_n)$; so $\gamma = b_1\beta_1 + \cdots + b_n\beta_n$. Now, $[\gamma]_\mathfrak{B} M$ is a matrix with one row; hence, we can interpret $[\gamma]_\mathfrak{B} M$ as an n-vector. By Definition 3.3.3

$$[\gamma]_\mathfrak{B} M = b_1 M_1 + \cdots + b_n M_n = b_1 [\beta_1]_\mathfrak{a} + \cdots + b_n [\beta_n]_\mathfrak{a}$$

$$= [b_1 \beta_1 + \cdots + b_n \beta_n]_\mathfrak{a} \qquad \text{by Lemma 7.3.3 .}$$

The content of Theorem 7.3.2 is clarified by introducing the notion of the *matrix of an ordered basis* with respect to a given ordered basis.

Definition 7.3.2: Let $\mathfrak{a}$ and $\mathfrak{B} = (\beta_1, \ldots, \beta_n)$ be ordered bases for an n-dimensional subspace W. The $n \times n$ matrix whose ith row vector is $[\beta_i]_\mathfrak{a}$, $i = 1, \ldots, n$, is said to be the *matrix of $\mathfrak{B}$ with respect to $\mathfrak{a}$*, and is denoted by $[\mathfrak{B}]_\mathfrak{a}$. If $\mathfrak{a} = (\epsilon_1, \ldots, \epsilon_n)$ then $[\mathfrak{B}]_\mathfrak{a}$ is called the *matrix of $\mathfrak{B}$* and is denoted by $[\mathfrak{B}]$.

We can now formulate Theorem 7.3.2 as follows.

Theorem 7.3.2: Let $\mathfrak{a}$ and $\mathfrak{B}$ be any ordered bases for a finite-dimensional subspace W. Then $[\gamma]_\mathfrak{a} = [\gamma]_\mathfrak{B} [\mathfrak{B}]_\mathfrak{a}$ whenever $\gamma \in W$.

We now illustrate Definition 7.3.2.

Example 3: Consider the vector space $\Re_3$. Let $\mathcal{Q} = ((2, 0, 1), (1, 1, 0),$ $(1, 1, 1))$ and let $\mathcal{B} = ((-1, -3, -2), (7, 7, 5), (4, 4, 4))$. Determine $[\mathcal{B}]_{\mathcal{Q}}$.

Solution: First, we point out that $\mathcal{Q}$ and $\mathcal{B}$ are ordered bases for $\Re_3$. Now, the row vectors of $[\mathcal{B}]_{\mathcal{Q}}$ are $[(-1, -3, -2)]_{\mathcal{Q}}$, $[(7, 7, 5)]_{\mathcal{Q}}$, and $[(4, 4, 4)]_{\mathcal{Q}}$. In particular, (x_1, x_2, x_3) is the first row vector of $[\mathcal{B}]_{\mathcal{Q}}$ provided that $x_1(2, 0, 1)$ $+ x_2(1, 1, 0) + x_3(1, 1, 1) = (-1, -3, -2)$, i.e.,

$$\begin{cases} 2x_1 + x_2 + x_3 = -1 \\ \quad\quad x_2 + x_3 = -3 \\ x_1 \quad\quad + x_3 = -2 \end{cases}.$$

Solving this linear system we find that $x_1 = 1$, $x_2 = 0$, and $x_3 = -3$; so $(1, 0, -3)$ is the first row vector of $[\mathcal{B}]_{\mathcal{Q}}$. Similarly, we find that $(7, 7, 5) = 2(1, 1, 0)$ $+ 5(1, 1, 1)$ and that $(4, 4, 4) = 4(1, 1, 1)$. Thus $[(7, 7, 5)]_{\mathcal{Q}} = (0, 2, 5)$ and $[(4, 4, 4)]_{\mathcal{Q}} = (0, 0, 4)$. We conclude that

$$[\mathcal{B}]_{\mathcal{Q}} = \begin{pmatrix} 1 & 0 & -3 \\ 0 & 2 & 5 \\ 0 & 0 & 4 \end{pmatrix}.$$

Next, we bring out a useful relationship between the matrices $[\mathcal{Q}]_{\mathcal{B}}$ and $[\mathcal{B}]_{\mathcal{Q}}$.

Lemma 7.3.4: Let $\mathcal{Q}$ and $\mathcal{B}$ be ordered bases for an n-dimensional subspace W. Then $[\mathcal{Q}]_{\mathcal{B}} [\mathcal{B}]_{\mathcal{Q}} = I_n$.

Proof: Let $\mathcal{Q} = (\alpha_1, \ldots, \alpha_n)$. Consider the ith row vector of $[\mathcal{Q}]_{\mathcal{B}}[\mathcal{B}]_{\mathcal{Q}}$:

$$([\mathcal{Q}]_{\mathcal{B}} [\mathcal{B}]_{\mathcal{Q}})_i = [\alpha_i]_{\mathcal{B}} [\mathcal{B}]_{\mathcal{Q}} \quad\quad \text{by Lemma 3.3.3}$$

$$= [\alpha_i]_{\mathcal{Q}} \quad\quad\quad\quad\quad \text{by Theorem 7.3.2}$$

$$= \epsilon_i.$$

So $[\mathcal{Q}]_{\mathcal{B}} [\mathcal{B}]_{\mathcal{Q}} = I_n$.

This result is useful because it enables us to compute $[\mathcal{B}]_{\mathcal{Q}}$ given $[\mathcal{Q}]_{\mathcal{B}}$.

Theorem 7.3.3: Let $\mathcal{Q}$ and $\mathcal{B}$ be ordered bases for a finite-dimensional subspace. Then $[\mathcal{B}]_{\mathcal{Q}}$ is the inverse of $[\mathcal{Q}]_{\mathcal{B}}$.

We point out that $[\mathcal{Q}]_{\mathcal{B}}$ is nonsingular whenever $\mathcal{Q}$ and $\mathcal{B}$ are ordered bases for a finite-dimensional subspace.

Let us illustrate Theorem 7.3.3.

Example 4: Determine $[\mathcal{Q}]_{\mathcal{B}}$ where $\mathcal{Q}$ and $\mathcal{B}$ are the ordered bases for $\Re_3$ given in Example 3.

Solution: As we saw in Example 3, $[\mathscr{B}]_\alpha = \begin{pmatrix} 1 & 0 & -3 \\ 0 & 2 & 5 \\ 0 & 0 & 4 \end{pmatrix}$. Now, the inverse of this matrix is $\frac{1}{8}\begin{pmatrix} 8 & 0 & 6 \\ 0 & 4 & -5 \\ 0 & 0 & 2 \end{pmatrix}$. Therefore, by Theorem 7.3.3, $[\alpha]_\mathscr{B} = \frac{1}{8}\begin{pmatrix} 8 & 0 & 6 \\ 0 & 4 & -5 \\ 0 & 0 & 2 \end{pmatrix}$.

Let us prove, next, that given any ordered basis α for an n-dimensional subspace W and given any nonsingular $n \times n$ matrix M, there is a unique ordered basis for W, say $\mathscr{B}$, such that $[\mathscr{B}]_\alpha = M$.

Theorem 7.3.4: Let α be an ordered basis for an n-dimensional subspace W and let M be any nonsingular $n \times n$ matrix. Then there is a unique ordered basis for W, say $\mathscr{B}$, such that $[\mathscr{B}]_\alpha = M$.

Proof: For each i, let β_i be the unique member of W such that $[\beta_i]_\alpha = M_i$. In view of Definition 7.3.2, if $\mathscr{B}$ is an ordered basis for W such that $[\mathscr{B}]_\alpha = M$, then $\mathscr{B} = (\beta_1, \ldots, \beta_n)$. We claim that $(\beta_1, \ldots, \beta_n)$ is an ordered basis for W. To this purpose we must prove that $\{\beta_1, \ldots, \beta_n\}$ is linearly independent. Let $k_1, \ldots, k_n$ be scalars such that $k_1\beta_1 + \cdots + k_n\beta_n = 0$. Now, $[0]_\alpha = 0$; therefore

$$0 = [k_1\beta_1 + \cdots + k_n\beta_n]_\alpha$$

$$= k_1 [\beta_1]_\alpha + \cdots + k_n [\beta_n]_\alpha \qquad \text{by Lemma 7.3.3}$$

$$= k_1 M_1 + \cdots + k_n M_n .$$

But M is nonsingular, so $\{M_1, \ldots, M_n\}$ has n members and is linearly independent; hence $k_i = 0$, $i = 1, \ldots, n$. We conclude that $\{\beta_1, \ldots, \beta_n\}$ is linearly independent. This establishes our theorem.

Corollary 7.3.1: Let α be an ordered basis for an n-dimensional subspace W and let M be any nonsingular $n \times n$ matrix. Then there is a unique ordered basis for W, say $\mathscr{B}$, such that $[\alpha]_\mathscr{B} = M$.

Proof: First we point out that M^{-1} is nonsingular. Now, by Theorem 7.3.4, there is a unique ordered basis for W, say $\mathscr{B}$, such that $[\mathscr{B}]_\alpha = M^{-1}$. So, by Theorem 7.3.3, $[\alpha]_\mathscr{B} = M$.

We now present some examples that demonstrate why we are interested in changing a basis for a subspace. In elementary analytic geometry we are accustomed to describe or characterize a set of vectors by stating a condition on the terms of a vector which is satisfied by each member of the set, and only by the members of the set. For example, $\mathcal{P} = \{(x, y, z) \mid 2x - y + z = 6\}$ is the set of vectors such that $(x, y, z) \in \mathcal{P}$ if and only if $2x - y + z = 6$. Let us see if we can simplify the relationship between the terms of a member of this set, by introducing a suitable basis for $\mathscr{R}_3$, say $\mathscr{B}$, and characterizing the statement $\alpha \in \mathcal{P}$ by means of a condition on the terms of $[\alpha]_\mathscr{B}$.

Example 5:   Simplify $\mathcal{P} = \{(x, y, z) \mid 2x - y + z = 6\}$.

Solution: Notice that $\mathcal{P} \subset \mathcal{R}_3$. By Theorem 7.3.4 there is a unique ordered basis for $\mathcal{R}_3$, say $\mathcal{B}$, such that $[\mathcal{B}] = \begin{pmatrix} 2 & -1 & 1 \\ 0 & 1 & 1 \\ 2 & 2 & -2 \end{pmatrix}$; indeed $\mathcal{B} = ((2, -1, 1),$

$(0, 1, 1), (2, 2, -2))$. Notice that $[\mathcal{B}]_1$ is a direction of a normal to $\mathcal{P}$ and that $[\mathcal{B}]_2$ and $[\mathcal{B}]_3$ are orthogonal to $[\mathcal{B}]_1$. Let $\alpha = (x, y, z)$ and let $[\alpha]_\mathcal{B} = (x', y', z')$; by Theorem 7.3.2, $[\alpha] = [\alpha]_\mathcal{B}[\mathcal{B}]$, i.e.

$$\begin{cases} x = 2x' \quad\quad\ + 2z' \\ y = -x' + y' + 2z' \\ z = \quad x' + y' - 2z' \end{cases}.$$

So

$$2x - y + z = 2(2x' + 2z') - (-x' + y' + 2z') + (x' + y' - 2z') = 6x'.$$

Thus

$$\mathcal{P} = \{(x, y, z) \mid 2x - y + z = 6\}$$

$$= \{\alpha \mid \text{there are scalars } x', y', \text{ and } z' \text{ such that}$$
$$[\alpha]_\mathcal{B} = (x', y', z') \text{ and } x' = 1\}$$

$$= \{\alpha \mid 1 \text{ is the first term of } [\alpha]_\mathcal{B}\}.$$

Notice that expressing $\mathcal{P}$ in terms of $\mathcal{B}$ amounts to setting up a coordinate system for which the direction and scale of each coordinate axis is given by a term of $\mathcal{B}$.

Here is another example of this sort.

Example 6:   Simplify $\{(x, y, z) \mid 34x^2 + y^2 + 41z^2 - 24zx - 36x + 48z = 1000 \text{ and } 3x - 4z = 25\}$.

Solution: Let $\mathcal{B}$ be the ordered basis for R_3 with matrix $\begin{pmatrix} 4 & 0 & 3 \\ 0 & 1 & 0 \\ 3 & 0 & -4 \end{pmatrix}$. Let $\alpha \in R_3$; by Theorem 7.3.2, if $\alpha = (x, y, z)$ and $[\alpha]_\mathcal{B} = (x', y', z')$, then

(3)
$$\begin{cases} x = 4x' + 3z' \\ y = y' \\ z = 3x' - 4z' \end{cases}.$$

So $3x - 4z = 3(4x' + 3z') - 4(3x' - 4z') = 25z'$. This means that if α is a member of the given set, then the third term of $[\alpha]_\mathcal{B}$ is 1. Let $\alpha = (x, y, z)$ be a member of our set; then, from (3),

$$1000 = 34x^2 + y^2 + 41z^2 - 24zx - 36x + 48z$$

$$= 34(4x' + 3)^2 + y'^2 + 41(3x' - 4)^2 - 24(3x' - 4)(4x' + 3)$$
$$- 36(4x' + 3) + 48(3x' - 4)$$

$$= 625x'^2 + y'^2 + 950.$$

We conclude that the given set is $\{\alpha \mid$ there are scalars x' and y' such that $[\alpha]_\mathcal{B} = (x', y', 1)$ and $625x'^2 + y'^2 = 50\}$. For completeness, we point out that $\mathcal{B} = ((4, 0, 3), (0, 1, 0), (3, 0, -4))$.

We now introduce the *Kronecker delta*, a useful mapping of $N \times N$ into $\{0, 1\}$ which is denoted by δ. It is customary to abbreviate $\delta(i, j)$ by writing δ_{ij}.

Definition 7.3.3:   Let $(i, j) \in N \times N$; then $\delta_{ij} = \begin{cases} 1 & \text{if } i = j \\ 0 & \text{if } i \neq j \end{cases}$.

For example, $\delta_{25} = 0$ and $\delta_{55} = 1$.

Recall that a subset of R_n, say A, is orthogonal if $\alpha \cdot \beta = 0$ whenever α and β are distinct members of A. Now, an orthogonal set B is said to be *orthonormal* if and only if $\|\alpha\| = 1$ whenever $\alpha \in B$. In Chapter 3 (see Theorem 3.1.6) we showed that each nontrivial subspace of $\mathcal{R}_n$ has an orthogonal basis. Now, it is easy to construct an orthonormal basis from an orthogonal basis; simply divide each member of the orthogonal basis by its length. This proves that $\mathcal{R}_n$ has an orthonormal basis whenever $n \in N$. We now present some properties of orthonormal bases.

Lemma 7.3.5:   Let $\mathcal{B}$ be any ordered orthonormal basis for $\mathcal{R}_n$; then $[\mathcal{B}]^{-1} = [\mathcal{B}]^t$.

Proof: Let $\mathcal{B} = (\beta_1, \ldots, \beta_n)$; then $\beta_i \cdot \beta_j = \delta_{ij}$ for each i and j. Thus $[\mathcal{B}][\mathcal{B}]^t = I_n$; so $[\mathcal{B}]^t = [\mathcal{B}]^{-1}$.

Lemma 7.3.6:   Let $\mathcal{B}$ be an ordered orthonormal basis for $\mathcal{R}_n$ and let $M = [\mathcal{B}]$. Then $({}_1M, \ldots, {}_nM)$ is an ordered orthonormal basis for $\mathcal{R}_n$.

Proof: By Lemma 7.3.5, $M \cdot M^t = I_n$; therefore, by Theorem 3.4.4, $M^t \cdot M = I_n$. Thus, for each i and j, ${}_iM \cdot {}_jM = \delta_{ij}$. But $\{{}_1M, \ldots, {}_nM\}$ has n members and is linearly independent since M is nonsingular. We conclude that $({}_1M, \ldots, {}_nM)$ is an ordered orthonormal basis for $\mathcal{R}_n$.

Lemma 7.3.7:   Let $\mathcal{B}$ be any ordered orthonormal basis for $\mathcal{R}_n$. Then $[\gamma]_\mathcal{B} = \gamma[\mathcal{B}]^t$ whenever $\gamma \in R_n$.

Proof: Let $\mathcal{C} = (\epsilon_1, \ldots, \epsilon_n)$ and let $\gamma \in R_n$. Now,

$$[\gamma]_\mathcal{B} = [\gamma]_\mathcal{C}[\mathcal{C}]_\mathcal{B} \qquad \text{by Theorem 7.3.2}$$
$$= \gamma[\mathcal{B}]^{-1} \qquad \text{by Theorem 7.3.3}$$
$$= \gamma[\mathcal{B}]^t \qquad \text{by Lemma 7.3.5 .}$$

Our next theorem is particularly important because of its application to geometry.

Theorem 7.3.5: Let M be any nonsingular $n \times n$ matrix such that $M^{-1} = M^t$. Then there is a unique ordered orthonormal basis for $\mathcal{R}_n$, say $\mathcal{B}$, such that $[\gamma]_\mathcal{B} = \gamma M$ whenever $\gamma \in R_n$; moreover, $\mathcal{B} = ({}_1M, \ldots, {}_nM)$.

Proof: Let $\mathcal{Q} = (\epsilon_1, \ldots, \epsilon_n)$. By Corollary 7.3.1 there is a unique ordered basis for $\mathcal{R}_n$, say $\mathcal{B}$, such that $[\mathcal{Q}]_\mathcal{B} = M$. Considering the proof of Corollary 7.3.1 we see that $[\mathcal{B}] = M^{-1} = M^t$; so $\mathcal{B} = ({}_1M, \ldots, {}_nM)$. Also

$$[\gamma]_\mathcal{B} = [\gamma]_\mathcal{Q}[\mathcal{Q}]_\mathcal{B} \qquad \text{by Theorem 7.3.2}$$

$$= \gamma M$$

whenever $\gamma \in R_n$. Since $M^{-1} = M^t$ we conclude that $\mathcal{B}$ is orthonormal. This completes our proof.

In Chapter 9 we present the notion of a *linear transformation* on a vector space. In view of Lemmas 7.3.1 and 7.3.2 we can associate a linear transformation with each ordered basis for the vector space. In this sense, linear transformations generalize the ideas of this section. This is particularly valuable because the algebra of linear transformations is highly developed (indeed, the algebra of linear transformations on a finite-dimensional vector space is precisely the algebra of $m \times n$ matrices). There is a nice interaction between the two concepts which centers around Theorem 7.3.2; so we can use the ideas of this section to develop our ideas about linear transformations, a generalization of the main concepts of this section.

EXERCISES

1. Let $\mathcal{B} = ((2, 0, 1), (1, 1, -1), (0, 0, 1))$.

   (a) Show that $\mathcal{B}$ is an ordered basis for $\mathcal{R}_3$.
   (b) Compute $[(5, -1, 3)]_\mathcal{B}$.

2. Let $W = \{(a, b, c, a) \mid (a, b, c) \in R_3\}$.

   (a) Show that W is a subspace of $\mathcal{R}_4$.
   (b) Determine the dimension of W.
   (c) Find an ordered basis $\mathcal{B}$ for W.
   (d) Compute $[(3, -1, 2, 3)]_\mathcal{B}$ where $\mathcal{B}$ is your answer to part (c).

3. Let $\mathcal{Q}$ be an ordered basis for $\mathcal{R}_n$; determine $[\mathcal{Q}]_\mathcal{Q}$.

4. Let $\mathcal{Q} = ((2, 0, -1), (1, 1, 0), (0, -1, 1))$ and let $\mathcal{B} = ((0, 1, 3), (1, 1, -1), (0, 5, -2))$.

   (a) Show that $\mathcal{Q}$ and $\mathcal{B}$ are ordered bases for $\mathcal{R}_3$.
   (b) Determine $[\mathcal{B}]_\mathcal{Q}$ directly from Definition 7.3.2.
   (c) Determine $[\mathcal{Q}]_\mathcal{B}$ directly from Definition 7.3.2.
   (d) Compute $[\mathcal{Q}]_\mathcal{B}[\mathcal{B}]_\mathcal{Q}$.

5. Let $\alpha = (\alpha_1, \alpha_2, \alpha_3, \alpha_4)$ and $\mathcal{B} = (\beta_1, \beta_2, \beta_3, \beta_4)$ be ordered bases for $\mathcal{R}_4$ where $\beta_1 = \alpha_1 + \alpha_4$, $\beta_2 = 2\alpha_1 - \alpha_2 + \alpha_3$, $\beta_3 = \alpha_2 + 2\alpha_3$, and $\beta_4 = \alpha_3 - \alpha_4$.

   (a) Compute $[\gamma]_\alpha$, given that $[\gamma]_\mathcal{B} = (4, -1, 0, 3)$.
   (b) Compute $[\gamma]_\alpha$, given that $[\gamma]_\mathcal{B} = (0, 1, -1, 3)$.
   (c) Determine $[\alpha]_\mathcal{B}$.
   (d) Compute $[\gamma]_\mathcal{B}$, given that $[\gamma]_\alpha = (0, 1, 1, 0)$.

6. Let α and $\mathcal{B}$ be ordered bases for $\mathcal{R}_4$ such that

$$[\alpha]_\mathcal{B} = \begin{pmatrix} 2 & 0 & -1 & 1 \\ 3 & 1 & 2 & 0 \\ 0 & -1 & 1 & 4 \\ 1 & 0 & 0 & -1 \end{pmatrix}.$$

   (a) Determine α, given that $\mathcal{B} = ((1, 0, 1, 1), (-1, 1, 2, 0), (0, 1, 1, 1), (1, 1, 0, 0))$.
   (b) Determine $\mathcal{B}$, given that $\alpha = ((3, 4, -1, 2), (6, 1, 4, -1), (8, 3, -5, 2), (-1, 0, 1, -1))$.

7. Let $\alpha = (\alpha_1, \ldots, \alpha_n)$ be an ordered basis for $\mathcal{R}_n$, and let Π be a permutation of $\{1, \ldots, n\}$. Determine $[\mathcal{B}]_\alpha$ where $\mathcal{B} = (\alpha_{\Pi(1)}, \ldots, \alpha_{\Pi(n)})$.

8. Let α and $\mathcal{B}$ be any ordered bases for a finite-dimensional subspace W and let $\gamma \in W$.

   (a) Prove that $[\gamma]_\alpha = (0, \ldots, 0)$ if and only if $\gamma = \mathbf{0}$, the zero vector of W.
   (b) Prove that $[\gamma]_\alpha = (0, \ldots, 0)$ if and only if $[\gamma]_\mathcal{B} = (0, \ldots, 0)$.
   (c) Is $[0]_\alpha$ necessarily the zero vector of W?

9. Working in the vector space $\mathcal{R}_3$, simplify each of the following:

   (a) $\{(x, y, z) \mid x + y - 2z = 5\}$;
   (b) $\{(x, y, z) \mid x + y - 2z = 5 \text{ and } 2x^2 - y^2 + 3z^2 - 4yz + zx = 10\}$.

10. Working in the vector space $\mathcal{R}_2$, simplify each of the following:

   (a) $\{(x, y) \mid x^2 - y^2 + 23xy = 2\}$;
   (b) $\{(x, y) \mid x^2 + y^2 + 3xy - 1\}$;
   (c) $\{(x, y) \mid 4x^2 - 3y^2 + 24xy - 2x + 3y = 3\}$.

11. Criticize the following "proof" of Lemma 7.3.4.
    Let $\gamma \in W$; now

$$\begin{aligned} [\gamma]_\alpha &= [\gamma]_\mathcal{B}[\mathcal{B}]_\alpha && \text{by Theorem 7.3.2} \\ &= ([\gamma]_\alpha[\alpha]_\mathcal{B})[\mathcal{B}]_\alpha && \text{by Theorem 7.3.2} \\ &= [\gamma]_\alpha([\alpha]_\mathcal{B}[\mathcal{B}]_\alpha) && \text{since matrix multiplication} \\ &&& \text{is associative.} \end{aligned}$$

   Therefore $[\alpha]_\mathcal{B}[\mathcal{B}]_\alpha = I_n$.

12. Prove Corollary 7.3.1 directly, i.e., without using Theorem 7.3.4.

13. Let α be an ordered basis for an n-dimensional subspace W, and let $S \subset W$. Prove that S is linearly independent if and only if $\{[\gamma]_\alpha \mid \gamma \in S\}$ is linearly independent.

14. (a) Let $n \in N$ and let $\mathcal{B}$ be any ordered orthonormal basis for $\mathcal{R}_n$. Prove that $|[\mathcal{B}]|^2 = 1$.

     (b) Let $n \in N$, let W be any nontrivial subspace of $\mathcal{R}_n$, and let α and $\mathcal{B}$ be any ordered orthonormal bases for W. Prove that $|[\mathcal{B}]_\alpha|^2 = 1$.

15. Let α and $\mathcal{B}$ be ordered bases for $\mathcal{R}_n$. Prove that $[\mathcal{B}]_\alpha = [\mathcal{B}][\alpha]^{-1}$.

8

POLYNOMIALS

8.1 VECTOR SPACE OF POLYNOMIALS

We have now acquired a great deal of experience at handling vector spaces in which the vectors are n-tuples of real numbers, where n is a specific natural number. In this section we present an important vector space in which the vectors are the 1-tuple (0) and all tuples of real numbers with nonzero final term. These objects are called *polynomials*. For example, (0), $(1, 0, 3)$, $(0, 1, -1, 0, 0, 0, 5)$, $(0, 0, 0, 0, 1)$, $(0, 5)$, (-3), $(.5, -\sqrt{2})$, $(0, \pi)$, $(1, 1, 1, 1)$ are polynomials, whereas none of $(1, 0, 3, -2, 0)$, $(0, 0, 0)$, $(1, 0)$ is a polynomial.

Our goal is to construct a vector space in which the vectors are the objects described above. In carrying out our construction it is not necessary to tie ourselves to the real number field; we can generalize the situation and achieve much more with the same effort by using any field $\mathfrak{F} = (F, +, \cdot, 0, 1)$ in place of the real number field. Any member of F is called a *scalar*. Consider (0) and each tuple of scalars whose final term is not 0 (remember that 0 is the additive identity of the field $\mathfrak{F}$, i.e., its fourth term); each of these objects is said to be a *polynomial over F*. To construct our vector space we must introduce scalar multiplication and vector addition; as usual, these algebraic operations will be defined in terms of the operations of addition and multiplication of the field $\mathfrak{F}$.

We point out that the polynomial $(a_0, a_1, \ldots, a_n)$ can be thought of in terms of the expression $a_0 + a_1x + \cdots + a_nx^n$; indeed, you may be firmly convinced that this expression is the polynomial. We shall soon establish the connection between tuples and expressions of this sort; in fact, by assigning a meaning to the x^m and to the $+$ that occur in this expression, we shall prove that $(a_0, a_1, \ldots, a_n) = a_0 + a_1x + \cdots + a_nx^n$.

Unfortunately, there is a basic distinction between polynomials which complicates matters; i.e., some polynomials are triples, some are 7-tuples, and some are 10^6-tuples. To avoid this difficulty we shall adopt a notation for polynomials which presents all polynomials in a uniform manner. Now, the polynomial of our intuition, $a_0 + a_1 x + \cdots + a_n x^n$, can be regarded as $a_0 + a_1 x + \cdots + a_n x^n + 0 x^{n+1} + \cdots + 0 x^{n+t} + \cdots$, an infinite sum which involves only a finite number of nonzero coefficients. This infinite expression can be represented by the infinite sequence $(a_0, a_1, \ldots, a_n, 0, \ldots, 0, \ldots)$, a very special kind of infinite sequence with the property that only a finite number of its terms are nonzero. Clearly, there is a one-one correspondence between the set of all polynomials and the set of all sequences which have only a finite number of nonzero terms. It is not unreasonable, then, to identify a given polynomial with the corresponding sequence. Let us agree, here and now, to *denote* any polynomial by the corresponding sequence. For example, the polynomial $(3, -2, 4)$ and the sequence $(3, -2, 4, 0, 0, \ldots, 0, \ldots)$ correspond, so we write $(3, -2, 4) = (3, -2, 4, 0, 0, \ldots, 0, \ldots)$; of course, this means that $(3, 2, 4, 0, 0, \ldots, 0, \ldots)$ is a name for $(3, -2, 4)$. Also, the polynomial (0) and the sequence $(0, 0, \ldots, 0, \ldots)$ correspond, so we write $(0) = (0, 0, \ldots, 0, \ldots)$; again, this means that $(0, 0, \ldots, 0, \ldots)$ is a name for (0). Recall that a sequence is a mapping of N into F, and that the sequence that associates a_n with n whenever $n \in N$ is denoted by (a_n) (actually, a_n is a prescription for obtaining the scalar that this mapping associates with the natural number n, whenever $n \in N$). We propose to define scalar multiplication and vector addition in terms of corresponding operations on sequences. Let (a_n) and (b_n) be any polynomials over F, and let $k \in F$; then we say that $k(a_n)$ denotes (ka_n) and that $(a_n) + (b_n)$ denotes $(a_n + b_n)$.

The following examples are intended to clarify the above definition of scalar multiplication and vector addition.

Example 1:   Determine $3(-2, 0, 5, 1)$.

Solution: First, we represent the given polynomial by a sequence: $(-2, 0, 5, 1) = (-2, 0, 5, 1, 0, 0, \ldots, 0, \ldots)$. By definition,

$$3(-2, 0, 5, 1) = 3(-2, 0, 5, 1, 0, 0, \ldots, 0, \ldots)$$
$$= (-6, 0, 15, 3, 0, 0, \ldots, 0, \ldots)$$
$$= (-6, 0, 15, 3) .$$

Example 2:   Determine $(4, 2) + (-2, 0, 5, 1)$.

Solution: Now, $(4, 2) = (4, 2, 0, \ldots, 0, \ldots)$

and $(-2, 0, 5, 1) = (-2, 0, 5, 1, 0, \ldots, 0, \ldots)$

So $(4, 2) + (-2, 0, 5, 1) = (4, 2, 0, \ldots, 0, \ldots)$
$$+ (-2, 0, 5, 1, 0, \ldots, 0, \ldots)$$
$$= (2, 2, 5, 1, 0, \ldots, 0, \ldots)$$
$$= (2, 2, 5, 1) .$$

We point out that the vector sum of two n-tuples is not necessarily an n-tuple.

Example 3: Determine $(1, 3, -5, -1) + (-2, 0, 5, 1)$.

Solution: Clearly,

$$(1, 3, -5, -1) + (-2, 0, 5, 1) = (1, 3, -5, -1, 0, \ldots, 0, \ldots)$$
$$+ (-2, 0, 5, 1, 0, \ldots, 0, \ldots)$$
$$= (-1, 3, 0, 0, \ldots, 0, \ldots)$$
$$= (-1, 3).$$

We now introduce some useful terminology and notation. The set of all polynomials over F is customarily denoted by $F[x]$; this convention contributes to the mystique of x, perhaps $\mathcal{P}[F]$ is a more appropriate name for the set of all polynomials over F. Considering the definition of polynomial addition, it is clear that (0) is an additive identity; so we shall denote this particular polynomial by 0. Accordingly, (0) is called the *zero* polynomial; any other polynomial is said to be a *nonzero* polynomial. With each nonzero polynomial we shall associate a nonnegative integer called its *degree*. Let $(a_0, a_1, \ldots, a_t)$ be any polynomial where $a_t \neq 0$; we shall say that t is the *degree* of this polynomial and we shall write $\deg(a_0, a_1, \ldots, a_t) = t$. In particular, if $a \neq 0$ then $\deg(a) = 0$ and $\deg(b, a) = 1$. We point out that the zero polynomial has no degree.

We are now ready to establish some facts.

Theorem 8.1.1: Let $\mathfrak{F}$ be any field; then $(F[x], +, 0)$ is an abelian group.

Proof: Here, $+$ is the binary operation on $F[x]$ introduced above, and 0 denotes the zero polynomial (0). It is easy to verify that the algebraic system $(F[x], +, 0)$ is an abelian group. The details are left as an exercise.

Theorem 8.1.2: Let $\mathfrak{F}$ be any field, let $\mathcal{U} = (F[x], +, 0)$, and let $\circ$ denote the mapping of $F \times F[x]$ into $F[x]$ introduced above; then $(\mathfrak{F}, \mathcal{U}, \circ)$ is a vector space.

Proof: The algebraic system $(\mathfrak{F}, \mathcal{U}, \circ)$ satisfies the conditions of Definition 7.1.1; so this algebraic system is a vector space.

Since $(F[x], +, 0)$ is a group, it is natural to introduce the usual unary operation $-$ (inverse of), and the usual binary operation $-$ (subtraction). So $-q$ denotes the polynomial r such that $q + r = 0$, and $p - q$ denotes the polynomial $p + (-q)$. In particular, let us consider polynomials over R. Then $-(2, 0, -1) = (-2, 0, 1)$ and $(3, 2) - (2, 0, -1) = (3, 2) + (-2, 0, 1) = (1, 2, 1)$.

EXERCISES

1. Simplify the following polynomials over R.

   (a) $(0, 1) + (2, 0, -3)$
   (b) $(1, 2) + (3, -2)$
   (c) $5(0, 1, -1)$
   (d) $(1, 2, -3) + (-1, -2, 3)$
   (e) $(1, 2, -3) - (-1, -2, 3)$.

2. Prove Theorem 8.1.1.

3. Consider the field $(F, +, \cdot, 0, 1)$ where $F = \{0, 1\}$, $+ = \{(0, 0, 0),$ $(0, 1, 1), (1, 0, 1), (1, 1, 0)\}$, and $\cdot = \{(0, 0, 0), (0, 1, 0),$ $(1, 0, 0), (1, 1, 1)\}$.

   (a) Exhibit all members of $F[x]$ which have degree two.
   (b) Compute $(1, 1, 0, 1) + (1, 1)$.
   (c) Compute $(1, 0, 0, 1) + (1, 1, 0, 1)$.
   (d) Compute $(0, 1, 0, 1, 1) + (1, 0, 0, 1, 1)$.
   (e) Compute $-(0, 1, 1)$.
   (f) Compute $(1, 1) - (0, 1, 1)$.
   (g) Compute $(0, 0, 1) - (0, 1)$.

4. Prove Theorem 8.1.2.

5. Let p and q be any nonzero polynomials; show that $p + q = 0$ or else $\deg(p + q)$ $\leq \max\{\deg p, \deg q\}$.

6. Consider the vector space V of Theorem 8.1.2.

   (a) Prove that $\{(1), (0, 1), (0, 0, 1), (0, 0, 0, 1), (0, 0, 0, 0, 1)\}$ is linearly independent.
   (b) Let $t \in N$; prove that $\{(1), (0, 1), (0, 0, 1), \ldots, \underbrace{(0, \ldots, 0, 1)}_{t0\text{'s}}\}$

   is linearly independent.
   (c) Show that V has infinite dimension.
   (d) Exhibit a basis for V.

8.2 RING OF POLYNOMIALS

In this section we demonstrate that the algebraic system $(F[x], +, 0)$ of Theorem 8.1.1 can be extended to a commutative ring with identity. To this purpose we must introduce a second binary operation on $F[x]$. Let $(a_1, \ldots, a_s)$ and $(b_1, \ldots, b_t)$ be any polynomials over F; these polynomials lead us to a polynomial by first forming the $s \times t$ matrix P such that $P_i = a_i(b_1, \ldots, b_t)$, $i = 1, \ldots, s$. The idea is to take subtotals of the entries of P, so that products $a_i b_j$ and $a_u b_v$ appear in the same subtotal if and only if $i + j = u + v$. These subtotals, starting with the subtotal $a_1 b_1$, will be the terms of the desired polynomial. An example will clarify our construction.

Example 1: The product of $(3, 5, 2)$ and $(1, -1, 4, -2)$ is found by considering the following array.

	1	-1	4	-2
3	3	-3	12	-6
5	5	-5	20	-10
2	2	-2	8	-4

Taking subtotals as indicated by the dashed lines, we obtain $3, 2, 9, 12, -2, -4$. So the required polynomial is $(3, 2, 9, 12, -2, -4)$.

We now formalize this operation; remember that each polynomial is represented by a sequence possessing only a finite number of nonzero terms. Remember that a sequence is a mapping of N into F, so $(a_n) = (a_1, a_2, a_3, \dots)$.

Definition 8.2.1: Let (a_n) and (b_n) be any polynomials over F; then $(a_n) \cdot (b_n)$ denotes $\left(\sum_{i+j=n+1} a_i b_j \right)$.

We point out that $\left(\sum_{i+j=n+1} a_i b_j \right) = (c_n)$ where $c_n = \sum_{i+j=n+1} a_i b_j$ whenever $n \in N$; so $c_1 = a_1 b_1$, $\quad c_2 = a_1 b_2 + a_2 b_1$, $\quad c_3 = a_1 b_3 + a_2 b_2 + a_3 b_1$, $\quad c_4 = a_1 b_4 + a_2 b_3 + a_3 b_2 + a_4 b_1$, and so on.

Here are two more examples.

Example 2: Compute $(a_1, a_2) \cdot (b_1, b_2, b_3, b_4)$ where $a_2 \neq 0$ and $b_4 \neq 0$.

Solution: $(a_1, a_2) \cdot (b_1, b_2, b_3, b_4)$

$= (a_1, a_2, 0, 0, 0, \dots) \cdot (b_1, b_2, b_3, b_4, 0, 0, 0, \dots)$

$= (a_1 b_1, a_1 b_2 + a_2 b_1, a_1 b_3 + a_2 b_2, a_1 b_4 + a_2 b_3, a_2 b_4, 0, 0, 0, \dots)$

by Definition 8.2.1

$= (a_1 b_1, a_1 b_2 + a_2 b_1, a_1 b_3 + a_2 b_2, a_1 b_4 + a_2 b_3, a_2 b_4) .$

Example 3: Compute $(2, 1, -3, 4) \cdot (-5, 0, 2, 3, -2, 4)$.

Solution: We use the device of Example 1 to assist in the computations.

	-5	0	2	3	-2	4
2	-10	0	4	6	-4	8
1	-5	0	2	3	-2	4
-3	15	0	-6	-9	6	-12
4	-20	0	8	12	-8	16

So $(2, 1, -3, 4) \cdot (-5, 0, 2, 3, -2, 4) = (-10, -5, 19, -12, -7, 5, 22, -20, 16)$.

A computational error can usually be detected by summing the terms of the product, and summing the entries of the matrix P. These totals must agree.

We now consider some important algebraic properties of polynomial multiplication. Remember that our goal is to prove that $(F[x], +, \cdot, 0)$ is a commutative ring with identity. First, we prove that multiplication is commutative.

Theorem 8.2.1: $p \cdot q = q \cdot p$ whenever p and q are polynomials.

Proof: Let $p = (a_n)$ and let $q = (b_n)$. First we point out that if $p = 0$ or $q = 0$ then $p \cdot q = 0$ and $q \cdot p = 0$. So, we can assume that both p and q are nonzero polynomials; accordingly, let deg $p = s - 1$ and let deg $q = t - 1$. We use the device of Example 1 to establish that $p \cdot q = q \cdot p$ as follows.

	b_1	b_2	$\cdots$	b_t			a_1	a_2	$\cdots$	a_s
a_1						b_1				
a_2						b_2				
$\cdot$						$\cdot$				
$\cdot$			P			$\cdot$			P^t	
$\cdot$						$\cdot$				
a_s						b_t				

Here, P is the $s \times t$ matrix involved in computing $(a_1, \ldots, a_s) \cdot (b_1, \ldots, b_t)$; clearly, its transpose P^t is the matrix involved in computing $(b_1, \ldots, b_t) \cdot (a_1, \ldots, a_s)$. Notice that corresponding subtotals are the same for P and P^t. Thus, $(a_1, \ldots, a_s) \cdot (b_1, \ldots, b_t) = (b_1, \ldots, b_t) \cdot (a_1, \ldots, a_s)$. Alternatively, we can establish this result in a purely formal manner. By Definition 8.2.1,

$$p \cdot q = \left(\sum_{i+j=n+1} a_i b_j \right) = \left(\sum_{i+j=n+1} b_j a_i \right) = \left(\sum_{j+i=n+1} b_j a_i \right) = q \cdot p .$$

Next, we consider the distributive laws.

Theorem 8.2.2: $p \cdot r + q \cdot r = (p + q) \cdot r$ whenever p, q, and r are polynomials.

Proof: First, we point out that if $p = 0$, $q = 0$, or $r = 0$ then $p \cdot r + q \cdot r = (p + q) \cdot r$. So, we assume that p, q, and r are nonzero polynomials. In order to use our matrix approach to multiplication in an uncomplicated manner, we consider the case in which p, q, and r have the same degree. Let $p = (p_1, \ldots, p_n)$, $q = (q_1, \ldots, q_n)$, and let $r = (r_1, \ldots, r_n)$; moreover, let A be the matrix involved in computing $p \cdot r$, let B be the matrix involved in computing $q \cdot r$, and let C be the matrix involved in computing $(p + q) \cdot r$. Symbolically, the situation can be represented as follows.

	r_1	$\cdots$	r_n			r_1	$\cdots$	r_n			r_1	$\cdots$	r_n
p_1					q_1					$p_1 + q_1$			
$\cdot$					$\cdot$					$\cdot$			
$\cdot$		A			$\cdot$		B			$\cdot$		C	
$\cdot$					$\cdot$					$\cdot$			
p_n					q_n					$p_n + q_n$			

But matrix addition is term by term addition; so $C = A + B$. It is now easy to see that $p \cdot r + q \cdot r = (p + q) \cdot r$. If p, q, and r do not have the same degree, insert zeros so that the resulting tuples have the same length, and apply the preceding procedure.

This establishes our distributive law. Alternatively, this fact can be proved by a formal argument as follows: let $p = (a_n)$, $q = (b_n)$, and $r = (c_n)$. Then $(p + q) \cdot r = (a_n + b_n) \cdot (c_n)$ whose nth term is $\sum_{i+j=n+1} (a_i + b_i)c_j$ for each n. Also, $p \cdot r + q \cdot r = (a_n) \cdot (c_n) + (b_n) \cdot (c_n)$ whose nth term is $\sum_{i+j=n+1} a_i c_j + \sum_{i+j=n+1} b_i c_j$, namely $\sum_{i+j=n+1} (a_i + b_i)c_j$ for each n. Thus $p \cdot r + q \cdot r = (p + q) \cdot r$.

Of course, the following distributive law is easy to prove.

Theorem 8.2.3: $r \cdot (p + q) = r \cdot p + r \cdot q$ whenever p, q, and r are polynomials.

Proof: Apply Theorem 8.2.1 and Theorem 8.2.2.

Mathematicians usually think of a polynomial as an expression of the form $a_0 + a_1 x + \cdots + a_t x^t$. Let us see about this. The polynomial $(0 , 1)$ is the key to the situation; we must give this polynomial a name so we use the symbol that appears in the expression $F[x]$, namely x, as a name for this polynomial. So, $x = (0, 1)$. We define powers of x in the usual way; thus $x^1 = x$ and $x^{n+1} = x^n \cdot x$ whenever $n \in N$. Notice that $x^2 = x^1 \cdot x = (0, 1) \cdot (0, 1) = (0, 0, 1)$ and that $x^3 = x^2 \cdot x = (0, 0, 1) \cdot (0, 1) = (0, 0, 0, 1)$. Indeed, using mathematical induction we can prove that $x^t = (0, \ldots, 0, 1)$, the $t + 1$-tuple whose first t terms are each 0 and whose last term is 1, whenever $t \in N$. It is convenient to define x^0 to be (1); so x^n is defined whenever n is a nonnegative integer.

Recall that we have agreed to denote the polynomial (0) by 0; let us extend this convention as follows. Let a be any scalar; then we denote the polynomial (a) by writing a. This is a parentheses-omitting convention.

We can now prove that $B = \{x^n \mid n \text{ is a nonnegative integer}\}$ is a basis for the vector space $(\mathfrak{F} , \mathfrak{V} , \circ)$ of Theorem 8.1.2. Since no two members of B have the same degree and since $\deg(p + q) = \max\{\deg p, \deg q\}$ if $\{p,q\} \subset B$, it follows that when we multiply a finite number of members of B by scalars, not all zero, and add, we obtain a polynomial that possesses a degree, hence is not 0. This proves that B is linearly independent. It remains to prove that LB, the set of all linear combinations of B, is $F[x]$. Let $p = (a_0 , a_1 , \ldots , a_t)$ be any polynomial; then

$$p = (a_0) + (0 , a_1) + \cdots + (\underbrace{0 , \ldots , 0}_{t \text{ 0's}}, a_t)$$

$$= a_0(1) + a_1(0 , 1) + \cdots + a_t(\underbrace{0 , \ldots , 0}_{t \text{ 0's}}, 1)$$

$$= a_0 + a_1 x + \cdots + a_t x^t.$$

We conclude that $p \in LB$; indeed $p \in L\{1 , x , \ldots , x^t\}$. This proves that $\{x^n \mid n \text{ is a nonnegative integer}\}$ is a basis for our vector space. Moreover, we have shown that the polynomial $(a_0 , a_1 , \ldots , a_t)$ is represented by the expression $a_0 + a_1 x + \cdots + a_t x^t$. In fact, we have given a precise meaning to the symbols x^m and $+$ that appear in this expression.

Before considering the associative law for multiplication we bring out the connection between multiplication of a polynomial by a scalar, and multiplication of a polynomial by a 1-tuple.

Lemma 8.2.1: The product of the polynomials (a) and p is the scalar product ap.

Proof: Obvious.

Lemma 8.2.2: Let p and q be any polynomials and let a be any scalar; then $[ap] \cdot q = a[p \cdot q]$, a scalar product.

Proof: Use the matrix device of Example 1.

In view of Lemma 8.2.1, we can regard Lemma 8.2.2 as a special case of the associative law for multiplication. Here is another special case of this law.

Lemma 8.2.3: Let p and q be any polynomials; then $x \cdot (p \cdot q) = (x \cdot p) \cdot q$.

Proof: Use the matrix device of Example 1; recall that $x = (0, 1)$.

Using mathematical induction it is easy to generalize Lemma 8.2.3.

Lemma 8.2.4: Let p and q be any polynomials and let $n \in N$; then $x^n \cdot (p \cdot q) = (x^n \cdot p) \cdot q$.

Proof: Clearly 1 has this property (see Lemma 8.2.3). Let t be a natural number with the property (i.e., x^t satisfies the associative law); we shall show that $t + 1$ has this property also. Let p and q be any polynomials; now

$$\begin{aligned}
x^{t+1} \cdot (p \cdot q) &= (x^t \cdot x) \cdot (p \cdot q) \\
&= x^t \cdot [x \cdot (p \cdot q)] && \text{by the induction assumption} \\
&= x^t \cdot [(x \cdot p) \cdot q] && \text{by Lemma 8.2.3} \\
&= [x^t \cdot (x \cdot p)] \cdot q && \text{by the induction assumption} \\
&= [(x^t \cdot x) \cdot p] \cdot q && \text{by the induction assumption} \\
&= (x^{t+1} \cdot p) \cdot q \ .
\end{aligned}$$

So $t + 1$ has this property whenever t has the property. We conclude, by mathematical induction, that each natural number has the property.

Indeed, we can generalize still further.

Lemma 8.2.5: Let p and q be any polynomials, let $n \in N$, and let a be any scalar; then $(ax^n) \cdot (p \cdot q) = [(ax^n) \cdot p] \cdot q$.

Proof: Lemmas 8.2.2 and 8.2.4.

We are now ready to consider the associative law itself.

Theorem 8.2.4: $(p \cdot q) \cdot r = p \cdot (q \cdot r)$ whenever p, q, and r are polynomials.

Proof: If $p = 0$ then $(p \cdot q) \cdot r = 0 \cdot r = 0$ and $p \cdot (q \cdot r) = 0$. So, we shall assume that $p \neq 0$. Now, each nonzero polynomial has a degree; we prove our theorem by applying mathematical induction to the degree of p. First, we must show that $(p \cdot q) \cdot r = p \cdot (q \cdot r)$ whenever deg $p = 0$; but this has already been established (see the comment following Lemma 8.2.2). Next, assume that $(p \cdot q) \cdot r = p \cdot (q \cdot r)$ whenever deg $p \leq k$, a nonnegative integer. We must show that $(p_1 \cdot q) \cdot r = p_1 \cdot (q \cdot r)$ whenever deg $p_1 = k + 1$. Let a be the final term of p_1; so, $p_1 = p + ax^{k+1}$ where p is a polynomial such that deg $p \leq k$ or else $p = 0$. Thus

$$(p_1 \cdot q) \cdot r = [(p + ax^{k+1}) \cdot q] \cdot r$$

$$= [p \cdot q + (ax^{k+1}) \cdot q] \cdot r \qquad \text{by Theorem 8.2.2}$$

$$= (p \cdot q) \cdot r + [(ax^{k+1}) \cdot q] \cdot r \qquad \text{by Theorem 8.2.2}$$

$$= p \cdot (q \cdot r) + (ax^{k+1}) \cdot (q \cdot r) \qquad \text{by the induction assumption and Lemma 8.2.5}$$

$$= (p + ax^{k+1}) \cdot (q \cdot r) \qquad \text{by Theorem 8.2.2}$$

$$= p_1 \cdot (q \cdot r) \ .$$

This proves that $k + 1$ has the property if each nonnegative integer that does not exceed k has the property. So, by mathematical induction, each nonnegative integer has the property. We conclude that $(p \cdot q) \cdot r = p \cdot (q \cdot r)$ whenever $\{p, q, r\} \subset F[x]$.

In view of Theorem 8.1.1 and the preceding results it is clear that $(F[x], +, \cdot, 0)$ is a commutative ring. Moreover, it is evident that $p \cdot 1 = p$ whenever $p \in F[x]$; so, the polynomial 1 is the multiplicative identity of this ring. We have established the following result.

Theorem 8.2.5: Let $(F, +, \cdot, 0, 1)$ be a field; then $(F[x], +, \cdot, 0, 1)$ is a commutative ring with identity.

It is easy to strengthen this result; we need the following lemma.

Lemma 8.2.6: Let p and q be polynomials such that $p \cdot q = 0$; then $p = 0$ or $q = 0$.

Proof: The product of nonzero scalars is a nonzero scalar; therefore, the product of nonzero polynomials is a nonzero polynomial.

Theorem 8.2.6: Let $(F, +, \cdot, 0, 1)$ be a field; then $(F[x], +, \cdot, 0, 1)$ is an integral domain.

Proof: Recall that a commutative ring with identity is an integral domain if and only if 0 has no proper divisors and $0 \neq 1$.

EXERCISES

1. Compute $(2, 3, -1) \cdot (4, 0, 5, 2, 3)$ where these are polynomials over R.

2. Compute $(1, 0, 0, 1) \cdot (1, 1)$ where these are polynomials over $\{0, 1\}$ where the field involved is

   $(\{0, 1\}, \{(0, 0, 0), (1, 0, 1), (0, 1, 1), (1, 1, 0)\}, \{(0, 0, 0),$
   $(1, 0, 0), (0, 1, 0), (1, 1, 1)\}, 0, 1)$.

3. Let $(F, +, \cdot, 0, 1)$ be a field; express the polynomial $x^2 - x$ as an ordered triple of members of F.

4. Prove that $x^n = (\underbrace{0, \ldots, 0}_{n \text{ 0's}}, 1)$ whenever n is a nonnegative integer.

5. Let $a \in F$, let $p \in F[x]$, and let $q \in F[x]$; prove that $[ap] \cdot q = a[p \cdot q]$.

6. Show that $\deg(p \cdot q) = \deg p + \deg q$ whenever p and q are nonzero polynomials.

7. Exhibit a field of characteristic 2 whose basic set is infinite.
   Hint: Consider the integral domain $(F[x], +, \cdot, 0, 1)$ where $F = \{0, 1\}$.

8.3 POLYNOMIAL FUNCTIONS

People who are familiar with calculus usually think of a polynomial as a function, i.e., a mapping of R into R. Here, we investigate the connection between our view that a polynomial is a tuple, and the calculus view that a polynomial is a function. To minimize confusion we use the term *polynomial function* for the function, and reserve *polynomial* exclusively for the tuple.

The main idea is that a polynomial, say $a_0 + a_1x + \cdots + a_mx^m$, leads us to a function in a natural and direct way as follows: to find the scalar that our mapping associates with a scalar t, replace x throughout by t; the resulting expression can be regarded as a direction for computing a scalar (by interpreting the polynomial operations of addition and multiplication as the corresponding scalar operations), namely $a_0 + a_1t + \cdots + a_mt^m$. This scalar is the value of our function at t. In other words, the function f associated with the polynomial $a_0 + a_1x + \cdots + a_mx^m$ is such that $f(t) = a_0 + a_1t + \cdots + a_mt^m$ whenever t is a scalar. For example, the function associated with the polynomial $1 + x^2 - 3x^4$ is f, where $f(t) = 1 + t^2 - 3t^4$ whenever t is a scalar.

A function is said to be a *polynomial function* provided it can be constructed from a polynomial in the above manner. Unfortunately, the simple manner in which the values of a polynomial function are yielded by the polynomial involved, makes it appear that there is little difference between the polynomial and the resulting mapping. After all, the scalar that a polynomial function associates with a given scalar t is obtained from the polynomial involved by merely replacing its x's by t's. It is important to distinguish clearly between polynomials and polynomial functions; therefore, we present another method of defining the polynomial function that we have already agreed to associate with a given polynomial.

Definition 8.3.1: The polynomial function associated with a polynomial $p = (a_0, a_1, \ldots, a_m)$, $m \geq 0$, is the mapping whose value at t is $(a_0, a_1, \ldots, a_m)$ $\cdot (1, t, \ldots, t^m)$ whenever t is a scalar; we denote this mapping by writing p_f.

Notice that the scalar $p_f(t)$ is the dot product of p and the tuple having the same length as p, whose first term is 1 and such that each remaining term is obtained by multiplying the preceding term by t. For example, let $p = (1, 0, 1, -3)$; to compute $p_f(2)$ we form the 4-tuple $(1, 2, 4, 8)$ and take its dot product with p; i.e.,

$$p_f(2) = (1, 0, 1, -3) \cdot (1, 2, 4, 8) = -19 .$$

Example 1: Let $p = (1, 0, 1)$ be a polynomial over R; determine p_f.

Solution: Let $t \in R$; then $p_f(t) = (1, 0, 1) \cdot (1, t, t^2) = 1 + t^2$. So $p_f = \{(t, 1 + t^2) \mid t \in R\}$.

If it is clear that we are dealing with a polynomial function rather than a polynomial, it is customary to denote the polynomial function by writing down a name for the polynomial involved, i.e., to suppress the subscript f. This convention is particularly convenient when we are referring to the values of a polynomial function; so, we usually write $p(t)$ rather than $p_f(t)$. Of course, this widely used convention compounds the confusion between polynomials and polynomial functions. We must remember that a polynomial is a tuple, whereas a polynomial function is a mapping.

The algebra of functions is well-known to any calculus student. We recall that the *sum* or *product* of functions f and g are defined as follows: $f + g = \{(a, b) \mid b = f(a) + g(a)\}$ and $f \cdot g = \{(a, b) \mid b = f(a)g(a)\}$. Consider the following quesions. Is the sum, or product, of polynomial functions necessarily a polynomial function? If so, which polynomial is involved? These questions are answered by the following theorems which assert that the sum of polynomial functions is the polynomial function associated with the sum of the corresponding polynomials, and that the product of polynomial functions is the polynomial function associated with the product of the corresponding polynomials.

Theorem 8.3.1: $p_f + q_f = (p + q)_f$ whenever p and q are polynomials.

Proof: We must show that $p(t) + q(t) = [p + q](t)$ whenever t is a scalar. Let $p = (a_1, \ldots, a_r) = (a_n)$ and let $q = (b_1, \ldots, b_s) = (b_n)$. Now, $p + q = (a_n + b_n)$; so

$$[p + q](t) = (a_n + b_n)(t)$$

$$= (a_1 + b_1) + (a_2 + b_2)t + \cdots + (a_m + b_m)t^{m-1} \quad \text{where } m = \max\{r, s\}$$

$$= (a_1 + a_2t + \cdots + a_rt^{r-1}) + (b_1 + b_2t + \cdots + b_st^{s-1})$$

$$= p(t) + q(t) .$$

whenever t is a scalar. This establishes our result.

Theorem 8.3.2: $p_f \cdot q_f = (p \cdot q)_f$ whenever p and q are polynomials.

Proof: We must show that $p(t)q(t) = [p \cdot q](t)$ whenever t is a scalar. Let $p = (a_1, \ldots, a_r)$ and let $q = (b_1, \ldots, b_s)$. Now,

$$p \cdot q = (a_1 + a_2 x + \cdots + a_r x^{r-1}) \cdot q$$

$$= a_1 \cdot q + a_2 x \cdot q + \cdots + a_r x^{r-1} \cdot q \qquad \text{by a distributive law}$$

so $[p \cdot q](t) = [a_1 \cdot q](t) + [a_2 x \cdot q](t) + \cdots + [a_r x^{r-1} \cdot q](t)$ by Theorem 8.3.1

$$= \sum_{i=1}^{s} a_1 b_i t^{i-1} + \sum_{i=1}^{s} a_2 b_i t^{i} + \cdots + \sum_{i=1}^{s} a_r b_i t^{i+r-2}$$

$$= (a_1 + a_2 t + \cdots + a_r t^{r-1}) \sum_{i=1}^{s} b_i t^{i-1} \qquad \begin{array}{l} \text{by a distributive law} \\ \text{for the field} \end{array}$$

$$= p(t)q(t) \; .$$

whenever t is a scalar. This establishes our result.

The fact that the basic algebraic operations on polynomials are so closely related to the corresponding operations on polynomial functions, suggests that polynomials and polynomial functions are fundamentally the same (from an algebraic viewpoint). Indeed, in view of the preceding theorems, to establish that our ring of polynomials is algebraically the same as the algebraic system that involves polynomial functions, it is necessary only to show that distinct poly-nomials yield distinct polynomial functions, i.e., that $p_f \neq q_f$ whenever $p \neq q$. It turns out that the truth of this statement depends upon the field involved. For example, in the case of the real number field and in the case of the complex number field, distinct polynomials yield distinct polynomial functions (this follows from the *Fundamental Theorem of Algebra* see Exercise 10, Section 8.4). Don't yield to the conjecture that this is so for any field. A counter-example easily disproves that idea. Consider the field $(\{0, 1\}, +, \cdot, 0, 1)$ where $+ = \{(0, 0, 0), (0, 1, 1), (1, 0, 1), (1, 1, 0)\}$ and $\cdot = \{(0, 0, 0), (0, 1, 0), (1, 0, 0), (1, 1, 1)\}$. Clearly, $(0, 1) \neq (0, 0, 1)$; however, the corresponding polynomial functions are the same: $(0, 1)_f = \{(0, 0), (1, 1)\}$ and $(0, 0, 1)_f = \{(0, 0), (1, 1)\}$.

We now introduce one more technical term. Let $(F, +, \cdot, 0, 1)$ be any field and let g be any mapping of F into F; by a *zero* of g we mean any member of F, say t, such that $g(t) = 0$. So it is meaningful to talk about a zero of a polynomial function. The point is that it is convenient to refer to a zero of a *polynomial*. Let p be any polynomial; then t is said to be a *zero* of p if and only if t is a zero of p_f. For example, 2 and -3 are the zeros of $(-6, 1, 1)$.

EXERCISES

1. (a) Exhibit the polynomial function associated with the polynomial $(2, 0, 3)$, where the field involved is the real number field.
    (b) Does the polynomial function of part (a) have a zero?

2. (a) Exhibit $(0, -1, 0, 1)_f$ where the field involved is the real number field.
   (b) Does the polynomial function of part (a) have a zero?

3. (a) Exhibit $(2, 3, 0, 5, -3)_f$ where the field involved is the real number field.
   (b) Does the polynomial function of part (a) have a zero?

4. Consider the field with basic set $\{0, 1\}$ of the text.

   (a) Represent the polynomial $x^2 - x$ as a triple.
   (b) Is $x^2 - x$ the zero polynomial?
   (c) Show that the polynomial functions $(x^2 - x)_f$ and 0_f are the same.
   (d) Simplify $(1, 0, -1)_f$.
   (e) Find the zeros of the polynomial $x^2 - x$.
   (f) Find the zeros of the polynomial $x^2 - x + 1$.
   (g) Find the zeros of $(1, 0, 1)$.

5. Consider the field $(\{0, 1, 2\}, +, \cdot, 0, 1)$ where $+$ and $\cdot$ are given by the following tables.

$+$	0	1	2		$\cdot$	0	1	2
0	0	1	2		0	0	0	0
1	1	2	0		1	0	1	2
2	2	0	1		2	0	2	1

   (a) Exhibit $(1, 2, 0, 1)_f$.
   (b) Exhibit $(2, 0, 1, 0, 2)_f$.
   (c) Compute $(1, 2, 0, 1)(2) + (2, 0, 1, 0, 2)(2)$.
   (d) Compute $(0, 2, 1, 1, 2)(2)$.
   (e) Exhibit two polynomials such that the associated polynomial functions are the same.

6. Given that p and q are polynomials, prove that $p(t) - q(t) = [p - q](t)$ whenever t is a scalar.

7. Prove that $p_f \neq q_f$ whenever p and q are distinct polynomials over F if and only if $r_f \neq \{(t, 0) \mid t \in F\}$ whenever r is a nonzero polynomial over F.

8.4 THE DIVISION THEOREM

Just as there is a *division theorem* for the system of integers, so there is a *division theorem* for the integral domain of Section 8.2 that involves polynomials. The key to the division process for polynomials is contained in the following result.

Lemma 8.4.1: Let p_1 and p_2 be nonzero polynomials such that $\deg p_2 \leq \deg p_1$; then there is a polynomial q such that $p_1 - p_2 \cdot q = 0$ or $\deg(p_1 - p_2 \cdot q) < \deg p_1$.

Proof: Let $p_1 = (a_1, \ldots, a_r)$ and let $p_2 = (b_1, \ldots, b_s)$ where $b_s \neq 0$ and

$r \geq s$. Let $q = (a_r/b_s)x^{r-s}$; clearly, the polynomial $p_1 - p_2 \cdot q$ is either 0 or else has degree less than $r - 1$, the degree of p_1. This establishes our lemma.

This result can be formulated as follows, which we shall refer to as our *basic lemma*.

Lemma 8.4.1:   Let p_1 and p_2 be nonzero polynomials such that $\deg p_2 \leq \deg p_1$; then there are polynomials q and r such that $p_1 = p_2 \cdot q + r$, and $r = 0$ or $\deg r < \deg p_1$.

Note: Here $r = p_1 - p_2 \cdot q$.

We are now ready to consider the Division Theorem.

Theorem 8.4.1: (*Division Theorem*):   Let p_1 be any polynomial and let p_2 be any nonzero polynomial; there are unique polynomials q and r, where $r = 0$ or $\deg r < \deg p_2$, such that $p_1 = p_2 \cdot q + r$.

Proof: First, we show that there exist polynomials q and r with the required properties. If $p_1 = 0$ or if $\deg p_1 < \deg p_2$, take $q = 0$ and $r = p_1$. If $\deg p_2 \leq \deg p_1$, then by our basic lemma there are polynomials q_1 and r_1 such that

$$(1) \qquad\qquad p_1 = p_2 \cdot q_1 + r_1, \quad \text{and} \quad r_1 = 0 \quad \text{or} \quad \deg r_1 < \deg p_1 .$$

If $r_1 = 0$ or if $\deg r_1 < \deg p_2$ we have finished.   Assume that $\deg p_2 \leq \deg r_1$. Then, by our basic lemma, there are polynomials q_2 and r_2 such that

$$(2) \qquad\qquad r_1 = p_2 \cdot q_2 + r_2, \quad \text{and} \quad r_2 = 0 \quad \text{or} \quad \deg r_2 < \deg r_1 .$$

If $r_2 = 0$ or if $\deg r_2 < \deg p_2$ we have finished.   Assume that $\deg p_2 \leq \deg r_2$. Then, by our basic lemma, there are polynomials q_3 and r_3 such that

$$(3) \qquad\qquad r_2 = p_2 \cdot q_3 + r_3, \quad \text{and} \quad r_3 = 0 \quad \text{or} \quad \deg r_3 < \deg r_2 .$$

If $r_3 = 0$ or if $\deg r_2 < \deg p_2$ we have finished.   Otherwise, we continue this process, namely we apply our basic lemma to r_3 and p_2. Notice that the degree of the remainder produced at each stage is less than that of the remainder produced at the preceding stage; i.e.,

$$\deg p_1 > \deg r_1 > \deg r_2 > \deg r_3 > \cdots$$

Therefore, applying our basic lemma n times, where $n \leq \deg p_1 - \deg p_2 + 1$, must produce a remainder r_n such that $r_n = 0$ or $\deg r_n < \deg p_2$. So, the nth and final application of our basic lemma produces

$$(n) \qquad\qquad r_{n-1} = p_2 \cdot q_n + r_n, \quad \text{and} \quad r_n = 0 \quad \text{or} \quad \deg r_n < \deg p_2 .$$

Thus, from (1), (2), . . . , (n),

$$p_1 = p_2 \cdot q_1 + p_2 \cdot q_2 + \cdots + p_2 \cdot q_n + r_n = p_2 \cdot (q_1 + \cdots + q_n) + r_n .$$

So $q = q_1 + \cdots + q_n$ and $r = r_n$. This demonstrates the existence of polynomials q and r with the required properties.   Next, we establish the uniqueness of q and r.

Suppose that there also exist polynomials q' and r' such that $p_1 = p_2 \cdot q' + r'$ and $r' = 0$ or deg $r' <$ deg p_2. Then $p_2 \cdot q + r = p_2 \cdot q' + r'$; so $p_2 \cdot (q - q') = r' - r$. If $r' \neq r$ then $r' - r \neq 0$ and $\deg(r' - r) <$ deg p_2; therefore, $p_2 \cdot (q - q')$ is nonzero and its degree is less than that of p_2. Clearly, this is impossible. This proves that $r' = r$. But then $p_2 \cdot (q - q') = 0$; so $q = q'$ since $p_2 \neq 0$. This completes our proof of Theorem 8.4.1.

The next example illustrates the Division Theorem.

Example 1: Let $p_1 = (3, 15, 13, 2, 4, 1)$ and let $p_2 = (3, -1, 1)$. Find polynomials q and r such that $p_1 = p_2 \cdot q + r$ and deg $r < 2$.

Solution: We illustrate our proof of the Division Theorem by using our basic lemma to build up q and r. Now

$$p_1 = p_2 \cdot x^3 + (3, 15, 13, -1, 5)$$

$$(3, 15, 13, -1, 5) = p_2 \cdot 5x^2 + (3, 15, -2, 4)$$

$$(3, 15, -2, 4) = p_2 \cdot 4x + (3, 3, 2)$$

$$(3, 3, 2) = p_2 \cdot (2) + (-3, 5)$$

so $p_1 = p_2 \cdot [(2) + 4x + 5x^2 + x^3] + (-3, 5) = p_2 \cdot (2, 4, 5, 1) + (-3, 5)$. Thus $q = (2, 4, 5, 1)$ and $r = (-3, 5)$.

The computations involved in determining the quotient q and the remainder r in the above example can be carried out efficiently as follows.

						2	4	5	1
3	−1	1	3	15	13	2	4	1
			3	15	13	−1	5	0
			3	15	−2	4	0	
			3	3	2	0		
			−3	5	0			

The quotient q is displayed in the first line of this array; the remainder r is displayed in the last line to the left of the dotted line. Let us explain how this array is constructed. We begin by setting up the given polynomials in the usual form for long division.

$$3 \quad -1 \quad 1 \mid 3 \quad 15 \quad 13 \quad 2 \quad 4 \quad 1$$

Next, we insert a dotted line before the third term of p_1 (in general, after the mth term of p_1, where m is the degree of p_2); its purpose is to tell us when we have completed the division process. The next step is to apply our basic lemma, multiplying p_2 by x^3 and subtracting the result from p_1. So we obtain:

$$3 \quad -1 \quad 1 \mid 3 \quad 15 \vdots 13 \quad 2 \quad 4 \quad 1 \; .$$
$$3 \quad 15 \vdots 13 \quad -1 \quad 5 \quad 0$$

The fact that we have multiplied by x^3 is recorded by inserting the final term of this polynomial, namely 1, above the line. Remember that when we apply our basic lemma we divide the final term of p_1 by the final term of p_2, and then multiply by the appropriate power of x. For the next application of our basic lemma we divide the final term of the displayed remainder (the bottom line of our table), namely 5, by the final term of p_2, obtaining 5. This means that we shall multiply p_2 by $5x^2$ and shall subtract the result from the previous remainder; this yields

$$
\begin{array}{ccc|ccccccc}
 & & & & & & & & 5 & 1 \\
\hline
3 & -1 & 1 & 3 & 15 & \vdots & 13 & 2 & 4 & 1 \, . \\
 & & & 3 & 15 & \vdots & 13 & -1 & 5 & \underline{0} \\
 & & & 3 & 15 & \vdots & -2 & 4 & \underline{0} \\
\end{array}
$$

Recording our results in this manner, we obtain the array displayed above by two more applications of the basic lemma.

The Division Theorem is of great theoretical importance; for example, it helps us to determine the greatest common divisor of two polynomials. Here we demonstrate its value by an application to calculus.

Example 2: Compute $\int_0^1 x^2/(x+1)$.

Solution: Notice that the integrand is the quotient of two polynomial functions. In view of the fact that *polynomial functions* and *polynomials* are algebraically the same (see Section 8.3), we can simplify the function $x^2/(x+1)$ by applying the Division Theorem to the polynomials $(0, 0, 1)$ and $(1, 1)$. Now, by the Division Theorem, $(0, 0, 1) = (1, 1)\cdot(-1, 1) + (1)$; so, the functions $x^2/(x+1)$ and $x - 1 + 1/(x+1)$ are the same. Thus

$$
\int_0^1 x^2/(x+1) = \int_0^1 (x-1) + \int_0^1 1/(x+1) = -.5 + \log 2 \approx .19315 \, .
$$

The special case of the Division Theorem for which deg $p_2 = 1$ leads us to the *Remainder Theorem*. Notice that our proof uses facts about polynomial functions.

Theorem 8.4.2 (*Remainder Theorem*): Let p be any polynomial and let k be any scalar; then there is a polynomial q such that $p = (x - k)\cdot q + r$ where r is the 1-tuple $(p(k))$.

Proof: By the Division Theorem there exist polynomials q and r such that $p = (x - k)\cdot q + r$ and r is a 1-tuple. Consider the corresponding polynomial functions. Clearly,

$$p(k) = [(x-k)\cdot q + r](k)$$

$$= r(k) \qquad \text{by Theorem 8.3.1 and Theorem 8.3.2} \, .$$

Therefore, $r = (p(k))$. This establishes our result.

A polynomial p_2 is said to be a *divisor*, or *factor*, of a polynomial p_1 if and only if there is a polynomial q such that $p_1 = p_2\cdot q$ (i.e., the remainder on dividing p_1 by

p_2 is 0). We abbreviate the statement "p_2 is a divisor of p_1" by writing $p_2 \mid p_1$. For example, $(-1, 1) \mid (-1, 0, 1)$ and $(2, 1) \mid (2, 5, 4, 1)$.

Our next result follows immediately from the Remainder Theorem.

Corollary 8.4.1 (*Factor Theorem*): Let p be any polynomial and let k be any scalar; then $(x - k) \mid p$ if and only if $p(k) = 0$.

EXERCISES

1. Exhibit polynomials over R, say q and r, such that:

   (a) $(-6, 7, -2, -3, 2) = (7, -2, -3, 2) \cdot q + r$ where $r = 0$ or deg $r < 3$,

   (b) $2x^5 - x^4 + 5x^3 + x^2 - 3x + 12 = (x^2 + 3) \cdot q + r$ where $r = 0$ or deg $r < 2$.

2. Consider the field $(\{0, 1\}, +, \cdot, 0, 1)$ where $+$ and $\cdot$ are defined as follows.

+	0	1
0	0	1
1	1	0

$\cdot$	0	1
0	0	0
1	0	1

   Exhibit polynomials q and r over $\{0, 1\}$ such that:

   (a) $(0, 1, 1, 0, 1) = (1, 0, 0, 1) \cdot q + r$ where $r = 0$ or deg $r < 3$,

   (b) $x^5 - x^2 + x - 1 = (x^2 - x) \cdot q + r$ where $r = 0$ or deg $r < 2$.

3. Consider the field $(\{0, 1, 2\}, +, \cdot, 0, 1)$ where $+$ and $\cdot$ are defined as follows.

+	0	1	2
0	0	1	2
1	1	2	0
2	2	0	1

$\cdot$	0	1	2
0	0	0	0
1	0	1	2
2	0	2	1

   Exhibit polynomials q and r over $\{0, 1, 2\}$ such that:

   (a) $(0, 2, 0, 2, 0, 1, 2) = (0, 2, 0, 0, 1) \cdot q + r$ where $r = 0$ or deg $r < 4$;

   (b) $(-2, 0, 2, -1, 0, 0, 1) = (-1, 0, 1) \cdot q + r$ where $r = 0$ or deg $r < 2$.

4. Use the Factor Theorem to obtain the zeros of the following polynomials over R:

   (a) $(6, 5, 1)$;   (b) $x^2 - 2x - 3$;   (c) $(-1, 3, -3, 1)$.

5. Use the Factor Theorem to obtain the first degree divisors of the following polynomials over R:

   (a) $x^2 + 6x + 5$,   (b) $(-2, -3, 0, 1)$,   (c) $(-3, 2, 0, 0, 1)$.

6. Prove that k is a zero of multiplicity m of a polynomial p if and only if

   (*i*) k is a zero of p,
   (*ii*) k is a zero of the derivative of p with multiplicity $m - 1$.

   Note: A zero k of p has multiplicity m if and only if $(x - k)^m \mid p$ whereas $(x - k)^{m+1}$ is not a divisor of p.

7. Let r/s be a rational number such that r and s have no prime divisors and r/s is a zero of $(a_1 , \ldots , a_n)$, a polynomial whose terms are integers. Prove that $r \mid a_1$ and $s \mid a_n$. Use this test to find the rational zeros of $(2 , 3 , 0 , -1)$ and of $(1 , 4 , 12 , 29 , 6)$.

8. Let p be a polynomial over C whose terms are real (imaginary part zero). Prove that a complex number k is a zero of p if and only if $\bar{k}$ (the complex conjugate of k) is a zero of p.
   Hint: Use the terms of p to compute the complex conjugate of $p(k)$.

9. The *Fundamental Theorem of Algebra* asserts that each polynomial over C with positive degree has at least one zero. Use this fact to establish the following statements.

   (a) Each nonzero polynomial over C can be expressed as the product of polynomials of degree 0 or 1.
   (b) Each nonzero polynomial over R can be expressed as the product of polynomials of degree 0, 1, or 2.
   Hint: Consider the corresponding polynomial over C and apply Exercise 8.

10. (a) Use Exercise 9(a) to prove that $p_f \neq q_f$ whenever p and q are distinct polynomials over C.
    (b) Use Exercise 9(b) to prove that $p_f \neq q_f$ whenever p and q are distinct polynomials over R.

8.5 MATRIC POLYNOMIALS AND POLYNOMIAL MATRICES

It is customary to extend the notion of a polynomial by using a ring with identity, whose basic set has at least two members, in place of a field. Thus, let $\mathfrak{B} = (B , + , \cdot , 0 , 1)$ be a ring with identity where $0 \neq 1$. The idea is to carry out the construction of Section 8.1 in the context of the ring $\mathfrak{B}$ rather than a field; so, we define a polynomial over B to be (0) and each tuple of members of B whose final term is not 0, and we introduce the usual operations of addition and multiplication on polynomials. It is easy to see that the resulting algebraic system $(B[x] , + , \cdot , 0 , 1)$ is a ring with identity, where 0 and 1 denote the polynomials (0) and (1) respectively. If the given ring $\mathfrak{B}$ possesses divisors of zero, then so does the resulting polynomial ring; for example, $(0 , a) \cdot (0 , b) = 0$ if a and b are nonzero members of B such that $a \cdot b = 0$.

Next, consider the ring $(M , + , \cdot , (0) , I_n)$ where M is the set of all $n \times n$ real matrices. Clearly, this is a noncommutative ring with identity. The resulting polynomial ring is of special interest to us; here multiplication is defined just as before. These polynomials are called *matric* polynomials since their terms are matrices. Now, matrix multiplication is not commutative; so the rule for forming the product of matric polynomials must be applied with care. However, (0) and I_n commute with each member of M; thus x^t commutes with each member of $M[x]$ whenever $t \in N$, i.e., $x^t \cdot p = p \cdot x^t$ whenever p is a matric polynomial and t is a natural number.

So far we have considered only matrices whose entries are real numbers; of course, this simplifies the notion of a matrix so that we can think about matrices more effectively. It is time, now, that we extend this notion by permitting the entries of a matrix to be members of F, where $(F, +, \cdot, 0, 1)$ is any field. A matrix of this sort is called a *matrix over F*. The usual operations of matrix addition, matrix multiplication, and scalar multiplication are defined in terms of the field operations, just as for matrices over R. We mention that matrices of this sort possess all the algebraic properties that we have established for matrices over R. It is useful to generalize our notion of a matrix still further by using a ring with identity in place of a field. So let $(B, +, \cdot, 0, 1)$ be a ring with identity, where $0 \neq 1$, and consider all $n \times n$ matrices over B, where n is a specific natural number. Here, our matrix operations are defined in terms of the ring operations. Notice that the resulting algebraic system is a noncommutative ring with identity.

We are specially interested in matrices whose entries are polynomials over R; these matrices are called *polynomial* matrices. The idea is to apply the above construction to the ring of real polynomials $(R[x], +, \cdot, 0, 1)$; so we obtain a ring of polynomial matrices. We claim that this ring is isomorphic to the ring of matric polynomials exhibited above. Now, we have two procedures for constructing a ring from a ring; one is based on polynomials, the other is based on matrices. Our claim is that the ring obtained by applying both constructions in succession is independent of the order, from the algebraic viewpoint. The situation is clarified by the following diagram, where M is the set of all $n \times n$ matrices over R.

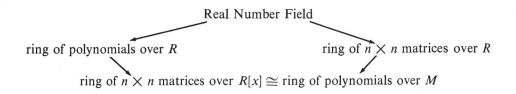

Real Number Field

ring of polynomials over R ring of $n \times n$ matrices over R

ring of $n \times n$ matrices over $R[x] \cong$ ring of polynomials over M

To establish our claim we must present a suitable method of associating a matric polynomial with a polynomial matrix. First, we illustrate the idea. Let $A = \begin{pmatrix} (3, 0, -2, 1) & (5, 2) \\ (-1, 4, 1) & (3) \end{pmatrix}$; in view of the ring properties we can break down A as follows:

(1) $$A = \begin{pmatrix} 3 & 5 \\ -1 & 3 \end{pmatrix} + \begin{pmatrix} 0 & 2x \\ 4x & 0 \end{pmatrix} + \begin{pmatrix} -2x^2 & 0 \\ x^2 & 0 \end{pmatrix} + \begin{pmatrix} x^3 & 0 \\ 0 & 0 \end{pmatrix}.$$

Here polynomials are scalars; so a common divisor of each entry of a matrix can be factored out, and the matrix can be replaced by a scalar product. Thus

$$(2) \qquad A = \begin{pmatrix} 3 & 5 \\ -1 & 3 \end{pmatrix} + x\begin{pmatrix} 0 & 2 \\ 4 & 0 \end{pmatrix} + x^2\begin{pmatrix} -2 & 0 \\ 1 & 0 \end{pmatrix} + x^3\begin{pmatrix} 1 & 0 \\ 0 & 0 \end{pmatrix}.$$

The matric polynomial that we associate with A is obtained from the right-hand side of (2) by an obvious maneuver, as follows:

$$(3) \qquad \begin{pmatrix} 3 & 5 \\ -1 & 3 \end{pmatrix} + \begin{pmatrix} 0 & 2 \\ 4 & 0 \end{pmatrix}x + \begin{pmatrix} -2 & 0 \\ 1 & 0 \end{pmatrix}x^2 + \begin{pmatrix} 1 & 0 \\ 0 & 0 \end{pmatrix}x^3.$$

Of course, this is the matric polynomial (a_1, a_2, a_3, a_4) where $a_1 = \begin{pmatrix} 3 & 5 \\ -1 & 3 \end{pmatrix}$, $a_2 = \begin{pmatrix} 0 & 2 \\ 4 & 0 \end{pmatrix}$, $a_3 = \begin{pmatrix} -2 & 0 \\ 1 & 0 \end{pmatrix}$, and $a_4 = \begin{pmatrix} 1 & 0 \\ 0 & 0 \end{pmatrix}$. Clearly the matric polynomial 0 corresponds to the polynomial matrix (0). We claim that a sum (or product) of polynomial matrices corresponds to the sum (or product) of the corresponding matric polynomials. To see this, notice that we can calculate the sum (or product) of polynomial matrices by first expressing them in the standard form of (2), and then carrying out the matrix addition (or multiplication). This involves applying the distributive laws of the ring and grouping together terms that involve the same power of x. Clearly, the same operation on the corresponding matric polynomials produces corresponding matric polynomials at each step of the computation. So the resulting polynomial matrix and matric polynomial correspond. This demonstrates that our rings are isomorphic. The following example illustrates our observation that each operation on polynomial matrices of the form (2) is reflected by the same operation on the corresponding matric polynomials.

Example 1: Compute

$$\begin{pmatrix} (0, 1) & (-2, 0, 1) & 0 \\ 1 & (5, 2) & (0, 1) \end{pmatrix} \cdot \begin{pmatrix} (-2, 3) & (0, 1) \\ (0, 3) & 0 \\ (0, 1) & 1 \end{pmatrix}.$$

Solution: Now,

$$\begin{pmatrix} (0, 1) & (-2, 0, 1) & 0 \\ 1 & (5, 2) & (0, 1) \end{pmatrix} = \begin{pmatrix} 0 & -2 & 0 \\ 1 & 5 & 0 \end{pmatrix} + x\begin{pmatrix} 1 & 0 & 0 \\ 0 & 2 & 1 \end{pmatrix} + x^2\begin{pmatrix} 0 & 1 & 0 \\ 0 & 0 & 0 \end{pmatrix}$$

and

$$\begin{pmatrix} (-2, 3) & (0, 1) \\ (0, 3) & 0 \\ (0, 1) & 1 \end{pmatrix} = \begin{pmatrix} -2 & 0 \\ 0 & 0 \\ 0 & 1 \end{pmatrix} + x\begin{pmatrix} 3 & 1 \\ 3 & 0 \\ 1 & 0 \end{pmatrix}.$$

So the required matrix product is:

$$\left[\begin{pmatrix} 0 & -2 & 0 \\ 1 & 5 & 0 \end{pmatrix} + x\begin{pmatrix} 1 & 0 & 0 \\ 0 & 2 & 1 \end{pmatrix} + x^2\begin{pmatrix} 0 & 1 & 0 \\ 0 & 0 & 0 \end{pmatrix}\right] \cdot \left[\begin{pmatrix} -2 & 0 \\ 0 & 0 \\ 0 & 1 \end{pmatrix} + x\begin{pmatrix} 3 & 1 \\ 3 & 0 \\ 1 & 0 \end{pmatrix}\right]$$

$$= \begin{pmatrix} 0 & 0 \\ -2 & 0 \end{pmatrix} + x\left[\begin{pmatrix} -6 & 0 \\ 18 & 1 \end{pmatrix} + \begin{pmatrix} -2 & 0 \\ 0 & 1 \end{pmatrix}\right] + x^2\left[\begin{pmatrix} 3 & 1 \\ 7 & 0 \end{pmatrix} + \begin{pmatrix} 0 & 0 \\ 0 & 0 \end{pmatrix}\right] + x^3\begin{pmatrix} 3 & 0 \\ 0 & 0 \end{pmatrix}$$
by a distributive law

$$= \begin{pmatrix} 0 & 0 \\ -2 & 0 \end{pmatrix} + x\begin{pmatrix} -8 & 0 \\ 18 & 2 \end{pmatrix} + x^2\begin{pmatrix} 3 & 1 \\ 7 & 0 \end{pmatrix} + x^3\begin{pmatrix} 3 & 0 \\ 0 & 0 \end{pmatrix} = \begin{pmatrix} (0, -8, 3, 3) & (0, 0, 1) \\ (-2, 18, 7) & (0, 2) \end{pmatrix}.$$

In this example the matrix product is obtained by applying matrix operations; at each step, however, the objects involved can be interpreted as matric polynomials and the operations effected can be interpreted as operations on polynomials.

In the following chapters we utilize the *determinant* of a polynomial matrix. This should be regarded as a straightforward generalization of Definition 1.3.1; since the entries are polynomials, the object that our mapping determinant associates with a polynomial matrix is a polynomial, namely the polynomial obtained by applying the recursive construction of Definition 1.3.1. For example, the determinant of

$$\begin{pmatrix} (3,\ 0,\ -2,\ 1) & (5,\ 2) \\ (-1,\ 4,\ 1) & 3 \end{pmatrix}$$

is $3(3,\ 0,\ -2,\ 1) - (5,\ 2)\cdot(-1,\ 4,\ 1)$, i.e., $(14,\ -18,\ -19,\ 1)$.

There is one more idea that we need later (see Chapter 10). As we observed in Section 8.3, each polynomial over F, where $(F,\ +,\ \cdot,\ 0,\ 1)$ is a field, leads us to a mapping of F into F. This is a way of *using* polynomials. In exactly the same way, a polynomial over B, where $\circledB = (B,\ +,\ \cdot,\ 0,\ 1)$ is a ring with identity and $0 \neq 1$, provides us with a mapping of B into B. Applying the terminology and notation of Section 8.3 we call the resulting mapping a *polynomial function* and we denote by p_f the mapping yielded by a polynomial p. Thus, let $p = (a_0,\ \ldots,\ a_m)$ be a polynomial over B, and let $t \in B$; then we say that the corresponding polynomial function p_f associates $(a_0,\ \ldots,\ a_m)\cdot(1,\ t,\ \ldots,\ t^m)$ with t, and we denote this scalar by writing $p(t)$. Of course, these mappings can be added and multiplied just as in the case of polynomials over a field. However, these operations do not possess the nice properties that we established in Section 8.3. There we proved two results, Theorem 8.3.1 and Theorem 8.3.2. The first of these applies in our present situation, which is very fortunate, but Theorem 8.3.2 fails here, if the ring $\circledB$ involved is not commutative. Here is the analogue of Theorem 8.3.1.

Theorem 8.5.1: Let $(B,\ +,\ \cdot,\ 0,\ 1)$ be a ring with identity where $0 \neq 1$, and let p and q be polynomials over B. Then $[p + q]_f = p_f + q_f$.

Proof: See the proof of Theorem 8.3.1.

Let us show that Theorem 8.3.2 is false for the case of a noncommutative ring.

Example 2: Consider the ring whose basic set consists of all 2×2 real matrices. Let $p = \begin{pmatrix} 1 & 0 \\ -1 & 1 \end{pmatrix} + \begin{pmatrix} 0 & 1 \\ 1 & 2 \end{pmatrix}x$, and let $q = \begin{pmatrix} 1 & 2 \\ 3 & 4 \end{pmatrix}x$. So $p\cdot q = \begin{pmatrix} 1 & 2 \\ 2 & 2 \end{pmatrix}x + \begin{pmatrix} 3 & 4 \\ 7 & 10 \end{pmatrix}x^2$. We point out that $[p\cdot q]_f$ associates $\begin{pmatrix} 17 & 17 \\ 38 & 38 \end{pmatrix}$ with $\begin{pmatrix} 1 & 1 \\ 1 & 1 \end{pmatrix}$; whereas p_f associates $\begin{pmatrix} 2 & 1 \\ 2 & 4 \end{pmatrix}$ with $\begin{pmatrix} 1 & 1 \\ 1 & 1 \end{pmatrix}$, and q_f associates $\begin{pmatrix} 3 & 3 \\ 7 & 7 \end{pmatrix}$ with $\begin{pmatrix} 1 & 1 \\ 1 & 1 \end{pmatrix}$, so $\begin{pmatrix} 13 & 13 \\ 34 & 34 \end{pmatrix}$ is the product of the matrices that p_f and q_f associate with $\begin{pmatrix} 1 & 1 \\ 1 & 1 \end{pmatrix}$. Thus

$$[p\cdot q]\begin{pmatrix} 1 & 1 \\ 1 & 1 \end{pmatrix} \neq p\begin{pmatrix} 1 & 1 \\ 1 & 1 \end{pmatrix}\cdot q\begin{pmatrix} 1 & 1 \\ 1 & 1 \end{pmatrix}.$$

Luckily, we can salvage a weakened form of Theorem 8.3.2 which we need to prove the *Cayley–Hamilton Theorem* of Section 10.3.

Theorem 8.5.2:   Let $\mathfrak{B} = (B, +, \cdot, 0, 1)$ be any ring with identity, $0 \neq 1$, and let p and q be polynomials over B.   Then $p(t) \cdot q(t) = [p \cdot q](t)$ provided that t commutes with each term of q.

Proof: We follow through the proof of Theorem 8.3.2.   Let $p = (a_1, \ldots, a_r)$, let $q = (b_1, \ldots, b_s)$, and let t be a member of B such that $b_1 \cdot t = t \cdot b_1, \ldots, b_s \cdot t = t \cdot b_s$.   Now,

$$p \cdot q = a_1 \cdot q + a_2 x \cdot q + \cdots + a_r x^{r-1} \cdot q$$

so $[p \cdot q](t) = [a_1 \cdot q](t) + [a_2 x \cdot q](t) + \cdots + [a_r x^{r-1} \cdot q](t)$ by Theorem 8.5.1

$$= \sum_{i=1}^{s} a_1 b_i t^{i-1} + \sum_{i=1}^{s} a_2 b_i t^{i} + \cdots + \sum_{i=1}^{s} a_r b_i t^{i+r-2}$$

$$= a_1 \sum_{i=1}^{s} b_i t^{i-1} + a_2 t \sum_{i=1}^{s} b_i t^{i-1} + \cdots + a_r t^{r-1} \sum_{i=1}^{s} b_i t^{i-1}$$

since $b_i t = t b_i$, $i = 1, \ldots, s$

$$= (a_1 + a_2 t + \cdots + a_r t^{r-1}) \sum_{i=1}^{s} b_i t^{i-1}$$

by a distributive law for $\mathfrak{B}$

$$= p(t) \cdot q(t) \ .$$

This establishes Theorem 8.5.2.

EXERCISES

1. Consider the integral domain $(I, +, \cdot, 0, 1)$ where I is the set of all integers, and $+$ and $\cdot$ are the usual operations of addition and multiplication.

    (a) Define $I[x]$.
    (b) Define addition and multiplication on $I[x]$.
    (c) Show that $(I[x], +, 0)$ is an abelian group, where 0 denotes the polynomial (0).
    (d) Show that $(I[x], +, \cdot, 0)$ is an integral domain.
    (e) Show that Lemma 8.4.1 does not apply to $(I[x], +, \cdot, 0)$.
    (f) Let p_1 and p_2 be any nonzero members of $I[x]$ such that $\deg p_2 \leq \deg p_1$. Show that there is an integer k and a polynomial q such that $k p_1 - q \cdot p_2 = 0$ or $\deg(k p_1 - q \cdot p_2) < \deg p_1$.

2. Consider the ring $(B, +, \cdot, 0)$ where $B = \{0, 1, 2, 3, 4, 5\}$, and $+$ and $\cdot$ denote addition modulo 6 and multiplication modulo 6, respectively.

    (a) Define $B[x]$.
    (b) Define addition and multiplication on $B[x]$.

(c) Show that $(B[x], +, 0)$ is an abelian group, where 0 denotes the polynomial (0).

(d) Show that $(B[x], +, \cdot, 0)$ is a commutative ring with identity, and that this ring is *not* an integral domain.

3. Show that the ring whose basic set consists of all 2×2 real matrices, is non-abelian and possesses divisors of zero.

4. Prove Theorem 8.5.1.

5. (a) Find 2×2 real matrices, say A and B, such that $[A - B][A + B] \neq A^2 - B^2$.

(b) Given that D and E are real square matrices such that $DE = ED$, prove that $D^2 - E^2 = [D - E][D + E]$.

(c) Given that D and E are real square matrices such that $DE = ED$, prove that $D^n - E^n$ is divisible by $D - E$ whenever $n \in N$.

(d) Let D and E be square matrices over F, where $(F, +, \cdot, 0, 1)$ is a field, such that $DE = ED$, and let $p \in F[x]$. Prove that there is a matrix M over F such that $p(D) - p(E) = (D - E)M$.

9

LINEAR OPERATORS

9.1 LINEAR TRANSFORMATIONS

In Section 7.3 we found that for certain problems it is helpful to use one ordered basis rather than another ordered basis. There we deliberately avoided the question: "How do we find an ordered basis that suits a particular problem?" It turns out that this is a rather large question. In this chapter we make a small start towards solving this problem by developing the notion of a linear operator.

First, we introduce the notion of a *vector function*. By a *vector function* we mean any mapping of a set of vectors into a set of vectors; so a vector function is a set of ordered pairs whose terms are vectors. Using the customary functional notation, $f(\gamma)$ denotes the vector that the vector function f associates with γ. A vector function possesses both a *domain* and an *image;* the *domain* of f is the set of all first terms of members of f, and the *image* of f is the set of all second terms of members of f. The term image can be generalized as follows: let S be any subset of the domain of f, then $f(S) = \{f(\gamma) \mid \gamma \in S\}$ is called the *image of S*. For example, consider the vector space $\mathcal{R}_3$ and let f be the vector function such that $f(\gamma) = (2, -1, 3) + \gamma$ whenever $\gamma \in R_3$. Clearly, R_3 is the domain of f; moreover, $f(R_3) = R_3$ so R_3 is the image of f. On the other hand, let g be the vector function such that $g(\gamma) = (1, 2)$ whenever $\gamma \in R_3$; here, the domain of g is R_3 but its image is $\{(1, 2)\}$.

In this chapter we concentrate on certain vector functions known as *linear transformations*. This notion is based on the observation that each ordered basis for a vector space leads us to a vector function. To clarify this point, consider Example 1 of Section 7.3; there, using the ordered basis $\mathcal{B} = ((1, 0, 0, 0), (0, 1, 0, 0), (0, 0, 1, 0))$, we associate the 3-vector $[\gamma]_{\mathcal{B}}$ with γ whenever γ is a 4-vector with 4th term 0. Notice that the domain of this vector function is

$\{(a, b, c, 0) \mid \{a, b, c\} \subset R\}$, a proper subset of R_4. Essentially, then, we can regard an ordered basis as a vector function; this is an effective method of studying ordered bases since the algebra of functions is highly developed. As always, an approach that permits the application of algebraic processes is extremely fruitful.

Now, in Lemmas 7.3.1 and 7.3.2 we display two useful properties of an ordered basis. We use these properties to delimit the class of vector functions considered in this section. Here is our definition.

Definition 9.1.1: Let $V = (\mathfrak{F}, \mathcal{V}, \circ)$ and $V' = (\mathfrak{F}, \mathcal{V}', \circ')$ be vector spaces with the same supporting field $\mathfrak{F}$, where $\mathcal{V} = (V, +, 0)$ and $\mathcal{V}' = (V', +', 0')$. Then T is said to be a *linear transformation of* V *into* V' if and only if:

(*i*) T is a mapping of V into V';
(*ii*) $T(\alpha + \beta) = T(\alpha) +' T(\beta)$ whenever $\{\alpha, \beta\} \subset V$;
(*iii*) $T(k \circ \alpha) = k \circ' T(\alpha)$ whenever $\alpha \in V$ and $k \in F$.

We have used $'$ to help separate the two vector spaces involved in this definition; the vector operations of the vector spaces V and V' are usually different, and should be kept distinct. Sometimes, however, we deal with vector spaces for which vector addition is denoted by the same symbol and for which scalar multiplication is denoted by juxtaposition (e.g. $\mathcal{R}_3$ and $\mathcal{R}_4$). Keep alert to this possibility.

Let us illustrate Definition 9.1.1. Our first example points out that a linear transformation can be constructed from an ordered basis for a finite-dimensional vector space.

Example 1: Let $V = (\mathcal{R}, \mathcal{V}, \circ)$ be any n-dimensional real vector space, let $\mathcal{B}$ be any ordered basis for V, and let $T = \{(\gamma, [\gamma]_\mathcal{B}) \mid \gamma \in V\}$. Certainly T is a mapping of V into R_n; moreover

$$T(\alpha + \gamma) = [\alpha + \gamma]_\mathcal{B} = [\alpha]_\mathcal{B} + [\gamma]_\mathcal{B} \qquad \text{by Lemma 7.3.1}$$
$$= T(\alpha) + T(\gamma)$$

and $$T(k \circ \alpha) = [k \circ \alpha]_\mathcal{B} = k[\alpha]_\mathcal{B} \qquad \text{by Lemma 7.3.2}$$
$$= k\,T(\alpha)$$

whenever $\{\alpha, \gamma\} \subset V$ and $k \in R$. So, T is a linear transformation of V into $\mathcal{R}_n$.

Example 2: Consider the vector spaces $\mathcal{R}_3$ and $\mathcal{R}_4$, and let T be the mapping of R_3 into R_4 such that $T(a, b, c) = (a, b, c, a + b + c)$ whenever $(a, b, c) \in R_3$. It is easy to verify that $T(\alpha + \beta) = T(\alpha) + T(\beta)$ and that $T(k\alpha) = k\,T(\alpha)$ whenever $\{\alpha, \beta\} \subset R_3$ and $k \in R$. So, T is a linear transformation of $\mathcal{R}_3$ into $\mathcal{R}_4$.

Example 3: Let V be the vector space of Example 3, Section 7.1, that involves all mappings of $\{0, 1\}$ into F. Let T be the mapping of V into R_2 such that $T(f) = (f(0), f(1))$ whenever $f \in V$. It is easy to verify that $T(f + g) = T(f) + T(g)$ and that $T(kf) = k\,T(f)$ whenever $\{f, g\} \subset V$ and $k \in F$. So, T is a linear transformation of V into $\mathcal{R}_2$.

Example 4: Let V be the vector space of Example 5, Section 7.1, that involves all continuous functions with domain $[0, 1]$. Let I be the mapping of V into R such that $I(f) = \int_0^1 f$ whenever $f \in V$. We point out that $I(f + g) = I(f) + I(g)$ and that $I(kf) = k\,I(f)$ whenever $\{f, g\} \subset V$ and $k \in R$. So, I is a linear transformation of V into $\mathfrak{R}_1$.

Example 5: Let $V = (\mathfrak{R}, \mathfrak{M}, \circ)$ be the vector space of Example 8, Section 7.1, and let T be the mapping of M into R_n such that $T(A) = A_1$ whenever A is an $m \times n$ matrix. Now,

$$T(A + B) = (A + B)_1 = A_1 + B_1 = T(A) + T(B)$$

and

$$T(k\,A) = (k\,A)_1 = k\,A_1 = k\,T(A)$$

whenever A and B are $m \times n$ matrices and $k \in R$. So, T is a linear transformation of V into $\mathfrak{R}_n$.

Example 6: Let V be the vector space of Example 5 with $m = n$, and let trace $A = \sum_{i=1}^{n} a_{ii}$ whenever $A = (a_{ij})$ is an $n \times n$ matrix (see Exercise 16, Section 3.4). Notice that *trace* is a mapping of M into R. Clearly, trace$(A + B)$ = trace A + trace B and trace$(k\,A) = k$ trace A whenever A and B are $n \times n$ matrices and $k \in R$. So, *trace* is a linear transformation of V into $\mathfrak{R}_1$.

Example 7: Let C be any $m \times n$ matrix, and let T be the mapping that associates γC with γ whenever $\gamma \in R_m$. It is easy to verify that T is a linear transformation of $\mathfrak{R}_m$ into $\mathfrak{R}_n$.

The idea of Example 7 can be generalized by utilizing ordered bases for the vector spaces involved. For simplicity we shall take $m = n$, which eliminates one basis. We rely on the following result throughout Section 9.2.

Lemma 9.1.1: Let $\mathfrak{B}$ be any ordered basis for V, an n-dimensional vector space, and let C be an $n \times n$ matrix. Then there is a unique mapping of V into V, say T, such that $[T(\gamma)]_{\mathfrak{B}} = [\gamma]_{\mathfrak{B}} C$ whenever $\gamma \in V$.

Proof: Let $\mathfrak{B} = (\beta_1, \ldots, \beta_n)$ and let $\gamma \in V$. We must show that there is a unique vector γ' such that

$$(1) \qquad\qquad [\gamma']_{\mathfrak{B}} = [\gamma]_{\mathfrak{B}} C$$

Now, $[\gamma]_{\mathfrak{B}} C$ is a $1 \times n$ matrix which we shall interpret as an n-vector; let $[\gamma]_{\mathfrak{B}} C = (t_1, \ldots, t_n)$. Notice that $\gamma' = t_1 \beta_1 + \cdots + t_n \beta_n$ satisfies (1); moreover, by Theorem 7.3.1, this is the only vector that satisfies (1). We conclude that $T(\gamma) = t_1 \beta_1 + \cdots + t_n \beta_n$. This establishes our result. We mention that T is a linear transformation of V into V (see Theorem 9.2.1).

Let us illustrate Lemma 9.1.1.

Example 8: Let W be the subspace of Example 2, Section 7.3. Exhibit T, the mapping of W into W such that $[T(\gamma)]_\mathfrak{B} = [\gamma]_\mathfrak{B} C$ whenever $\gamma \in W$, where $\mathfrak{B} = ((2, 0, -1), (1, 2, 0))$ and $C = \begin{pmatrix} 2 & 0 \\ 1 & -1 \end{pmatrix}$.

Solution: Let $\gamma = a(2, 0, -1) + b(1, 2, 0)$ be any member of W; so $[\gamma]_\mathfrak{B} = (a, b)$. Thus

$$[\gamma]_\mathfrak{B} C = (a, b) \begin{pmatrix} 2 & 0 \\ 1 & -1 \end{pmatrix} = (2a + b, -b) .$$

Therefore, $T(\gamma) = (2a + b)(2, 0, -1) + (-b)(1, 2, 0) = (4a + b, -2b, -2a - b)$. Summarizing, if $[\gamma]_\mathfrak{B} = (a, b)$ then $T(\gamma) = (4a + b, -2b, -2a - b)$ a member of W. So T is the required mapping.

EXERCISES

1. Let T be the vector function such that $T(a_1, a_2, a_3) = (a_2, 0)$ whenever $(a_1, a_2, a_3) \in R_3$.

    (a) Show that T is a linear transformation of $\mathfrak{R}_3$ into $\mathfrak{R}_2$.
    (b) Compute the dimension of the subspace $T(R_3)$.

2. Let T be the vector function such that $T(a_1, a_2, a_3) = (a_1, a_2)$ whenever $(a_1, a_2, a_3) \in R_3$.

    (a) Show that T is a linear transformation of $\mathfrak{R}_3$ into $\mathfrak{R}_2$.
    (b) Compute the dimension of $T(R_3)$.

3. Let T be the vector function such that $T(a_1, a_2, a_3) = (0, a_1)$ whenever $(a_1, a_2, a_3) \in R_3$.

    (a) Show that T is a linear transformation of $\mathfrak{R}_3$ into $\mathfrak{R}_2$.
    (b) Compute the dimension of $T(R_3)$.

4. Let T be the vector function such that $T(a_1, a_2, a_3) = (a_1 + a_2, 0, 0)$ whenever $(a_1, a_2, a_3) \in R_3$.

    (a) Show that T is a linear transformation of $\mathfrak{R}_3$ into $\mathfrak{R}_3$.
    (b) Compute the dimension of $T(R_3)$.

5. Let T be the vector function such that $T(a_1, a_2, a_3) = (a_1 + a_2, a_2, a_3)$ whenever $(a_1, a_2, a_3) \in R_3$.

    (a) Show that T is a linear transformation of $\mathfrak{R}_3$ into $\mathfrak{R}_3$.
    (b) Find a basis for the subspace $T(R_3)$.

6. Show that T is a linear transformation of V into V, given that $T(\alpha) = \alpha$ whenever $\alpha \in V$.

7. Show that T is a linear transformation of $\mathfrak{R}_3$ into $\mathfrak{R}_2$, given that $T(a, b, c) = (a + b, a + c)$ whenever $(a, b, c) \in R_3$.

8. Show that T is a linear transformation of $\mathcal{R}_3$ into $\mathcal{R}_2$, given that $T(a, b, c) = (a + b, a - c)$ whenever $(a, b, c) \in R_3$.

9. Show that T is a linear transformation of $\mathcal{R}_3$ into $\mathcal{R}_2$, given that $T(a, b, c) = (a, b)$ whenever $(a, b, c) \in R_3$.

10. Show that T is a linear transformation of $\mathcal{R}_2$ into $\mathcal{R}_3$, given that $T(a, b) = (a, b, 0)$ whenever $(a, b) \in R_2$.

11. Show that T is *not* a linear transformation of $\mathcal{R}_3$ into $\mathcal{R}_3$, given that $T(a_1, a_2, a_3) = (1 + a_1, a_2, a_3)$ whenever $(a_1, a_2, a_3) \in R_3$.

12. Show that T is *not* a linear transformation of $\mathcal{R}_3$ into $\mathcal{R}_2$, given that $T(a, b, c) = (a, 1)$ whenever $(a, b, c) \in R_3$.

13. Let T be a linear transformation of V into V'.

    (a) Prove that $T(0) = 0'$.
    (b) Prove that $T(\alpha - \gamma) = T(\alpha) -' T(\gamma)$ whenever $\{\alpha, \gamma\} \subset V$.
    (c) Prove that $T(W)$ is a subspace of V' if W is a subspace of V.
    (d) Prove that the image of T is a subspace of V'.

14. Let T be the mapping of Example 7; verify that T is a linear transformation of $\mathcal{R}_m$ into $\mathcal{R}_n$.

15. Let $T(\gamma) = \gamma \begin{pmatrix} 2 & 0 \\ 1 & -1 \\ 4 & 5 \end{pmatrix}$ whenever $\gamma \in R_3$.

    (a) Exhibit $T(a, b, c)$.
    (b) Simplify $T(3, -1, 1) + T(5, 1, -2) + 2\,T(-4, 0, 1)$.

16. Prove that the mapping of Lemma 9.1.1 is a linear transformation of V into V.

17. Let $W = L\{(3, 0, 1, 2), (1, 4, 0, 1), (2, 1, 0, 0)\}$, let $\mathcal{B} = ((3, 0, 1, 2), (1, 4, 0, 1), (2, 1, 0, 0))$, and let $C = \begin{pmatrix} 1 & 0 & 1 \\ 2 & 1 & -1 \\ 0 & 2 & 1 \end{pmatrix}$.
    Exhibit T, the mapping of W into W such that $[T(\gamma)]_\mathcal{B} = [\gamma]_\mathcal{B} C$ whenever $\gamma \in W$.

18. Exhibit T, the mapping of R_4 into R_4 such that $[T(\gamma)]_\mathcal{B} = [\gamma]_\mathcal{B} C$ whenever $\gamma \in R_4$, where $\mathcal{B} = ((1, 0, -1, 0), (2, 0, 0, 3), (0, 1, \cdot 1, 0),$
    $(0, 2, 0, 0))$ and $C = \begin{pmatrix} 1 & 1 & 3 & 1 \\ 2 & 4 & -3 & 2 \\ 0 & 1 & 0 & 0 \\ 6 & 0 & -6 & 0 \end{pmatrix}$.

19. Let $\mathcal{B}$ be an ordered basis for V, an m-dimensional real vector space, let $\mathcal{B}'$ be an ordered basis for V', an n-dimensional real vector space, and let C be any $m \times n$ matrix. Prove that there is a unique mapping T of V into V'

such that $[T(\gamma)]_{\mathcal{B}'} = [\gamma]_{\mathcal{B}} C$ whenever $\gamma \in V$. Show that T is a linear transformation of V into V'.

20. Exhibit T, the mapping of R_2 into R_3 such that $[T(\gamma)]_{\mathcal{B}'} = [\gamma]_{\mathcal{B}} C$ whenever $\gamma \in R_2$, where $\mathcal{B} = ((1, 1), (1, 0))$, $\mathcal{B}' = ((1, 0, 1), (0, 1, 1), (1, 1, 0))$, and $C = \begin{pmatrix} 2 & 1 & 0 \\ 0 & -1 & 1 \end{pmatrix}$. Use Definition 9.1.1 to show that T is a linear transformation of $\mathcal{R}_2$ into $\mathcal{R}_3$.

9.2 LINEAR OPERATORS

We now concentrate on linear transformations of a special class, namely linear transformations of a vector space into itself. This sort of linear transformation is called a *linear operator*.

Definition 9.2.1: A linear transformation of V into V is said to be a *linear operator* on V.

So, a mapping T of V into V is a linear operator on V if and only if $T(\alpha + \gamma) = T(\alpha) + T(\gamma)$ and $T(k\alpha) = kT(\alpha)$ whenever $\{\alpha, \gamma\} \subset V$ and k is a scalar. Here are some examples.

Example 1: Let A be an $n \times n$ matrix over R, and let T be the mapping of R_n into R_n such that $T(\gamma) = \gamma A$ whenever $\gamma \in R_n$. Now, $T(\alpha + \gamma) = (\alpha + \gamma)A = \alpha A + \gamma A = T(\alpha) + T(\gamma)$ and $T(k\alpha) = (k\alpha)A = k(\alpha A) = kT(\alpha)$ whenever $\{\alpha, \gamma\} \subset R_n$ and $k \in R$. Thus, T is a linear operator on $\mathcal{R}_n$.

Example 2: Let V be the vector space of Theorem 8.1.2, where $\mathfrak{F} = \mathcal{R}$, that involves polynomials over R. Let D be the mapping of $R[x]$ into $R[x]$ that associates $(a_2, 2a_3, \ldots, (s-1)a_s)$ with $(a_1, \ldots, a_s)$; i.e., $D(p)$ is the derivative of p whenever $p \in R[x]$. It is easy to verify that $D(p + q) = D(p) + D(q)$ and $D(kp) = kD(p)$ whenever $\{p, q\} \subset R[x]$ and $k \in R$; so, D is a linear operator on V.

Example 3: Let V be the vector space of Example 2. Let I be the mapping of $R[x]$ into $R[x]$ such that $I(p) = (0, a_1, a_2/2, \ldots, a_s/s)$ whenever $p = (a_1, \ldots, a_s)$. Notice that $I(p)$ is the polynomial that associates $\int_0^t p$ with t, whenever $t \in R$. Using this fact, we see that $I(p + q) = I(p) + I(q)$ and $I(kp) = kI(p)$ whenever $\{p, q\} \subset R[x]$ and $k \in R$. So, I is a linear operator on V.

Example 4: Let V be any vector space and let a be any scalar. Let μ be the mapping of V into V such that $\mu(\gamma) = a\gamma$ whenever $\gamma \in V$. Here, $\mu(\alpha + \gamma) = a(\alpha + \gamma) = a\alpha + a\gamma = \mu(\alpha) + \mu(\gamma)$ and $\mu(k\gamma) = a(k\gamma) = k(a\gamma) = k\mu(\gamma)$ whenever $\{\alpha, \gamma\} \subset V$ and k is a scalar. So, μ is a linear operator on V; i.e., scalar multiplication by a fixed scalar is a linear operator on the vector space involved.

The following lemmas are easy to establish.

Lemma 9.2.1: Let T be a linear operator on a vector space V; then $T(0) = 0$.

Lemma 9.2.2: Let T be a linear operator on a vector space V; then $T(\alpha - \gamma) = T(\alpha) - T(\gamma)$ whenever $\{\alpha, \gamma\} \subset V$.

Lemma 9.2.3: Let T be a linear operator on a vector space V; then $T\left(\sum_{i=1}^{n} k_i \gamma_i\right) = \sum_{i=1}^{n} k_i T(\gamma_i)$ whenever the γ's are vectors and the k's are scalars.

In Example 1 we used a matrix to construct a linear operator on $\mathfrak{R}_n$; this idea can be generalized to any finite-dimensional vector space.

Theorem 9.2.1: Let $\mathfrak{B}$ be an ordered basis for V, an n-dimensional vector space, and let C be any $n \times n$ matrix. Let T be the mapping of V into V such that $[T(\gamma)]_\mathfrak{B} = [\gamma]_\mathfrak{B} C$ whenever $\gamma \in V$; then T is a linear operator on V.

Proof: By Lemma 9.1.1 there is a unique mapping T of V into V such that $[T(\gamma)]_\mathfrak{B} = [\gamma]_\mathfrak{B} C$ whenever $\gamma \in V$. We must prove that T is a linear operator on V. Let $\{\alpha, \gamma\} \subset V$ and let k be any scalar; then

$$\begin{aligned}
[T(\alpha + \gamma)]_\mathfrak{B} &= [\alpha + \gamma]_\mathfrak{B} C \\
&= ([\alpha]_\mathfrak{B} + [\gamma]_\mathfrak{B})C \qquad \text{by Lemma 7.3.1} \\
&= [\alpha]_\mathfrak{B} C + [\gamma]_\mathfrak{B} C \\
&= [T(\alpha)]_\mathfrak{B} + [T(\gamma)]_\mathfrak{B}
\end{aligned}$$

and it follows that $T(\alpha + \gamma) = T(\alpha) + T(\gamma)$. Also,

$$\begin{aligned}
[T(k\gamma)]_\mathfrak{B} &= [k\gamma]_\mathfrak{B} C = (k[\gamma]_\mathfrak{B})C \qquad \text{by Lemma 7.3.2} \\
&= k([\gamma]_\mathfrak{B} C) = k[T(\gamma)]_\mathfrak{B}
\end{aligned}$$

and it follows that $T(k\gamma) = k T(\gamma)$. We conclude that T is a linear operator on V.

The matrix C that characterizes the linear operator of Theorem 9.2.1 is particularly interesting and valuable. Here is a key property of this matrix.

Lemma 9.2.4: Let T be the linear operator of Theorem 9.2.1 and let $\mathfrak{B} = (\beta_1, \ldots, \beta_n)$; then $C_i = [T(\beta_i)]_\mathfrak{B}$, $i = 1, \ldots, n$.

Proof: By Theorem 9.2.1, $[T(\beta_i)]_\mathfrak{B} = [\beta_i]_\mathfrak{B} C = \epsilon_i C = C_i$, $i = 1, \ldots, n$.

We must give C a name.

Definition 9.2.2: Let $\mathfrak{B} = (\beta_1, \ldots, \beta_n)$ be an ordered basis for V, let T be a linear operator on V, and let C be the $n \times n$ matrix such that $C_i = [T(\beta_i)]_\mathfrak{B}$, $i = 1, \ldots, n$. Then C is said to be *the matrix of T with respect to $\mathfrak{B}$*, and is denoted by $[T]_\text{ß}$. If ß $= (\epsilon_1 , \ldots , \epsilon_n)$ then $[T]_\text{ß}$ is said to be *the matrix of T* and is denoted by $[T]$.

Let us illustrate this notion.

Example 5: Let ß $= (\beta_1 , \beta_2 , \beta_3 , \beta_4)$ where $\beta_1 = (3 , 0 , 1 , -1)$, $\beta_2 = (1 , 1 , -1 , 0)$, $\beta_3 = (1 , 0 , 0 , 2)$, and $\beta_4 = (0 , 1 , -1 , 1)$; clearly, ß is an ordered basis for $\Re_4$. Let T be the linear operator on $\Re_4$ such that $T(\beta_1) = (6 , -1 , 3 , -3)$, $T(\beta_2) = (4 , -1 , 2 , 0)$, $T(\beta_3) = (7 , 1 , 1 , -2)$, and $T(\beta_4) = (3 , 1 , 0 , 0)$. Notice that $T(\beta_1) = 2\beta_1 - \beta_4$, $T(\beta_2) = \beta_1 + \beta_3 - \beta_4$, $T(\beta_3) = 2\beta_1 + \beta_2$, and $T(\beta_4) = \beta_1 + \beta_4$. So, by Definition 9.2.2,

$$[T]_\text{ß} = \begin{pmatrix} 2 & 0 & 0 & -1 \\ 1 & 0 & 1 & -1 \\ 2 & 1 & 0 & 0 \\ 1 & 0 & 0 & 1 \end{pmatrix} .$$

Continuing our example, let us work out the terms of $T(\gamma)$ where $\gamma = (11 , -1 , 4 , 2) = 3\beta_1 - 2\beta_2 + 4\beta_3 + \beta_4$.   By Lemma 9.2.3,

$$T(\gamma) = 3T(\beta_1) - 2T(\beta_2) + 4T(\beta_3) + T(\beta_4)$$

$$= 3(2\beta_1 - \beta_4) - 2(\beta_1 + \beta_3 - \beta_4) + 4(2\beta_1 + \beta_2) + (\beta_1 + \beta_4)$$

$$= 13\beta_1 + 4\beta_2 - 2\beta_3 .$$

So $[T(\gamma)]_\text{ß} = (13 , 4 , -2 , 0)$. To motivate our next theorem, we point out that $[\gamma]_\text{ß}[T]_\text{ß} = (3 , -2 , 4 , 1) \begin{pmatrix} 2 & 0 & 0 & -1 \\ 1 & 0 & 1 & -1 \\ 2 & 1 & 0 & 0 \\ 1 & 0 & 0 & 1 \end{pmatrix} = (13 , 4 , -2 , 0)$.

We point out that each linear operator on a finite-dimensional vector space can be characterized in the manner of Theorem 9.2.1.

Theorem 9.2.2: Let T be a linear operator on V, a finite-dimensional vector space, and let ß be an ordered basis for V. Then $[T(\gamma)]_\text{ß} = [\gamma]_\text{ß}[T]_\text{ß}$ whenever $\gamma \in V$.

Proof: Let ß $= (\beta_1 , \ldots , \beta_n)$ and let $C = [T]_\text{ß}$. Let $\gamma \in V$ and let $[\gamma]_\text{ß} = (k_1 , \ldots , k_n)$; so $T(\gamma) = T\left(\sum_{i=1}^{n} k_i \beta_i\right) = \sum_{i=1}^{n} k_i T(\beta_i)$ by Lemma 9.2.3.   Thus,

$$[T(\gamma)]_\text{ß} = k_1 [T(\beta_1)]_\text{ß} + \cdots + k_n [T(\beta_n)]_\text{ß} \qquad \text{by Lemmas 7.3.1 and 7.3.2}$$

$$= k_1 C_1 + \cdots + k_n C_n$$

$$= [\gamma]_\text{ß} C$$

$$= [\gamma]_\text{ß} [T]_\text{ß} .$$

This completes our proof.

We have mentioned that Lemma 9.2.4 is a key property; indeed, this is a subtle and significant result. To make our point, we formulate Lemma 9.2.4 as follows.

Lemma 9.2.4: Let T be a linear operator on V, a finite-dimensional vector space with ordered basis $\mathcal{B}$ such that $[T(\gamma)]_\mathcal{B} = [\gamma]_\mathcal{B} C$ whenever $\gamma \in V$. Then $C = [T]_\mathcal{B}$.

To bring out the power of Lemma 9.2.4, we now consider the relation between $[T]_\alpha$ and $[T]_\mathcal{B}$ where α and $\mathcal{B}$ are ordered bases for V.

Lemma 9.2.5: Let α and $\mathcal{B}$ be ordered bases for V, a finite-dimensional vector space, and let T be a linear operator on V. Then $[T]_\alpha = [\alpha]_\mathcal{B} [T]_\mathcal{B} [\mathcal{B}]_\alpha$.

Proof: Let $\gamma \in V$; then

$$[T(\gamma)]_\alpha = [T(\gamma)]_\mathcal{B} [\mathcal{B}]_\alpha \qquad \text{by Theorem 7.3.2}$$

$$= [\gamma]_\mathcal{B} [T]_\mathcal{B} [\mathcal{B}]_\alpha \qquad \text{by Theorem 9.2.2}$$

$$= [\gamma]_\alpha [\alpha]_\mathcal{B} [T]_\mathcal{B} [\mathcal{B}]_\alpha \qquad \text{by Theorem 7.3.2 .}$$

So, by Lemma 9.2.4, $[T]_\alpha = [\alpha]_\mathcal{B} [T]_\mathcal{B} [\mathcal{B}]_\alpha$.

Example 6: Let $\alpha = ((2, 0, 1), (1, 1, 0), (1, 1, 1))$, let $\mathcal{B} = ((-1, -3, -2), (7, 7, 5), (4, 4, 4))$, and let T be the linear operator on $\mathcal{R}_3$ such that $[T]_\alpha = \begin{pmatrix} 4 & -1 & 0 \\ 2 & 3 & -1 \\ 1 & -2 & 5 \end{pmatrix}$. Determine $[T]_\mathcal{B}$ and compute $T(-1, -3, -2)$.

Solution: We shall obtain $[T]_\mathcal{B}$ by applying Lemma 9.2.5. By Examples 3 and 4 of Section 7.3, $[\mathcal{B}]_\alpha = \begin{pmatrix} 1 & 0 & -3 \\ 0 & 2 & 5 \\ 0 & 0 & 4 \end{pmatrix}$ and $[\alpha]_\mathcal{B} = \frac{1}{8}\begin{pmatrix} 8 & 0 & 6 \\ 0 & 4 & -5 \\ 0 & 0 & 2 \end{pmatrix}$. So, by

Lemma 9.2.5, $[T]_\mathcal{B} = \frac{1}{8}\begin{pmatrix} 1 & 0 & -3 \\ 0 & 2 & 5 \\ 0 & 0 & 4 \end{pmatrix}\begin{pmatrix} 4 & -1 & 0 \\ 2 & 3 & -1 \\ 1 & -2 & 5 \end{pmatrix}\begin{pmatrix} 8 & 0 & 6 \\ 0 & 4 & -5 \\ 0 & 0 & 2 \end{pmatrix}$

$$= \frac{1}{8}\begin{pmatrix} 8 & 20 & -49 \\ 72 & -16 & 120 \\ 32 & -32 & 104 \end{pmatrix} .$$

Noting that $(-1, -3, -2)$ is a basis vector of $\mathcal{B}$, and considering the significance of $[T]_\mathcal{B}$, we see that

$$T(-1, -3, -2) = \tfrac{1}{8}[8(-1, -3, -2) + 20(7, 7, 5) - 49(4, 4, 4)]$$

$$= (-8, -10, -14).$$

EXERCISES

1. Prove Lemma 9.2.1.

2. Prove Lemma 9.2.2.

3. Prove Lemma 9.2.3.

4. Let $(\beta_1, \ldots, \beta_n)$ be an ordered basis for a vector space V, and let $\{\alpha_1, \ldots, \alpha_n\} \subset V$. Prove that there is a unique linear operator on V, say T, such that $T(\beta_i) = \alpha_i$, $i = 1, \ldots, n$.

5. Let T be the linear operator on $\mathcal{R}_3$ such that $T(\epsilon_1) = (2, 0, 1)$, $T(\epsilon_2) = (1, 1, 0)$, and $T(\epsilon_3) = (0, 1, -1)$.

   (a) Write down $[T]$.
   (b) Compute $T(3, 1, -1)$.
   (c) Compute $T(4, 0, 2)$.

6. Let T be the linear operator on $\mathcal{R}_3$ such that $T(1, 1, -1) = (2, 0, 1)$, $T(0, 0, 1) = (0, 1, 2)$, and $T(1, 0, 1) = (2, 1, -1)$; let $\mathcal{B} = ((1, 1, -1), (0, 0, 1), (1, 0, 1))$.

   (a) Determine $[(2, 0, 1)]_{\mathcal{B}}$, $[(0, 1, 2)]_{\mathcal{B}}$, $[(2, 1, -1)]_{\mathcal{B}}$.
   (b) Exhibit $[T]_{\mathcal{B}}$.
   (c) Compute $[T(\epsilon_1)]_{\mathcal{B}}$.
   (d) Compute $T(\epsilon_1)$.

7. Let $\alpha = ((1, 1, -1), (0, 0, 1), (1, 0, 1))$, let $\mathcal{B} = ((2, 0, 1), (1, 1, 0), (0, 1, -1))$, and let T be the linear operator on $\mathcal{R}_3$ such that

$$[T]_\alpha = \begin{pmatrix} 0 & 1 & 1 \\ 1 & 0 & -1 \\ 1 & 1 & 2 \end{pmatrix}. \text{ Find } [T]_{\mathcal{B}}.$$

8. Let $(\beta_1, \ldots, \beta_n)$ be an ordered orthonormal basis for $\mathcal{R}_n$, i.e., $\beta_i \cdot \beta_j = \delta_{ij}$ for each i and j. Let T be the mapping of R_n into R_n such that $T(\gamma) = (a_1, \ldots, a_n)$ where $a_i = \beta_i \cdot \gamma$, $i = 1, \ldots, n$, whenever $\gamma \in R_n$.

   (a) Show that T is a linear operator on $\mathcal{R}_n$.
   (b) Show that $T(\gamma) = \gamma C$ whenever $\gamma \in R_n$, where C is the $n \times n$ matrix such that $_iC = \beta_i$, $i = 1, \ldots, n$.
   (c) Show that $_i[T] = \beta_i$, $i = 1, \ldots, n$.
   (d) Show that T is a one-one mapping of R_n onto R_n.

9. Let T be a linear operator on a finite-dimensional vector space V, and let α and $\mathcal{B}$ be ordered bases for V such that $[T]_\alpha = [T]_{\mathcal{B}}$. Prove that $[T]_\alpha [\mathcal{B}]_\alpha = [\mathcal{B}]_\alpha [T]_\alpha$.

10. A linear operator on $\mathcal{R}_n$, say T, is said to be *orthogonal* if and only if $\|T(\gamma)\| = \|\gamma\|$ whenever $\gamma \in R_n$. Show that the linear operator with matrix

$$\frac{1}{3} \begin{pmatrix} 1 & 2 & -2 \\ 2 & 1 & 2 \\ -2 & 2 & 1 \end{pmatrix} \text{ is orthogonal.}$$

11. Prove that a linear operator on $\mathcal{R}_n$, say T, is orthogonal if and only if $T(\alpha) \cdot T(\gamma) = \alpha \cdot \gamma$ whenever $\{\alpha, \gamma\} \subset R_n$.

12. A linear operator on $\mathcal{R}_n$, say T, is said to be *symmetric* if and only if there is an ordered orthonormal basis $\mathcal{C}$ for $\mathcal{R}_n$ such that $[T]_\mathcal{C}$ is symmetric (i.e., is the same as its transpose). Prove that a linear operator on $\mathcal{R}_n$, say T, is symmetric if and only if $T(\alpha) \cdot \gamma = \alpha \cdot T(\gamma)$ whenever $\{\alpha, \gamma\} \subset R_n$.

9.3 ALGEBRA OF LINEAR OPERATORS

The first step in developing the algebra of linear operators on a vector space **V**, is to show that these mappings form a vector space over the supporting field $\mathfrak{F}$ of **V**. Let $\mathcal{L}(V)$ denote the set of all linear operators on **V**; we now introduce vector addition and scalar multiplication.

Definition 9.3.1: Let T and U be any linear operators on **V**; then $T + U = \{(\alpha, \beta) \mid \alpha \in V \text{ and } \beta = T(\alpha) + U(\alpha)\}$.

Definition 9.3.2: Let T be any linear operator on **V** and let k be any scalar; then $kT = \{(\alpha, \beta) \mid \alpha \in V \text{ and } \beta = k T(\alpha)\}$.

We illustrate these concepts.

Example 1: Let T and U be the linear operators on $\mathcal{R}_3$ such that $T(\gamma) = \gamma \begin{pmatrix} 0 & 1 & 0 \\ 1 & 0 & 0 \\ 0 & 0 & -1 \end{pmatrix}$ and $U(\gamma) = \gamma \begin{pmatrix} 0 & 0 & 1 \\ 0 & -1 & 0 \\ 1 & 0 & 0 \end{pmatrix}$ whenever $\gamma \in R_3$. Then $T + U$ is the mapping that associates $\gamma \begin{pmatrix} 0 & 1 & 0 \\ 1 & 0 & 0 \\ 0 & 0 & -1 \end{pmatrix} + \gamma \begin{pmatrix} 0 & 0 & 1 \\ 0 & -1 & 0 \\ 1 & 0 & 0 \end{pmatrix}$ with γ whenever $\gamma \in R_3$; so

$$(T + U)(\gamma) = \gamma \begin{pmatrix} 0 & 1 & 1 \\ 1 & -1 & 0 \\ 1 & 0 & -1 \end{pmatrix}$$

whenever $\gamma \in R_3$. Here, $T + U$ is a linear operator on $\mathcal{R}_3$. Also, $3T$ denotes the mapping that associates $3\gamma \begin{pmatrix} 0 & 1 & 0 \\ 1 & 0 & 0 \\ 0 & 0 & -1 \end{pmatrix}$ with γ whenever $\gamma \in R_3$; i.e., $(3T)(\gamma) = \gamma \begin{pmatrix} 0 & 3 & 0 \\ 3 & 0 & 0 \\ 0 & 0 & -3 \end{pmatrix}$ whenever $\gamma \in R_3$. Here, $3T$ is a linear operator on $\mathcal{R}_3$. Notice that $[T + U] = \begin{pmatrix} 0 & 1 & 1 \\ 1 & -1 & 0 \\ 1 & 0 & -1 \end{pmatrix}$ and $[3T] = \begin{pmatrix} 0 & 3 & 0 \\ 3 & 0 & 0 \\ 0 & 0 & -3 \end{pmatrix}$. We point out that $[T + U] = [T] + [U]$ and that $[3T] = 3[T]$.

We mention that the mappings of Definitions 9.3.1 and 9.3.2 are linear operators on **V**.

Lemma 9.3.1: $+$ is a binary operation on $\mathcal{L}(V)$.

Note: We must show that $T + U$ is a linear operator on **V** whenever T and U are linear operators on **V**. The details are easy and are left as an exercise.

Lemma 9.3.2: $kT \in \mathcal{L}(V)$ whenever $T \in \mathcal{L}(V)$ and k is a scalar.

Next, we shall establish that $(\mathcal{L}(V), +, 0)$ is an abelian group, where $0 = \{(\alpha, \mathbf{0}) \mid \alpha \in V\}$.

Lemma 9.3.3: $0 \in \mathcal{L}(V)$.

Proof: Obvious.

Theorem 9.3.1: $(\mathcal{L}(V), +, 0)$ is an abelian group.

Proof: Show that $+$ is associative and commuta tive, that 0 is a right identity, and that $T + (-1)T = 0$ whenever $T \in \mathcal{L}(V)$.

It is easy, now, to demonstrate that linear operators form a vector space.

Theorem 9.3.2: $(\mathcal{F}, \mathcal{G}, \circ)$ is a vector space, where $\mathcal{G}$ is the group of Theorem 9.3.1, $\mathcal{F}$ is the field of, **V**, and $\circ$ is the scalar multiplication of Definition 9.3.2.

Proof: Consider Definition 7.1.1.

Let us show that we can extend $(\mathcal{L}(V), +, 0)$ to a ring. Of course, we need another binary operation on $\mathcal{L}(V)$.

Definition 9.3.3:   Let T and U be any linear operators on **V**; then $T \cdot U = \{(\alpha, \beta) \mid \alpha \in V \text{ and } \beta = U(T(\alpha))\}$.

Practicing our usual convention, we shall freely suppress the dot for multiplication. We mention that $\{(\alpha, \beta) \mid \alpha \in V \text{ and } \beta = T(U(\alpha))\}$, the *composite* of T and U, is sometimes defined to be the product of these mappings; we choose our notion of *product* in order to strengthen the connection between linear operators and matrices (see Theorem 9.3.4).

Example 2:   Let T and U be the linear operators of Example 1. Then $(TU)(\epsilon_1) = U(T(\epsilon_1)) = U(0, 1, 0) = (0, -1, 0)$, $(TU)(\epsilon_2) = U(T(\epsilon_2)) = U(1, 0, 0) = (0, 0, 1)$, and $(TU)(\epsilon_3) = U(T(\epsilon_3)) = U(0, 0, -1) = (-1, 0, 0)$. So

$$[TU] = \begin{pmatrix} 0 & -1 & 0 \\ 0 & 0 & 1 \\ -1 & 0 & 0 \end{pmatrix}.$$ Notice that $[T][U] = \begin{pmatrix} 0 & 1 & 0 \\ 1 & 0 & 0 \\ 0 & 0 & -1 \end{pmatrix}\begin{pmatrix} 0 & 0 & 1 \\ 0 & -1 & 0 \\ 1 & 0 & 0 \end{pmatrix} =$

$$\begin{pmatrix} 0 & -1 & 0 \\ 0 & 0 & 1 \\ -1 & 0 & 0 \end{pmatrix} = [TU].$$ We shall prove that this is always so (see Lemma 9.3.6).

Our goal is to show that $(\mathcal{L}(V), +, \cdot, 0)$ is a ring. First, we must be sure that $\cdot$ is a binary operation on $\mathcal{L}(V)$.

Lemma 9.3.4: $T \cdot U \in \mathcal{L}(V)$ whenever $\{T, U\} \subset \mathcal{L}(V)$.

Proof: This is left as an exercise.

We now present our main result.

Theorem 9.3.3: $(\mathcal{L}(V), +, \cdot, 0)$ is a ring.

Proof: In view of Theorem 6.1.1 and the fact that composition of mappings is associative, we see that $\cdot$ is associative. We now verify the distributive laws. Let $\{T_1, T_2, T_3\} \subset \mathcal{L}(V)$ and let $\gamma \in V$; then

$$\begin{aligned}
((T_2 + T_3) \cdot T_1)(\gamma) &= T_1((T_2 + T_3)(\gamma)) \\
&= T_1(T_2(\gamma) + T_3(\gamma)) && \text{by Definition 9.3.1} \\
&= T_1(T_2(\gamma)) + T_1(T_3(\gamma)) && \text{since } T_1 \in \mathcal{L}(V) \\
&= (T_2 \cdot T_1 + T_3 \cdot T_1)(\gamma) \ .
\end{aligned}$$

Therefore, $(T_2 + T_3) \cdot T_1 = T_2 \cdot T_1 + T_3 \cdot T_1$. It is easier to prove that $T_1 \cdot (T_2 + T_3) = T_1 \cdot T_2 + T_1 \cdot T_3$. Observe that

$$(T_1 \cdot (T_2 + T_3))(\gamma) = (T_2 + T_3)(T_1(\gamma)) = T_2(T_1(\gamma)) + T_3(T_1(\gamma)) = (T_1 T_2 + T_1 T_3)(\gamma)$$

whenever $\gamma \in V$; this establishes our second distributive law. We conclude that $(\mathcal{L}(V), +, \cdot, 0)$ is a ring.

In fact, $(\mathcal{L}(V), +, \cdot, 0)$ is a ring with identity; we note that $1 = \{(\alpha, \alpha) \mid \alpha \in V\}$ is a linear operator on V. Clearly, $T \cdot 1 = 1 \cdot T = T$ whenever $T \in \mathcal{L}(V)$.

We mention that the algebra of linear operators on a finite-dimensional vector space V, is really the algebra of matrices. We must clarify this statement. Let $\dim V = n$ and let M be the set of all $n \times n$ matrices over F; then $(\mathcal{L}(V), +, \cdot, 0)$ is isomorphic to $(M, +, \cdot, (0))$. By this we mean that the terms of these algebraic systems correspond exactly. We must show that there is a one-one mapping of $\mathcal{L}(V)$ onto M, say μ, such that applying μ to each term of $(\mathcal{L}(V), +, \cdot, 0)$ produces $(M, +, \cdot, (0))$. Thus, to demonstrate our claim that these algebraic systems are algebraically the same, we must produce a method of associating an $n \times n$ matrix with each linear operator on V, that transforms $(\mathcal{L}(V), +, \cdot, 0)$ into $(M, +, \cdot, (0))$. The idea is to choose an ordered basis $\mathcal{B}$ for V and to associate

$[T]_\mathfrak{B}$ with T whenever $T \in \mathfrak{L}(V)$. We have already suggested in our examples that this method of associating a matrix with a linear operator has the required properties. Let us prove this.

Lemma 9.3.5: Let $\mathfrak{B}$ be an ordered basis for V, a finite-dimensional vector space, and let $\{T,\ U\} \subset \mathfrak{L}(V)$. Then $[T + U]_\mathfrak{B} = [T]_\mathfrak{B} + [U]_\mathfrak{B}$.

Proof: Let $\mathfrak{B} = (\beta_1,\ \ldots,\ \beta_n)$, let $C = [T]_\mathfrak{B}$, and let $D = [U]_\mathfrak{B}$. Then

$$[(T + U)(\beta_i)]_\mathfrak{B} = [T(\beta_i) + U(\beta_i)]_\mathfrak{B}$$

$$= [T(\beta_i)]_\mathfrak{B} + [U(\beta_i)]_\mathfrak{B} \qquad \text{by Lemma 7.3.1}$$

$$= C_i + D_i \qquad \text{by Definition 9.2.2}$$

$$= (C + D)_i\ .$$

So, by Definition 9.2.2, $[T + U]_\mathfrak{B} = C + D$.

Lemma 9.3.6: Let $\mathfrak{B}$ be an ordered basis for V, a finite-dimensional vector space, and let $\{T,\ U\} \subset \mathfrak{L}(V)$. Then $[TU]_\mathfrak{B} = [T]_\mathfrak{B}\,[U]_\mathfrak{B}$.

Proof: Let $\mathfrak{B} = (\beta_1,\ \ldots,\ \beta_n)$, let $C = [T]_\mathfrak{B}$, and let $D = [U]_\mathfrak{B}$. Then

$$((TU))(\beta_i)]_\mathfrak{B} = [U(T(\beta_i))]_\mathfrak{B}$$

$$= [T(\beta_i)]_\mathfrak{B}\,[U]_\mathfrak{B} \qquad \text{by Theorem 9.2.2}$$

$$= C_i \cdot D \qquad \text{by Definition 9.2.2}$$

$$= (CD)_i \qquad \text{by Lemma 3.3.3}\ .$$

So, by Definition 9.2.2, $[TU]_\mathfrak{B} = CD$.

Let us illustrate these results.

Example 3: Let T and U be the linear operators on $\mathfrak{R}_3$ such that $[T] = \begin{pmatrix} 2 & 0 & 1 \\ 1 & -1 & 2 \\ 3 & 0 & 2 \end{pmatrix}$ and $[U] = \begin{pmatrix} -1 & 1 & 0 \\ 0 & 1 & 1 \\ 1 & -2 & 0 \end{pmatrix}$. Then $[T + U] = \begin{pmatrix} 1 & 1 & 1 \\ 1 & 0 & 3 \\ 4 & -2 & 2 \end{pmatrix}$ and

$[TU] = \begin{pmatrix} -1 & 0 & 0 \\ 1 & -4 & -1 \\ -1 & -1 & 0 \end{pmatrix}$. So, by Theorem 9.2.2, $(T + U)(\gamma) = \gamma \begin{pmatrix} 1 & 1 & 1 \\ 1 & 0 & 3 \\ 4 & -2 & 2 \end{pmatrix}$ and

$(TU)(\gamma) = \gamma \begin{pmatrix} -1 & 0 & 0 \\ 1 & -4 & -1 \\ -1 & -1 & 0 \end{pmatrix}$ whenever $\gamma \in R_3$. In particular, $(TU)(2,\ 4,\ -1) =$

$(2,\ 4,\ -1)\begin{pmatrix} -1 & 0 & 0 \\ 1 & -4 & -1 \\ -1 & -1 & 0 \end{pmatrix} = (3,\ -15,\ -4)$. Checking, $T(2,\ 4,\ -1) =$

$(2,\ 4,\ -1)[T] = (5,\ -4,\ 8)$;   so $(TU)(2,\ 4,\ -1) = U(5,\ -4,\ 8) =$
$(5,\ -4,\ 8)[U] = (3,\ -15,\ -4)$.

In view of Lemmas 9.3.5 and 9.3.6, it is now clear that our method of associating a matrix with each linear operator on V, achieves our goal. The point is that we can carry out calculations on linear operators by performing corresponding calculations on matrices, so obtaining a matrix; by reversing our mapping, this matrix leads us to the required linear operator. All this is expressed mathematically by the following theorem.

Theorem 9.3.4: Let $V = (\mathcal{F}, \mathcal{V}, \circ)$ be any n-dimensional vector space and let M be the set of all $n \times n$ matrices over F. Then $(\mathcal{L}(V), +, \cdot, 0) \cong (M, +, \cdot, (0))$.

We mention that the vector space of Theorem 9.3.2 is isomorphic to the vector space of Example 8, Section 7.1, with $m = n$. This relies on the following lemma.

Lemma 9.3.7: Let $\mathcal{B}$ be an ordered basis for V, a finite-dimensional vector space, let $T \in \mathcal{L}(V)$, and let k be a scalar. Then $[kT]_\mathcal{B} = k[T]_\mathcal{B}$.

Proof: The details are easy and are left as an exercise.

In this section we have introduced the linear operator $1 = \{(\alpha, \alpha) \mid \alpha \in V\}$ and the scalar product $kT = \{(\alpha, \beta) \mid \alpha \in V \text{ and } \beta = kT(\alpha)\}$. In particular, $k1 = \{(\alpha, \beta) \mid \alpha \in V \text{ and } \beta = k\alpha\}$ is a linear operator on V; we denote this linear operator by writing k, but only if it is obvious from the context that we have mentioned a linear operator and not a scalar.

EXERCISES

1. Let T and U be the linear operators on $\mathcal{R}_3$ such that

$$[T] = \begin{pmatrix} 2 & 0 & 1 \\ 1 & 1 & -2 \\ 3 & 1 & -1 \end{pmatrix} \quad \text{and} \quad [U] = \begin{pmatrix} -1 & 2 & 2 \\ 3 & 1 & 0 \\ 1 & 1 & -1 \end{pmatrix}.$$

   (a) Exhibit $[T + U]$.
   (b) Exhibit $[5T]$.
   (c) Use (a) to compute $(T + U)(\epsilon_1)$.
   (d) Compute $(T + U)(\epsilon_1)$ directly from Definition 9.3.1.

2. Let T and U be the linear operators on $\mathcal{R}_4$ such that

$$[T] = \begin{pmatrix} 3 & 1 & 0 & -1 \\ 2 & 0 & 1 & 2 \\ 1 & 1 & 2 & 2 \\ 0 & 2 & 3 & 1 \end{pmatrix} \quad \text{and} \quad [U] = \begin{pmatrix} 2 & 2 & 1 & 0 \\ 3 & 1 & 2 & 1 \\ -1 & 2 & -1 & 0 \\ -2 & 0 & 1 & 1 \end{pmatrix}.$$

   (a) Exhibit $[T + U]$.
   (b) Exhibit $[2T]$.
   (c) Compute $(T + U)(4, 1, 0, -1)$.

3. Prove Lemma 9.3.1.

4. Prove Lemma 9.3.2.

5. Prove Lemma 9.3.3.

6. Prove Theorem 9.3.1.

7. Prove Theorem 9.3.2.

8. Let T and U be the linear operators of Exercise 1.

   (a) Exhibit $[TU]$.
   (b) Use (a) to compute $(TU)(\epsilon_1)$.
   (c) Compute $(TU)(\epsilon_1)$ directly from Definition 9.3.3.

9. Let T and U be the linear operators of Exercise 2.

   (a) Exhibit $[TU]$.
   (b) Use (a) to compute $(TU)(2, 0, 1, -1)$.
   (c) Compute $(TU)(2, 0, 1, -1)$ directly from Definition 9.3.3.

10. Prove Lemma 9.3.4.

11. Prove Lemma 9.3.7.

10

CHARACTERISTIC POLYNOMIALS

10.1 CHARACTERISTIC VECTORS

Let T be a linear operator on a vector space V. We are interested in knowing whether there is a vector α and a scalar k such that $T(\alpha) = k\alpha$. Clearly, 0 has this property; any nonzero vector with the property is said to be a *characteristic vector* of T (or an *eigenvector* of T) and the scalar involved is said to be a *characteristic root* (or *characteristic value* or *eigenvalue*) of T.

Definition 10.1.1: A vector α is said to be a *characteristic vector* of a linear operator T if and only if:

   (*i*) $\alpha \neq 0$;
   (*ii*) There is a scalar k such that $T(\alpha) = k\alpha$.

Definition 10.1.2: A scalar k is said to be a *characteristic root* of a linear operator T if and only if there is a nonzero vector α such that $T(\alpha) = k\alpha$.

Here is an example.

Example 1: Find the characteristic vectors and the characteristic roots of T, where T is the linear operator on $\Re_3$ such that

$$[T] = \begin{pmatrix} 6 & 3 & -3 \\ -2 & -1 & 2 \\ 16 & 8 & -7 \end{pmatrix} .$$

213

Solution: Let $(a, b, c) \in R_3$; then

$$T(a, b, c) = (a, b, c) \begin{pmatrix} 6 & 3 & -3 \\ -2 & -1 & 2 \\ 16 & 8 & -7 \end{pmatrix}$$

$$= (6a - 2b + 16c, \ 3a - b + 8c, \ -3a + 2b - 7c).$$

Thus, (a, b, c) is a characteristic vector of T if and only if $(a, b, c) \neq 0$ and there is a real number k such that

$$(6a - 2b + 16c, \ 3a - b + 8c, \ -3a + 2b - 7c) = k(a, b, c).$$

We conclude that the characteristic vectors of T are the nonzero vector solutions of the homogeneous linear system

(I)
$$\begin{cases} (6 - k)a - 2b + 16c = 0 \\ 3a - (1 + k)b + 8c = 0 \ . \\ -3a + 2b - (7 + k)c = 0 \end{cases}$$

Let us regard k as a parameter so that the unknowns are a, b, and c. In view of Corollary 2.4.1, this homogeneous linear system has a nontrivial solution if and only if its coefficient matrix is singular, i.e.,

$$\begin{vmatrix} 6 - k & -2 & 16 \\ 3 & -1 - k & 8 \\ -3 & 2 & -7 - k \end{vmatrix} = 0 \ .$$

This condition enables us to determine the values of the parameter k that lead to a nonzero vector solution of the linear system (I). Simplifying the above condition we obtain $-k^3 - 2k^2 + 3k = 0$; so $-k(k - 1)(k + 3) = 0$. Thus $k = 0, 1, -3$. This means that 0, 1, and -3 are the values of the parameter k of the linear system (I) that lead to nontrivial solutions of the system. We conclude that 0, 1, and -3 are the characteristic roots of T. Using these values of the parameter k in (I), we readily determine the corresponding characteristic vectors.

$$k = 0: \quad \begin{pmatrix} 6 & -2 & 16 \\ 3 & -1 & 8 \\ -3 & 2 & -7 \end{pmatrix} \sim \begin{pmatrix} 0 & 0 & 0 \\ 3 & -1 & 8 \\ 0 & 1 & 1 \end{pmatrix} \sim \begin{pmatrix} 0 & 0 & 0 \\ 3 & 0 & 9 \\ 0 & 1 & 1 \end{pmatrix} \sim \begin{pmatrix} 0 & 0 & 0 \\ 1 & 0 & 3 \\ 0 & 1 & 1 \end{pmatrix}$$

Therefore $t(3, 1, -1)$ is a characteristic vector of T whenever $t \neq 0$.

$$k = 1: \quad \begin{pmatrix} 5 & -2 & 16 \\ 3 & -2 & 8 \\ -3 & 2 & -8 \end{pmatrix} \sim \begin{pmatrix} 5 & -2 & 16 \\ 1 & -2 & 0 \\ 0 & 0 & 0 \end{pmatrix} \sim \begin{pmatrix} 0 & 8 & 16 \\ 1 & -2 & 0 \\ 0 & 0 & 0 \end{pmatrix} \sim \begin{pmatrix} 0 & 1 & 2 \\ 1 & -2 & 0 \\ 0 & 0 & 0 \end{pmatrix}$$

Therefore $t(4, 2, -1)$ is a characteristic vector of T whenever $t \neq 0$.

$$k = -3: \quad \begin{pmatrix} 9 & -2 & 16 \\ 3 & 2 & 8 \\ -3 & 2 & -4 \end{pmatrix} \sim \begin{pmatrix} 3 & 2 & 8 \\ 0 & 4 & 4 \\ 0 & 4 & 4 \end{pmatrix} \sim \begin{pmatrix} 3 & 0 & 6 \\ 0 & 1 & 1 \\ 0 & 0 & 0 \end{pmatrix} \sim \begin{pmatrix} 1 & 0 & 2 \\ 0 & 1 & 1 \\ 0 & 0 & 0 \end{pmatrix}$$

Therefore $t(2, 1, -1)$ is a characteristic vector of T whenever $t \neq 0$.

Notice that in the case of Example 1, the characteristic vectors of T that correspond to one characteristic root of T, together with 0, form a subspace of $\mathfrak{R}_3$. In view of Theorem 2.4.1 it is clear that this will be the case whenever dim V is finite. Let us prove that this is so even if dim V is infinite.

Lemma 10.1.1: Let T be a linear operator on a vector space V, and let k be any characteristic root of T. Then $\{\gamma \mid T(\gamma) = k\gamma\}$ is a subspace of V.

Proof: Let $T(\alpha) = k\alpha$, let $T(\beta) = k\beta$, and let c be a scalar. We must show that $T(\alpha + \beta) = k(\alpha + \beta)$ and that $T(c\alpha) = k(c\alpha)$. Since T is a linear operator on V, $T(\alpha + \beta) = T(\alpha) + T(\beta) = k\alpha + k\beta = k(\alpha + \beta)$; and $T(c\alpha) = cT(\alpha) = c(k\alpha) = (ck)\alpha = k(c\alpha)$. This establishes our lemma.

Moreover, we can prove that subspaces corresponding to distinct characteristic roots of T, have exactly one member in common, namely 0.

Lemma 10.1.2: Let T be a linear operator on a vector space V, and let k_1 and k_2 be two characteristic roots of T. Then $\{\gamma \mid T(\gamma) = k_1\gamma\} \cap \{\gamma \mid T(\gamma) = k_2\gamma\} = \{0\}$.

Proof: Clearly, 0 is a member of both sets. Let α be a vector such that $T(\alpha) = k_1\alpha$ and $T(\alpha) = k_2\alpha$. Then $k_1\alpha = k_2\alpha$, so $(k_1 - k_2)\alpha = 0$. Since $k_1 \neq k_2$ by assumption, we conclude that $\alpha = 0$. This establishes our result.

Let us return to Example 1. This example does more than solve a problem; it illustrates *how* to obtain the characteristic vectors of a linear operator on $\mathfrak{R}_n$. We now examine the method of this example. First, we write down $[T]$. Next, we form the matrix equation

$$(1) \qquad\qquad \alpha[T] = k\alpha$$

where α is the unknown and k is regarded as a parameter. Notice that we regard α both as a vector and a matrix. Clearly, each value of the parameter k that leads to a nonzero vector solution of (1) is a characteristic root of T; moreover, the corresponding nonzero vector solutions of (1) are characteristic vectors of T. Now, the matrix equation (1) represents a homogeneous linear system whose coefficient matrix is $[T]^t - kI_n$ (here $[T]^t$ is the transpose of the matrix $[T]$, not its tth power). Now, a homogeneous linear system has a nontrivial solution if and only if its coefficient matrix is singular. Therefore, (1) possesses a nonzero vector solution if and only if k is chosen so that $|[T]^t - kI_n| = 0$. The left-hand side of this equation is the scalar that a certain polynomial function associates with k; the polynomial involved is $|[T]^t - xI_n|$, the determinant of a polynomial matrix, which is called the *characteristic polynomial* of T. By construction, the zeros of $|[T]^t - xI_n|$ are the characteristic roots of T. Finally, we substitute a characteristic root of T for the parameter k in (1); this gives us a homogeneous linear system whose nonzero vector solutions are the characteristic vectors of T that correspond to the characteristic root in question.

The point of all this is that we can automatically write down the key matrix $[T]^t - kI_n$ to begin our solution. Next, we read off the characteristic polynomial of T

and find its zeros; these are the characteristic roots of T. Finally, we substitute a characteristic root for k in the key matrix and reduce the resulting matrix. We can then read off the corresponding characteristic vectors. So, the idea is to work directly from the matrix $[T]^t - kI_n$. We now illustrate our method.

Example 2:   Find the characteristic vectors of T, where T is the linear operator

on $\mathfrak{R}_3$ such that $[T] = \begin{pmatrix} 5 & 1 & -1 \\ -6 & 0 & 2 \\ 0 & 0 & 2 \end{pmatrix}$.

Solution: Our key matrix is $[T]^t - kI_3$, namely

$$\begin{pmatrix} 5-k & -6 & 0 \\ 1 & -k & 0 \\ -1 & 2 & 2-k \end{pmatrix}$$

so $(5 - x)(x^2 - 2x) + 6(2 - x)$ is the characteristic polynomial of T; this polynomial is $(12, -16, 7, -1)$ and its zeros are 2 and 3. Therefore, the characteristic roots of T are 2 and 3. We now determine the corresponding characteristic vectors.

$$k = 2: \quad \begin{pmatrix} 3 & -6 & 0 \\ 1 & -2 & 0 \\ -1 & 2 & 0 \end{pmatrix} \sim \begin{pmatrix} 1 & -2 & 0 \\ 0 & 0 & 0 \\ 0 & 0 & 0 \end{pmatrix}$$

Therefore, $(2, 1, 0)$ and $(2, 1, 1)$ are characteristic vectors of T; so each nonzero member of $L\{(2, 1, 0), (2, 1, 1)\}$ is a characteristic vector of T.

$$k = 3: \quad \begin{pmatrix} 2 & -6 & 0 \\ 1 & -3 & 0 \\ -1 & 2 & -1 \end{pmatrix} \sim \begin{pmatrix} 1 & -3 & 0 \\ 0 & 0 & 0 \\ 0 & -1 & -1 \end{pmatrix} \sim \begin{pmatrix} 1 & 0 & 3 \\ 0 & 1 & 1 \\ 0 & 0 & 0 \end{pmatrix}$$

Therefore, $t(3, 1, -1)$ is a characteristic vector of T whenever $t \neq 0$.

Clearly, the key to the characteristic vectors of a linear operator is its characteristic polynomial. Now, a polynomial matrix and its transpose have the same determinant (see Theorem 1.6.1); so the characteristic polynomial of a linear operator T is the determinant of $([T]^t - xI_n)^t$. But $([T]^t - xI_n)^t = [T] - xI_n$; thus $|[T] - xI_n|$ is the characteristic polynomial of T. Let us illustrate this point.

Example 3:   Compute the characteristic polynomial of the linear operator of Example 2.

Solution: Now, $[T] = \begin{pmatrix} 5 & 1 & -1 \\ -6 & 0 & 2 \\ 0 & 0 & 2 \end{pmatrix}$; so $\begin{vmatrix} 5-x & 1 & -1 \\ -6 & -x & 2 \\ 0 & 0 & 2-x \end{vmatrix}$ is the charac-

teristic polynomial of T. Expanding by the entries of the third row we obtain the polynomial $(2 - x)(x^2 - 5x + 6)$. Thus $(12, -16, 7, -1)$ is the characteristic polynomial of T, as before.

EXERCISES

1. Find the characteristic roots and the characteristic vectors of T, given that $T(a, b, c) = (0, b, 0)$ whenever $(a, b, c) \in R_3$.

2. Find the characteristic roots and the characteristic vectors of T, given that $T(a, b, c) = (3a, 0, 0)$ whenever $(a, b, c) \in R_3$.

3. Find the characteristic roots and the characteristic vectors of T, given that $T(a, b, c, d) = (-a, -b, -c, -d)$ whenever $(a, b, c, d) \in R_4$.

4. Find the characteristic roots and the characteristic vectors of T, given that $T(a, b, c, d) = (a + b + c + d, 0, 0, 0)$ whenever $(a, b, c, d) \in R_4$.

5. Show that ϵ_1 is a characteristic vector of T and that 4 is a characteristic root of T, given that T is the linear operator on $\mathcal{R}_3$ such that $[T] = \begin{pmatrix} 4 & 0 & 0 \\ 1 & 3 & -1 \\ 2 & 2 & 5 \end{pmatrix}$.

6. Let T be the linear operator on $\mathcal{R}_3$ such that $[T] = \begin{pmatrix} 2 & 5 & -1 \\ 0 & -2 & 0 \\ 0 & -3 & 1 \end{pmatrix}$.

   (a) Determine the characteristic polynomial of T.
   (b) Find the characteristic roots and the characteristic vectors of T.

7. Let T be the linear operator on $\mathcal{R}_3$ such that $[T] = \begin{pmatrix} 2 & 1 & -1 \\ -6 & -3 & 2 \\ 0 & 0 & -1 \end{pmatrix}$.

   (a) Determine the characteristic polynomial of T.
   (b) Find the characteristic roots and the characteristic vectors of T.

8. Let T be the linear operator on $\mathcal{R}_4$ such that $[T] = \begin{pmatrix} 0 & -6 & -3 & 3 \\ 3 & 9 & 3 & -3 \\ -6 & 0 & 3 & 0 \\ 0 & 24 & 12 & -9 \end{pmatrix}$.

   (a) Determine the characteristic polynomial of T.
   (b) Find the characteristic roots and the characteristic vectors of T.

10.2   THE CHARACTERISTIC POLYNOMIAL OF A MATRIX

Since the ideas of Section 10.1 center around a matrix, it is convenient to formulate these ideas directly in terms of a matrix. First, we present the notion of the characteristic polynomial of a square matrix. Notice that this is the determinant of a polynomial matrix.

Definition 10.2.1: Let A be any $n \times n$ matrix; then the polynomial $|A - xI_n|$ is said to be the *characteristic polynomial* of A.

For example, $\begin{vmatrix} 2-x & 1 \\ 3 & 3-x \end{vmatrix}$ is the characteristic polynomial of $\begin{pmatrix} 2 & 1 \\ 3 & 3 \end{pmatrix}$.

Simplifying, we see that $(3, -5, 1)$ is the characteristic polynomial of this matrix. Next, we present the notion of a characteristic root of a square matrix.

Definition 10.2.2: Each zero of the characteristic polynomial of a square matrix A is said to be a *characteristic root* of A.

Let k be a characteristic root of a square matrix A; then $|A - kI_n| = 0$ and it follows that $|(A - kI_n)^t| = 0$. Therefore, the homogeneous linear system represented by the matrix $(A - kI_n)^t$ has a nonzero vector solution, say α. Thus $\alpha A = k\alpha$. Any nonzero vector α with this property is said to be a *characteristic vector* of the matrix A.

Definition 10.2.3: A nonzero vector α is said to be a *characteristic vector* of a square matrix A if and only if there is a scalar k such that $\alpha A = k\alpha$.

These ideas enable us to think about the characteristic polynomial of a linear operator T in terms of the characteristic polynomial of $[T]$; really, this is precisely how we defined the characteristic polynomial of a linear operator.

Example 1: Exhibit the characteristic polynomial, the characteristic roots, and the characteristic vectors of

$$A = \begin{pmatrix} 0 & 0 & 0 & 0 \\ 1 & 0 & 0 & 0 \\ -2 & 0 & 0 & 0 \\ 0 & -1 & 1 & 0 \end{pmatrix}.$$

Solution: Now, the characteristic polynomial of A is $\begin{vmatrix} -x & 0 & 0 & 0 \\ 1 & -x & 0 & 0 \\ -2 & 0 & -x & 0 \\ 0 & -1 & 1 & -x \end{vmatrix}$,

namely x^4. So 0 is the only characteristic root of A. To determine the characteristic vectors of A that correspond to a characteristic root k, we must solve the homogeneous linear system whose matrix is $(A - kI_4)^t$; here, $k = 0$, so we shall row-reduce A^t. Now,

$$\begin{pmatrix} 0 & 1 & -2 & 0 \\ 0 & 0 & 0 & -1 \\ 0 & 0 & 0 & 1 \\ 0 & 0 & 0 & 0 \end{pmatrix} \sim \begin{pmatrix} 0 & 1 & -2 & 0 \\ 0 & 0 & 0 & -1 \\ 0 & 0 & 0 & 0 \\ 0 & 0 & 0 & 0 \end{pmatrix}.$$

Therefore, $(1, 0, 0, 0)$ and $(0, 2, 1, 0)$ are characteristic vectors of A; so each nonzero member of $L\{\epsilon_1, (0, 2, 1, 0)\}$ is a characteristic vector of A. Moreover, A has no other characteristic vectors.

EXERCISES

1. Let $A = \begin{pmatrix} 0 & 0 & 0 & 0 \\ 1 & 0 & 0 & 0 \\ -2 & 1 & 0 & 0 \\ 0 & -1 & 1 & 0 \end{pmatrix}$.

   (a) Write down the characteristic polynomial of A.
   (b) Compute the characteristic roots of A.
   (c) Exhibit the characteristic vectors of A.

2. Let $A = \begin{pmatrix} 3 & 2 & -1 \\ -4 & -3 & 1 \\ 8 & 4 & -3 \end{pmatrix}$.

   (a) Write down the characteristic polynomial of A.
   (b) Compute the characteristic roots of A.
   (c) Exhibit the characteristic vectors of A.

3. Let A be any nonsingular matrix.

   (a) Show that 0 is *not* a characteristic root of A.
   (b) Prove that the characteristic roots of A^{-1} are the reciprocals of the characteristic roots of A.
   (c) Prove that A and A^{-1} have the same characteristic vectors.

4. (a) Given that k is a characteristic root of a matrix A, prove that ck is a characteristic root of cA whenever c is a scalar.
   (b) Given that α is a characteristic vector of A, prove that α is a characteristic vector of cA whenever c is a scalar.

5. (a) Prove that α is a characteristic vector of AB if α is a characteristic vector of both A and B.
   (b) Let α be a characteristic vector of A. Prove that α is a characteristic vector of A^n whenever $n \in N$.
   (c) Let k be a characteristic root of A. Prove that k^n is a characteristic root of A^n whenever $n \in N$.

10.3 SIMILAR MATRICES

In Section 9.2 we proved that if T is a linear operator on a finite-dimensional vector space V with ordered bases α and $\mathcal{B}$, then $[T]_\mathcal{B} = [\mathcal{B}]_\alpha [T]_\alpha [\alpha]_\mathcal{B}$. Now, $[\alpha]_\mathcal{B}$ is the inverse of $[\mathcal{B}]_\alpha$; so, letting $[\alpha]_\mathcal{B} = P$, we see that

(1) $$[T]_\mathcal{B} = P^{-1} [T]_\alpha P .$$

Seizing on this relationship between the square matrices $A = [T]_\alpha$ and $B = [T]_\mathcal{B}$, we introduce the notion of *similar* matrices.

Definition 10.3.1: A matrix B is said to be *similar* to a matrix A if and only if there is a nonsingular matrix P such that $B = P^{-1}AP$.

So, real $n \times n$ matrices A and B are similar if and only if there is a linear operator T on $\Re_n$, and ordered bases α and β for $\Re_n$ such that $[T]_\alpha = A$ and $[T]_\beta = B$ (prove this statement!).

Next, we mention that *similarity* is an equivalence relation on the set of all square matrices; this is easy to prove.

For simplicity, let us take scalars to be real numbers and confine ourselves to real matrices. We must confess that usually it is difficult to establish whether two matrices are similar. However, we can settle this question in case one of the given matrices is a diagonal matrix.

Let A be any $n \times n$ matrix over R. Now, A is similar to a diagonal matrix, say $D = \mathrm{diag}(k_1, \ldots, k_n)$, if and only if there is a nonsingular matrix P such that $PA = DP$. Let us see what we can learn about P. Clearly, $PA = DP$ if and only if $(PA)_i = (DP)_i$ for each i. Now, for each i,

$$(PA)_i = P_i \cdot A$$

and
$$(DP)_i = \sum_{j=1}^{n} d_{ij} P_j \qquad \text{where } D_i = (d_{i1}, \ldots, d_{in})$$

$$= k_i P_i .$$

since $d_{ij} = 0$ if $i \neq j$, and $d_{ii} = k_i$. Thus $PA = DP$ if and only if $P_i \cdot A = k_i P_i$ for each i. But this means that P_i is a characteristic vector of A which corresponds to the characteristic root k_i (note that if $P_i = \mathbf{0}$, then P is singular). We conclude that A is similar to $\mathrm{diag}(k_1, \ldots, k_n)$ if and only if

(*i*)   Each k_i is a characteristic root of A;

(*ii*) There exist n characteristic vectors $\alpha_1, \ldots, \alpha_n$ corresponding to $k_1, \ldots, k_n$, respectively, such that $\{\alpha_1, \ldots, \alpha_n\}$ is linearly independent.

Moreover, P is the $n \times n$ matrix such that $P_i = \alpha_i, i = 1, \ldots, n$.

In view of (*ii*) it is clear that P is nonsingular. We now summarize this result as follows.

Theorem 10.3.1: An $n \times n$ matrix A is similar to a diagonal matrix D if and only if there is a basis for $\Re_n$, say $\{\alpha_1, \ldots, \alpha_n\}$, such that each α_i is a characteristic vector of A. Moreover, $D = \mathrm{diag}(k_1, \ldots, k_n)$ where $\alpha_i A = k_i \alpha_i$, and $A = P^{-1}DP$ where $P_i = \alpha_i, i = 1, \ldots, n$.

Let us illustrate our method.

Example 1: Show that $\begin{pmatrix} 8 & 3 & -3 \\ -6 & -1 & 3 \\ 12 & 6 & -4 \end{pmatrix}$ is similar to a diagonal matrix,

exhibit the diagonal matrix, and exhibit the matrix P of Theorem 10.3.1.

Solution: The characteristic polynomial of the given matrix is $(-4, 0, 3, -1)$, i.e., $-(x + 1)(x - 2)^2$; so its characteristic roots are -1 and 2. We must determine corresponding characteristic vectors that form a basis for $\mathfrak{R}_3$.

$$k = -1: \quad \begin{pmatrix} 9 & -6 & 12 \\ 3 & 0 & 6 \\ -3 & 3 & -3 \end{pmatrix} \sim \begin{pmatrix} 1 & 0 & 2 \\ 0 & -6 & -6 \\ 0 & 3 & 3 \end{pmatrix} \sim \begin{pmatrix} 1 & 0 & 2 \\ 0 & 1 & 1 \\ 0 & 0 & 0 \end{pmatrix}$$

So $(-2, -1, 1)$ is a characteristic vector which corresponds to the characteristic root -1 (take 1 for the third term of a characteristic vector).

$$k = 2: \quad \begin{pmatrix} 6 & -6 & 12 \\ 3 & -3 & 6 \\ -3 & 3 & -6 \end{pmatrix} \sim \begin{pmatrix} 1 & -1 & 2 \\ 0 & 0 & 0 \\ 0 & 0 & 0 \end{pmatrix}$$

So $(1, 1, 0)$ and $(-2, 0, 1)$ are characteristic vectors which correspond to the characteristic root 2 (first take 0 for the third term of a characteristic vector; next, take 0 for the second term). Since $\{(-2, -1, 1), (1, 1, 0), (-2, 0, 1)\}$ is linearly independent, we conclude that the given matrix is similar to diag$(-1, 2, 2)$

and that $P = \begin{pmatrix} -2 & -1 & 1 \\ 1 & 1 & 0 \\ -2 & 0 & 1 \end{pmatrix}$. As a check, we point out that $P^{-1} = \begin{pmatrix} 1 & 1 & -1 \\ -1 & 0 & 1 \\ 2 & 2 & -1 \end{pmatrix}$

and that

$$\begin{pmatrix} 1 & 1 & -1 \\ -1 & 0 & 1 \\ 2 & 2 & -1 \end{pmatrix} \begin{pmatrix} -1 & 0 & 0 \\ 0 & 2 & 0 \\ 0 & 0 & 2 \end{pmatrix} \begin{pmatrix} -2 & -1 & 1 \\ 1 & 1 & 0 \\ -2 & 0 & 1 \end{pmatrix} = \begin{pmatrix} 8 & 3 & -3 \\ -6 & -1 & 3 \\ 12 & 6 & -4 \end{pmatrix}$$

There is a variation of Theorem 10.3.1 which provides us with a simple method of finding a diagonal matrix similar to a given matrix (if the given matrix is similar to a diagonal matrix and meets the requirements of Theorem 10.3.2, which follows). First, we need the following fact about characteristic vectors.

Lemma 10.3.1: Let $k_1, \ldots, k_m$ be distinct characteristic roots of a real $n \times n$ matrix A, and let $\alpha_1, \ldots, \alpha_m$ be corresponding characteristic vectors of A. Then

    (i) $\alpha_1, \ldots, \alpha_m$ are distinct;

    (ii) $\{\alpha_1, \ldots, \alpha_m\}$ is linearly independent.

Proof: It is convenient to use the language of linear operators. Let T be the linear operator on $\mathfrak{R}_n$ such that $[T] = A$; so $T(\alpha_i) = k_i\alpha_i$ and $\alpha_i \neq 0$, $i = 1, \ldots, m$. Clearly *(i)* follows from Lemma 10.1.2. Having established that $\{\alpha_1, \ldots, \alpha_m\}$ has m members, let us prove that this set is linearly independent. Certainly $\{\alpha_1\}$ is linearly independent; assume that $\{\alpha_1, \ldots, \alpha_t\}$ is linearly independent and that $\{\alpha_{t+1}, \ldots, \alpha_m\} \subset L\{\alpha_1, \ldots, \alpha_t\}$ (at worst, this involves renumbering the α's). In view of the Steinitz Replacement Theorem, we can assume that $k_m \neq 0$ (bear in mind the possibility that $t = m - 1$ and $k_m = 0$). Now, there are scalars $a_1, \ldots, a_t$

such that $\alpha_m = \sum_{i=1}^{t} a_i \, \alpha_i$; thus $T(\alpha_m) = \sum_{i=1}^{t} a_i \, T(\alpha_i)$, i.e., $k_m \alpha_m = \sum_{i=1}^{t} (a_i k_i) \alpha_i$; so,

$\sum_{i=1}^{t} a_i (1 - k_i/k_m) \alpha_i = \mathbf{0}$. But $\{\alpha_1, \ldots, \alpha_t\}$ is linearly independent; so $a_i(1 - k_i/k_m) = 0$ for each i. We conclude that $a_i = 0$, $i = 1, \ldots, t$; thus $\alpha_m = \mathbf{0}$. This contradiction establishes Lemma 10.3.1.

It is easy, now, to demonstrate the following theorem.

Theorem 10.3.2: Let A be a real $n \times n$ matrix with n characteristic roots $k_1, \ldots, k_n$. Then A is similar to $\mathrm{diag}(k_1, \ldots, k_n)$.

Proof: Let $\alpha_1, \ldots, \alpha_n$ be characteristic vectors of A corresponding to $k_1, \ldots, k_n$, respectively. By Lemma 10.3.1, $\{\alpha_1, \ldots, \alpha_n\}$ is a basis for $\mathcal{R}_n$; thus, by Theorem 10.3.1, A is similar to $\mathrm{diag}(k_1, \ldots, k_n)$.

Of course, the point of Theorem 10.3.2 is that we avoid the step of computing characteristic vectors of A.

Example 2: Exhibit a diagonal matrix similar to $A = \begin{pmatrix} 6 & 3 & -3 \\ -2 & -1 & 2 \\ 16 & 8 & -7 \end{pmatrix}$.

Solution: This is the matrix of Example 1, Section 10.1. There, we saw that its characteristic roots are 0, 1, and -3. So, by Theorem 10.3.2, A is similar to $\mathrm{diag}(0, 1, -3)$.

EXERCISES

1. Show that $\begin{pmatrix} 1 & 0 & 0 \\ 2 & 0 & 0 \\ 3 & -1 & 0 \end{pmatrix}$ is not similar to $\begin{pmatrix} 2 & 0 & 0 \\ 2 & 0 & 0 \\ 3 & -1 & 0 \end{pmatrix}$.

2. Show that $\begin{pmatrix} 2 & 1 & -1 \\ -6 & -3 & 2 \\ 0 & 0 & -1 \end{pmatrix}$ is not similar to $\begin{pmatrix} 3 & 2 & -1 \\ -4 & -3 & 1 \\ 8 & 4 & -3 \end{pmatrix}$.

3. Show that $\begin{pmatrix} 0 & 0 & 0 & 0 \\ 1 & 0 & 0 & 0 \\ -2 & 1 & 0 & 0 \\ 0 & -1 & 1 & 0 \end{pmatrix}$ is not similar to $\begin{pmatrix} 1 & 0 & 0 & -1 \\ -1 & 1 & 0 & 1 \\ 2 & -2 & 1 & -1 \\ 0 & 0 & 1 & 2 \end{pmatrix}$.

4. Let A and B be 1×1 matrices; prove that A is similar to B if and only if $A = B$.

5. Show that $\begin{pmatrix} 5 & 1 & -1 \\ -6 & 0 & 2 \\ 0 & 0 & 2 \end{pmatrix}$ is similar to a diagonal matrix, exhibit the diagonal matrix, and exhibit the matrix P of Theorem 10.3.1.

6. Show that $\begin{pmatrix} 0 & 1 & 0 & 0 \\ 0 & 0 & 1 & 0 \\ 0 & 0 & 0 & 1 \\ -1 & 0 & 2 & 0 \end{pmatrix}$ is similar to a diagonal matrix, exhibit the diagonal matrix, and exhibit the matrix P of Theorem 10.3.1.

7. Let A and B be real $n \times n$ matrices such that $B = P^{-1}AP$ for some nonsingular matrix P. Find an ordered basis α for $\mathcal{R}_n$ and a linear operator T on $\mathcal{R}_n$, such that $[T] = B$ and $[T]_\alpha = A$.

8. Prove that *similarity* is an equivalence relation.

9. Prove that similar matrices have the same characteristic polynomial.

10. Prove that 2×2 matrices are similar if and only if they have the same characteristic polynomial.

11. Let A be a nonsingular matrix which is similar to A^{-1}. Prove that k is a characteristic root of A if and only if $1/k$ is a characteristic root of A.

10.4 THE CAYLEY–HAMILTON THEOREM

We have mentioned that a polynomial can be used to obtain a mapping of the basic set of a ring into that set. Thus, let $(B, +, \cdot, 0)$ be any ring and let $p = (a_0, \ldots, a_m)$ be any polynomial over B; then $p(t)$ denotes $a_0 + a_1 t + \cdots + a_m t^m$ whenever $t \in B$. Notice that the ring operations are involved in the definition of this mapping. Now, consider the ring of $n \times n$ matrices over R, and let $p = (a_0, \ldots, a_m)$ be any polynomial over R; then $p(A)$ denotes $a_0 I_n + a_1 A + \cdots + a_m A^m$ whenever A is an $n \times n$ matrix. Our point is that a polynomial can be used to associate a square matrix with each square matrix. We are now ready to present the surprising fact that the characteristic polynomial of a matrix A associates the zero matrix with A.

Theorem 10.4.1 (*Cayley–Hamilton*): Let A be any square matrix and let f be its characteristic polynomial; then $f(A) = (0)$.

Proof: Let A be $n \times n$; notice that $f = |A - xI_n|$. Accordingly, we consider the polynomial matrix $A - xI_n$ and let $B = \text{adj}(A - xI_n)$; then

(1) $$(A - xI_n)B = |A - xI_n|I_n = fI_n.$$

Now, (1) is a statement about polynomial matrices (i.e., matrices whose entries are polynomials). Consider the corresponding statement about matric polynomials. To this purpose we use the isomorphism between the ring of polynomial matrices and the ring of matric polynomials which is discussed in Section 8.5. Clearly, $A - I_n x$ is the matric polynomial that corresponds to $A - xI_n$. To find the image of fI_n, let $f = \sum_{i=0}^{n} c_i x^i$; notice that

$$fI_n = \text{diag}(f, \ldots, f) = \text{diag}\left(\sum_{i=0}^{n} c_i x^i, \ldots, \sum_{i=0}^{n} c_i x^i\right) = c_0 I_n + c_1 x I_n + \cdots + c_n x^n I_n.$$

So the matric polynomial $c_0 I_n + c_1 I_n x + \cdots + c_n I_n x^n$ is the image of $f I_n$ under our isomorphism. Let $B*$ be the image of B; using our isomorphism, we obtain from (1) the following statement about matric polynomials:

$$(2) \qquad (A - I_n x)B* = c_0 I_n + c_1 I_n x + \cdots + c_n I_n x^n .$$

Notice that $\deg B* = n - 1$; so, there are matrices $B_0, B_1, \ldots, B_{n-1}$ such that $B* = B_0 + B_1 x + \cdots + B_{n-1} x^{n-1}$. Thus

$$(3) \quad (A - I_n x)(B_0 + B_1 x + \cdots + B_{n-1} x^{n-1}) = c_0 I_n + c_1 I_n x + \cdots + c_n I_n x^n .$$

Multiplying out the left-hand side of (3) we obtain:

$$(4) \qquad \begin{cases} AB_0 = c_0 I_n \\ AB_1 - B_0 = c_1 I_n \\ AB_2 - B_1 = c_2 I_n \\ \qquad \cdot \\ \qquad \cdot \\ \qquad \cdot \\ AB_{n-1} - B_{n-2} = c_{n-1} I_n \\ -B_{n-1} = c_n I_n \end{cases}$$

Notice that $f(A) = c_0 I_n + c_1 A + \cdots + c_n A^n = c_0 I_n + c_1 I_n A + \cdots + c_n I_n A^n$; so, we can build up $f(A)$ by multiplying the left-hand sides of (4) by $I_n, A, \ldots, A^n$ respectively, and summing. We obtain:

$$f(A) = AB_0 + A(AB_1 - B_0) + A^2(AB_2 - B_1) + \cdots + A^{n-1}(AB_{n-1} - B_{n-2}) - A^n B_{n-1}$$

$$= (0) .$$

This completes our proof of the Cayley–Hamilton Theorem.

Although the Cayley–Hamilton Theorem is largely of theoretical value, it does possess some practical and immediate applications.

Lemma 10.4.1: Let $f = (c_0, \ldots, c_n)$ be the characteristic polynomial of a matrix A, where $c_0 \neq 0$. Then A is nonsingular and

$$A^{-1} = \frac{-1}{c_0}(c_1 I_n + c_2 A + \cdots + c_n A^{n-1}) .$$

Proof: Clearly, 0 is not a characteristic root of A; so $|A| \neq 0$ (recall the significance of characteristic roots), i.e., A is nonsingular. By the Cayley–Hamilton Theorem $f(A) = (0)$, i.e.,

$$c_0 I_n + c_1 A + \cdots + c_n A^n = (0) .$$

Multiplying both sides of this equation by A^{-1}, we obtain

$$A^{-1} = \frac{-1}{c_0}(c_1 I_n + c_2 A + \cdots + c_n A^{n-1}) .$$

This proves Lemma 10.4.1.

Let us illustrate this idea; notice that we prefer to work directly from the characteristic polynomial, rather than apply the formula contained in Lemma 10.4.1.

Example 1: Compute A^{-1} where $A = \begin{pmatrix} 5 & 1 & -1 \\ -6 & 0 & 2 \\ 0 & 0 & 2 \end{pmatrix}$.

Solution: Considering Example 2, Section 10.1, we see that $(12, -16, 7, -1)$ is the characteristic polynomial of A. So

$$12I_3 - 16A + 7A^2 - A^3 = (0)$$

thus

$$A^{-1} = \frac{1}{12}(16I_3 - 7A + A^2) .$$

Now

$$A^2 = \begin{pmatrix} 19 & 5 & -5 \\ -30 & -6 & 10 \\ 0 & 0 & 4 \end{pmatrix}$$

so

$$A^{-1} = \frac{1}{12}\begin{pmatrix} 0 & -2 & 2 \\ 12 & 10 & -4 \\ 0 & 0 & 6 \end{pmatrix} .$$

Of course, we can also use the Cayley–Hamilton Theorem to obtain powers of an $n \times n$ matrix A; the fact is that $A^m \in L\{I_n, A, \ldots, A^{n-1}\}$ whenever $m > 0$. Indeed, $A^{-m} \in L\{I_n, A, \ldots, A^{n-1}\}$ whenever $m > 0$, if A is nonsingular.

Example 2: Compute A^4 where A is the matrix of Example 1.

Solution: From Example 1,

$$A^3 = 12I_3 - 16A + 7A^2$$

so

$$A^4 = 12A - 16A^2 + 7A^3$$

$$= 84I_3 - 100A + 33A^2$$

$$= \begin{pmatrix} 211 & 65 & -65 \\ -390 & -114 & 130 \\ 0 & 0 & 16 \end{pmatrix} .$$

EXERCISES

1. Let $A = \begin{pmatrix} -1 & 3 \\ 4 & 5 \end{pmatrix}$.

   (a) Determine f, the characteristic polynomial of A.

   (b) Show directly that $f(A) = \begin{pmatrix} 0 & 0 \\ 0 & 0 \end{pmatrix}$.

2. Let $A = \begin{pmatrix} 2 & 1 & 0 \\ 3 & -1 & 4 \\ -1 & 0 & 2 \end{pmatrix}$.

   (a) Determine f, the characteristic polynomial of A.

   (b) Show directly that $f(A) = \begin{pmatrix} 0 & 0 & 0 \\ 0 & 0 & 0 \\ 0 & 0 & 0 \end{pmatrix}$.

3. Let $A = \begin{pmatrix} 1 & 2 & 0 & 0 \\ 3 & 0 & 1 & -2 \\ 0 & -2 & 3 & 4 \\ 1 & 0 & 1 & -1 \end{pmatrix}$.

   (a) Determine f, the characteristic polynomial of A.

   (b) Show directly that $f(A) = \begin{pmatrix} 0 & 0 & 0 & 0 \\ 0 & 0 & 0 & 0 \\ 0 & 0 & 0 & 0 \\ 0 & 0 & 0 & 0 \end{pmatrix}$.

4. Let T be the linear operator on $\Re_3$ such that $[T] = \begin{pmatrix} 2 & 0 & 0 \\ -1 & 1 & 0 \\ 1 & -4 & 0 \end{pmatrix}$.

   (a) Show that 2 is a characteristic root of T.
   (b) Compute $[T^3]$.
   (c) Show directly that 8 is a characteristic root of T^3.

5. Let A be any $n \times n$ matrix and let $c_0 + c_1 x + \cdots + c_{n-1} x^{n-1} + (-1)^n x^n$ be the characteristic polynomial of A. Show that

   (a) $A^{-1} = \dfrac{-1}{c_0}(c_1 I_n + c_2 A + \cdots + c_{n-1} A^{n-2} + (-1)^n A^{n-1})$ provided that A is nonsingular.

   (b) $A^{n+1} = (-1)^{n+1}[c_0 A + c_1 A^2 + \cdots + c_{n-2} A^{n-1}] + c_{n-1}[c_0 I_n + c_1 A + \cdots + c_{n-1} A^{n-1}]$

   (c) A^s is a linear combination of $\{I_n, A, A^2, \ldots, A^{n-1}\}$ whenever $s \in N$.

   (d) A^{-s} is a linear combination of $\{I_n, A, A^2, \ldots, A^{n-1}\}$ whenever $s \in N$, provided that A is nonsingular. Here A^{-s} denotes $(A^{-1})^s$.

6. (a) Compute A^{-1} where A is the matrix of Exercise 2.
   (b) Compute A^{-1} where A is the matrix of Exercise 3.
   (c) Compute A^{-3} where A is the matrix of Exercise 2.

7. Let A be any $n \times n$ matrix with characteristic polynomial $c_0 + c_1 x + \cdots + c_n x^n$.

   (a) Prove that $-[c_1 I_n + c_2(A + x I_n) + c_3(A^2 + x A + x^2 I_n) + \cdots + c_n(A^{n-1} + x A^{n-2} + \cdots + x^{n-2} A + x^{n-1} I_n)]$ is the adjoint of $A - x I_n$.
   (b) Use (a) to prove that $-(c_1 I_n + c_2 A + \cdots + c_n A^{n-1})$ is the adjoint of A.
   (c) Use (b) to obtain a formula for A^{-1}, provided that A is nonsingular.
   (d) Develop a formula for $(A - I_n)^{-1}$, provided that $A - I_n$ is nonsingular.
   (e) Develop a formula for $(A + I_n)^{-1}$, provided that $A + I_n$ is nonsingular.

8. Let $f = 2 - x + x^2$ and let A be an $n \times n$ matrix such that $f(A) = (0)$.

    (a)   Prove that A is nonsingular.
    (b)   Show that $A^{-1} \in L\{A, I_n\}$.

10.5   COMPUTING CHARACTERISTIC POLYNOMIALS

We now present a very pretty method of obtaining each term of the characteristic polynomial of an $n \times n$ matrix A. We make use of the fact that *det* is multilinear. Let B be any $n \times n$ matrix. By Lemma 1.4.6 we can represent $|B|$ as a sum by regarding a row vector of B as the sum of two vectors; to be specific, let $B_r = \alpha + \beta$ and consider the two matrices obtained from B by replacing B_r by α and by β in turn. Then $|B|$ is the sum of the determinants of the resulting matrices.

It is easy to generalize this observation: regard *each* row vector of B as a sum of two vectors, and apply Lemma 1.4.6 2^n times, representing $|B|$ as the sum of the determinants of all the matrices obtained from B by choosing one of the two possible row vectors to represent each row of B. Thus, our generalized observation amounts to this:

$$\det(\alpha_1 + \beta_1, \ldots, \alpha_n + \beta_n) = \sum_{\gamma_i = \alpha_i \text{ or } \beta_i} \det(\gamma_1, \ldots, \gamma_n) \; ;$$

where the sum is taken over all possible choices of $\gamma_1, \ldots, \gamma_n$.

To illustrate we take $n = 3$; then

$$\det(\alpha_1 + \beta_1, \alpha_2 + \beta_2, \alpha_3 + \beta_3) =$$

$$\det(\alpha_1, \alpha_2, \alpha_3) + \det(\beta_1, \alpha_2, \alpha_3) + \det(\alpha_1, \beta_2, \alpha_3) + \det(\alpha_1, \alpha_2, \beta_3)$$

$$+ \det(\alpha_1, \beta_2, \beta_3) + \det(\beta_1, \alpha_2, \beta_3) + \det(\beta_1, \beta_2, \alpha_3) + \det(\beta_1, \beta_2, \beta_3) .$$

Now, let us see about the characteristic polynomial of A, an $n \times n$ matrix. We want to compute $|A - xI_n|$; notice that the row vectors of I_n are $\epsilon_1, \ldots, \epsilon_n$. Thus, the ith row vector of $A - xI_n$ is $A_i - x\epsilon_i$ whenever $1 \leq i \leq n$. Hence,

$$(1) \qquad\qquad |A - xI_n| = \sum_{\gamma_i = A_i \text{ or } -x\epsilon_i} \det(\gamma_1, \ldots, \gamma_n)$$

where the sum is over all possible choices of $\gamma_1, \ldots, \gamma_n$.

Consider any term which appears in the right-hand side of (1), say $\det(\gamma_1, \ldots, \gamma_n)$. If some of the γ's have the form $-x\epsilon_i$ we can factor out $-x$ from these row vectors. Then the resulting matrix involves only row vectors of A or unit vectors; moreover, the unit vector ϵ_i occurs as the ith row vector of the matrix. This is particularly fortunate, since the determinant of a matrix whose ith row vector is ϵ_i, is easily obtained by expanding in terms of the entries of the ith row, and turns out to be the determinant of the submatrix of the given matrix obtained by deleting its ith row and ith column. To illustrate the situation let us take $n = 4$.

Example 1: Let A be any 4×4 matrix, then the characteristic polynomial of A is $|A - xI_4| = \det(A_1, A_2, A_3, A_4) + \det(-x\epsilon_1, A_2, A_3, A_4)$

$+ \det(A_1, -x\epsilon_2, A_3, A_4) + \det(A_1, A_2, -x\epsilon_3, A_4) + \det(A_1, A_2, A_3, -x\epsilon_4)$

$+ \det(-x\epsilon_1, -x\epsilon_2, A_3, A_4) + \det(-x\epsilon_1, A_2, -x\epsilon_3, A_4)$

$+ \det(-x\epsilon_1, A_2, A_3, -x\epsilon_4) + \det(A_1, -x\epsilon_2, -x\epsilon_3, A_4)$

$+ \det(A_1, -x\epsilon_2, A_3, -x\epsilon_4) + \det(A_1, A_2, -x\epsilon_3, -x\epsilon_4)$

$+ \det(A_1, -x\epsilon_2, -x\epsilon_3, -x\epsilon_4) + \det(-x\epsilon_1, A_2, -x\epsilon_3, -x\epsilon_4)$

$+ \det(-x\epsilon_1, -x\epsilon_2, A_3, -x\epsilon_4) + \det(-x\epsilon_1, -x\epsilon_2, -x\epsilon_3, A_4)$

$+ \det(-x\epsilon_1, -x\epsilon_2, -x\epsilon_3, -x\epsilon_4)$

$= \det(A_1, A_2, A_3, A_4) - x[\det(\epsilon_1, A_2, A_3, A_4)$

$+ \det(A_1, \epsilon_2, A_3, A_4)$

$+ \det(A_1, A_2, \epsilon_3, A_4) + \det(A_1, A_2, A_3, \epsilon_4)] + x^2[\det(\epsilon_1, \epsilon_2, A_3, A_4)$

$+ \det(\epsilon_1, A_2, \epsilon_3, A_4) + \det(\epsilon_1, A_2, A_3, \epsilon_4) + \det(A_1, \epsilon_2, \epsilon_3, A_4)$

$+ \det(A_1, \epsilon_2, A_3, \epsilon_4) + \det(A_1, A_2, \epsilon_3, \epsilon_4)] - x^3[\det(A_1, \epsilon_2, \epsilon_3, \epsilon_4)$

$+ \det(\epsilon_1, A_2, \epsilon_3, \epsilon_4) + \det(\epsilon_1, \epsilon_2, A_3, \epsilon_4) + \det(\epsilon_1, \epsilon_2, \epsilon_3, A_4)]$

$+ x^4\det(\epsilon_1, \epsilon_2, \epsilon_3, \epsilon_4) \; .$

To see what we have here, let $A = \begin{pmatrix} a_{11} & a_{12} & a_{13} & a_{14} \\ a_{21} & a_{22} & a_{23} & a_{24} \\ a_{31} & a_{32} & a_{33} & a_{34} \\ a_{41} & a_{42} & a_{43} & a_{44} \end{pmatrix} \; .$

Then $|A - xI_4| =$

$$|A| - x\left(\begin{vmatrix} a_{22} & a_{23} & a_{24} \\ a_{32} & a_{33} & a_{34} \\ a_{42} & a_{43} & a_{44} \end{vmatrix} + \begin{vmatrix} a_{11} & a_{13} & a_{14} \\ a_{31} & a_{33} & a_{34} \\ a_{41} & a_{43} & a_{44} \end{vmatrix} + \begin{vmatrix} a_{11} & a_{12} & a_{14} \\ a_{21} & a_{22} & a_{24} \\ a_{41} & a_{42} & a_{44} \end{vmatrix} + \begin{vmatrix} a_{11} & a_{12} & a_{13} \\ a_{21} & a_{22} & a_{23} \\ a_{31} & a_{32} & a_{33} \end{vmatrix}\right)$$

$$+ x^2\left(\begin{vmatrix} a_{33} & a_{34} \\ a_{43} & a_{44} \end{vmatrix} + \begin{vmatrix} a_{22} & a_{24} \\ a_{42} & a_{44} \end{vmatrix} + \begin{vmatrix} a_{22} & a_{23} \\ a_{32} & a_{33} \end{vmatrix} + \begin{vmatrix} a_{11} & a_{14} \\ a_{41} & a_{44} \end{vmatrix}\right)$$

$$- x^3(|a_{11}| + |a_{22}| + |a_{33}| + |a_{44}|) + x^4.$$

(Here $|b|$ denotes the determinant of the 1×1 matrix (b); so $|b| = b$, not the absolute value of b.) Examining the matrices that appear in the coefficients of x, x^2, and x^3, we see that in each case the main diagonal is part of the main diagonal of A; moreover, the coefficient of x involves each 3×3 submatrix of A whose main diagonal is part of the main diagonal of A, the coefficient of x^2 involves each 2×2 submatrix of A whose main diagonal is part of the main diagonal of A, and the coefficient of x^3 involves each 1×1 submatrix of A whose main diagonal is part of the main diagonal of A. It is convenient, now, to introduce the term *principal submatrix*. A submatrix of A is said to be a *principal submatrix* of A if and only if its main diagonal is part of the main diagonal of A. In other words, a principal submatrix of an $n \times n$

matrix A is obtained from A by deleting both A_i and $_iA$ or neither of A_i and $_iA$, $i = 1, \ldots, n$.

Now we are ready to consider the general situation in which A is an $n \times n$ matrix where n is any natural number. Let the characteristic polynomial of A be $c_0 + c_1x + \cdots + c_nx^n$. Clearly, $c_0 = |A|$ and $c_n = (-1)^n$. We shall now characterize $c_i, 1 \leq i < n$. In carrying out the above procedure, illustrated for $n = 4$, we obtain a term which involves x^i by choosing i of the row vectors $-x\epsilon_1, \ldots, -x\epsilon_n$ and choosing $n - i$ of the row vectors $A_1, \ldots, A_n$. Factoring out $-x$ from each of i row vectors, we obtain the factor $(-1)^ix^i$; this leaves us with matrices that involve $n - i$ row vectors of A, and i unit vectors; moreover if A_j appears, then it is the jth row vector of our matrix, and if ϵ_j appears, then it is the jth row vector of our matrix. Hence, the determinant of this matrix is precisely the determinant of the submatrix of A obtained by deleting the jth row and column whenever ϵ_j has been chosen to be the jth row vector. In short, the coefficient of x^i is the product of $(-1)^i$ and the sum of the determinants of all the $n - i \times n - i$ principal submatrices of A.

Example 2: Determine the characteristic polynomial of

$$\begin{pmatrix} 5 & 1 & 3 \\ 2 & -3 & 1 \\ -4 & 2 & 6 \end{pmatrix} .$$

Solution: Let the characteristic polynomial of the given matrix be (c_0, c_1, c_2, c_3); then

$$c_0 = \begin{vmatrix} 5 & 1 & 3 \\ 2 & -3 & 1 \\ -4 & 2 & 6 \end{vmatrix} = -140 .$$

$$c_1 = -\left(\begin{vmatrix} -3 & 1 \\ 2 & 6 \end{vmatrix} + \begin{vmatrix} 5 & 3 \\ -4 & 6 \end{vmatrix} + \begin{vmatrix} 5 & 1 \\ 2 & -3 \end{vmatrix} \right) = -5 .$$

$$c_2 = (5 - 3 + 6) = 8 .$$

$$c_3 = -1 .$$

Thus the characteristic polynomial of the given matrix is $(-140, -5, 8, -1)$.

Example 3: Determine the characteristic polynomial of

$$\begin{pmatrix} 2 & 0 & 1 & 3 \\ 4 & 2 & -2 & 1 \\ -3 & 0 & 1 & 5 \\ 7 & 4 & 3 & 2 \end{pmatrix} .$$

Solution: Let the characteristic polynomial of the given matrix be $(c_0, c_1, c_2, c_3, c_4)$; then

$$c_0 = \begin{vmatrix} 2 & 0 & 1 & 3 \\ 4 & 2 & -2 & 1 \\ -3 & 0 & 1 & 5 \\ 7 & 4 & 3 & 2 \end{vmatrix} = -270 .$$

$$c_1 = -\left(\begin{vmatrix} 2 & -2 & 1 \\ 0 & 1 & 5 \\ 4 & 3 & 2 \end{vmatrix} + \begin{vmatrix} 2 & 1 & 3 \\ -3 & 1 & 5 \\ 7 & 3 & 2 \end{vmatrix} + \begin{vmatrix} 2 & 0 & 3 \\ 4 & 2 & 1 \\ 7 & 4 & 2 \end{vmatrix} + \begin{vmatrix} 2 & 0 & 1 \\ 4 & 2 & -2 \\ -3 & 0 & 1 \end{vmatrix}\right) = 87 \ .$$

$$c_2 = \begin{vmatrix} 1 & 5 \\ 3 & 2 \end{vmatrix} + \begin{vmatrix} 2 & 1 \\ 4 & 2 \end{vmatrix} + \begin{vmatrix} 2 & -2 \\ 0 & 1 \end{vmatrix} + \begin{vmatrix} 2 & 3 \\ 7 & 2 \end{vmatrix} + \begin{vmatrix} 2 & 1 \\ -3 & 1 \end{vmatrix} + \begin{vmatrix} 2 & 0 \\ 4 & 2 \end{vmatrix} = -19 \ .$$

$$c_3 = -(2 + 2 + 1 + 2) = -7 \ .$$

$$c_4 = 1 \ .$$

Thus the characteristic polynomial of the given matrix is $(-270, 87, -19, -7, 1)$.

Example 4: Find the fourth term of the characteristic polynomial of

$$\begin{pmatrix} 2 & 0 & 1 & 3 & -4 \\ 0 & 1 & 3 & 5 & 2 \\ -3 & 2 & 1 & -2 & 0 \\ 1 & 4 & -1 & 0 & 1 \\ 0 & -3 & 2 & 1 & 2 \end{pmatrix} \ .$$

Solution: Let $(c_0, c_1, c_2, c_3, c_4, c_5)$ be the characteristic polynomial of the given matrix A; then

$$c_3 = (-1)^3(\det(\epsilon_1, \epsilon_2, \epsilon_3, A_4, A_5) + \det(\epsilon_1, \epsilon_2, A_3, \epsilon_4, A_5)$$

$$+ \det(\epsilon_1, \epsilon_2, A_3, A_4, \epsilon_5) + \det(\epsilon_1, A_2, \epsilon_3, \epsilon_4, A_5) + \det(\epsilon_1, A_2, \epsilon_3, A_4, \epsilon_5)$$

$$+ \det(\epsilon_1, A_2, A_3, \epsilon_4, \epsilon_5) + \det(A_1, \epsilon_2, \epsilon_3, \epsilon_4, A_5) + \det(A_1, \epsilon_2, \epsilon_3, A_4, \epsilon_5)$$

$$+ \det(A_1, \epsilon_2, A_3, \epsilon_4, \epsilon_5) + \det(A_1, A_2, \epsilon_3, \epsilon_4, \epsilon_5))$$

$$= -\left(\begin{vmatrix} 0 & 1 \\ 1 & 2 \end{vmatrix} + \begin{vmatrix} 1 & 0 \\ 2 & 2 \end{vmatrix} + \begin{vmatrix} 1 & -2 \\ -1 & 0 \end{vmatrix} + \begin{vmatrix} 1 & 2 \\ -3 & 2 \end{vmatrix} + \begin{vmatrix} 1 & 5 \\ 4 & 0 \end{vmatrix} + \begin{vmatrix} 1 & 3 \\ 2 & 1 \end{vmatrix} + \begin{vmatrix} 2 & -4 \\ 0 & 2 \end{vmatrix}\right.$$

$$\left. + \begin{vmatrix} 2 & 3 \\ 1 & 0 \end{vmatrix} + \begin{vmatrix} 2 & 1 \\ -3 & 1 \end{vmatrix} + \begin{vmatrix} 2 & 0 \\ 0 & 1 \end{vmatrix}\right)$$

$$= -(-1 + 2 - 2 + 8 + 1 - 5 + 4 - 3 + 5 + 2)$$

$$= -11 \ .$$

In this section we have presented a method of obtaining each term of the characteristic polynomial of a given matrix. Although we cannot go into the matter here, this result also possesses theoretical value.

EXERCISES

1. (a) Verify that $\det(\alpha_1 + \beta_1, \alpha_2 + \beta_2, \alpha_3 + \beta_3, \alpha_4 + \beta_4) = \displaystyle\sum_{\gamma_i = \alpha_i \text{ or } \beta_i} \det(\gamma_1, \gamma_2, \gamma_3, \gamma_4) \ .$

    (b) How many terms appear in the sum on the right-hand side of the equation of part (a)?

2. Simplify:

(a) $\det(\alpha + \epsilon_1, \beta + \epsilon_2, \gamma + \epsilon_3)$;

(b) $\det(\alpha + k\epsilon_1, \beta + k\epsilon_2, \gamma + k\epsilon_3)$,

(c) $\det(\alpha - k\epsilon_1, \beta - k\epsilon_2, \gamma - k\epsilon_3)$.

3. Exhibit the characteristic polynomial of each of the following matrices.

(a) $\begin{pmatrix} 2 & 6 & 1 \\ -3 & 4 & 5 \\ 1 & -1 & -2 \end{pmatrix}$

(b) $\begin{pmatrix} 7 & 1 & -1 \\ 2 & -3 & 1 \\ -4 & 2 & -2 \end{pmatrix}$

(c) $\begin{pmatrix} 1 & -1 & 2 & 2 \\ 3 & 0 & 1 & 0 \\ 2 & -2 & 1 & 1 \\ 1 & 1 & 0 & 3 \end{pmatrix}$

(d) $\begin{pmatrix} 2 & 1 & 0 & -1 \\ 3 & 4 & 2 & 5 \\ -1 & 0 & 3 & -2 \\ 4 & 1 & 1 & 0 \end{pmatrix}$

(e) $\begin{pmatrix} 2 & 0 & 1 & 3 & 0 \\ 3 & -1 & 0 & 0 & 1 \\ -2 & 0 & 1 & -1 & 1 \\ 0 & 1 & 2 & -2 & 0 \\ 1 & 1 & -1 & 0 & 3 \end{pmatrix}$

4. Find the third term of the characteristic polynomial of

$$\begin{pmatrix} 1 & 1 & -1 & 0 & 1 \\ 0 & 2 & 1 & 1 & 2 \\ -1 & 1 & 3 & -1 & 2 \\ 0 & 4 & 0 & 1 & 1 \\ -1 & -1 & 2 & 2 & -1 \end{pmatrix} .$$

11

INNER PRODUCT SPACES

11.1 BILINEAR FORMS

In Section 3.1 we introduced a certain mapping of $R_n \times R_n$ into R, where $n \in N$, which we called the *dot product*. We used this mapping throughout Chapter 3 in connection with the algebra of matrices. Moreover, the dot product is a key concept in our applications to geometry; recall that Chapters 4 and 5 make extensive use of this mapping. Of course, the dot product applies only to vectors of a vector space $\mathfrak{R}_n$; clearly, this mapping can be generalized by replacing the real number field by any field. In this chapter we investigate a much broader generalization of our dot product called an *inner product*. We begin by introducing the notion of a *bilinear form* on a vector space. This is the basic concept of this chapter. Intuitively, a bilinear form on $(\mathfrak{F}, \mathfrak{V}, \circ)$ is a mapping of $V \times V$ into F which is linear in both of its arguments. Here is our formal definition.

Definition 11.1.1: A mapping B of $V \times V$ into F is said to be a *bilinear form* on the vector space $(\mathfrak{F}, \mathfrak{V}, \circ)$ if and only if:

(i) $B(k\alpha_1 + \alpha_2, \gamma) = k\,B(\alpha_1, \gamma) + B(\alpha_2, \gamma)$ whenever $\{\alpha_1, \alpha_2, \gamma\} \subset V$ and $k \in F$;

(ii) $B(\alpha, k\gamma_1 + \gamma_2) = k\,B(\alpha, \gamma_1) + B(\alpha, \gamma_2)$ whenever $\{\alpha, \gamma_1, \gamma_2\} \subset V$ and $k \in F$.

We now present some examples.

Example 1: Consider the vector space $\mathfrak{R}_3$ and the mapping f of $R_3 \times R_3$ into R such that $f(\alpha, \gamma) = \alpha \cdot \gamma$ whenever $(\alpha, \gamma) \in R_3 \times R_3$.

Now, $f(k\alpha_1 + \alpha_2\,,\,\gamma) = (k\alpha_1 + \alpha_2)\cdot\gamma = (k\alpha_1)\cdot\gamma + \alpha_2\cdot\gamma = k(\alpha_1\cdot\gamma) + \alpha_2\cdot\gamma$

$$= k\,f(\alpha_1\,,\,\gamma) + f(\alpha_2\,,\,\gamma)\ \text{whenever}$$

$$\{\alpha_1\,,\,\alpha_2\,,\,\gamma\} \subset R_3\ \text{and}\ k \in R.$$

Similarly, we see that $f(\alpha\,,\,k\gamma_1 + \gamma_2) = k\,f(\alpha\,,\,\gamma_1) + f(\alpha\,,\,\gamma_2)$ whenever $\{\alpha\,,\,\gamma_1\,,\,\gamma_2\} \subset R_3$ and $k \in R$. So, f is a bilinear form on $\Re_3$.

Example 2: Consider the vector space $\Re_2$ and the mapping f of $R_2 \times R_2$ into R such that $f(\alpha\,,\,\gamma) = \left[\alpha\begin{pmatrix}2 & 0\\1 & -1\end{pmatrix}\right]\cdot\gamma$ whenever $(\alpha\,,\,\gamma)$ is an ordered pair of vectors. To be explicit, let $\alpha = (a_1\,,\,a_2)$ and let $\gamma = (b_1\,,\,b_2)$; it is easy to see that $f(\alpha\,,\,\gamma) = 2\,a_1\,b_1 + a_2\,b_1 - a_2\,b_2$. Now,

$$f(k\alpha_1 + \alpha_2\,,\,\gamma) = \left[(k\alpha_1 + \alpha_2)\begin{pmatrix}2 & 0\\1 & -1\end{pmatrix}\right]\cdot\gamma$$

$$= k\left[\alpha_1\begin{pmatrix}2 & 0\\1 & -1\end{pmatrix}\right]\cdot\gamma + \left[\alpha_2\begin{pmatrix}2 & 0\\1 & -1\end{pmatrix}\right]\cdot\gamma$$

$$= k\,f(\alpha_1\,,\,\gamma) + f(\alpha_2\,,\,\gamma)\ .$$

Similarly, we see that $f(\alpha\,,\,k\gamma_1 + \gamma_2) = k\,f(\alpha\,,\,\gamma_1) + f(\alpha\,,\,\gamma_2)$. So f is a bilinear form on $\Re_2$. Notice here that the statement "$f(\alpha\,,\,\gamma) = f(\gamma\,,\,\alpha)$ whenever $\{\alpha\,,\,\gamma\} \subset R_2$" is false.

We present a few basic facts about bilinear forms.

Lemma 11.1.1: Let B be a bilinear form on a vector space; then

(i) $B(\alpha_1 + \alpha_2\,,\,\gamma) = B(\alpha_1\,,\,\gamma) + B(\alpha_2\,,\,\gamma)$ whenever $\alpha_1, \alpha_2, \gamma$ are vectors,

(ii) $B(\alpha\,,\,\gamma_1 + \gamma_2) = B(\alpha\,,\,\gamma_1) + B(\alpha\,,\,\gamma_2)$ whenever $\alpha, \gamma_1, \gamma_2$ are vectors,

(iii) $B(0\,,\,\alpha) = B(\alpha\,,\,0) = 0$ whenever α is a vector,

(iv) $B(k\alpha\,,\,\gamma) = k\,B(\alpha\,,\,\gamma)$ whenever k is a scalar and α and γ are vectors,

(v) $B(\alpha\,,\,k\gamma) = k\,B(\alpha\,,\,\gamma)$ whenever k is a scalar and α and γ are vectors,

(vi) $B(a\alpha\,,\,c\gamma) = ac\,B(\alpha\,,\,\gamma)$ whenever a and c are scalars, and α and γ are vectors.

Proof: Let 1 be the multiplicative identity of the supporting field. Then $B(\alpha_1 + \alpha_2\,,\,\gamma) = B(1\alpha_1 + \alpha_2\,,\,\gamma) = 1\,B(\alpha_1\,,\,\gamma) + B(\alpha_2\,,\,\gamma) = B(\alpha_1\,,\,\gamma) + B(\alpha_2\,,\,\gamma)$. This establishes (i); (ii) can be established in a similar way. To verify (iii) consider $B(0 + 0\,,\,\alpha)$ and consider $B(\alpha\,,\,0 + 0)$. Next, we demonstrate (iv). Now, $B(k\alpha\,,\,\gamma) = B(k\alpha + 0\,,\,\gamma) = k\,B(\alpha\,,\,\gamma) + B(0\,,\,\gamma) = k\,B(\alpha\,,\,\gamma)$ by (iii); a similar argument verifies (v). Clearly, (vi) follows from (iv) and (v).

Lemma 11.1.2: Let B be a bilinear form on a vector space; then

(i) $B\left(\sum\limits_{i=1}^{n} \alpha_i\,,\,\gamma\right) = B(\alpha_1\,,\,\gamma) + \cdots + B(\alpha_n\,,\,\gamma)$ whenever $\alpha_1, \ldots, \alpha_n, \gamma$ are vectors,

(ii) $B\left(\alpha, \sum_{i=1}^{n} \gamma_i\right) = B(\alpha, \gamma_1) + \cdots + B(\alpha, \gamma_n)$ whenever $\alpha, \gamma_1, \ldots, \gamma_n$ are vectors.

Proof: Use mathematical induction over n.

We now establish a key result.

Lemma 11.1.3:   Let B be a bilinear form on a vector space; then

$$B\left(\sum_{i=1}^{n} \alpha_i, \sum_{i=1}^{n} \gamma_i\right) = \sum_{(i,j) \in C_n} B(\alpha_i, \gamma_j) \text{ whenever } \alpha_1, \ldots, \alpha_n, \gamma_1, \ldots, \gamma_n \text{ are vectors.}$$

Proof: We use mathematical induction over n. Clearly, 1 has the property. Assume that k is a natural number with the property; we must show that $k + 1$ has the property. Now,

$$B\left(\sum_{i=1}^{k+1} \alpha_i, \sum_{i=1}^{k+1} \gamma_i\right) = B\left(\sum_{i=1}^{k} \alpha_i + \alpha_{k+1}, \sum_{i=1}^{k} \gamma_i + \gamma_{k+1}\right)$$

$$= B\left(\sum_{i=1}^{k} \alpha_i, \sum_{i=1}^{k} \gamma_i\right) + B\left(\sum_{i=1}^{k} \alpha_i, \gamma_{k+1}\right) + B\left(\alpha_{k+1}, \sum_{i=1}^{k} \gamma_i\right)$$

$$+ B(\alpha_{k+1}, \gamma_{k+1}) \qquad \text{by Lemma 11.1.1}$$

$$= \sum_{(i,j) \in C_k} B(\alpha_i, \gamma_j) + \sum_{i=1}^{k} B(\alpha_i, \gamma_{k+1}) + \sum_{i=1}^{k} B(\alpha_{k+1}, \gamma_i)$$

$$+ B(\alpha_{k+1}, \gamma_{k+1})$$

$$= \sum_{(i,j) \in C_{k+1}} B(\alpha_i, \gamma_j) .$$

This demonstrates that $k + 1$ has the property whenever k has the property. So, by mathematical induction, each natural number has the property. This establishes Lemma 11.1.3.

Corollary 11.1.1:   Let B be a bilinear form on a vector space; then

$$B\left(\sum_{i=1}^{n} a_i \alpha_i, \sum_{i=1}^{n} c_i \gamma_i\right) = \sum_{(i,j) \in C_n} a_i c_j B(\alpha_i, \gamma_j) \text{ whenever the } \alpha\text{'s and } \gamma\text{'s are}$$

vectors, and the a's and c's are scalars.

Proof: $B\left(\sum_{i=1}^{n} a_i \alpha_i, \sum_{i=1}^{n} c_i \gamma_i\right) = \sum_{(i,j) \in C_n} B(a_i \alpha_i, c_j \gamma_j) \qquad \text{by Lemma 11.1.3}$

$$= \sum_{(i,j) \in C_n} a_i c_j B(\alpha_i, \gamma_j) \qquad \text{by Lemma 11.1.1 .}$$

Next, we present a very important fact about bilinear forms.

Theorem 11.1.1:   Let B be a bilinear form on a finite-dimensional vector space, let $\mathcal{B} = (\beta_1, \ldots, \beta_n)$ be any ordered basis for this vector space, and let

$b_{ij} = B(\beta_i, \beta_j)$ whenever $(i, j) \in C_n$. Then $B(\alpha, \gamma) = ([\alpha]_\mathfrak{B} (b_{ij})) \cdot [\gamma]_\mathfrak{B}$ whenever α and γ are vectors.

Proof: Let $[\alpha]_\mathfrak{B} = (a_1, \ldots, a_n)$ and let $[\gamma]_\mathfrak{B} = (c_1, \ldots, c_n)$. Now,

$$B(\alpha, \gamma) = B\left(\sum_{i=1}^{n} a_i \beta_i, \sum_{i=1}^{n} c_i \beta_i\right) = \sum_{(i,j) \in C_n} a_i c_j B(\beta_i, \beta_j) = \sum_{(i,j) \in C_n} a_i c_j b_{ij}.$$

Notice that the sum on the right can be represented by a matrix with multipliers, namely

$$\begin{array}{c}\\ a_1 \\ \\ \\ \\ \\ a_n \end{array}\begin{array}{ccc} c_1 & \cdots & c_n \\ \left(\begin{matrix} b_{11} & \cdots & b_{1n} \\ & \cdot & \\ & \cdot & \\ & \cdot & \\ b_{n1} & \cdots & b_{nn} \end{matrix}\right).\end{array}$$

So $\displaystyle\sum_{(i,j) \in C_n} a_i c_j b_{ij} = [(a_1, \ldots, a_n)(b_{ij})] \cdot (c_1, \ldots, c_n)$

$$= [[\alpha]_\mathfrak{B} (b_{ij})] \cdot [\gamma]_\mathfrak{B} .$$

This proves that $B(\alpha, \gamma) = [[\alpha]_\mathfrak{B} (b_{ij})] \cdot [\gamma]_\mathfrak{B} .$

The preceding result brings out the importance of the $n \times n$ matrix $(B(\beta_i, \beta_j))$, where B is a bilinear form on a vector space with ordered basis $\mathfrak{B} = (\beta_1, \ldots, \beta_n)$. This matrix is called the *matrix of B with respect to* $\mathfrak{B}$.

Definition 11.1.2: Let B be a bilinear form on a finite-dimensional vector space with basis $\mathfrak{B} = (\beta_1, \ldots, \beta_n)$. Then the $n \times n$ matrix $(B(\beta_i, \beta_j))$ is said to be the *matrix of B with respect to* $\mathfrak{B}$ and is denoted by $[B]_\mathfrak{B}$. If $\mathfrak{B} = (\epsilon_1, \ldots, \epsilon_n)$ then $[B]_\mathfrak{B}$ is called the *matrix of B* and is denoted by $[B]$.

Example 3: Consider the bilinear form f of Example 1. Notice that $f(\epsilon_i, \epsilon_j) = \delta_{ij}$ whenever $(i, j) \in C_3$; so $[f] = I_3$.

Example 4: Consider the bilinear form f of Example 2. Notice that $f(\epsilon_1, \epsilon_1) = 2, f(\epsilon_1, \epsilon_2) = 0, f(\epsilon_2, \epsilon_1) = 1$, and $f(\epsilon_2, \epsilon_2) = -1$. So

$$[f] = \begin{pmatrix} 2 & 0 \\ 1 & -1 \end{pmatrix} .$$

Let us express Theorem 11.1.1 in this terminology.

Theorem 11.1.1: Let B be a bilinear form on a finite-dimensional vector space, and let $\mathfrak{B}$ be any ordered basis for this vector space. Then $B(\alpha, \gamma) = ([\alpha]_\mathfrak{B} [B]_\mathfrak{B}) \cdot [\gamma]_\mathfrak{B}$ whenever α and γ are vectors.

We need the following fact.

Theorem 11.1.2: Let B be a bilinear form on a finite-dimensional vector space with ordered basis $\mathfrak{B}$, and let M be a square matrix such that $B(\alpha, \gamma) = ([\alpha]_\mathfrak{B} M) \cdot [\gamma]_\mathfrak{B}$ whenever α and γ are vectors. Then $M = [B]_\mathfrak{B}$.

Proof: Let $\mathfrak{B} = (\beta_1, \ldots, \beta_n)$, let $M = (m_{ij})$, and let $(i, j) \in C_n$.

By assumption

$$B(\beta_i, \beta_j) = ([\beta_i]_\mathfrak{B} M) \cdot [\beta_j]_\mathfrak{B} = (\epsilon_i M) \cdot \epsilon_j = M_i \cdot \epsilon_j = m_{ij}.$$

Thus $M = [B]_\mathfrak{B}$.

There is a nice relationship between $[B]_\mathfrak{a}$ and $[B]_\mathfrak{B}$, where B is a bilinear form and $\mathfrak{a}$ and $\mathfrak{B}$ are ordered bases for the vector space involved.

Theorem 11.1.3: Let B be a bilinear form on a finite-dimensional vector space with ordered bases $\mathfrak{a}$ and $\mathfrak{B}$. Then $[B]_\mathfrak{B} = [\mathfrak{B}]_\mathfrak{a} [B]_\mathfrak{a} [\mathfrak{B}]_\mathfrak{a}^t$.

Proof: Let α and γ be any vectors; then

$$\begin{aligned}
B(\alpha, \gamma) &= ([\alpha]_\mathfrak{a} [B]_\mathfrak{a}) \cdot [\gamma]_\mathfrak{a} && \text{by Theorem 11.1.1} \\
&= ([\alpha]_\mathfrak{B} [\mathfrak{B}]_\mathfrak{a} [B]_\mathfrak{a}) \cdot ([\gamma]_\mathfrak{B} [\mathfrak{B}]_\mathfrak{a}) && \text{by Theorem 7.3.2} \\
&= ([\alpha]_\mathfrak{B} [\mathfrak{B}]_\mathfrak{a} [B]_\mathfrak{a} [\mathfrak{B}]_\mathfrak{a}^t) \cdot [\gamma]_\mathfrak{B} && \text{by Lemma 3.3.5.}
\end{aligned}$$

Thus, by Theorem 11.1.2, $[B]_\mathfrak{B} = [\mathfrak{B}]_\mathfrak{a} [B]_\mathfrak{a} [\mathfrak{B}]_\mathfrak{a}^t$.

Next, we introduce the notion of a *symmetric* bilinear form.

Definition 11.1.3: A bilinear form B is said to be *symmetric* if and only if $B(\alpha, \gamma) = B(\gamma, \alpha)$ whenever α and γ are vectors.

The bilinear form of Example 1 is symmetric, whereas the bilinear form of Example 2 is not symmetric.

The following theorem discloses the reason for the choice of the term *symmetric*.

Theorem 11.1.4: Let B be a bilinear form on a finite-dimensional vector space with ordered basis $\mathfrak{a}$. Then B is symmetric if and only if $[B]_\mathfrak{a}$ is symmetric.

Proof: Let $\mathfrak{a} = (\alpha_1, \ldots, \alpha_n)$ be an ordered basis for the vector space involved.

1. Assume that B is symmetric. Then $B(\alpha_i, \alpha_j) = B(\alpha_j, \alpha_i)$ whenever $(i, j) \in C_n$. Thus, $[B]_\mathfrak{a} = [B]_\mathfrak{a}^t$.

2.   Let $A = [B]_a$ and assume that $A = A^t$. We must show that

$B(\beta, \gamma) = B(\gamma, \beta)$ whenever β and γ are vectors. Now,

$$B(\beta, \gamma) = ([\beta]_a\, A) \cdot [\gamma]_a \qquad \text{by Theorem 11.1.1}$$

$$= [\beta]_a \cdot ([\gamma]_a\, A^t) \qquad \text{by Lemma 3.3.5}$$

$$= ([\gamma]_a\, A) \cdot [\beta]_a \qquad \begin{array}{l}\text{since } A^t = A \text{ and the dot}\\ \text{product is commutative}\end{array}$$

$$= B(\gamma, \beta) \qquad \text{by Theorem 11.1.1 .}$$

Thus B is symmetric. This completes our proof.

EXERCISES

1.   Consider the vector space $\mathfrak{R}_2$. Let f be the mapping of $R_2 \times R_2$ into R such that $f(\alpha, \beta) = a_1 b_1$ whenever $\alpha = (a_1, a_2)$ and $\beta = (b_1, b_2)$.

    (a)   Use Definition 11.1.1 to show that f is a bilinear form on $\mathfrak{R}_2$.
    (b)   Exhibit $[f]$.
    (c)   Represent $f(\alpha, \beta)$ by a matrix with multipliers, where $\alpha = (a_1, a_2)$ and $\beta = (b_1, b_2)$.
    (d)   Let $\mathfrak{B} = ((1, 1), (1, -1))$; exhibit $[f]_\mathfrak{B}$.
    (e)   Is f symmetric?

2.   Consider the vector space $\mathfrak{R}_2$. Let f be the mapping of $R_2 \times R_2$ into R such that $f(\alpha, \beta) = a_1(b_1 + b_2)$ whenever $\alpha = (a_1, a_2)$ and $\beta = (b_1, b_2)$.

    (a)   Show that f is a bilinear form on $\mathfrak{R}_2$.
    (b)   Exhibit $[f]$.
    (c)   Represent $f(\alpha, \beta)$ by a matrix with multipliers, where $\alpha = (a_1, a_2)$ and $\beta = (b_1, b_2)$.
    (d)   Let $\mathfrak{B} = ((2, 5), (-3, 1))$; exhibit $[f]_\mathfrak{B}$.
    (e)   Is f symmetric?

3.   Consider the vector space $\mathfrak{R}_3$. Let f be the mapping of $R_3 \times R_3$ into R such that $f(\alpha, \beta) = a_1(b_1 + 2)$ whenever $\alpha = (a_1, a_2, a_3)$ and $\beta = (b_1, b_2, b_3)$. Is f a bilinear form on $\mathfrak{R}_3$?

4.   Consider the vector space $\mathfrak{R}_3$. Let f be the mapping of $R_3 \times R_3$ into R such that $f(\alpha, \beta) = a_1(b_1 + 2b_2 - b_3)$ whenever $\alpha = (a_1, a_2, a_3)$ and $\beta = (b_1, b_2, b_3)$.

    (a)   Show that f is a bilinear form on $\mathfrak{R}_3$.
    (b)   Exhibit $[f]$.
    (c)   Represent $f(\alpha, \beta)$ by a matrix with multipliers, where $\alpha = (a_1, a_2, a_3)$ and $\beta = (b_1, b_2, b_3)$.
    (d)   Is f symmetric?

5. Prove Lemma 11.1.1.

6. Prove Lemma 11.1.2.

7. Let B be the bilinear form on $\mathfrak{R}_2$ such that $[B] = \begin{pmatrix} 2 & 1 \\ -1 & 3 \end{pmatrix}$.

    (a) Determine $[B]_{\mathfrak{a}}$ where $\mathfrak{a} = ((0, 1), (1, 0))$.
    (b) Determine $[B]_{\mathfrak{a}}$ where $\mathfrak{a} = ((1, 3), (1, -1))$.

8. Let B be the bilinear form on $\mathfrak{R}_3$ such that $[B] = \begin{pmatrix} 2 & 0 & -1 \\ 0 & 1 & 1 \\ 1 & 3 & 1 \end{pmatrix}$.

    (a) Determine $[B]_{\mathfrak{a}}$ where $\mathfrak{a} = (\epsilon_3, \epsilon_2, \epsilon_1)$.
    (b) Determine $[B]_{\mathfrak{a}}$ where $\mathfrak{a} = ((0, 1, 1), (1, 0, 1), (1, 1, 0))$.

9. Let B be a bilinear form on a finite-dimensional vector space with ordered basis $(\alpha_1, \ldots, \alpha_n)$. Prove that B is symmetric if and only if $B(\alpha_i, \alpha_j) = B(\alpha_j, \alpha_i)$ whenever $(i, j) \in C_n$.

10. Let B and C be bilinear forms on a vector space V. Show that $B + C = \{(\alpha, \gamma, k) \mid (\alpha, \gamma) \in V \times V$ and $k = B(\alpha, \gamma) + C(\alpha, \gamma)\}$ is a bilinear form on V.

11. A bilinear form B is said to be *skew-symmetric* if and only if $B(\alpha, \alpha) = 0$ whenever α is a vector.

    (a) Given that B is skew-symmetric, show that $B(\alpha, \gamma) = -B(\gamma, \alpha)$ whenever α and γ are vectors.
    (b) Let B be a bilinear form on a vector space $(\mathfrak{F}, \mathfrak{V}, \circ)$ where the characteristic of $\mathfrak{F}$ is not 2. Prove that there is a unique symmetric bilinear form C and a unique skew-symmetric bilinear form D such that $B = C + D$.

11.2   REAL INNER PRODUCT SPACES

In this section we consider the mathematical system obtained by adjoining a bilinear form of a special type, called an *inner product*, to a real vector space.

Definition 11.2.1: A bilinear form $*$ on a real vector space $V = (\mathfrak{R}, \mathfrak{V}, \circ)$ is said to be an *inner product* on V if and only if:

    (*i*) $*$ is symmetric;
    (*ii*) $\alpha * \alpha > 0$ whenever $\alpha \neq \mathbf{0}$.

Notice that we donote the scalar that the mapping $*$ associates with (β, γ) by writing $\beta * \gamma$. This is the convention that we followed in the case of the dot product of Section 3.1. Obviously, this notation is much more efficient than the notation of Section 11.1. We point out that the concept of an inner product on a real vector space is a generalization of the dot product in two senses. First, it is evident that the dot product is an inner product on $\mathfrak{R}_n$. Secondly, recall that the development of Section 3.1 is based largely on the properties of the dot product contained in Theorem 3.1.1. Well, each inner product on a real vector space possesses these properties also.

Theorem 11.2.1: Let $*$ be an inner product on a real vector space **V**. Then

(*i*) $\alpha * \gamma = \gamma * \alpha$ whenever $\{\alpha, \gamma\} \subset V$,

(*ii*) $\alpha * (\beta + \gamma) = \alpha * \beta + \alpha * \gamma$ whenever $\{\alpha, \beta, \gamma\} \subset V$,

(*iii*) $(k\alpha) * \beta = k(\alpha * \beta)$ whenever $k \in R$ and $\{\alpha, \beta\} \subset V$,

(*iv*) $\alpha * \alpha > 0$ whenever $\alpha \neq \mathbf{0}; \mathbf{0} * \mathbf{0} = 0$.

Proof: Apply Lemma 11.1.1.

This theorem is particularly significant for the following reason. Throughout Section 3.1 we carefully established many of our results by using the algebraic properties of the dot product contained in Theorem 3.1.1, rather than the definition of the dot product. Now, Theorem 11.2.1 ensures that those results hold for any inner product on a real vector space. The point is that we can obtain a proof for any inner product by considering the corresponding proof of Section 3.1 and using Theorem 11.2.1 in place of Theorem 3.1.1.

A real vector space $V = (\mathfrak{R}, \mathcal{U}, \circ)$ and an inner product $*$ together constitute a mathematical system which is somewhat more complicated than the vector space itself. This mathematical system is called a *real inner product space* and is denoted by $(V, *)$, or by $(\mathfrak{R}, \mathcal{U}, \circ, *)$ if we wish to exhibit the components of the vector space.

Definition 11.2.2: $(V, *)$ is said to be a *real inner product space* if and only if:

(*i*)   **V** is a real vector space;

(*ii*) $*$ is an inner product on **V**.

Here are some examples.

Example 1: $(\mathfrak{R}_n, \cdot)$ is a real inner product space, whenever $n \in N$, where $\cdot$ denotes the dot product of Definition 3.1.1.

Example 2:   Let **V** be a real, finite-dimensional vector space, and let $\mathfrak{B}$ be an ordered basis for **V**. Let $*$ be the mapping of $V \times V$ into R such that $\alpha * \gamma = [\alpha]_{\mathfrak{B}} \cdot [\gamma]_{\mathfrak{B}}$ whenever $(\alpha, \gamma) \in V \times V$. It is easy to see that $*$ is a symmetric bilinear form on **V** and that $\alpha * \alpha > 0$ whenever $\alpha \neq \mathbf{0}$.   Thus, $(V, *)$ is a real inner product space.

Example 3:   Let **V** be the real vector space of Example 5, Section 7.1. There, vectors are continuous functions with domain $[0, 1]$. Clearly, each function with these properties is integrable over $[0 , 1]$; moreover, the product of functions with these properties is integrable over $[0 , 1]$. Let $*$ be the mapping of $V \times V$ into R such that $f * g = \int_0^1 f \cdot g$ when f and g are vectors (i.e., continuous functions with domain $[0 , 1]$). It is easy to see that $*$ is a symmetric bilinear form on V. It is usually shown in an advanced calculus course that $\int_0^1 g > 0$ if g is continuous on $[0 , 1]$, $g \neq \mathbf{0}$, and if $g(t) \geq 0$ whenever $t \in [0 , 1]$. Thus $f * f > 0$ whenever $f \neq \mathbf{0}$. We conclude that $*$ is an inner product on V; so $(V , *)$ is a real inner product space. Notice that this inner product space has infinite dimension.

Example 4:　Let V be the real vector space involving polynomials over R (see Theorem 8.1.2). Let $\sum_{i=0}^{s} a_i x^i$ and $\sum_{j=0}^{t} b_j x^j$ be any polynomials, and let

$$\sum_{i=0}^{s} a_i x^i * \sum_{j=0}^{t} b_j x^j = \sum_{(i,j)} \frac{a_i b_j}{i + j + 1}$$ summed over all members (i , j) of $\{0 , \dots , s\} \times \{0 , \dots , t\}$. Now, V is a subsystem of the vector space of Example 3; moreover, the mapping of this example is the restriction of the inner product of Example 3 to polynomial functions. Thus $*$ is an inner product on V; so, $(V , *)$ is a real inner product space.

Example 5:　Let V be the real vector space involving all $m \times n$ matrices over R (see Example 8, Section 7.1). We define $*$ as follows. Let A and B be any $m \times n$ matrices; then $A * B = \sum_{i=1}^{m} A_i \cdot B_i$. It is easy to verify that $*$ is an inner product on V. Thus $(V , *)$ is a real inner product space. Notice that $A * B = \sum_{j=1}^{n} {}_j A \cdot {}_j B$; indeed, $A * B$ can be obtained by multiplying each entry of A by the corresponding entry of B, and summing the resulting products.

When we look for an inner product on a real vector space it soon becomes clear that interesting examples are few and far between. In particular, condition (ii) is difficult to satisfy. In Example 2, we pointed out a general procedure for obtaining an inner product on a real, finite-dimensional vector space. Here is another method of manufacturing inner products.

Example 6:　Let $(V , *)$ be any real inner product space, let $t > 0$, and let $\Diamond$ be the mapping of $V \times V$ into R such that $\alpha \Diamond \beta = t(\alpha * \beta)$ whenever $(\alpha , \beta) \in V \times V$. Since $*$ is an inner product on V it follows that $\Diamond$ is an inner product on V also. Thus $(V , \Diamond)$ is a real inner product space.

Notice that the inner products $*$ and $\Diamond$ of Example 6 are related by the fact that $\alpha * \beta = 0$ if and only if $\alpha \Diamond \beta = 0$. In view of the general difficulty in constructing inner products, this observation suggests the following conjecture.

CONJECTURE:　Let $(V , *)$ be a real inner product space; then each inner product on V, say $\Diamond$, has the property that $\alpha \Diamond \beta = 0$ whenever $\alpha * \beta = 0$.

Think about this statement for a moment; is it true or false? Well, the shortage of inner products is *not* as severe as described in this conjecture. The conjecture is false! To demonstrate this, we must exhibit a real vector space which possesses two essentially different inner products. The key is contained in Example 2 which asserts that each ordered basis for a real finite-dimensional vector space, leads us to an inner product on the vector space.

Example 7: Consider the real vector space $\mathfrak{R}_2$. Now, $\cdot$ is an inner product on $\mathfrak{R}_2$. We use Example 2 to construct another inner product on $\mathfrak{R}_2$. Notice that $\mathfrak{B} = ((1, 0), (1, 1))$ is an ordered basis for $\mathfrak{R}_2$. So, by Example 2, the mapping $*$ such $\alpha * \gamma = [\alpha]_{\mathfrak{B}} \cdot [\gamma]_{\mathfrak{B}}$ whenever $(\alpha, \gamma) \in R_2 \times R_2$ is an inner product on $\mathfrak{R}_2$. To be specific, $(a_1, a_2) * (b_1, b_2) = (a_1 - a_2)(b_1 - b_2) + a_2 b_2$ whenever $(a_1, a_2) \in R_2$ and $(b_1, b_2) \in R_2$. Clearly, $*$ is a symmetric bilinear form on $\mathfrak{R}_2$ and $\alpha * \alpha > 0$ if $\alpha \neq (0, 0)$; indeed, $(a_1, a_2) * (a_1, a_2) = (a_1 - a_2)^2 + a_2^2$. So $(\mathfrak{R}_2, *)$ is a real inner product space. We wish to show that $*$ is essentially different from $\cdot$ in the sense that $*$ does not preserve orthogonality. Now,

$$\epsilon_1 * \epsilon_2 = [\epsilon_1]_{\mathfrak{B}} \cdot [\epsilon_2]_{\mathfrak{B}} = (1, 0) \cdot (-1, 1) = -1 .$$

Also, $(2, 3) * (4, 1) = (-1, 3) \cdot (3, 1) = 0$. This demonstrates that the conjecture is false.

It is now clear that there exist a variety of inner products on a real vector space. However, remember that Example 2 refers *only* to finite-dimensional vector spaces. Perhaps the conjecture applies to infinite-dimensional vector spaces! We can dispose of this suggestion by exhibiting some inner products on the vector space of Example 4, which is infinite-dimensional.

Example 8: Let V be the vector space involving polynomials over R. Let $\mathfrak{B} = (\beta_0, \ldots, \beta_n, \ldots)$ be any ordered basis for V such that $\deg \beta_n = n$ for each n. Let p and q be any polynomials; there is a natural number m such that $\{p, q\} \subset L\{\beta_0, \ldots, \beta_m\}$, indeed $m = \max\{\deg p, \deg q\}$ or $m = 0$ if $p = q = 0$. Let $\mathfrak{B}' = (\beta_0, \ldots, \beta_m)$. We define a mapping $*$ as follows: $p * q = [p]_{\mathfrak{B}'} \cdot [q]_{\mathfrak{B}'}$. It is easy to verify that $*$ is an inner product on V. Take $\mathfrak{B} = (1, x, \ldots, x^{n-1}, \ldots)$. Let $m = \max\{\deg p, \deg q\}$; then $p * q = [p]_{\mathfrak{B}'} \cdot [q]_{\mathfrak{B}'}$ where $\mathfrak{B}' = (1, x, \ldots, x^m)$. For example, $(3 - x^2 + 2x^3) * (x + x^2) = (3, 0, -1, 2) \cdot (0, 1, 1, 0) = -1$. Take $\mathfrak{B} = (1, 1 + x, \ldots, 1 + x + \cdots + x^{n-1}, \ldots)$. Let $m = \max\{\deg p, \deg q\}$; then $p * q = [p]_{\mathfrak{B}'} \cdot [q]_{\mathfrak{B}'}$ where $\mathfrak{B}' = (1, 1 + x, \ldots, 1 + x + \cdots + x^m)$. For example, $(2 + 3x) * (4 + x) = (-1, 3) \cdot (3, 1) = 0$. This establishes our point.

EXERCISES

1. Prove Theorem 11.2.1.

2. Let $\mathcal{V} = (R, +, 0)$; show that $(\mathfrak{R}, \mathcal{V}, \cdot, \cdot)$ is a real inner product space, where $\cdot$ denotes multiplication in the real number field.

3. Let $\mathcal{U} = (R, +, 0)$; show that $(\mathcal{R}, \mathcal{U}, \cdot, +)$ is *not* a real inner product space, where $+$ denotes addition in the real number field.

4. Let $*$ be the mapping of $R_2 \times R_2$ into R such that $\alpha * \beta = a_1(b_1 + b_2) + a_2(b_1 + 2b_2)$ whenever $\alpha = (a_1, a_2)$ and $\beta = (b_1, b_2)$. Show that $*$ is an inner product on $\mathcal{R}_2$.

5. Let V be any real vector space and let $\alpha * \beta = 0$ whenever $(\alpha, \beta) \in V \times V$. Show that $*$ is *not* an inner product on V.

6. Let $(V, *)$ be any real inner product space, let V' be any real vector space, and let T be a one-one mapping of V' into V such that T is a linear transformation of V into V'. Let $*'$ be the mapping of $V' \times V'$ into R such that $\alpha *' \beta = T(\alpha) * T(\beta)$ whenever $(\alpha, \beta) \in V' \times V'$. Show that $*'$ is an inner product on V'.

7. Let V be the set of all mappings f of $\{0, 1\}$ into R such that $f(0)$ and $f(1)$ have the same algebraic sign. Let $+$, $\mathbf{0}$, and $\circ$ be defined as in Example 3, Section 7.1, and let

$$f * g = (f(0) + f(1))(g(0) + g(1))$$

whenever $(f, g) \in V \times V$. Let $\mathcal{U} = (V, +, \mathbf{0})$; show that $(\mathcal{R}, \mathcal{U}, \circ, *)$ is *not* a real inner product space.

8. Let $n \in N$ and consider the real vector space $\mathcal{R}_n$. Let

$$\alpha * \beta = \left(\sum_{i=1}^{n} a_i \right)\left(\sum_{i=1}^{n} b_i \right)$$

whenever $\alpha = (a_1, \ldots, a_n)$ and $\beta = (b_1, \ldots b_n)$. Show that $(\mathcal{R}_n, *)$ is *not* a real inner product space.

9. Let $n \in N$ and let V be the set of all members of R_n, say $(a_1, \ldots, a_n)$, such that $a_1, \ldots, a_n$ have the same algebraic sign. Let $+$, $\mathbf{0}$, and $\circ$ be defined as in Example 1, Section 7.1. Let $\alpha * \beta = \left(\sum_{i=1}^{n} a_i \right)\left(\sum_{i=1}^{n} b_i \right)$ whenever $\alpha = (a_1, \ldots, a_n)$ and $\beta = (b_1, \ldots, b_n)$. Let $\mathcal{U} = (V, +, \mathbf{0})$; show that $(\mathcal{R}, \mathcal{U}, \circ, *)$ is *not* a real inner product space.

10. Let V be the vector space of Example 5, Section 7.1. Let h be a member of V such that $h(t) > 0$ whenever $t \in [0, 1]$, and let $f * g = \int_0^1 (f \cdot g \cdot h)$ whenever $(f, g) \in V \times V$. Show that $(V, *)$ is a real inner product space.

11. Let V be the vector space of Example 8, Section 7.1 and let $*$ be an inner product on $\mathcal{R}_m$. Let $A \diamond B = \sum_{i=1}^{m} (A_i * B_i)$ whenever A and B are $m \times n$ matrices. Show that $(V, \diamond)$ is a real inner product space.

11.3 PROPERTIES OF REAL INNER PRODUCT SPACES

In Section 3.2 we introduced the notion of the *length* of a vector. There, we were concerned primarily with the geometric applications of this concept, as the term suggests. It is not wise, however, to become tied to one application of an idea. Here, we use the term *norm* in an effort to free our minds from the domination of geometry.

Definition 11.3.1: Let $(V, *)$ be a real inner product space; then $\sqrt{\alpha * \alpha}$ is said to be the *norm* of α whenever $\alpha \in V$, and is denoted by $\|\alpha\|$.

Notice that *norm* is a mapping of V into R.

As we have already observed, the properties of *length* discussed in Section 3.2 can be established in this more general setting by similar arguments. We now state some of these results in the language of this section.

Theorem 11.3.1 (*Schwarz Inequality*)**:** Let $(V, *)$ be a real inner product space. Then $|\alpha * \gamma| \leq \|\alpha\| \, \|\gamma\|$ whenever α and γ are vectors.

Theorem 11.3.2 (*Triangle Inequality*)**:** Let $(V, *)$ be a real inner product space. Then $\|\alpha + \gamma\| \leq \|\alpha\| + \|\gamma\|$ whenever α and γ are vectors.

Here is an important application to analysis of these ideas. Consider the real inner product space of Example 3, Section 11.2. There $\|f\| = (\int_0^1 f^2)^{\frac{1}{2}}$ whenever f is a continuous function with domain $[0, 1]$. Applying Theorems 11.3.1 and 11.3.2 in this real inner product space, we establish the following theorems of analysis.

SCHWARZ INEQUALITY: Let f and g be any continuous functions with domain $[0, 1]$; then $|\int_0^1 f \cdot g| \leq (\int_0^1 f^2 \int_0^1 g^2)^{\frac{1}{2}}$.

MINKOWSKI INEQUALITY: Let f and g be any continuous functions with domain $[0, 1]$; then $[\int_0^1 (f + g)^2]^{\frac{1}{2}} \leq (\int_0^1 f^2)^{\frac{1}{2}} + (\int_0^1 g^2)^{\frac{1}{2}}$.

Just as in Section 3.1 we present the notion of *orthogonal vectors*, the notion of an *orthogonal set*, and the notion of an *orthonormal* set.

Definition 11.3.2: Let $(V, *)$ be any real inner product space. Vectors α and γ are said to be *orthogonal* if and only if $\alpha * \gamma = 0$. A nonempty set of vectors is said to be *orthogonal* if and only if any two of its members are orthogonal. An orthogonal set is said to be *orthonormal* if and only if $\|\alpha\| = 1$ whenever α is a member of the set.

Notice that the significance of the terms "orthogonal" and "orthonormal" depends upon the inner product involved in the real inner product space.

Using this language we can strengthen the Gram–Schmidt Theorem (Theorem 3.1.6) as follows.

Theorem 11.3.3: Each finite-dimensional subspace of a real inner product space possesses an orthonormal basis.

Proof: Let W be a finite-dimensional subspace of $(V, *)$, a real inner product space. Since W possesses a dimension, it is clear that W is not the trivial subspace of V. Applying the method of the proof of Theorem 3.1.6 it is easy to verify that W possesses an orthogonal basis, say $\{\beta_1, \ldots, \beta_t\}$. Thus $\{\beta_1/\|\beta_1\|, \ldots, \beta_t/\|\beta_t\|\}$ is an orthonormal basis for W.

We now present some properties of real inner product spaces.

Lemma 11.3.1: Let $(V, *)$ be an n-dimensional, real inner product space, and let $\mathcal{B}$ be an ordered orthonormal basis for V. Then $[*]_\mathcal{B} = I_n$.

Proof: Let $\mathcal{B} = (\beta_1, \ldots, \beta_n)$; then

$$[*]_\mathcal{B} = (\beta_i * \beta_j) \qquad \text{by Definition 11.1.2}$$

$$= (\delta_{ij}) \qquad \text{since } \mathcal{B} \text{ is orthonormal}$$

$$= I_n \ .$$

Our next result is important.

Theorem 11.3.4: Let $(V, *)$ be a finite-dimensional, real inner product space and let $\mathcal{B}$ be an orthonormal basis for V. Then $\alpha * \gamma = [\alpha]_\mathcal{B} \cdot [\gamma]_\mathcal{B}$ whenever α and γ are vectors.

Proof: $\alpha * \gamma = ([\alpha]_\mathcal{B} [*]_\mathcal{B}) \cdot [\gamma]_\mathcal{B} \qquad \text{by Theorem 11.1.1}$

$\qquad = ([\alpha]_\mathcal{B} I_n) \cdot [\gamma]_\mathcal{B} \qquad \text{by Lemma 11.3.1}$

$\qquad = [\alpha]_\mathcal{B} \cdot [\gamma]_\mathcal{B} \ .$

This completes our proof.

The following corollary to Theorem 11.3.4 shows how easy it is to determine the matrix of a vector with respect to an orthonormal basis.

Corollary 11.3.1: Let $(V, *)$ be a finite-dimensional, real inner product space and let $\mathcal{B} = (\beta_1, \ldots, \beta_n)$ be an ordered orthonormal basis for V. Then $[\gamma]_\mathcal{B} = (\gamma * \beta_1, \ldots, \gamma * \beta_n)$ whenever $\gamma \in V$.

Proof: Let $\gamma \in V$ and let $i \in \{1, \ldots, n\}$. By Theorem 11.3.4

$$\gamma * \beta_i = [\gamma]_\mathcal{B} \cdot [\beta_i]_\mathcal{B} = [\gamma]_\mathcal{B} \cdot \epsilon_i \ .$$

So $\gamma * \beta_i$ is the ith term of $[\gamma]_\mathcal{B}$. Thus $[\gamma]_\mathcal{B} = (\gamma * \beta_1, \ldots, \gamma * \beta_n)$.

Next, we introduce the notion of the *orthogonal complement* of a nonempty set of vectors.

Definition 11.3.3: Let $(V, *)$ be a real inner product space and let A be a nonempty subset of V. Then $\{\gamma \mid \gamma \in V$ and $\gamma * \alpha = 0$ whenever $\alpha \in A\}$ is said to be the *orthogonal complement of A* and is denoted by $A^\perp$.

For example, $V^\perp = \{0\}$ and $\{0\}^\perp = V$. Consider $(\Re_3, \cdot)$; here $\{\epsilon_1\}^\perp = L\{\epsilon_2, \epsilon_3\}$ and $\{\epsilon_1, \epsilon_2\}^\perp = L\{\epsilon_3\}$.

In this connection the following facts are easily established.

Lemma 11.3.2: Let $(V, *)$ be a real inner product space and let A be any nonempty subset of V. Then $A^\perp = (LA)^\perp$.

Proof: See Theorem 3.1.3.

Lemma 11.3.3: Let $(V, *)$ be a real inner product space and let A be any nonempty subset of V. Then $A^\perp$ is a subspace of V.

EXERCISES

1. Let $(V, *)$ be a real inner product space. Prove each of the following statements.

    (a) $\|\alpha\| > 0$ if $\alpha \neq 0$.
    (b) $\|0\| = 0$.
    (c) $\|k\alpha\| = |k|\|\alpha\|$ whenever $\alpha \in V$ and $k \in R$.
    (d) $\|\alpha + \beta\| = \sqrt{\alpha * \alpha + \beta * \beta + 2(\alpha * \beta)}$ whenever $\{\alpha, \beta\} \subset V$.
    (e) $\|\alpha - \beta\| = \sqrt{\alpha * \alpha + \beta * \beta - 2(\alpha * \beta)}$ whenever $\{\alpha, \beta\} \subset V$.

2. Let $(V, *)$ be a real inner product space. Prove that $|\alpha * \beta| \leq 1$ whenever $\|\alpha\| = \|\beta\| = 1$.

3. Prove Theorem 11.3.1.

4. Prove Theorem 11.3.2.

5. Let f and g be any continuous functions with domain $[0, 1]$ such that $\int_0^1 f^2 = \int_0^1 g^2 = 1$; prove that $|\int_0^1 f \cdot g| \leq 1$.

6. Complete the proof of Theorem 11.3.3.

7. Consider the real inner product space $(\Re_3, \cdot)$.

    (a) Find a basis for $\{(1, -1, 0)\}^\perp$.
    (b) Find a basis for $\{(1, -1, 0), (1, 0, -1)\}^\perp$.

8. Consider the real inner product space $(\Re_4, \cdot)$.

    (a) Find a basis for $\{(1, 1, 0, 0)\}^\perp$.
    (b) Find a basis for $\{(1, 1, 0, 0), (0, 0, 1, 1)\}^\perp$.
    (c) Find a basis for $\{(1, 1, 0, 0), (0, 0, 1, 1), (1, 0, 0, 1)\}^\perp$.

9. Prove Lemma 11.3.2.

10. Prove Lemma 11.3.3.

11. Let $(V, *)$ be a finite-dimensional, real inner product space, and let $\mathfrak{A}$ and $\mathfrak{B}$ be ordered orthonormal bases for V. Prove that $[\gamma_1]_{\mathfrak{A}} \cdot [\gamma_2]_{\mathfrak{A}} = [\gamma_1]_{\mathfrak{B}} \cdot [\gamma_2]_{\mathfrak{B}}$ whenever $\{\gamma_1, \gamma_2\} \subset V$.

11.4 QUADRATIC FORMS

In Chapter 12 we come to grips with *quadric surfaces;* there, we utilize the notion of a *quadratic form.* Indeed, our analysis of a quadric surface centers around two quadratic forms that are associated with it. The goal of this section, then, is to present the notion of a quadratic form and to develop some of the properties of quadratic forms.

Definition 11.4.1: A mapping Q of V into F is said to be a *quadratic form* on the vector space $V = (\mathfrak{F}, \mathfrak{V}, \circ)$ if and only if there is a symmetric bilinear form on V, say B, such that $Q(\alpha) = B(\alpha, \alpha)$ whenever $\alpha \in V$.

We now illustrate this notion.

Example 1: Consider $\mathfrak{R}_3$ and let Q be the mapping of R_3 into R such that
$$Q(\alpha) = \left[\alpha \begin{pmatrix} 1 & 2 & 0 \\ 2 & 0 & 1 \\ 0 & 1 & -1 \end{pmatrix} \right] \cdot \alpha$$
whenever $\alpha \in R_3$. We claim that Q is a quadratic form on $\mathfrak{R}_3$; accordingly, we must exhibit a symmetric bilinear form on $\mathfrak{R}_3$ that leads to Q in the sense of Definition 11.4.1. Let B be the bilinear form on $\mathfrak{R}_3$ such that $[B] = \begin{pmatrix} 1 & 2 & 0 \\ 2 & 0 & 1 \\ 0 & 1 & -1 \end{pmatrix}$. Clearly, B is symmetric; moreover $Q(\alpha) = B(\alpha, \alpha)$ whenever $\alpha \in R_3$. So, Q is a quadratic form on $\mathfrak{R}_3$.

Here is an important property of quadratic forms.

Lemma 11.4.1: Let Q be a quadratic form on a vector space V; then $Q(k\alpha) = k^2 Q(\alpha)$ whenever $\alpha \in V$ and k is a scalar.

Proof: Let B be a symmetric bilinear form on V such that $Q(\alpha) = B(\alpha, \alpha)$ whenever $\alpha \in V$. Then
$$Q(k\alpha) = B(k\alpha, k\alpha) = k^2 B(\alpha, \alpha) = k^2 Q(\alpha)$$
whenever $\alpha \in V$ and k is a scalar.

It turns out that there is just one symmetric bilinear form that leads to a particular quadratic form in the sense of Definition 11.4.1. This point is easily established by considering the following lemma.

Lemma 11.4.2: Let Q be a quadratic form on a vector space V and let B be a symmetric bilinear form on V such that $Q(\alpha) = B(\alpha, \alpha)$ whenever $\alpha \in V$. Then $Q(\alpha + \gamma) = Q(\alpha) + Q(\gamma) + 2B(\alpha, \gamma)$ whenever $\{\alpha, \gamma\} \subset V$.

Proof: By Lemma 11.1.3

$$Q(\alpha + \gamma) = B(\alpha + \gamma, \alpha + \gamma) = B(\alpha, \alpha) + B(\gamma, \gamma) + B(\alpha, \gamma) + B(\gamma, \alpha)$$

$$= Q(\alpha) + Q(\gamma) + 2B(\alpha, \gamma)$$

since B is symmetric.

In Chapter 12 we shall be involved with quadratic forms on $\Re_3$ and $\Re_4$. Here is an appropriate *unique-existence* theorem.

Theorem 11.4.1: Let Q be a quadratic form on $\Re_n$; then there is a unique symmetric bilinear form on $\Re_n$, say B, such that $Q(\alpha) = B(\alpha, \alpha)$ whenever $\alpha \in R_n$.

Proof: By Definition 11.4.1 there is at least one symmetric bilinear form with the stated property. We must show that there is just one. Let B_1 and B_2 be symmetric bilinear forms on $\Re_n$ such that $Q(\alpha) = B_1(\alpha, \alpha)$ and $Q(\alpha) = B_2(\alpha, \alpha)$ whenever $\alpha \in R_n$. We now show that $B_1(\beta, \gamma) = B_2(\beta, \gamma)$ whenever $\{\beta, \gamma\} \subset R_n$. By Lemma 11.4.2

$$Q(\beta + \gamma) = Q(\beta) + Q(\gamma) + 2B_1(\beta, \gamma)$$

and $$Q(\beta + \gamma) = Q(\beta) + Q(\gamma) + 2B_2(\beta, \gamma) .$$

Thus $B_1(\beta, \gamma) = B_2(\beta, \gamma)$ whenever $\{\beta, \gamma\} \subset R_n$. We conclude that $B_1 = B_2$; this completes our proof.

Note: The unique symmetric bilinear form of Theorem 11.4.1 is said to be the bilinear form *associated* with Q.

The following theorem provides us with a wholesale method of constructing quadratic forms on a finite-dimensional vector space.

Theorem 11.4.2: Let $V = (\mathcal{F}, \mathcal{V}, \circ)$ be any n-dimensional vector space, let $\mathcal{B}$ be an ordered basis for V, let A be any symmetric $n \times n$ matrix over F, and let Q be the mapping of V into F such that $Q(\alpha) = ([\alpha]_{\mathcal{B}} A) \cdot [\alpha]_{\mathcal{B}}$ whenever $\alpha \in V$. Then Q is a quadratic form on V.

Proof: Let B be the bilinear form on V such that $[B]_{\mathcal{B}} = A$; by Theorem 11.1.4, B is symmetric. But, by Theorem 11.1.1, $Q(\alpha) = B(\alpha, \alpha)$ whenever $\alpha \in V$. We conclude that Q is a quadratic form on V and that B is the bilinear form associated with Q.

As usual, we need the notion of the *matrix* of a quadratic form with respect to an ordered basis.

Definition 11.4.2: Let V be any finite-dimensional vector space, let $\mathcal{B}$ be an ordered basis for V, and let Q be a quadratic form on V with associated bilinear form B. Then $[B]_\mathcal{B}$ is said to be the matrix of Q with respect to $\mathcal{B}$ and is denoted by $[Q]_\mathcal{B}$. If $\mathcal{B} = (\epsilon_1, \ldots, \epsilon_n)$ then $[Q]_\mathcal{B}$ is called *the* matrix of Q and is denoted by $[Q]$.

To illustrate, let Q be the quadratic form of Example 1; then $[Q] = \begin{pmatrix} 1 & 2 & 0 \\ 2 & 0 & 1 \\ 0 & 1 & -1 \end{pmatrix}$.

The following lemma exhibits the value of the concept of Definition 11.4.2.

Lemma 11.4.3: Let Q be a quadratic form on a finite-dimensional vector space V with ordered basis $\mathcal{B}$. Then $Q(\alpha) = ([\alpha]_\mathcal{B} [Q]_\mathcal{B}) \cdot [\alpha]_\mathcal{B}$ whenever $\alpha \in V$.

Proof: Apply Theorem 11.1.1.

We need the following fact in Chapter 12.

Lemma 11.4.4: Let Q be a quadratic form on $\mathcal{R}_n$; then $Q(\alpha + \gamma) = Q(\alpha) + Q(\gamma) + 2(\alpha[Q]) \cdot \gamma$ whenever $\{\alpha, \gamma\} \subset R_n$.

Proof: By Lemma 11.4.3

$$Q(\alpha + \gamma) = ((\alpha + \gamma)[Q]) \cdot (\alpha + \gamma)$$
$$= (\alpha[Q]) \cdot \alpha + (\alpha[Q]) \cdot \gamma + (\gamma[Q]) \cdot \alpha + (\gamma[Q]) \cdot \gamma$$
$$= Q(\alpha) + Q(\gamma) + 2(\alpha[Q]) \cdot \gamma \ .$$

This completes our proof.

Next, we present the relationship between $[Q]_\alpha$ and $[Q]_\mathcal{B}$, where α and $\mathcal{B}$ are ordered bases for the vector space involved.

Theorem 11.4.3: Let Q be a quadratic form on a finite-dimensional vector space with ordered bases α and $\mathcal{B}$. Then $[Q]_\mathcal{B} = [\mathcal{B}]_\alpha [Q]_\alpha [\mathcal{B}]_\alpha'$.

Proof: Apply Theorem 11.1.3.

To explain our interest in quadratic forms we now present an application to geometry. We are sometimes interested in discussing a set of vectors, of a finite-dimensional vector space, characterized by a condition on the coordinates of a vector with respect to a given ordered basis. In particular, we are interested in sets of vectors that can be characterized by an equation of the second degree. This equation can sometimes be simplified by choosing a suitable ordered basis. We now illustrate the idea.

Example 2: Simplify $\{(x, y) \mid x^2 + 4y^2 - 4xy - 2x - y = 5\}$.

Solution: The quadratic part of the given equation, namely $x^2 + 4y^2 - 4xy$, can be expressed by the quadratic form Q such that $[Q] = \begin{pmatrix} 1 & -2 \\ -2 & 4 \end{pmatrix}$. Indeed,

$$Q(x, y) = ((x, y)[Q]) \cdot (x, y) = \begin{matrix} x \\ y \end{matrix}\begin{pmatrix} 1 & -2 \\ -2 & 4 \end{pmatrix} = x^2 + 4y^2 - 4xy.$$ So, the given

set is $\{\alpha \mid x$ and y exist such that $[\alpha] = (x, y)$ and $Q(\alpha) - 2x - y = 5\}$. Our object is to find an ordered basis $\mathcal{B}$ for $\mathcal{R}_2$ such that $[Q]_\mathcal{B}$ is simpler than $[Q]$ (i.e., involves more zeros); in short, we wish to simplify the quadratic part of our equation Consider the ordered basis $\mathcal{B} = ((1, -2), (2, 1))$; by Theorem 11.4.3

$$[Q]_\mathcal{B} = \begin{pmatrix} 1 & -2 \\ 2 & 1 \end{pmatrix}[Q]\begin{pmatrix} 1 & 2 \\ -2 & 1 \end{pmatrix} = \begin{pmatrix} 25 & 0 \\ 0 & 0 \end{pmatrix}.$$

Next, let $\alpha \in R_2$, let $[\alpha] = (x, y)$, and let $[\alpha]_\mathcal{B} = (x', y')$. By Theorem 7.3.2, $(x, y) = (x', y')\begin{pmatrix} 1 & -2 \\ 2 & 1 \end{pmatrix} = (x' + 2y', -2x' + y')$; so $x = x' + 2y'$ and $y = -2x' + y'$. Moreover, by Lemma 11.4.3,

$$Q(\alpha) = \left[(x', y')\begin{pmatrix} 25 & 0 \\ 0 & 0 \end{pmatrix} \right] \cdot (x', y') = \begin{matrix} x' \\ y' \end{matrix}\begin{pmatrix} 25 & 0 \\ 0 & 0 \end{pmatrix} = 25x'^2.$$

We conclude that the given set is $\{\alpha \mid x'$ and y' exist such that $[\alpha]_\mathcal{B} = (x', y')$ and $25x'^2 - 2(x' + 2y') - (-2x' + y') = 5\}$, namely $\{\alpha \mid x'$ and y' exist such that $[\alpha]_\mathcal{B} = (x', y')$ and $5x'^2 - y' = 1\}$, a parabola.

This method works just as well in a vector space of higher dimension.

Example 3: Simplify $\{(x, y, z) \mid 5x^2 + 5y^2 + z^2 + 2xz + 4yz - 2x - 4y + 10z = 0\}$.

Solution: Notice that the quadratic part of the key equation is given by the quadratic form Q, where $[Q] = \begin{pmatrix} 5 & 0 & 1 \\ 0 & 5 & 2 \\ 1 & 2 & 1 \end{pmatrix}$. The idea is to choose an ordered basis $\mathcal{B}$ for $\mathcal{R}_3$ so that $[Q]_\mathcal{B}$ takes on a simple form. Consider $\mathcal{B} = ((2, -1, 0), (1, 2, 1), (-1, -2, 5))$; by Theorem 11.4.3 $[Q]_\mathcal{B} =$

$$\begin{pmatrix} 2 & -1 & 0 \\ 1 & 2 & 1 \\ -1 & -2 & 5 \end{pmatrix}[Q]\begin{pmatrix} 2 & 1 & -1 \\ -1 & 2 & -2 \\ 0 & 1 & 5 \end{pmatrix} = \begin{pmatrix} 25 & 0 & 0 \\ 0 & 36 & 0 \\ 0 & 0 & 0 \end{pmatrix}.$$ Next, let $\alpha \in R_3$, let $[\alpha] = (x, y, z)$, and let $[\alpha]_\mathcal{B} = (x', y', z')$. By Theorem 7.3.2 $(x, y, z) = (x', y', z')\begin{pmatrix} 2 & -1 & 0 \\ 1 & 2 & 1 \\ -1 & -2 & 5 \end{pmatrix}$; so $x = 2x' + y' - z'$, $y = -x' + 2y' - 2z'$, and $z = y' + 5z'$. Moreover, by Lemma 11.4.3,

$$Q(\alpha) = \left[(x',\ y',\ z') \begin{pmatrix} 25 & 0 & 0 \\ 0 & 36 & 0 \\ 0 & 0 & 0 \end{pmatrix} \right] \cdot (x',\ y',\ z') = \begin{matrix} & \overset{x'\quad y'\quad z'}{} \\ \begin{matrix} x' \\ y' \\ z' \end{matrix} & \begin{pmatrix} 25 & 0 & 0 \\ 0 & 36 & 0 \\ 0 & 0 & 0 \end{pmatrix} \end{matrix}$$

$$= 25x'^2 + 36y'^2\ .$$

Thus, the given set is $\{\alpha \mid x',\ y',$ and z' exist such that $[\alpha]_\mathfrak{B} = (x',\ y',\ z')$ and $25x'^2 + 36y'^2 + 60z' = 0\}$, an elliptic paraboloid.

Finally, we present a fact about quadratic forms on $\mathfrak{R}_n$ that we shall need in connection with the notion of a *center* of a quadric surface (see Theorem 12.3.2). A quadratic form Q on $\mathfrak{R}_n$ is said to be *nonzero* if and only if $[Q] \neq (0)$.

Lemma 11.4.5: Let $n \in N$ and let Q be any nonzero quadratic form on $\mathfrak{R}_n$; then there is a basis $\mathfrak{B}$ for $\mathfrak{R}_n$ such that $Q(\beta) \neq 0$ whenever $\beta \in \mathfrak{B}$.

Proof: The idea is to use mathematical induction over n. Clearly 1 has the property. Assume that k has the property. Let Q' be any nonzero quadratic form on $\mathfrak{R}_{k+1}$; then $[Q']$ possesses a nonzero $k \times k$ submatrix which, for simplicity, we assume consists of its first k rows and its first k columns. Let Q be the quadratic form whose matrix this is. By assumption, there is a basis $\mathfrak{B} = \{\beta_1,\ \ldots,\ \beta_k\}$ for $\mathfrak{R}_k$ such that $Q(\beta_i) \neq 0$, $i = 1,\ \ldots,\ k$. Now extend each member of $\mathfrak{B}$ to a member of R_{k+1} by adjoining 0 as $k + 1$st term. Then $Q'(\beta_i') \neq 0$ whenever β_i' is obtained from β_i in this fashion. If the entry of $[Q']$ in the position $(k + 1,\ k + 1)$ is not zero, then $Q'(\epsilon_{k+1}) \neq 0$ and $\{\beta_i',\ \ldots,\ \beta_k',\ \epsilon_{k+1}\}$ is a suitable basis for $\mathfrak{R}_{k+1}$. If this entry of $[Q']$ is 0, then it is easy to compute a scalar t such that $Q'(\beta_{k+1}) \neq 0$ where β_{k+1} is the vector obtained from β_1' by replacing its $k + 1$st term by t. Clearly, $\{\beta_1',\ \ldots,\ \beta_k',\ \beta_{k+1}\}$ is a basis for $\mathfrak{R}_{k+1}$ with the required property. This demonstrates that $k + 1$ has the property of the lemma whenever k has the property. So, by mathematical induction, each natural number has this property. This establishes Lemma 11.4.5.

EXERCISES

1. Let Q be the mapping of R_2 into R such that $Q(\alpha) = \left[\alpha \begin{pmatrix} 3 & -1 \\ -1 & 0 \end{pmatrix} \right] \cdot \alpha$ whenever $\alpha \in R_2$. Show that Q is a quadratic form on $\mathfrak{R}_2$; display the associated bilinear form.

2. Let Q be the mapping of R_3 into R such that $Q(\alpha) = \left[\alpha \begin{pmatrix} 2 & 0 & -1 \\ 0 & 1 & 0 \\ -1 & 0 & 3 \end{pmatrix} \right] \cdot \alpha$ whenever $\alpha \in R_3$. Show that Q is a quadratic form on $\mathfrak{R}_3$; display the associated bilinear form.

3. Prove Lemma 11.4.3.

4. Prove Theorem 11.4.3.

5. Simplify $\{(x, y) \mid x^2 + 9y^2 - 6xy = 1\}$.

6. Simplify $\{(x, y) \mid x^2 + 9y^2 - 6xy - 2x + y = 5\}$.

7. Simplify $\{(x, y, z) \mid 23x^2 + y^2 + 2z^2 + 72zx = 1\}$.

8. Simplify $\{(x, y, z) \mid 23x^2 + y^2 + 2z^2 + 72zx - 15x + 20z = 25\}$.

9. Simplify $\{(x, y, z, w) \mid -x^2 + 3y^2 - z^2 + 3w^2 + 2yw + 2xz = 1\}$.

10. Let Q be any quadratic form on $\mathfrak{R}_n$ and let $\mathfrak{B}$ be any ordered basis for $\mathfrak{R}_n$. Prove that $[Q]_{\mathfrak{B}} = [\mathfrak{B}][Q][\mathfrak{B}]^t$.

11. Let Q be a quadratic form on a finite-dimensional vector space with ordered bases $\mathfrak{a}$ and $\mathfrak{B}$. Prove that rank $[Q]_{\mathfrak{a}} = $ rank $[Q]_{\mathfrak{B}}$.

12

QUADRIC SURFACES

12.1 QUADRIC SURFACES

In this chapter we work against the background of the real inner product space $(\mathfrak{R}_3, \cdot)$. In particular, we concentrate on subsets of R_3 that possess the form $\{\gamma \mid Q(\gamma) + 2\beta \cdot \gamma + d = 0\}$ where Q is a nonzero quadratic form on $\mathfrak{R}_3$, $\beta \in R_3$, and $d \in R$. Any such set is said to be a *quadric surface*. Notice that each quadric surface is characterized by three parameters, a nonzero 3×3 matrix, a 3-vector, and a real number, namely $[Q]$, β, and d.

Example 1: Let Q be the quadratic form on $\mathfrak{R}_3$ with matrix $\begin{pmatrix} 1 & 0 & 0 \\ 0 & 2 & 0 \\ 0 & 0 & 2 \end{pmatrix}$, let $\beta = (2, 0, -3)$, and let $d = 1$; then $\mathfrak{Q} = \{\gamma \mid Q(\gamma) + 2\beta \cdot \gamma + d = 0\}$ is a quadric surface. We point out that $(x, y, z) \in \mathfrak{Q}$ if and only if $x^2 + 2y^2 + 2z^2 + 4x - 6z + 1 = 0$. In particular, $(-1, 1, 0) \in \mathfrak{Q}$, whereas $(-1, 0, 0) \notin \mathfrak{Q}$.

Let us show that each quadric surface can be represented by a 4×4 matrix. Let $\mathfrak{Q} = \{\gamma \mid Q(\gamma) + 2\beta \cdot \gamma + d = 0\}$ be any quadric surface, where $[Q] = \begin{pmatrix} a & h & g \\ h & b & f \\ g & f & c \end{pmatrix}$ and $\beta = (q, r, s)$. Consider the matrix

$$(1) \qquad \begin{pmatrix} a & h & g & q \\ h & b & f & r \\ g & f & c & s \\ q & r & s & d \end{pmatrix}$$

253

which we call the *matrix* of Q and denote by $[Q]$. Clearly $[Q]$ exhibits the parameters of Q, since we can read off $[Q]$, β, and d. But $[Q]$ represents Q in a much deeper sense. Let $\gamma \in R_3$ and let γ^1 denote the 4-vector obtained from γ by adjoining 1 as fourth term; i.e., $\gamma^1 = (x, y, z, 1)$ whenever $\gamma = (x, y, z)$. We claim that $\gamma \in Q$ if and only if

$$
\begin{array}{c}
\begin{array}{cccc} x & y & z & 1 \end{array} \\
\begin{array}{c} x \\ y \\ z \\ 1 \end{array}
\begin{pmatrix}
a & h & g & q \\
h & b & f & r \\
g & f & c & s \\
q & r & s & d
\end{pmatrix} = 0 \ .
\end{array}
$$

We illustrate this statement before proving it. Let Q be the quadric surface of Example 1; so

$$
[Q] = \begin{pmatrix}
1 & 0 & 0 & 2 \\
0 & 2 & 0 & 0 \\
0 & 0 & 2 & -3 \\
2 & 0 & -3 & 1
\end{pmatrix} \ .
$$

Let us apply our test to $(-1, 1, 0)$, which is a member of Q. Now,

$$
\begin{array}{c}
\begin{array}{cccc} -1 & 1 & 0 & 1 \end{array} \\
\begin{array}{c} -1 \\ 1 \\ 0 \\ 1 \end{array}
\begin{pmatrix}
1 & 0 & 0 & 2 \\
0 & 2 & 0 & 0 \\
0 & 0 & 2 & -3 \\
2 & 0 & -3 & 1
\end{pmatrix} = -1 + 2 + 0 - 1 = 0 \ .
\end{array}
$$

We now prove our claim. Clearly, a matrix with multipliers can be evaluated by partitioning the matrix involved into disjoint submatrices. The idea is to take subtotals by submatrices, rather than by rows or columns. Let us partition the matrix (I) into four submatrices as follows:

$$
\left(\begin{array}{ccc|c}
a & h & g & q \\
h & b & f & r \\
g & f & c & s \\
\hline
q & r & s & d
\end{array} \right) \ ,
$$

i.e., our submatrices are $[Q]$, β, β^t, and (d). The corresponding subtotals are $Q(\gamma)$, $\beta \cdot \gamma$, $\beta \cdot \gamma$, and d. So $Q(\gamma) + 2\beta \cdot \gamma + d$ is the value of our matrix with multipliers. This establishes our claim, namely that $\gamma \in Q$ if and only if 0 is the value of our matrix with multipliers. It is important to think in terms of a matrix with multipliers; notice that we can denote the matrix and its multipliers by writing down a matrix flanked by vectors in the form of a dot product, in this case $(\gamma^1[Q]) \cdot \gamma^1$. Although this expression is a dot product, it represents a matrix with multipliers; we should practise visualizing a dot product of this form as a matrix with multipliers. Let us formalize our result.

Theorem 12.1.1: Let Q be a quadric surface; then $\gamma \in Q$ if and only if $(\gamma^1[Q]) \cdot \gamma^1 = 0$.

As a further illustration of the notion of a quadric surface we point out that the empty set is a quadric surface; indeed $\{(x, y, z) \mid x^2 = -1\}$ is a quadric surface; here, $[Q] = \begin{pmatrix} 1 & 0 & 0 \\ 0 & 0 & 0 \\ 0 & 0 & 0 \end{pmatrix}$, $\beta = 0$, and $d = 1$. A quadric surface which possesses no members is said to be *imaginary;* so there is exactly one imaginary quadric surface. On the other hand, a quadric surface which possesses members is said to be *real;* there are many real quadric surfaces. For example, $\{(x, y, z) \mid x^2 = 1\}$ is a real quadric surface.

We mention that the real quadric surfaces can be sorted into the following fourteen types, where a, b, and c are nonzero real numbers. More precisely, given any quadric surface Q there is a coordinate system C with respect to which Q comes under one of the following fourteen categories. In the sketchs, the coordinate axes of the coordinate system C are labeled X, Y, and Z.

We now present the fourteen types into which the real quadric surfaces can be classified.

1. $\{x, y, z) \mid x^2/a^2 + y^2/b^2 + z^2/c^2 - 1 = 0\}$. This quadric surface is called an *ellipsoid.* To sketch the graph of this surface, we consider the intersection of the surface with a plane parallel to a coordinate plane. The intersection of a quadric surface and a plane is called the *trace* of the surface in the plane. Consider the trace of our quadric surface in the plane $\{(x, y, z) \mid z = k\}$; namely, $\{(x, y, k) \mid x^2/a^2 + y^2/b^2 = 1 - k^2/c^2\}$ which is an ellipse if $|k| < |c|$. Again, the trace of our quadric surface in the plane $\{(x, y, z) \mid y = k\}$ is the ellipse $\{(x, k, z) \mid x^2/a^2 + z^2/c^2 = 1 - k^2/b^2\}$ if $|k| < |b|$; and the trace of our quadric surface in the plane $\{(x, y, z) \mid x = k\}$ is the ellipse $\{(k, y, z) \mid y^2/b^2 + z^2/c^2 = 1 - k^2/a^2\}$ if $|k| < |a|$. Thus, we obtain the sketch of the ellipsoid shown in Figure 12.1.1.

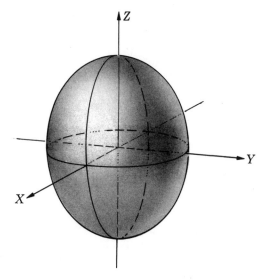

Figure 12.1.1

2. $\{(x, y, z) \mid x^2/a^2 + y^2/b^2 - z^2/c^2 - 1 = 0\}$. This quadric surface is called a *hyperboloid of one sheet*. The trace of this surface in any plane parallel to the XY-plane is an ellipse; the trace in a plane parallel to either of the remaining coordinate planes is a hyperbola or a pair of lines. So, we obtain the following sketch of the hyperboloid of one sheet (see Figure 12.1.2).

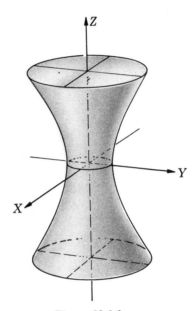

Figure 12.1.2

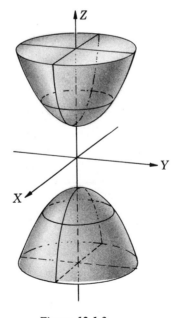

Figure 12.1.3

3. $\{(x, y, z) \mid x^2/a^2 + y^2/b^2 - z^2/c^2 + 1 = 0\}$. This quadric surface is called a *hyperboloid of two sheets*. The trace of this surface in the plane $\{(x, y, z) \mid z = k\}$ is an ellipse provided $|k| > |c|$. The trace of this surface in any plane parallel to the YZ-plane or the ZX-plane, is a hyperbola. Notice that this surface has two parts (see Figure 12.1.3).

4. $\{(x, y, z) \mid x^2/a^2 + y^2/b^2 - z^2/c^2 = 0\}$. This quadric surface is called an *elliptic cone*. The trace of this surface in the plane $\{(x, y, z) \mid z = k\}$, $k \neq 0$, is an ellipse. The trace of this surface in the plane $\{(x, y, z) \mid y = k\}$, $k \neq 0$, is a hyperbola. The trace of this surface in the plane $\{(x, y, z) \mid x = k\}$, $k \neq 0$, is a hyperbola. So, we obtain the following sketch of the elliptic cone (see Figure 12.1.4).

5. $\{(x, y, z) \mid x^2/a^2 + y^2/b^2 + z^2/c^2 = 0\}$. This quadric surface consists of the point $(0, 0, 0)$.

6. $\{(x, y, z) \mid x^2/a^2 + y^2/b^2 - 2z = 0\}$. This quadric surface is called an *elliptic paraboloid*. The trace of this surface in the plane $\{(x, y, z) \mid z = k\}$, $k > 0$, is an ellipse. Each trace in a plane parallel to the YZ-plane or the ZX-plane, is a parabola. So, we obtain the following sketch of the elliptic paraboloid (see Figure 12.1.5).

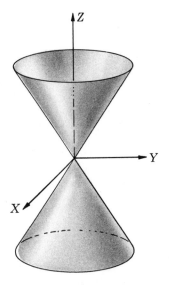

Figure 12.1.4

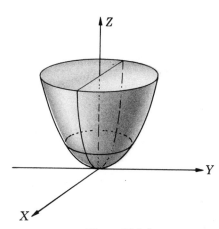

Figure 12.1.5

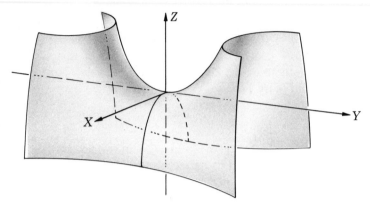

Figure 12.1.6

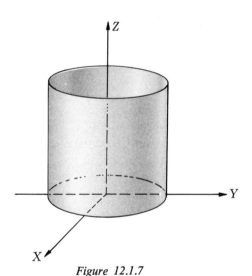

Figure 12.1.7

7. $\{(x, y, z) \mid x^2/a^2 - y^2/b^2 + 2z = 0\}$.   This quadric surface is called a *hyperbolic paraboloid*. The trace of this surface in the plane $\{(x, y, z) \mid z = k\}$, $k \neq 0$, is a hyperbola. Its trace in any plane parallel to the YZ-plane or the ZX-plane is a parabola. Notice that this surface is saddle-shaped (see Figure 12.1.6).

8. $\{(x, y, z) \mid x^2/a^2 + y^2/b^2 - 1 = 0\}$.   This quadric surface is called an *elliptic cylinder*. This surface consists of lines; namely the normals to the XY-plane which pass through a point of the ellipse $\{(x, y, 0) \mid x^2/a^2 + y^2/b^2 = 1\}$ (see Figure 12.1.7).

9. $\{(x, y, z) \mid x^2/a^2 - y^2/b^2 - 1 = 0\}$.   This quadric surface is called a *hyperbolic cylinder*. This surface consists of lines; namely, the normals to the XY-plane which pass through a point of the hyperbola $\{(x, y, 0) \mid x^2/a^2 - y^2/b^2 = 1\}$ (see Figure 12.1.8).

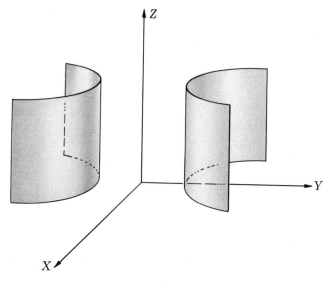

Figure 12.1.8

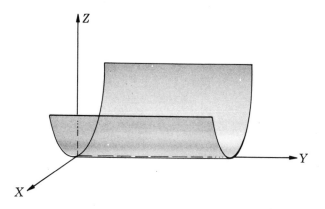

Figure 12.1.9

10. $\{(x, y, z) \mid x^2/a^2 - y^2/b^2 = 0\}$.   This quadric surface consists of two nonparallel planes.

11. $\{(x, y, z) \mid x^2/a^2 + y^2/b^2 = 0\}$.   This is the line $\{(0, 0, t) \mid t \in R\}$.

12. $\{(x, y, z) \mid x^2/a^2 - 2z = 0\}$.   This quadric surface is called a *parabolic cylinder*. This surface consists of lines; namely, the normals to the *ZX*-plane which pass through a point of the parabola $\{(x, 0, z) \mid x^2 = 2a^2z\}$ (see Figure 12.1.9).

13. $\{(x, y, z) \mid x^2/a^2 - 1 = 0\}$.   This quadric surface consists of two parallel planes; namely, the planes $\{(x, y, z) \mid x = a\}$ and $\{(x, y, z) \mid x = -a\}$.

14. $\{(x, y, z) \mid x^2/a^2 = 0\}$.   This quadric surface is the *YZ*-plane.

We say that an equation is in *standard* form if it is one of the fourteen equations considered above. Furthermore, we say that the equations $x^2/a^2 + y^2/b^2 + z^2c^2 + 1 = 0$, $x^2/a^2 + y^2/b^2 + 1 = 0$, $x^2/a^2 + 1 = 0$ are in standard form; each of these equations gives rise to the imaginary quadric surface. Thus, the imaginary quadric surface possesses the following standard forms.

15. $\{(x, y, z) \mid x^2/a^2 + y^2/b^2 + z^2/c^2 + 1 = 0\}$.

16. $\{(x, y, z) \mid x^2/a^2 + y^2/b^2 + 1 = 0\}$.

17. $\{(x, y, z) \mid x^2/a^2 + 1 = 0\}$.

EXERCISES

Write down the parameters $[Q]$, β, and d for each of the following quadric surfaces.

1. $\{(x, y, z) \mid 2x^2 - y^2 + 6yz - 4x + 2y - 1 = 0\}$.

2. $\{(x, y, z) \mid z^2 + 4xy + 2z + 3 = 0\}$.

3. $\{(x, y, z) \mid 3y^2 - x^2 + 4xy = 0\}$.

4. $\{(x, y, z) \mid z^2 - y^2 - 2zx + 4y + 5 = 0\}$.

5. $\{(x, y, z) \mid 5x^2 - 3y^2 + z^2 - 2xy + 4y + 5 = 0\}$.

6. $\{(x, y, z) \mid x^2 + y^2 - z^2 + 4yz - 2x + 3 = 0\}$.

7. $\{(x, y, z) \mid 2x^2 + z^2 - 2xy + 4y - 2z = 0\}$.

8. $\{(x, y, z) \mid z^2 - 3x^2 + 4xz + 2xy - 2x + 5 = 0\}$.

9. Let $Q = \{(x, y, z) \mid 3y^2 + z^2 - 4xy + 2z - 3 = 0\}$.

    (a) Write down the parameters $[Q]$, β, and d.
    (b) Write down $[Q]$.
    (c) Is $(2, -1, 1) \in Q$?
    (d) Is $(0, 0, 1) \in Q$?

(e) Use a matrix with multipliers to compute $((4, -1, 2, 1)[\varrho])$ $\cdot (4, -1, 2, 1)$.

(f) Use a matrix with multipliers to compute $((2, 0, -1, 3)[\varrho])$ $\cdot (1, 1, 0, -2)$.

10. Let $\varrho = \{(x, y, z) \mid 2x^2 + y^2 - z^2 + 2yz - 2zx + 4xy + 8z - 10 = 0\}$.

(a) Write down the parameters $[Q]$, β, and d.
(b) Write down $[\varrho]$.
(c) Is $(5, 0, -2) \in \varrho$?
(d) Is $(5, 0, 0) \in \varrho$?
(e) Use a matrix with multipliers to compute $((1, 2, -1, 1)[\varrho])$ $\cdot (1, 2, -1, 1)$.
(f) Use a matrix with multipliers to compute $((1, 0, -2, 2)[\varrho]$ $\cdot (3, -1, 0, 5)$.

Identify and sketch the following quadric surfaces.

11. $\{(x, y, z) \mid x^2 + 4y^2 + 9z^2 = 36\}$.

12. $\{(x, y, z) \mid 2x^2 + y^2 - z^2 = 1\}$.

13. $\{(x, y, z) \mid 4x^2 - y^2 + 2z^2 = 1\}$.

14. $\{(x, y, z) \mid x^2 + 2y^2 = 4z\}$.

15. $\{(x, y, z) \mid x = y^2 - 6z^2\}$.

16. $\{(x, y, z) \mid x^2 + y^2 = 1\}$.

17. $\{(x, y, z) \mid x^2 = 4\}$.

18. $\{(x, y, z) \mid x = 0\}$.

19. Let C be a *plane* curve (i.e., C is a subset of some plane), and let β be any nonzero vector; then the surface which consists of the lines with direction $[\beta]$ passing through a point of C, is said to be a *cylinder*. A cylinder is called a *right* cylinder if the lines of the cylinder are normals to the plane of the given curve.

(a) Show that $\{(x, y, z) \mid x^2 + y^2 = 9\}$ is a right cylinder.
(b) Show that each elliptic cylinder, hyperbolic cylinder, and parabolic cylinder, is a right cylinder.

20. Let $C = \{(x, y, z) \mid x^2 + (10 - x - z)^2 = 9\}$.

(a) Show that C is a plane curve. *Hint:* Consider $\{(x, y, z) \mid x + y + z = 10$ and $x^2 + y^2 = 9\}$.
(b) Show that the surface consisting of all lines through a point of C with direction $[\epsilon_3]$ is a cylinder.

21. Let ϱ be a real quadric surface characterized by the parameters $[Q]$, β, and d, and also by the parameters $[Q']$, β', and d'. Is it necessarily the case that there is a nonzero real number k such that $[Q'] = k[Q]$, $\beta' = k\beta$, and $d' = kd$?

12.2 INTERSECTION OF A QUADRIC SURFACE AND A LINE

As we have seen, we can characterize a specific quadric surface by means of three parameters, a 3×3 symmetric matrix $[Q]$, a 3-vector β, and a real number d. Now, the matrix of a quadric surface $\mathbb{Q}$ is a 4×4 symmetric matrix; so, by Theorem 11.4.2, there is a unique quadratic form on $\mathbb{R}_4$ whose matrix this is. We denote this quadratic form by Q'. To be specific, let $\mathbb{Q} = \{\gamma \mid Q(\gamma) + 2\beta \cdot \gamma + d = 0\}$ be any quadric surface, let $[Q] = \begin{pmatrix} a & h & g \\ h & b & f \\ g & f & c \end{pmatrix}$, and let $\beta = (q, r, s)$. Then Q' is the quadratic form on $\mathbb{R}_4$ such that $[Q'] = \begin{pmatrix} a & h & g & q \\ h & b & f & r \\ g & f & c & s \\ q & r & s & d \end{pmatrix}$.

In view of the discussion which precedes Theorem 12.1.1 it is easy to verify the following lemma.

Lemma 12.2.1: Let $\mathbb{Q} = \{\gamma \mid Q(\gamma) + 2\beta \cdot \gamma + d = 0\}$ be any quadric surface and let Q' be the associated quadratic form on $\mathbb{R}_4$. Then $Q'(\gamma^1) = Q(\gamma) + 2\beta \cdot \gamma + d$ whenever $\gamma \in R_3$.

Notice that the quadratic form Q' characterizes $\mathbb{Q}$ in the following sense.

Lemma 12.2.2: Let $\mathbb{Q} = \{\gamma \mid Q(\gamma) + 2\beta \cdot \gamma + d = 0\}$ be any quadric surface and let Q' be the associated quadratic form on $\mathbb{R}_4$. Then $\gamma_0 \in \mathbb{Q}$ if and only if $Q'(\gamma_0^1) = 0$.

Proof: Apply Lemma 12.2.1.

To get some idea of the value of all this, we now consider the problem of determining the points of intersection of a line and a quadric surface. The following theorem presents our main result; notice that a member of the given line is also a member of the given quadric surface if and only if the parameter t that produces the point on the line satisfies the quadratic equation $t^2 Q(\beta_0) + 2t(\alpha_0[Q] + \beta) \cdot \beta_0 + Q'(\alpha_0^1) = 0$.

Theorem 12.2.1: Let $L = \{\alpha_0 + t\beta_0 \mid t \in R\}$ be any line and let $\mathbb{Q} = \{\gamma \mid Q(\gamma) + 2\beta \cdot \gamma + d = 0\}$ be any quadric surface. Then $L \cap \mathbb{Q} = \{\alpha_0 + t\beta_0 \mid t^2 Q(\beta_0) + 2t(\alpha_0[Q] + \beta) \cdot \beta_0 + Q'(\alpha_0^1) = 0\}$.

Proof: We shall prove that $\alpha_0 + t\beta_0 \in \mathbb{Q}$ if and only if t is a real number such that $t^2 Q(\beta_0) + 2t(\alpha_0[Q] + \beta) \cdot \beta_0 + Q'(\alpha_0^1) = 0$. By Lemma 12.2.2, $a_0 + t\beta_0 \in \mathbb{Q}$ if and only if $Q'(\alpha_0 + t\beta_0)^1 = 0$. Now,

$$Q'(\alpha_0 + t\beta_0)^1 = Q(\alpha_0 + t\beta_0) + 2\beta \cdot (\alpha_0 + t\beta_0) + d \qquad \text{by Lemma 12.2.1}$$

$$= Q(\alpha_0) + Q(t\beta_0) + 2(\alpha_0[Q]) \cdot t\beta_0 + 2\beta \cdot \alpha_0 + 2t\beta \cdot \beta_0 + d$$
$$\text{by Lemma 11.4.4}$$

$$= t^2 Q(\beta_0) + 2t(\alpha_0[Q] \cdot \beta_0 + \beta \cdot \beta_0) + Q'(\alpha_0^1) \qquad \text{by Lemma 11.4.1}$$

$$= t^2 Q(\beta_0) + 2t(\alpha_0[Q] + \beta) \cdot \beta_0 + Q'(\alpha_0^1) .$$

We conclude that $\alpha_0 + t\beta_0 \in Q$ if and only if $t^2 Q(\beta_0) + 2t(\alpha_0[Q] + \beta) \cdot \beta_0 + Q'(\alpha_0^1) = 0$. This establishes Theorem 12.2.1.

Theorem 12.2.1 is useful because it enables us to predict the nature of the set $L \cap Q$ in terms of the size of the solution set of the quadratic equation involved. We can summarize the situation as follows.

SOLUTION OF QUADRATIC	$L \cap Q$
All real numbers	The line L
Two real numbers	A set with two members
One real number	A set with one member
No real number	The empty set

This observation has a bearing on the concept of a *diametral plane* which we discuss in Section 12.3. There, we are involved with the coefficients of the quadratic equation that appears in Theorem 12.2.1. Here is an interesting little result concerning $(\alpha_0[Q] + \beta) \cdot \beta_0$, the coefficient of $2t$. The point is that this scalar can be expressed by a matrix with multipliers; the matrix involved is the submatrix of $[Q]$ obtained by deleting its fourth row.

Lemma 12.2.3: Let $[Q] = \begin{pmatrix} a & h & g \\ h & b & f \\ g & f & c \end{pmatrix}$, $\beta = (q, r, s)$, $\beta_0 = (l, m, n)$, and $\alpha_0 = (x_0, y_0, z_0)$. Then

$$(\alpha_0[Q] + \beta) \cdot \beta_0 = \begin{matrix} & x_0 & y_0 & z_0 & 1 \\ l & \begin{pmatrix} a & h & g & q \\ m & h & b & f & r \\ n & g & f & c & s \end{pmatrix} \end{matrix} .$$

Proof: Obvious.

We must emphasize that the intersection of a particular line and a particular quadric surface can and should be found *without* using Theorem 12.2.1. This theorem has a useful role in our theory; it should not be used to work out particular problems.

Example 1: Determine the intersection of the line $L = \{t(0, 1, \sqrt{2}) \mid t \in R\}$ and the elliptic cone $Q = \{(x, y, z) \mid x^2 + 2y^2 - z^2 = 0\}$.

Solution: Let $t \in R$. Now, $t(0, 1, \sqrt{2}) \in Q \Leftrightarrow 2t^2 - (\sqrt{2}t)^2 = 0 \Leftrightarrow 2t^2 - 2t^2 = 0$. We conclude that each member of L is a member of Q. Thus, $L \cap Q = L$.

Example 2: Given that $\gamma \neq 0$, determine the intersection of the line $L = L\{\gamma\}$ and the sphere $Q = \{(x, y, z) \mid x^2 + y^2 + z^2 = 1\}$.

Solution: Let $t \in R$. Now, $t\gamma \in Q \Leftrightarrow \|t\gamma\|^2 = 1 \Leftrightarrow t^2 = 1/\|\gamma\|^2$. Thus, $t\gamma \in Q$ if and only if $t = 1/\|\gamma\|$ or $t = -1/\|\gamma\|$. We conclude that $L \cap Q = \{\gamma/\|\gamma\|, -\gamma/\|\gamma\|\}$, a set with two members.

EXERCISES

1. Find the points of intersection of the line $\{(0, 0, 8) + t(0, -1, 3) \mid t \in R\}$ and the quadric surface $\{(x, y, z) \mid 2x^2 + y^2 + 2zx + 4xy - 2z + 3 = 0\}$.

2. Find the points of intersection of the line $\{(1, 0, -1) + t(1, -1, 2) \mid t \in R\}$ and the quadric surface $\{(x, y, z) \mid x^2 + 2y^2 + 3z^2 - 12 = 0\}$.

3. Let $L = \{\alpha_0 + t\beta_0 \mid t \in R\}$ be any line, let $Q = \{\gamma \mid Q(\gamma) + 2\beta \cdot \gamma + d = 0\}$ be any quadric surface, and let $a = Q(\beta_0)$, $b = 2(\alpha_0[Q] + \beta) \cdot \beta_0$, $c = Q'(\alpha_0^1)$. Prove the following.

   (a) $L \cap Q = L$ if and only if $a = b = c = 0$.
   (b) $L \cap Q$ has exactly two members if and only if $a \neq 0$ and $b^2 > 4ac$.
   (c) $L \cap Q$ has exactly one member if and only if $a \neq 0$ and $b^2 = 4ac$, or $a = 0$ and $b \neq 0$.
   (d) $L \cap Q = \emptyset$ if and only if $a \neq 0$ and $b^2 < 4ac$, or $a = b = 0$ and $c \neq 0$.

12.3 DIAMETRAL PLANES; CENTERS

We now introduce a purely geometric concept, the notion of a *chord* of a quadric surface. A line-segment (see Definition 4.4.1) is said to be a chord of a quadric surface if and only if its endpoints are members of the quadric surface whereas no other member of the line-segment has this property.

Definition 12.3.1: A line-segment L with endpoints α_1 and α_2 is said to be a *chord* of a quadric surface Q if and only if $L \cap Q = \{\alpha_1, \alpha_2\}$.

Example 1: The line-segment $\{\epsilon_1 - 2t\epsilon_1 \mid t \in [0, 1]\}$ is a chord of the quadric surface $\{(x, y, z) \mid x^2 = 1\}$. Notice that this line-segment has endpoints ϵ_1 and $-\epsilon_1$.

Now, each chord is a subset of a line; so we can associate two directions with a chord, namely the directions of its line. Consider the family of all chords of a quadric surface $Q = \{\gamma \mid Q(\gamma) + 2\beta \cdot \gamma + d = 0\}$ that possess directions $[\beta_0]$ and $[-\beta_0]$ where $\beta_0 \neq \mathbf{0}$. Note that a chord with endpoints α_1 and α_2 is a member of this family if and only if $\alpha_2 - \alpha_1 \in L\{\beta_0\}$. It is the midpoints of these chords that interest us; let D be the resulting set. Clearly, $\frac{1}{2}(\alpha_1 + \alpha_2)$ is the midpoint of the line-segment with endpoints α_1 and α_2; so $\frac{1}{2}(\alpha_1 + \alpha_2) \in D$ whenever this line-segment is a member of our family. Let $\alpha_0 \in D$; in view of Theorem 12.2.1, the line $\{\alpha_0 + t\beta_0 \mid t \in R\}$ has exactly two members in common with Q, say $\alpha_0 + t_1\beta_0$ and $\alpha_0 - t_1\beta_0$ where $t_1 \in R$. So

$$t^2 Q(\beta_0) + 2t(\alpha_0[Q] + \beta) \cdot \beta_0 + Q'(\alpha_0^1) = 0$$

has distinct roots, namely t_1 and $-t_1$. In particular, this means that $Q(\beta_0) \neq 0$ and that $(\alpha_0[Q] + \beta) \cdot \beta_0 = 0$. We now extend D by adjoining to D each vector γ that satisfies the latter condition, i.e., such that $(\gamma[Q] + \beta) \cdot \beta_0 = 0$. The resulting set is said to be the *diametral plane* of Q with respect to β_0. Summarizing, Q possesses a diametral plane with respect to β_0 if and only if $Q(\beta_0) \neq 0$; moreover, γ is a member of this set if and only if $(\gamma[Q] + \beta) \cdot \beta_0 = 0$.

Definition 12.3.2:   Let $Q = \{\gamma \mid Q(\gamma) + 2\beta \cdot \gamma + d = 0\}$ be any quadric surface and let β_0 be any vector such that $Q(\beta_0) \neq 0$; then $\{\gamma \mid (\gamma[Q] + \beta) \cdot \beta_0 = 0\}$ is said to be the *diametral plane* of Q with respect to β_0.

We point out that Q does *not* possess a diametral plane with respect to β_0 if $Q(\beta_0) = 0$. Notice that $Q(\mathbf{0}) = 0$ whenever Q is a quadratic form; so no quadric surface possesses a diametral plane with respect to $\mathbf{0}$. We must mention that a diametral plane of a suitably chosen quadric surface may not possess any midpoints of chords of the quadric surface for the simple reason that the quadric surface has no chords. For example, the quadric surface $\{(x, y, z) \mid x^2 + y^2 + z^2 = 0\}$ has no chords; yet it has a diametral plane with respect to β_0 whenever $\beta_0 \neq \mathbf{0}$.

The submatrix of $[Q]$ consisting of its first three rows, leads us to each diametral plane of Q, as the following example shows.

Example 2:   Determine the diametral plane of $Q = \{(x, y, z) \mid x^2 + 4y^2 + 4yz + 4y + 8z - 10 = 0\}$ with respect to $(1, 2, -1)$.

Solution: Here $[Q] = \begin{pmatrix} 1 & 0 & 0 \\ 0 & 4 & 2 \\ 0 & 2 & 0 \end{pmatrix}$, $\beta = (0, 2, 4)$, and $d = -10$.   First, we must check that $Q(1, 2, -1) \neq 0$; now

$$Q(1, 2, -1) = \begin{array}{c} 1 \\ 2 \\ -1 \end{array} \begin{array}{ccc} 1 & 2 & -1 \\ \begin{pmatrix} 1 & 0 & 0 \\ 0 & 4 & 2 \\ 0 & 2 & 0 \end{pmatrix} \end{array} = 1 + 12 - 4 = 9 \ .$$

So Q possesses a diametral plane with respect to $(1, 2, -1)$. Next, let $\gamma = (x, y, z)$ be any 3-vector; then

$$(\gamma[Q] + \beta) \cdot \beta_0 = \begin{matrix} & \begin{matrix} x & y & z & 1 \end{matrix} \\ \begin{matrix} 1 \\ 2 \\ -1 \end{matrix} & \begin{pmatrix} 1 & 0 & 0 & 0 \\ 0 & 4 & 2 & 2 \\ 0 & 2 & 0 & 4 \end{pmatrix} \end{matrix} = x + 6y + 4z .$$

We conclude that $\{(x, y, z) \mid x + 6y + 4z = 0\}$ is the diametral plane of Q with respect to $(1, 2, -1)$.

Notice that in the case of Example 2 the diametral plane actually is a plane. In fact, this is always so.

Theorem 12.3.1: Each diametral plane is a plane.

Proof: Let $Q = \{\gamma \mid Q(\gamma) + 2\beta \cdot \gamma + d = 0\}$ be any quadric surface, let β_0 be any vector such that $Q(\beta_0) \neq 0$, and let $\mathcal{P}$ be the diametral plane of Q with respect to β_0, i.e., let $\mathcal{P} = \{\gamma \mid (\gamma[Q] + \beta) \cdot \beta_0 = 0\}$. Now, $(\gamma[Q]) \cdot \beta_0 = (\beta_0[Q]) \cdot \gamma$; so $\mathcal{P}$ is a plane if and only if $\beta_0[Q] \neq \mathbf{0}$. Suppose that $\mathcal{P}$ is not a plane; then $Q(\beta_0) = (\beta_0[Q]) \cdot \beta_0 = \mathbf{0} \cdot \beta_0 = 0$. This contradiction proves that $\beta_0[Q] \neq \mathbf{0}$; we conclude that $\mathcal{P}$ is a plane.

Our proof of Theorem 12.3.1 has brought out an important fact about diametral planes, which we now state.

Lemma 12.3.1: Let $Q = \{\gamma \mid Q(\gamma) + 2\beta \cdot \gamma + d = 0\}$ be any quadric surface and let β_0 be any vector such that $Q(\beta_0) \neq 0$. Then $[\beta_0[Q]]$ is a direction of a normal to the diametral plane of Q with respect to β_0.

We emphasize that the method of Example 2, which involves the first three rows of $[Q]$, is the simplest procedure for determining a diametral plane.

Example 3: Determine the diametral plane of $Q = \{(x, y, z) \mid 2x^2 + 4xy + 2x - 2z = 3\}$ with respect to $(2, -3, 0)$.

Solution: Here $[Q] = \begin{pmatrix} 2 & 2 & 0 & 1 \\ 2 & 0 & 0 & 0 \\ 0 & 0 & 0 & -1 \\ 1 & 0 & -1 & -3 \end{pmatrix}$. Using a matrix with multipliers

we verify that $Q(2, -3, 0) = -16$; so Q has a diametral plane with respect to $(2, -3, 0)$. Let $\gamma = (x, y, z)$ be any 3-vector; then

$$(\gamma[Q] + \beta) \cdot \beta_0 = \begin{matrix} & \begin{matrix} x & y & z & 1 \end{matrix} \\ \begin{matrix} 2 \\ -3 \\ 0 \end{matrix} & \begin{pmatrix} 2 & 2 & 0 & 1 \\ 2 & 0 & 0 & 0 \\ 0 & 0 & 0 & -1 \end{pmatrix} \end{matrix} = -2x + 4y + 2 .$$

We conclude that $\{(x, y, z) \mid x - 2y = 1\}$ is the diametral plane of Q with respect to $(2, -3, 0)$.

The following example motivates the notion of a *center* of a quadric surface.

Example 4: Determine the diametral plane of $Q = \{(x, y, z) \mid x^2 + y^2 + z^2 = 1\}$ with respect to β_0, where $\beta_0 \neq \mathbf{0}$.

Solution: Here $[\mathbb{Q}] = \begin{pmatrix} 1 & 0 & 0 & 0 \\ 0 & 1 & 0 & 0 \\ 0 & 0 & 1 & 0 \\ 0 & 0 & 0 & -1 \end{pmatrix}$; so $[Q] = I_3$, $\beta = \mathbf{0}$, and $d = -1$.

Clearly, $Q(\beta_0) = (\beta_0 I_3) \cdot \beta_0 = \beta_0 \cdot \beta_0 \neq 0$ since $\beta_0 \neq \mathbf{0}$; so Q has a diametral plane with respect to β_0 provided that $\beta_0 \neq \mathbf{0}$. Let γ be any 3-vector; then $(\gamma[Q] + \beta) \cdot \beta_0 = (\gamma I_3 + \mathbf{0}) \cdot \beta_0 = \gamma \cdot \beta_0$. Thus $\{\gamma \mid \beta_0 \cdot \gamma = 0\}$ is the diametral plane of the unit sphere with respect to β_0. Notice that $\mathbf{0}$ is a member of each of these planes; so the center of the unit sphere is a member of each of its diametral planes.

We base the general notion of a *center* of a quadric surface on the property of the center of the unit sphere brought out in Example 4.

Definition 12.3.3: α is said to be a *center* of a quadric surface Q if and only if α is a member of each diametral plane of Q.

Before illustrating this notion again, we must develop a technique for determining the centers, if any, of a quadric surface. Our goal is to establish Theorem 12.3.2. First, we present the following lemma which is easily verified.

Lemma 12.3.2: α is a center of the quadric surface $\{\gamma \mid Q(\gamma) + 2\beta \cdot \gamma + d = 0\}$ if and only if $(\alpha[Q] + \beta) \cdot \beta_0 = 0$ whenever $Q(\beta_0) \neq 0$.

Here is our main result.

Theorem 12.3.2: α is a center of the quadric surface $Q = \{\gamma \mid Q(\gamma) + 2\beta \cdot \gamma + d = 0\}$ if and only if $\alpha[Q] + \beta = \mathbf{0}$.

Proof: Our proof has two parts.

1. Assume that $\alpha[Q] + \beta = \mathbf{0}$. Then $(\alpha[Q] + \beta) \cdot \beta_0 = \mathbf{0} \cdot \beta_0 = 0$ whenever $Q(\beta_0) \neq 0$.

2. Assume that α is a center of Q. Then, by Lemma 12.3.2, $(\alpha[Q] + \beta) \cdot \beta_0 = 0$ whenever $Q(\beta_0) \neq 0$. By Lemma 11.4.5 there is a basis $\mathcal{B}$ for $\mathcal{R}_3$ such that $Q(\beta_i) \neq 0$ whenever $\beta_i \in \mathcal{B}$. So, $\alpha[Q] + \beta \in \mathcal{B}^\perp$; thus, by Theorem 3.1.3, $\alpha[Q] + \beta \in R_3^\perp$. But $R_3^\perp = \{\mathbf{0}\}$; so $\alpha[Q] + \beta = \mathbf{0}$. This completes our proof.

This result provides us with a simple technique for computing the centers of a quadric surface. Notice that $\alpha[Q] + \beta = \mathbf{0}$ if and only if α is a vector solution of the linear system whose coefficient matrix is $[Q]^t$, i.e., $[Q]$, and whose augmented matrix is the 3×4 submatrix of $[\mathbb{Q}]$ obtained by deleting its fourth row vector and multiplying its fourth column vector by -1. So, we can determine the centers of a quadric surface by reducing the 3×4 matrix that represents the linear system $\alpha[Q] = -\beta$. We now illustrate this technique.

Example 5: Determine the centers of $Q = \{(x, y, z) \mid 2x^2 + 2y^2 + 4z^2 - 4yz + 4zx + 10x + 2y + 8z + 11 = 0\}$.

Solution: Here $[Q] = \begin{pmatrix} 2 & 0 & 2 & 5 \\ 0 & 2 & -2 & 1 \\ 2 & -2 & 4 & 4 \\ 5 & 1 & 4 & 11 \end{pmatrix}$. Now,

$$\begin{pmatrix} 2 & 0 & 2 & -5 \\ 0 & 2 & -2 & -1 \\ 2 & -2 & 4 & -4 \end{pmatrix} \sim \begin{pmatrix} 2 & 0 & 2 & -5 \\ 0 & 2 & -2 & -1 \\ 0 & -2 & 2 & 1 \end{pmatrix} \sim \begin{pmatrix} 2 & 0 & 2 & -5 \\ 0 & 2 & -2 & -1 \\ 0 & 0 & 0 & 0 \end{pmatrix}.$$

Noting that 2 is the rank of the reduced matrix we conclude that Q possesses a line of centers; indeed, each member of the line $\{(-5/2, -1/2, 0) + t(-1, 1, 1) \mid t \in R\}$ is a center of Q.

Example 6: Determine the centers of $Q = \{(x, y, z) \mid 2xy + 2xz + 2y + 4z = 0\}$.

Solution: Here $[Q] = \begin{pmatrix} 0 & 1 & 1 & 0 \\ 1 & 0 & 0 & 1 \\ 1 & 0 & 0 & 2 \\ 0 & 1 & 2 & 0 \end{pmatrix}$; clearly, the linear system whose augmented matrix is $\begin{pmatrix} 0 & 1 & 1 & 0 \\ 1 & 0 & 0 & -1 \\ 1 & 0 & 0 & -2 \end{pmatrix}$ has no solution. Thus, by Theorem 12.3.2, Q has no center.

We now present some properties of centers.

Lemma 12.3.3: Let α be a center of the quadric surface $\{\gamma \mid Q(\gamma) + 2\beta \cdot \gamma + d = 0\}$; then $(\alpha[Q] + \beta) \cdot \gamma = 0$ whenever $\gamma \in R_3$.

Proof: Apply Theorem 12.3.2.

Lemma 12.3.4: Let $\{\gamma \mid Q(\gamma) + 2\beta \cdot \gamma + d = 0\}$ be a quadric surface with centers α_1 and α_2. Then $\beta \cdot \alpha_1 = \beta \cdot \alpha_2$.

Proof: Now, $(\alpha_1[Q] + \beta) \cdot \alpha_2 = 0$ and $(\alpha_2[Q] + \beta) \cdot \alpha_1 = 0$ by Lemma 12.3.3; so $(\alpha_1[Q]) \cdot \alpha_2 + \beta \cdot \alpha_2 = (\alpha_2[Q]) \cdot \alpha_1 + \beta \cdot \alpha_1$. But $(\alpha_1[Q]) \cdot \alpha_2 = (\alpha_2[Q]) \cdot \alpha_1$ since $[Q]$ is symmetric. Thus, $\beta \cdot \alpha_2 = \beta \cdot \alpha_1$.

Lemma 12.3.5: Let $Q = \{\gamma \mid Q(\gamma) + 2\beta \cdot \gamma + d = 0\}$ be a quadric surface with center α_1; then $Q'(\alpha_1^!) = \beta \cdot \alpha_1 + d$. Moreover, if α_2 is another center of Q, then $Q'(\alpha_1^!) = Q'(\alpha_2^!)$.

Proof: Now,

$$Q'(\alpha_1^!) = Q(\alpha_1) + 2\beta \cdot \alpha_1 + d \qquad\qquad \text{by Lemma 12.2.1}$$
$$= (\alpha_1[Q]) \cdot \alpha_1 + 2\beta \cdot \alpha_1 + d$$
$$= (\alpha_1[Q] + \beta) \cdot \alpha_1 + \beta \cdot \alpha_1 + d$$
$$= \beta \cdot \alpha_1 + d \qquad\qquad \text{by Theorem 12.3.2 .}$$

Next, let α_2 be another center of Q; then

$$Q'(\alpha_2^!) = \beta \cdot \alpha_2 + d \qquad \text{by the first part of this proof}$$
$$= \beta \cdot \alpha_1 + d \qquad \text{by Lemma 12.3.4}$$
$$= Q'(\alpha_1^!) \qquad \text{by the first part of this proof .}$$

This establishes Lemma 12.3.5.

EXERCISES

1. Show that $\{(-1, -1, 0) + t(2, 2, 0) \mid t \in [0, 1]\}$ is a chord of $\{(x, y, z) \mid x^2 + y^2 + z^2 = 2\}$.

2. Determine the diametral plane of $\{(x, y, z) \mid y^2 - 2yz + 4xy - 4x + 8y = 5\}$ with respect to $(1, 5, -2)$.

3. Determine the diametral plane of $\{(x, y, z) \mid x^2 + y^2 + z^2 = 1\}$ with respect to ϵ_1.

4. Determine the diametral plane of $\{(x, y, z) \mid x^2 - y^2 = 1\}$ with respect to ϵ_1.

5. Determine the diametral plane of $\{(x, y, z) \mid x^2 - y^2 = 1\}$ with respect to $(1, 1, 0)$.

6. Determine the diametral plane of $\{(x, y, z) \mid x^2 - y^2 = 1\}$ with respect to ϵ_3.

7. Let Q be any quadric surface and let $\mathcal{P}$ be the diametral plane of Q with respect to β_0. Prove that $\mathcal{P}$ is the diametral plane of Q with respect to $k\beta_0$ whenever $k \neq 0$.

8. Exhibit a quadratic form Q and a 3-vector β_0 such that $Q(\beta_0) = 0$ and $\beta_0[Q] \neq \mathbf{0}$.

9. Prove Lemma 12.3.3.

10. Let $Q = \{(x, y, z) \mid 2x^2 + 3y^2 - z^2 + 8yz - 2zx + 6xy - 2x - 28y + 18z = -7\}$.

    (a) Exhibit the diametral plane of Q with respect to (l, m, n), given that $Q(l, m, n) \neq 0$.
    (b) Use Definition 12.3.3 to show that $(3, -1, 2)$ is a center of Q.

11. Determine the centers of $\{(x, y, z) \mid 2x^2 + y^2 + 2zx + 4xy - 2z + 3 = 0\}$.

12. Determine the centers of $\{(x, y, z) \mid 3x^2 + 2y^2 + z^2 + 2zx - 2xy + 4x + 4z = 0\}$.

13. Determine the centers of $\{(x, y, z) \mid x^2 + y^2 - 2x + 2z - 4 = 0\}$.

14. Determine the centers of $\{(x, y, z) \mid x^2 + 2y^2 + 4z^2 + 4zx - 4x + 8y - 8z = 10\}$.

15. Determine the centers of $\{(x, y, z) \mid x^2 + y^2 + z^2 + 2yz + 2zx + 2xy - 4x - 4y - 4z = 0\}$.

16. Prove that a quadric surface $\{\gamma \mid Q(\gamma) + 2\beta \cdot \gamma + d = 0\}$ has a unique center if and only if $[Q]$ is nonsingular.

17. Prove that a quadric surface $\mathbb{Q} = \{\gamma \mid Q(\gamma) + 2\beta \cdot \gamma + d = 0\}$ possesses a center if and only if the submatrix of $[\mathbb{Q}]$ obtained by deleting its fourth row vector, has the same rank as $[\mathbb{Q}]$.

18. Let $\mathbb{Q} = \{\gamma \mid Q(\gamma) + 2\beta \cdot \gamma + d = 0\}$ be a quadric surface with a center. Prove that:

    (a) $\mathbb{Q}$ has a unique center if and only if rank $[Q] = 3$;
    (b) $\mathbb{Q}$ has a line of centers if and only if rank $[Q] = 2$;
    (c) $\mathbb{Q}$ has a plane of centers if and only if rank $[Q] = 1$.

19. Let $\{\gamma \mid Q(\gamma) + 2\beta \cdot \gamma + d = 0\}$ be a quadric surface with centers α_1 and α_2, and let B be the bilinear form associated with Q.

    (a) Prove that $\alpha_1[Q] = \alpha_2[Q]$.
    (b) Prove that $B(\alpha_1, \alpha_2) = Q(\alpha_1)$.
    (c) Prove that $Q(\alpha_1) = Q(\alpha_2)$.

12.4   PRINCIPAL PLANES

Consider the following example.

Example 1:   Determine the diametral plane of $\mathbb{Q} = \{(x, y, z) \mid x^2 + y^2 - 4zx + 2y + 4z - 10 = 0\}$ with respect to ϵ_2.

Solution: Here $[Q] = \begin{pmatrix} 1 & 0 & -2 \\ 0 & 1 & 0 \\ -2 & 0 & 0 \end{pmatrix}$, $\beta = (0, 1, 2)$, and $d = -10$. Now, $Q(\epsilon_2) = 1$; so $\mathbb{Q}$ has a diametral plane with respect to ϵ_2. Applying the technique of Section 12.3 we find that $\{\gamma \mid \epsilon_2 \cdot \gamma + 1 = 0\}$ is the required diametral plane.

Notice that $[\epsilon_2]$ is a direction of a normal to the diametral plane of Example 1. This means that the chords of $\mathbb{Q}$ that are bisected by $\{\gamma \mid \epsilon_2 \cdot \gamma + 1 = 0\}$ are perpendicular to this diametral plane. Any diametral plane that has this property is said to be a *principal plane* of the quadric surface involved. Let us clarify this notion.

Definition 12.4.1: $\mathcal{P}$ is said to be a *principal plane* of a quadric surface $\mathcal{Q}$ if and only if:

(i) There is a vector β_0 such that $\mathcal{P}$ is a diametral plane of $\mathcal{Q}$ with respect to β_0;

(ii) $[\beta_0]$ is a direction of a normal to $\mathcal{P}$.

Clearly, if $\mathcal{P}$ is a diametral plane of $\mathcal{Q}$ with respect to β_0, then $\beta_0 \neq 0$; thus, from (ii), if $\mathcal{P}$ is a principal plane of $\mathcal{Q}$ then β_0 is a characteristic vector of $[Q]$. The following result is easy to verify; this result is important because it provides us with an efficient technique for computing the principal planes of a quadric surface.

Lemma 12.4.1: Let $\mathcal{Q} = \{\gamma \mid Q(\gamma) + 2\beta \cdot \gamma + d = 0\}$ be any quadric surface. Then $\{\gamma \mid (\beta_0[Q]) \cdot \gamma + \beta \cdot \beta_0 = 0\}$ is a principal plane of $\mathcal{Q}$ if and only if $Q(\beta_0) \neq 0$ and β_0 is a characteristic vector of $[Q]$.

Proof: Consider Definition 12.4.1.

We point out that $Q(\beta_0) = 0$ if β_0 is a characteristic vector of $[Q]$ corresponding to the characteristic root 0. In this case β_0 does not lead us to a principal plane of $\mathcal{Q}$. Let us establish this fact.

Lemma 12.4.2: Let $\mathcal{Q} = \{\gamma \mid Q(\gamma) + 2\beta \cdot \gamma + d = 0\}$ be any quadric surface, let 0 be a characteristic root of $[Q]$, and let β_0 be a corresponding characteristic vector of $[Q]$. Then $\mathcal{Q}$ does *not* possess a diametral plane with respect to β_0.

Proof: By assumption, $\beta_0[Q] = \mathbf{0}$; so $Q(\beta_0) = (\beta_0[Q]) \cdot \beta_0 = \mathbf{0} \cdot \beta_0 = 0$. We conclude that $\mathcal{Q}$ does not possess a diametral plane with respect to β_0.

On the other hand, $Q(\beta_0) \neq 0$ whenever β_0 is a characteristic vector of $[Q]$ corresponding to a nonzero characteristic root of $[Q]$; in this case, then, we obtain a principal plane of $\mathcal{Q}$. Let us establish this fact.

Lemma 12.4.3: Let $\mathcal{Q} = \{\gamma \mid Q(\gamma) + 2\beta \cdot \gamma + d = 0\}$ be any quadric surface and let β_0 be a characteristic vector of $[Q]$ corresponding to a nonzero characteristic root of $[Q]$. Then $\mathcal{Q}$ possesses a diametral plane with respect to β_0 and this diametral plane is a principal plane of $\mathcal{Q}$.

Proof: Let k be a nonzero characteristic root of $[Q]$ and let β_0 be a corresponding characteristic vector of $[Q]$; so $\beta_0[Q] = k\beta_0$. Then

$$Q(\beta_0) = (\beta_0[Q]) \cdot \beta_0 = (k\beta_0) \cdot \beta_0 = k(\beta_0 \cdot \beta_0) = k\|\beta_0\|^2 \neq 0$$

since $k \neq 0$ and $\|\beta_0\|^2 \neq 0$. Thus, $\mathcal{Q}$ possesses a diametral plane with respect to β_0; moreover, by Lemma 12.4.1, this diametral plane is a principal plane of $\mathcal{Q}$.

Incidentally, our proof of Lemma 12.4.3 has disclosed a useful little fact that we shall want later on.

Lemma 12.4.4: Let $Q = \{\gamma \mid Q(\gamma) + 2\beta \cdot \gamma + d = 0\}$ be any quadric surface and let β_0 be a characteristic vector of $[Q]$ of unit length which corresponds to k, a characteristic root of $[Q]$. Then $Q(\beta_0) = k$.

We now summarize Lemmas 12.4.1, 12.4.2, and 12.4.3.

Theorem 12.4.1: Let $Q = \{\gamma \mid Q(\gamma) + 2\beta \cdot \gamma + d = 0\}$ be any quadric surface. Then $\{\gamma \mid (\beta_0[Q]) \cdot \gamma + \beta \cdot \beta_0 = 0\}$ is a principal plane of Q if and only if β_0 is a characteristic vector of $[Q]$ corresponding to a nonzero characteristic root of $[Q]$.

Clearly, this result enables us to determine the principal planes of a quadric surface $Q = \{\gamma \mid Q(\gamma) + 2\beta \cdot \gamma + d = 0\}$. First, we find the nonzero characteristic roots of $[Q]$; the corresponding characteristic vectors of $[Q]$ lead us to the principal planes of Q. Here is an example.

Example 2: Find the principal planes of $Q = \{(x, y, z) \mid x^2 + 4y^2 + z^2 + 4yz + 6y - 10 = 0\}$.

Solution: Here, $[Q] = \begin{pmatrix} 1 & 0 & 0 \\ 0 & 4 & 2 \\ 0 & 2 & 1 \end{pmatrix}$, $\beta = (0, 3, 0)$, and $d = -10$. The characteristic polynomial of $[Q]$ is $(1 - x)(x^2 - 5x)$; so the characteristic roots of $[Q]$ are 0, 1, and 5. We now determine characteristic vectors of $[Q]$ corresponding to 1 and 5, and the corresponding diametral planes of Q.

$k = 1$:   We want β_0 such that $\beta_0 \begin{pmatrix} 1 & 0 & 0 \\ 0 & 4 & 2 \\ 0 & 2 & 1 \end{pmatrix} = \beta_0$.

Now, $\begin{pmatrix} 0 & 0 & 0 \\ 0 & 3 & 2 \\ 0 & 2 & 0 \end{pmatrix} \sim \begin{pmatrix} 0 & 1 & 2 \\ 0 & 1 & 0 \end{pmatrix} \sim \begin{pmatrix} 0 & 0 & 1 \\ 0 & 1 & 0 \end{pmatrix}.$

So $\beta_0 \in L\{\epsilon_1\}$. Take $\beta_0 = \epsilon_1$. The diametral plane of Q with respect to ϵ_1 is $\{\gamma \mid \epsilon_1 \cdot \gamma = 0\}$, i.e., $\{(x, y, z) \mid x = 0\}$, which is a principal plane of Q.

$k = 5$:   We want β_0 such that $\beta_0 \begin{pmatrix} 1 & 0 & 0 \\ 0 & 4 & 2 \\ 0 & 2 & 1 \end{pmatrix} = 5\beta_0$.

Now, $\begin{pmatrix} -4 & 0 & 0 \\ 0 & -1 & 2 \\ 0 & 2 & -4 \end{pmatrix} \sim \begin{pmatrix} 1 & 0 & 0 \\ 0 & 1 & -2 \end{pmatrix}.$

So $\beta_0 \in L\{(0, 2, 1)\}$. Take $\beta_0 = (0, 2, 1)$. The diametral plane of Q with respect to $(0, 2, 1)$ is $\{\gamma \mid (0, 10, 5) \cdot \gamma + 6 = 0\}$, i.e., $\{(x, y, z) \mid 10y + 5z + 6 = 0\}$, which is a principal plane of Q. We conclude that Q has exactly two principal planes

We mention that the quadric surface of Example 2 has exactly two principal planes because $[Q]$ has exactly two nonzero characteristic roots and because the subspace of vector solutions of the linear system represented by $\beta_0[Q] = k\beta_0$, where k is a nonzero characteristic root of $[Q]$, in each case is one-dimensional. Now, the diametral plane of Q with respect to $t\beta_0$, where $t \neq 0$, is the diametral plane of Q with respect to β_0 (see Exercise 7, Section 12.3). So, each of these subspaces provides us with just one principal plane.

To develop our insight into principal planes, we now present an example of a quadric surface that possesses infinitely many principal planes.

Example 3: Find the principal planes of $Q = \{(x, y, z) \mid x^2 + y^2 + z^2 + 2x - y - 9 = 0\}$.

Solution: Here $[Q] = I_3$, $\beta = (1, -.5, 0)$, and $d = -9$. The characteristic polynomial of $[Q]$ is $(1, -3, 3, -1)$; so 1 is the only characteristic root of $[Q]$. Moreover, $\beta_0[Q] = \beta_0$ whenever $\beta_0 \in R_3$; thus each nonzero 3-vector is a characteristic vector of $[Q]$ corresponding to the characteristic root 1. We conclude that $\{\gamma \mid \beta_0 \cdot \gamma + \beta_0 \cdot \beta = 0\}$ is a principal plane of Q whenever $\beta_0 \neq \mathbf{0}$.

Here is another example of a quadric surface with infinitely many principal planes.

Example 4: Find the principal planes of $Q = \{(x, y, z) \mid 3x^2 + 3y^2 - 4x + 2z - 25 = 0\}$.

Solution: Here $[Q] = \begin{pmatrix} 3 & 0 & 0 \\ 0 & 3 & 0 \\ 0 & 0 & 0 \end{pmatrix}$, $\beta = (-2, 0, 1)$, and $d = -25$. The characteristic polynomial of $[Q]$ is $(0, 9, -6, 1)$; so 3 is the only nonzero characteristic root of $[Q]$. Clearly $\beta_0[Q] = 3\beta_0$ if and only if 0 is the third term of β_0; thus each nonzero vector with third term 0 is a characteristic vector of $[Q]$ corresponding to the characteristic root 3. We conclude that $\{\gamma \mid \beta_0 \cdot \gamma + \beta_0 \cdot \beta = 0\}$ is a principal plane of Q whenever β_0 is a nonzero vector with third term 0.

Now that we have seen that some quadric surfaces have infinitely many principal planes, let us demonstrate that each quadric surface has at least one principal plane. Our proof relies on the following fact.

Lemma 12.4.5: Let A be a symmetric matrix over R; then the characteristic polynomial of A is the product of polynomials of degree at most one.

Comment: A proof of this statement is beyond the scope of this book; it involves a study of matrices over C, and Hermitian matrices in particular.

We now present our *existence* theorem.

Theorem 12.4.2: Each quadric surface possesses a principal plane.

Proof: Let $Q = \{\gamma \mid Q(\gamma) + 2\beta \cdot \gamma + d = 0\}$ be any quadric surface; clearly it is enough to prove that $[Q]$ has a nonzero characteristic root. Suppose that $\mathbf{0}$ is the only characteristic root of $[Q]$; it follows from Lemma 12.4.5 that $(0, 0, 0, -1)$ is the characteristic polynomial of $[Q]$. Therefore, by the Cayley–Hamilton Theorem, $[Q]^3 = (0)$; so $[Q]^4 = (0)$. Now, each entry of the main diagonal of $[Q]^2$ is a sum of squares of the entries of $[Q]$ (indeed, the entries of the main diagonal of $[Q]^2$ are $[Q]_1 \cdot [Q]_1$, $[Q]_2 \cdot [Q]_2$, and $[Q]_3 \cdot [Q]_3$). Similarly, each entry of the main diagonal of $[Q]^4$ is a sum of squares of the entries of $[Q]^2$. Since $[Q]^4 = (0)$, we conclude that each entry of $[Q]^2$ is zero, so each entry of $[Q]$ is zero. But $[Q] \neq (0)$ since Q is a quadric surface. This contradiction establishes Theorem 12.4.2.

At this stage the obvious question is this: "For what are principal planes good?" The fact is that the principal planes of a quadric surface Q are the key to simplifying the parameters that represent Q. The idea is to choose a coordinate system so that a principal plane of Q is a coordinate plane. It turns out that in the resulting coordinate system, the parameters of Q are simplified. Let Q be a quadric surface with exactly three principal planes; a description of Q that refers to its principal planes is far superior (in the sense of being simpler) to a description of Q that refers to some other coordinate system. So, a quadric surface with exactly three principal planes has a built in coordinate system; using some other coordinate system complicates the description of Q. This explains our interest in the principal planes of a quadric surface.

EXERCISES

1. Show that $\{(x, y, z) \mid x + 2 = 0\}$ is a principal plane of the quadric surface $\{(x, y, z) \mid x^2 + 2y^2 - 2yz + 4x - 10 = 0\}$.

2. Show that $\{(x, y, z) \mid x + y = 0\}$ is a principal plane of the quadric surface $\{(x, y, z) \mid 2xy - 1 = 0\}$.

3. Let $[Q] = \begin{pmatrix} 1 & -2 & 2 \\ -2 & 1 & 2 \\ 2 & 2 & -8 \end{pmatrix}$.

    (a) Write down the characteristic polynomial of $[Q]$.
    (b) Compute the characteristic roots of $[Q]$.
    (c) Find the principal planes of the quadric surface

    $$\{(x, y, z) \mid x^2 + y^2 - 8z^2 + 4yz + 4zx - 4xy + 9y - 10 = 0\} .$$

4. Consider the quadric surface $Q = \{(x, y, z) \mid x^2 + 4y^2 + z^2 - 2zx + 4xy - 4yz = 16\}$.

    (a) Write down the matrix $[Q]$.
    (b) Write down the characteristic polynomial of $[Q]$.
    (c) Compute the characteristic roots of $[Q]$.
    (d) Find the principal planes of Q.

5. Consider the quadric surface $Q = \{(x, y, z) \mid x^2 + 9y^2 - 6xy + 6z - 4 = 0\}$.

    (a) Write down the matrix $[Q]$.
    (b) Write down the characteristic polynomial of $[Q]$.
    (c) Compute the characteristic roots of $[Q]$.
    (d) Find the principal planes of Q.

6. Consider the quadric surface $Q = \{(x, y, z) \mid x^2 + y^2 + 4z^2 + 4yz - 2x = -1\}$.

    (a) Write down the matrix $[Q]$.
    (b) Write down the characteristic polynomial of $[Q]$.
    (c) Compute the characteristic roots of $[Q]$.
    (d) Find the principal planes of Q.

7. Consider the quadric surface $Q = \{(x, y, z) \mid 9x^2 + 5y^2 - z^2 - 12xy - 2y - 4z = 4\}$.

    (a) Write down the matrix $[Q]$.
    (b) Write down the characteristic polynomial of $[Q]$.
    (c) Compute the characteristic roots of $[Q]$.
    (d) Find the principal planes of Q.

8. Determine the principal planes of the quadric surface
$\{(x, y, z) \mid x^2 + 2y^2 + 5z^2 - 4yz + 4zx - 2xy - 1 = 0\}$.

9. Determine the principal planes of the quadric surface
$\{(x, y, z) \mid 9x^2 + 13y^2 + 3z^2 + 12yz - 6xy + 1 = 0\}$.

10. Determine the principal planes of $\{(x, y, z) \mid 2x^2 + 2y^2 + 2z^2 - 2yz - 6x = -3\}$.

11. Determine the principal planes of $\{(x, y, z) \mid 2x^2 - y^2 - z^2 + 4yz + 2zx + 2xy + 6x + 6y = -3\}$.

TABLE 1 ARCCOS

T	.000	.001	.002	.003	.004	.005	.006	.007	.008	.009
-1.00	3.1415927	3.0968676	3.0783366	3.0641136	3.0521201	3.0415509	3.0319933	3.0232019	3.0150171	3.0073277
-0.99	3.0000532	2.9931324	2.9865180	2.9801723	2.9740648	2.9681703	2.9624678	2.9569395	2.9515702	2.9463468
-0.98	2.9412578	2.9362933	2.9314444	2.9267033	2.9220631	2.9175174	2.9130606	2.9086876	2.9043938	2.9001749
-0.97	2.8960271	2.8919469	2.8879305	2.8839762	2.8800800	2.8762397	2.8724529	2.8687174	2.8650311	2.8613921
-0.96	2.8577985	2.8542487	2.8507410	2.8472739	2.8438461	2.8404561	2.8371027	2.8337848	2.8305011	2.8272505
-0.95	2.8240322	2.8208451	2.8176883	2.8145609	2.8114620	2.8083909	2.8053469	2.8023291	2.7993369	2.7963696
-0.94	2.7934266	2.7905073	2.7876111	2.7847374	2.7818857	2.7790554	2.7762461	2.7734573	2.7706885	2.7679393
-0.93	2.7652092	2.7624978	2.7598048	2.7571299	2.7544722	2.7518319	2.7492085	2.7466016	2.7440109	2.7414361
-0.92	2.7388768	2.7363329	2.7338039	2.7312896	2.7287899	2.7263042	2.7238326	2.7213746	2.7189300	2.7164987
-0.91	2.7140804	2.7116748	2.7092818	2.7069011	2.7045326	2.7021760	2.6998312	2.6974980	2.6951761	2.6928655
-0.90	2.6905658	2.6882771	2.6859990	2.6837315	2.6814744	2.6792275	2.6769907	2.6747639	2.6725468	2.6703394
-0.89	2.6681415	2.6659530	2.6637738	2.6616036	2.6594425	2.6572903	2.6551469	2.6530121	2.6508859	2.6487680
-0.88	2.6466585	2.6445572	2.6424641	2.6403789	2.6383016	2.6362321	2.6341704	2.6321163	2.6300696	2.6280305
-0.87	2.6259986	2.6239741	2.6219567	2.6199464	2.6179431	2.6159467	2.6139572	2.6119744	2.6099983	2.6080289
-0.86	2.6060660	2.6041096	2.6021595	2.6002158	2.5982784	2.5963472	2.5944221	2.5925030	2.5905900	2.5886829
-0.85	2.5867816	2.5848862	2.5829965	2.5811126	2.5792342	2.5773615	2.5754943	2.5736325	2.5717762	2.5699252
-0.84	2.5680795	2.5662391	2.5644039	2.5625739	2.5607490	2.5589291	2.5571143	2.5553044	2.5534594	2.5516993
-0.83	2.5499040	2.5481135	2.5463278	2.5445467	2.5427703	2.5409985	2.5392313	2.5374686	2.5357104	2.5339567
-0.82	2.5322073	2.5304624	2.5287218	2.5269854	2.5252534	2.5235255	2.5218019	2.5200824	2.5183670	2.5166557
-0.81	2.5149484	2.5132452	2.5115460	2.5098507	2.5081593	2.5064718	2.5047882	2.5031083	2.5014323	2.4997601
-0.80	2.4980915	2.4964267	2.4947656	2.4931081	2.4914542	2.4898039	2.4881572	2.4865140	2.4848743	2.4832381
-0.79	2.4816053	2.4799760	2.4783501	2.4767275	2.4751083	2.4734925	2.4718799	2.4702706	2.4686646	2.4670617
-0.78	2.4654621	2.4638657	2.4622725	2.4606823	2.4590953	2.4575114	2.4559306	2.4543528	2.4527780	2.4512063
-0.77	2.4496375	2.4480717	2.4465088	2.4449489	2.4433918	2.4418377	2.4402864	2.4387379	2.4371923	2.4356495
-0.76	2.4341094	2.4325722	2.4310377	2.4295059	2.4279768	2.4264504	2.4249268	2.4234057	2.4218873	2.4203716
-0.75	2.4188584	2.4173478	2.4158399	2.4143344	2.4128315	2.4113312	2.4098333	2.4083380	2.4068451	2.4053547
-0.74	2.4038667	2.4023811	2.4008980	2.3994173	2.3979390	2.3964630	2.3949894	2.3935181	2.3920492	2.3905826
-0.73	2.3891183	2.3876562	2.3861965	2.3847390	2.3832837	2.3818307	2.3803799	2.3789313	2.3774849	2.3760407
-0.72	2.3745986	2.3731587	2.3717210	2.3702854	2.3688518	2.3674204	2.3659911	2.3645639	2.3631387	2.3617156
-0.71	2.3602945	2.3588755	2.3574585	2.3560435	2.3546305	2.3532195	2.3518104	2.3504034	2.3489982	2.3475951
-0.70	2.3461938	2.3447945	2.3433971	2.3420016	2.3406080	2.3392162	2.3378264	2.3364383	2.3350522	2.3336679
-0.69	2.3322854	2.3309047	2.3295258	2.3281488	2.3267735	2.3254000	2.3240283	2.3226584	2.3212901	2.3199237
-0.68	2.3185590	2.3171960	2.3158347	2.3144751	2.3131172	2.3117610	2.3104065	2.3090537	2.3077025	2.3063530
-0.67	2.3050051	2.3036589	2.3023143	2.3009713	2.2996299	2.2982901	2.2969519	2.2956154	2.2942804	2.2929470
-0.66	2.2916151	2.2902848	2.2889560	2.2876288	2.2863031	2.2849789	2.2836563	2.2823352	2.2810155	2.2796974

TABLE 1 Arccos

T	.000	.001	.002	.003	.004	.005	.006	.007	.008	.009
-0.65	2.2783808	2.2770656	2.2757519	2.2744397	2.2731289	2.2718196	2.2705117	2.2692053	2.2679003	2.2665967
-0.64	2.2652946	2.2639938	2.2626945	2.2613966	2.2601000	2.2588048	2.2575111	2.2562186	2.2549276	2.2536379
-0.63	2.2523495	2.2510625	2.2497769	2.2484925	2.2472095	2.2459279	2.2446475	2.2433684	2.2420907	2.2408142
-0.62	2.2395390	2.2382651	2.2369925	2.2357212	2.2344511	2.2331823	2.2319147	2.2306484	2.2293834	2.2281195
-0.61	2.2268569	2.2255955	2.2243354	2.2230764	2.2218187	2.2205622	2.2193069	2.2180527	2.2167998	2.2155480
-0.60	2.2142974	2.2130480	2.2117998	2.2105527	2.2093068	2.2080620	2.2068183	2.2055758	2.2043345	2.2030943
-0.59	2.2018552	2.2006172	2.1993803	2.1981446	2.1969099	2.1956764	2.1944439	2.1932126	2.1919823	2.1907531
-0.58	2.1895250	2.1882980	2.1870720	2.1858471	2.1846233	2.1834005	2.1821787	2.1809580	2.1797384	2.1785198
-0.57	2.1773022	2.1760856	2.1748701	2.1736556	2.1724421	2.1712296	2.1700181	2.1688076	2.1675981	2.1663896
-0.56	2.1651821	2.1639756	2.1627701	2.1615655	2.1603619	2.1591593	2.1579576	2.1567569	2.1555572	2.1543584
-0.55	2.1531606	2.1519637	2.1507677	2.1495727	2.1483786	2.1471854	2.1459932	2.1448019	2.1436115	2.1424220
-0.54	2.1412334	2.1400458	2.1388590	2.1376731	2.1364882	2.1353041	2.1341209	2.1329386	2.1317571	2.1305766
-0.53	2.1293969	2.1282181	2.1270401	2.1258630	2.1246868	2.1235114	2.1223369	2.1211632	2.1199904	2.1188184
-0.52	2.1176473	2.1164770	2.1153075	2.1141388	2.1129710	2.1118040	2.1106378	2.1094724	2.1083078	2.1071441
-0.51	2.1059811	2.1048190	2.1036576	2.1024970	2.1013373	2.1001783	2.0990201	2.0978627	2.0967060	2.0955502
-0.50	2.0943951	2.0932408	2.0920872	2.0909345	2.0897824	2.0886312	2.0874806	2.0863309	2.0851819	2.0840336
-0.49	2.0828861	2.0817393	2.0805932	2.0794479	2.0783033	2.0771595	2.0760164	2.0748740	2.0737323	2.0725913
-0.48	2.0714510	2.0703115	2.0691727	2.0680345	2.0668971	2.0657604	2.0646243	2.0634890	2.0623543	2.0612204
-0.47	2.0600871	2.0589545	2.0578226	2.0566914	2.0555608	2.0544309	2.0533017	2.0521732	2.0510453	2.0499181
-0.46	2.0487915	2.0476656	2.0465404	2.0454158	2.0442918	2.0431685	2.0420459	2.0409239	2.0398025	2.0386818
-0.45	2.0375617	2.0364422	2.0353234	2.0342051	2.0330876	2.0319706	2.0308542	2.0297385	2.0286234	2.0275089
-0.44	2.0263950	2.0252817	2.0241690	2.0230570	2.0219455	2.0208346	2.0197243	2.0186146	2.0175055	2.0163970
-0.43	2.0152891	2.0141818	2.0130750	2.0119688	2.0108632	2.0097582	2.0086538	2.0075499	2.0064466	2.0053438
-0.42	2.0042416	2.0031400	2.0020390	2.0009385	1.9998385	1.9987391	1.9976403	1.9965420	1.9954442	1.9943470
-0.41	1.9932504	1.9921543	1.9910587	1.9899636	1.9888691	1.9877752	1.9866817	1.9855888	1.9844964	1.9834045
-0.40	1.9823132	1.9812223	1.9801320	1.9790422	1.9779529	1.9768642	1.9757759	1.9746882	1.9736009	1.9725142
-0.39	1.9714279	1.9703422	1.9692569	1.9681722	1.9670879	1.9660041	1.9649209	1.9638381	1.9627558	1.9616740
-0.38	1.9605926	1.9595118	1.9584314	1.9573515	1.9562721	1.9551931	1.9541146	1.9530366	1.9519591	1.9508820
-0.37	1.9498053	1.9487292	1.9476535	1.9465782	1.9455035	1.9444291	1.9433553	1.9422818	1.9412088	1.9401363
-0.36	1.9390642	1.9379926	1.9369214	1.9358506	1.9347803	1.9337104	1.9326409	1.9315719	1.9305033	1.9294352
-0.35	1.9283674	1.9273001	1.9262332	1.9251668	1.9241007	1.9230351	1.9219699	1.9209051	1.9198407	1.9187768
-0.34	1.9177132	1.9166501	1.9155873	1.9145250	1.9134631	1.9124016	1.9113404	1.9102797	1.9092194	1.9081594
-0.33	1.9070999	1.9060408	1.9049820	1.9039236	1.9028656	1.9018081	1.9007508	1.8996940	1.8986376	1.8975815
-0.32	1.8965258	1.8954705	1.8944156	1.8933610	1.8923068	1.8912530	1.8901995	1.8891464	1.8880937	1.8870414
-0.31	1.8859894	1.8849377	1.8838864	1.8828355	1.8817850	1.8807348	1.8796849	1.8786354	1.8775862	1.8765374

TABLE 1 — Arccos

T	.000	.001	.002	.003	.004	.005	.006	.007	.008	.009
-0.30	1.8754890	1.8744409	1.8733931	1.8723457	1.8712986	1.8702518	1.8692054	1.8681594	1.8671136	1.8660682
-0.29	1.8650232	1.8639784	1.8629340	1.8618899	1.8608462	1.8598028	1.8587596	1.8577169	1.8566744	1.8556323
-0.28	1.8545904	1.8535489	1.8525077	1.8514669	1.8504263	1.8493860	1.8483461	1.8473064	1.8462671	1.8452281
-0.27	1.8441894	1.8431509	1.8421128	1.8410750	1.8400375	1.8390002	1.8379633	1.8369267	1.8358903	1.8348543
-0.26	1.8338185	1.8327831	1.8317479	1.8307130	1.8296784	1.8286440	1.8276100	1.8265762	1.8255427	1.8245095
-0.25	1.8234766	1.8224439	1.8214115	1.8203794	1.8193476	1.8183160	1.8172847	1.8162537	1.8152229	1.8141924
-0.24	1.8131622	1.8121322	1.8111025	1.8100730	1.8090438	1.8080149	1.8069862	1.8059578	1.8049296	1.8039017
-0.23	1.8028740	1.8018466	1.8008194	1.7997925	1.7987658	1.7977394	1.7967132	1.7956872	1.7946615	1.7936360
-0.22	1.7926108	1.7915858	1.7905610	1.7895365	1.7885122	1.7874882	1.7864643	1.7854407	1.7844174	1.7833942
-0.21	1.7823713	1.7813486	1.7803261	1.7793039	1.7782818	1.7772600	1.7762384	1.7752171	1.7741959	1.7731750
-0.20	1.7721542	1.7711337	1.7701134	1.7690933	1.7680735	1.7670538	1.7660343	1.7650150	1.7639960	1.7629771
-0.19	1.7619585	1.7609400	1.7599218	1.7589037	1.7578859	1.7568682	1.7558507	1.7548334	1.7538164	1.7527995
-0.18	1.7517628	1.7507663	1.7497499	1.7487338	1.7477179	1.7467021	1.7456865	1.7446711	1.7436559	1.7426409
-0.17	1.7416260	1.7406113	1.7395968	1.7385825	1.7375683	1.7365543	1.7355405	1.7345269	1.7335134	1.7325001
-0.16	1.7314870	1.7304740	1.7294612	1.7284486	1.7274361	1.7264238	1.7254116	1.7243996	1.7233878	1.7223761
-0.15	1.7213646	1.7203532	1.7193420	1.7183310	1.7173201	1.7163093	1.7152987	1.7142882	1.7132779	1.7122678
-0.14	1.7112577	1.7102479	1.7092381	1.7082285	1.7072191	1.7062098	1.7052006	1.7041916	1.7031827	1.7021739
-0.13	1.7011653	1.7001568	1.6991485	1.6981402	1.6971321	1.6961242	1.6951163	1.6941086	1.6931010	1.6920935
-0.12	1.6910862	1.6900790	1.6890719	1.6880649	1.6870581	1.6860513	1.6850447	1.6840382	1.6830318	1.6820255
-0.11	1.6810194	1.6800133	1.6790074	1.6780016	1.6769958	1.6759902	1.6749847	1.6739793	1.6729740	1.6719688
-0.10	1.6709637	1.6699588	1.6689539	1.6679491	1.6669444	1.6659398	1.6649353	1.6639309	1.6629266	1.6619224
-0.09	1.6609183	1.6599142	1.6589103	1.6579065	1.6569027	1.6558990	1.6548954	1.6538919	1.6528885	1.6518852
-0.08	1.6508819	1.6498787	1.6488756	1.6478726	1.6468697	1.6458668	1.6448640	1.6438613	1.6428587	1.6418561
-0.07	1.6408536	1.6398512	1.6388488	1.6378466	1.6368443	1.6358422	1.6348401	1.6338381	1.6328361	1.6318342
-0.06	1.6308324	1.6298306	1.6288289	1.6278272	1.6268256	1.6258241	1.6248226	1.6238212	1.6228198	1.6218185
-0.05	1.6208172	1.6198160	1.6188148	1.6178136	1.6168126	1.6158115	1.6148105	1.6138096	1.6128087	1.6118078
-0.04	1.6108070	1.6098062	1.6088055	1.6078048	1.6068041	1.6058035	1.6048029	1.6038023	1.6028018	1.6018013
-0.03	1.6008008	1.5998004	1.5988000	1.5977996	1.5967993	1.5957989	1.5947986	1.5937984	1.5927981	1.5917979
-0.02	1.5907977	1.5897975	1.5887973	1.5877971	1.5867970	1.5857969	1.5847968	1.5837967	1.5827966	1.5817965
-0.01	1.5807965	1.5797964	1.5787964	1.5777964	1.5767964	1.5757963	1.5747963	1.5737963	1.5727963	1.5717964
-0.00	1.5707963	1.5697963	1.5687963	1.5677963	1.5667963	1.5657963	1.5647963	1.5637963	1.5627962	1.5617962
0.01	1.5607962	1.5597961	1.5587960	1.5577960	1.5567959	1.5557958	1.5547956	1.5537955	1.5527954	1.5517952
0.02	1.5507950	1.5497948	1.5487946	1.5477943	1.5467940	1.5457937	1.5447934	1.5437930	1.5427927	1.5417923
0.03	1.5407918	1.5397914	1.5387909	1.5377903	1.5367898	1.5357892	1.5347885	1.5337879	1.5327872	1.5317864
0.04	1.5307857	1.5297848	1.5287840	1.5277831	1.5267821	1.5257811	1.5247801	1.5237790	1.5227779	1.5217767

279

TABLE 1   Arccos

T	.000	.001	.002	.003	.004	.005	.006	.007	.008	.009
0.05	1.5207755	1.5197742	1.5187729	1.5177715	1.5167700	1.5157686	1.5147670	1.5137654	1.5127638	1.5117620
0.06	1.5107603	1.5097584	1.5087565	1.5077546	1.5067526	1.5057505	1.5047483	1.5037461	1.5027438	1.5017415
0.07	1.5007390	1.4997365	1.4987340	1.4977313	1.4967286	1.4957258	1.4947230	1.4937200	1.4927170	1.4917139
0.08	1.4907107	1.4897075	1.4887042	1.4877007	1.4866972	1.4856936	1.4846900	1.4836862	1.4826824	1.4816784
0.09	1.4806744	1.4796703	1.4786660	1.4776617	1.4766573	1.4756528	1.4746483	1.4736436	1.4726388	1.4716339
0.10	1.4706289	1.4696238	1.4686186	1.4676133	1.4666079	1.4656024	1.4645968	1.4635911	1.4625853	1.4615793
0.11	1.4605733	1.4595671	1.4585608	1.4575545	1.4565479	1.4555413	1.4545346	1.4535277	1.4525208	1.4515137
0.12	1.4505064	1.4494991	1.4484916	1.4474841	1.4464763	1.4454685	1.4444605	1.4434524	1.4424442	1.4414358
0.13	1.4404273	1.4394187	1.4384100	1.4374011	1.4363920	1.4353829	1.4343736	1.4333641	1.4323545	1.4313448
0.14	1.4303349	1.4293249	1.4283147	1.4273044	1.4262940	1.4252834	1.4242726	1.4232617	1.4222506	1.4212394
0.15	1.4202281	1.4192165	1.4182049	1.4171930	1.4161810	1.4151689	1.4141566	1.4131441	1.4121314	1.4111186
0.16	1.4101057	1.4090925	1.4080792	1.4070658	1.4060521	1.4050383	1.4040243	1.4030102	1.4019958	1.4009813
0.17	1.3999667	1.3989518	1.3979368	1.3969215	1.3959061	1.3948906	1.3938748	1.3928588	1.3918427	1.3908264
0.18	1.3898099	1.3887932	1.3877763	1.3867592	1.3857419	1.3847245	1.3837068	1.3826889	1.3816709	1.3806526
0.19	1.3796342	1.3786155	1.3775967	1.3765776	1.3755583	1.3745389	1.3735192	1.3724993	1.3714792	1.3704589
0.20	1.3694384	1.3684177	1.3673967	1.3663756	1.3653542	1.3643326	1.3633108	1.3622888	1.3612665	1.3602441
0.21	1.3592214	1.3581984	1.3571753	1.3561519	1.3551283	1.3541045	1.3530804	1.3520561	1.3510316	1.3500069
0.22	1.3489819	1.3479566	1.3469311	1.3459054	1.3448795	1.3438533	1.3428269	1.3418002	1.3407732	1.3397461
0.23	1.3387186	1.3376910	1.3366630	1.3356349	1.3346064	1.3335778	1.3325488	1.3315196	1.3304902	1.3294605
0.24	1.3284305	1.3274002	1.3263697	1.3253390	1.3243079	1.3232766	1.3222451	1.3212132	1.3201811	1.3191487
0.25	1.3181161	1.3170831	1.3160499	1.3150164	1.3139827	1.3129486	1.3119143	1.3108797	1.3098448	1.3088096
0.26	1.3077741	1.3067384	1.3057023	1.3046660	1.3036293	1.3025924	1.3015552	1.3005177	1.2994798	1.2984417
0.27	1.2974033	1.2963646	1.2953255	1.2942862	1.2932466	1.2922066	1.2911664	1.2901258	1.2890849	1.2880437
0.28	1.2870022	1.2859604	1.2849182	1.2838758	1.2828330	1.2817899	1.2807465	1.2797027	1.2786586	1.2776142
0.29	1.2765695	1.2755244	1.2744790	1.2734333	1.2723872	1.2713408	1.2702941	1.2692470	1.2681996	1.2671518
0.30	1.2661037	1.2650552	1.2640064	1.2629573	1.2619078	1.2608579	1.2598077	1.2587571	1.2577062	1.2566549
0.31	1.2556033	1.2545513	1.2534990	1.2524462	1.2513931	1.2503397	1.2492858	1.2482317	1.2471771	1.2461222
0.32	1.2450668	1.2440112	1.2429551	1.2418986	1.2408418	1.2397846	1.2387270	1.2376690	1.2366107	1.2355519
0.33	1.2344928	1.2334332	1.2323733	1.2313129	1.2302522	1.2291911	1.2281296	1.2270676	1.2260053	1.2249426
0.34	1.2238794	1.2228159	1.2217519	1.2206875	1.2196227	1.2185575	1.2174919	1.2164259	1.2153594	1.2142925
0.35	1.2132252	1.2121575	1.2110893	1.2100207	1.2089517	1.2078823	1.2068124	1.2057420	1.2046713	1.2036001
0.36	1.2025284	1.2014563	1.2003838	1.1993108	1.1982374	1.1971635	1.1960892	1.1950144	1.1939392	1.1928635
0.37	1.1917873	1.1907107	1.1896336	1.1885561	1.1874780	1.1863996	1.1853206	1.1842412	1.1831613	1.1820809
0.38	1.1810000	1.1799187	1.1788369	1.1777546	1.1766718	1.1755885	1.1745047	1.1734205	1.1723357	1.1712505
0.39	1.1701647	1.1690785	1.1679917	1.1669045	1.1658167	1.1647285	1.1636397	1.1625504	1.1614606	1.1603703

TABLE 1 Arccos

T	.000	.001	.002	.003	.004	.005	.006	.007	.008	.009
0.40	1.1592795	1.1581881	1.1570963	1.1560039	1.1549105	1.1538175	1.1527235	1.1516290	1.1505340	1.1494384
0.41	1.1483423	1.1472456	1.1461484	1.1450507	1.1439524	1.1428535	1.1417541	1.1406542	1.1395537	1.1384526
0.42	1.1373510	1.1362488	1.1351461	1.1340428	1.1329389	1.1318344	1.1307294	1.1296238	1.1285176	1.1274109
0.43	1.1263035	1.1251956	1.1240871	1.1229780	1.1218683	1.1207581	1.1196472	1.1185357	1.1174236	1.1163109
0.44	1.1151977	1.1140838	1.1129693	1.1118541	1.1107384	1.1096221	1.1085051	1.1073875	1.1062693	1.1051505
0.45	1.1040310	1.1029109	1.1017902	1.1006688	1.0995468	1.0984241	1.0973008	1.0961769	1.0950523	1.0939270
0.46	1.0928011	1.0916746	1.0905474	1.0894195	1.0882909	1.0871617	1.0860318	1.0849013	1.0837700	1.0826381
0.47	1.0815055	1.0803723	1.0792383	1.0781037	1.0769683	1.0758323	1.0746956	1.0735581	1.0724200	1.0712812
0.48	1.0701416	1.0690014	1.0678604	1.0667187	1.0655763	1.0644332	1.0632893	1.0621447	1.0609994	1.0598534
0.49	1.0587066	1.0575590	1.0564108	1.0552618	1.0541120	1.0529615	1.0518102	1.0506582	1.0495054	1.0483519
0.50	1.0471976	1.0460425	1.0448866	1.0437300	1.0425726	1.0414144	1.0402554	1.0390956	1.0379350	1.0367737
0.51	1.0356115	1.0344486	1.0332848	1.0321203	1.0309549	1.0297887	1.0286217	1.0274538	1.0262852	1.0251157
0.52	1.0239454	1.0227742	1.0216022	1.0204294	1.0192557	1.0180812	1.0169058	1.0157296	1.0145525	1.0133746
0.53	1.0121958	1.0110161	1.0098355	1.0086541	1.0074718	1.0062886	1.0051045	1.0039195	1.0027337	1.0015469
0.54	1.0003592	0.9991706	0.9979812	0.9967908	0.9955994	0.9944072	0.9932141	0.9920200	0.9908249	0.9896290
0.55	0.9884321	0.9872342	0.9860355	0.9848357	0.9836350	0.9824334	0.9812307	0.9800271	0.9788226	0.9776170
0.56	0.9764105	0.9752030	0.9739945	0.9727850	0.9715746	0.9703631	0.9691506	0.9679371	0.9667226	0.9655070
0.57	0.9642905	0.9630729	0.9618543	0.9606346	0.9594139	0.9581922	0.9569694	0.9557455	0.9545206	0.9532947
0.58	0.9520676	0.9508395	0.9496103	0.9483801	0.9471487	0.9459163	0.9446827	0.9434481	0.9422123	0.9409755
0.59	0.9397375	0.9384984	0.9372582	0.9360168	0.9347743	0.9335307	0.9322859	0.9310400	0.9297929	0.9285446
0.60	0.9272952	0.9260446	0.9247929	0.9235399	0.9222858	0.9210305	0.9197739	0.9185162	0.9172573	0.9159971
0.61	0.9147357	0.9134731	0.9122093	0.9109442	0.9096779	0.9084104	0.9071415	0.9058715	0.9046001	0.9033275
0.62	0.9020536	0.9007784	0.8995020	0.8982242	0.8969452	0.8956648	0.8943831	0.8931001	0.8918158	0.8905301
0.63	0.8892431	0.8879548	0.8866651	0.8853740	0.8840816	0.8827878	0.8814926	0.8801961	0.8788981	0.8775988
0.64	0.8762981	0.8749959	0.8736923	0.8723873	0.8710809	0.8697730	0.8684637	0.8671530	0.8658407	0.8645271
0.65	0.8632119	0.8618952	0.8605771	0.8592575	0.8579363	0.8566137	0.8552895	0.8539639	0.8526366	0.8513079
0.66	0.8499776	0.8486457	0.8473123	0.8459773	0.8446407	0.8433025	0.8419627	0.8406214	0.8392784	0.8379338
0.67	0.8365875	0.8352397	0.8338901	0.8325390	0.8311861	0.8298316	0.8284754	0.8271176	0.8257580	0.8243967
0.68	0.8230337	0.8216690	0.8203025	0.8189343	0.8175643	0.8161926	0.8148191	0.8134439	0.8120668	0.8106879
0.69	0.8093073	0.8079248	0.8065405	0.8051543	0.8037663	0.8023764	0.8009847	0.7995911	0.7981956	0.7967982
0.70	0.7953988	0.7939976	0.7925944	0.7911893	0.7897822	0.7883732	0.7869622	0.7855492	0.7841342	0.7827172
0.71	0.7812981	0.7798771	0.7784539	0.7770288	0.7756015	0.7741722	0.7727408	0.7713073	0.7698717	0.7684339
0.72	0.7669540	0.7655520	0.7641090	0.7626613	0.7612127	0.7597672	0.7583089	0.7568537	0.7553962	0.7539364
0.73	0.7524744	0.7510101	0.7495434	0.7480745	0.7466032	0.7451296	0.7436537	0.7421754	0.7406946	0.7392115
0.74	0.7377260	0.7362380	0.7347476	0.7332547	0.7317593	0.7302615	0.7287611	0.7272582	0.7257528	0.7242448

TABLE 1   Arccos

r	.000	.001	.002	.003	.004	.005	.006	.007	.008	.009
0.75	0.7227342	0.7212211	0.7197053	0.7181869	0.7166659	0.7151422	0.7136158	0.7120868	0.7105550	0.7090205
0.76	0.7074832	0.7059432	0.7044004	0.7028547	0.7013063	0.6997550	0.6982008	0.6966438	0.6950839	0.6935210
0.77	0.6919552	0.6903864	0.6888146	0.6872399	0.6856621	0.6840812	0.6824973	0.6809103	0.6793202	0.6777269
0.78	0.6761305	0.6745309	0.6729281	0.6713221	0.6697128	0.6681002	0.6664843	0.6648651	0.6632426	0.6616167
0.79	0.6599873	0.6583546	0.6567184	0.6550787	0.6534355	0.6517887	0.6501385	0.6484846	0.6468271	0.6451659
0.80	0.6435011	0.6418326	0.6401603	0.6384843	0.6368045	0.6351209	0.6334334	0.6317420	0.6300467	0.6283474
0.81	0.6266442	0.6249370	0.6232257	0.6215103	0.6197908	0.6180671	0.6163393	0.6146072	0.6128709	0.6111303
0.82	0.6093853	0.6076360	0.6058822	0.6041240	0.6023613	0.6005941	0.5988223	0.5970459	0.5952649	0.5934791
0.83	0.5916886	0.5898934	0.5880933	0.5862883	0.5844784	0.5826635	0.5808437	0.5790187	0.5771887	0.5753535
0.84	0.5735131	0.5716674	0.5698165	0.5679601	0.5660984	0.5642312	0.5623584	0.5604801	0.5585961	0.5567065
0.85	0.5548110	0.5529098	0.5510027	0.5490896	0.5471706	0.5452455	0.5433142	0.5413768	0.5394331	0.5374831
0.86	0.5355267	0.5335638	0.5315943	0.5296182	0.5276355	0.5256460	0.5236496	0.5216463	0.5196360	0.5176186
0.87	0.5155940	0.5135622	0.5115230	0.5094764	0.5074223	0.5053605	0.5032910	0.5012138	0.4991286	0.4970354
0.88	0.4949341	0.4928246	0.4907068	0.4885805	0.4864458	0.4843023	0.4821501	0.4799890	0.4778189	0.4756397
0.89	0.4734512	0.4712533	0.4690459	0.4668288	0.4646019	0.4623651	0.4601182	0.4578611	0.4555936	0.4533156
0.90	0.4510268	0.4487272	0.4464165	0.4440947	0.4417614	0.4394166	0.4370600	0.4346915	0.4323108	0.4299178
0.91	0.4275123	0.4250939	0.4226626	0.4202181	0.4177601	0.4152884	0.4128028	0.4103030	0.4077888	0.4052598
0.92	0.4027158	0.4001566	0.3975818	0.3949915	0.3923842	0.3897607	0.3871204	0.3844629	0.3817879	0.3790948
0.93	0.3763835	0.3736534	0.3709042	0.3681354	0.3653466	0.3625373	0.3597070	0.3568553	0.3539816	0.3510853
0.94	0.3481660	0.3452230	0.3422558	0.3392636	0.3362458	0.3332017	0.3301306	0.3270318	0.3239044	0.3207475
0.95	0.3175604	0.3143421	0.3110916	0.3078079	0.3044899	0.3011365	0.2977466	0.2943187	0.2908516	0.2873439
0.96	0.2837941	0.2802005	0.2765615	0.2728752	0.2691397	0.2653529	0.2615126	0.2576164	0.2536617	0.2496458
0.97	0.2455655	0.2414177	0.2371989	0.2329051	0.2285321	0.2240753	0.2195296	0.2148893	0.2101482	0.2052994
0.98	0.2003348	0.1952459	0.1900224	0.1846531	0.1791248	0.1734223	0.1675278	0.1614204	0.1550747	0.1484603
0.99	0.1415395	0.1342649	0.1265756	0.1183907	0.1095994	0.1000417	0.0894726	0.0774790	0.0632561	0.0447251

TABLE 2 COS

T	.000	.001	.002	.003	.004	.005	.006	.007	.008	.009
-0.00	1.0000000	0.9999995	0.9999980	0.9999955	0.9999920	0.9999875	0.9999820	0.9999755	0.9999680	0.9999595
0.01	0.9999500	0.9999395	0.9999280	0.9999155	0.9999020	0.9998875	0.9998720	0.9998555	0.9998380	0.9998195
0.02	0.9998000	0.9997795	0.9997580	0.9997355	0.9997120	0.9996875	0.9996620	0.9996355	0.9996080	0.9995795
0.03	0.9995500	0.9995195	0.9994880	0.9994555	0.9994221	0.9993876	0.9993521	0.9993156	0.9992781	0.9992396
0.04	0.9992001	0.9991596	0.9991181	0.9990756	0.9990322	0.9989877	0.9989422	0.9988957	0.9988482	0.9987997
0.05	0.9987503	0.9986998	0.9986483	0.9985958	0.9985424	0.9984879	0.9984324	0.9983759	0.9983185	0.9982600
0.06	0.9982005	0.9981401	0.9980786	0.9980162	0.9979527	0.9978882	0.9978228	0.9977563	0.9976889	0.9976204
0.07	0.9975510	0.9974806	0.9974091	0.9973367	0.9972632	0.9971888	0.9971134	0.9970370	0.9969595	0.9968811
0.08	0.9968017	0.9967213	0.9966399	0.9965575	0.9964741	0.9963897	0.9963043	0.9962179	0.9961305	0.9960421
0.09	0.9959527	0.9958624	0.9957710	0.9956786	0.9955853	0.9954909	0.9953955	0.9952992	0.9952018	0.9951035
0.10	0.9950042	0.9949038	0.9948025	0.9947007	0.9945969	0.9944926	0.9943873	0.9942810	0.9941737	0.9940654
0.11	0.9939561	0.9938458	0.9937346	0.9936223	0.9935090	0.9933948	0.9932795	0.9931633	0.9930461	0.9929279
0.12	0.9928086	0.9926884	0.9925672	0.9924450	0.9923218	0.9921977	0.9920725	0.9919463	0.9918192	0.9916910
0.13	0.9915619	0.9914318	0.9913006	0.9911685	0.9910354	0.9909013	0.9907662	0.9906302	0.9904931	0.9903550
0.14	0.9902160	0.9900760	0.9899349	0.9897929	0.9896499	0.9895059	0.9893609	0.9892149	0.9890680	0.9889200
0.15	0.9887711	0.9886211	0.9884702	0.9883183	0.9881654	0.9880115	0.9878567	0.9877008	0.9875439	0.9873861
0.16	0.9872273	0.9870675	0.9869067	0.9867449	0.9865821	0.9864184	0.9862536	0.9860879	0.9859212	0.9857535
0.17	0.9855848	0.9854151	0.9852444	0.9850728	0.9849002	0.9847265	0.9845519	0.9843764	0.9841999	0.9840222
0.18	0.9838437	0.9836642	0.9834837	0.9833022	0.9831197	0.9829363	0.9827518	0.9825664	0.9823800	0.9821926
0.19	0.9820042	0.9818149	0.9816246	0.9814332	0.9812409	0.9810477	0.9808534	0.9806582	0.9804620	0.9802648
0.20	0.9800666	0.9798674	0.9796673	0.9794662	0.9792641	0.9790610	0.9788569	0.9786519	0.9784459	0.9782389
0.21	0.9780309	0.9778220	0.9776120	0.9774011	0.9771893	0.9769764	0.9767626	0.9765477	0.9763320	0.9761152
0.22	0.9758974	0.9756787	0.9754590	0.9752384	0.9750167	0.9747941	0.9745705	0.9743459	0.9741204	0.9738939
0.23	0.9736664	0.9734379	0.9732085	0.9729781	0.9727467	0.9725143	0.9722810	0.9720467	0.9718114	0.9715752
0.24	0.9713380	0.9710998	0.9708606	0.9706205	0.9703794	0.9701373	0.9698943	0.9696503	0.9694053	0.9691593
0.25	0.9689124	0.9686645	0.9684157	0.9681659	0.9679151	0.9676633	0.9674106	0.9671569	0.9669022	0.9666466
0.26	0.9663900	0.9661324	0.9658739	0.9656144	0.9653539	0.9650925	0.9648301	0.9645668	0.9643024	0.9640371
0.27	0.9637709	0.9635037	0.9632355	0.9629664	0.9626963	0.9624252	0.9621532	0.9618802	0.9616062	0.9613313
0.28	0.9610554	0.9607786	0.9605008	0.9602220	0.9599423	0.9596617	0.9593800	0.9590974	0.9588139	0.9585293
0.29	0.9582439	0.9579574	0.9576701	0.9573817	0.9570924	0.9568021	0.9565109	0.9562187	0.9559256	0.9556315
0.30	0.9553365	0.9550405	0.9547435	0.9544456	0.9541468	0.9538470	0.9535462	0.9532445	0.9529418	0.9526382
0.31	0.9523336	0.9520280	0.9517215	0.9514141	0.9511057	0.9507964	0.9504861	0.9501748	0.9498627	0.9495495
0.32	0.9492354	0.9489204	0.9486044	0.9482874	0.9479696	0.9476507	0.9473309	0.9470102	0.9466885	0.9463659
0.33	0.9460423	0.9457178	0.9453924	0.9450660	0.9447386	0.9444103	0.9440811	0.9437509	0.9434198	0.9430877
0.34	0.9427547	0.9424207	0.9420858	0.9417500	0.9414132	0.9410755	0.9407368	0.9403972	0.9400566	0.9397151

TABLE 2 Cos

T	.000	.001	.002	.003	.004	.005	.006	.007	.008	.009
0.35	0.9393727	0.9390293	0.9386850	0.9383398	0.9379936	0.9376465	0.9372984	0.9369494	0.9365995	0.9362486
0.36	0.9358968	0.9355441	0.9351904	0.9348358	0.9344802	0.9341238	0.9337663	0.9334080	0.9330487	0.9326885
0.37	0.9323273	0.9319653	0.9316023	0.9312383	0.9308734	0.9305076	0.9301409	0.9297732	0.9294046	0.9290351
0.38	0.9286646	0.9282933	0.9279209	0.9275477	0.9271735	0.9267984	0.9264224	0.9260455	0.9256676	0.9252888
0.39	0.9249091	0.9245284	0.9241468	0.9237643	0.9233809	0.9229966	0.9226113	0.9222251	0.9218380	0.9214500
0.40	0.9210610	0.9206711	0.9202803	0.9198886	0.9194960	0.9191024	0.9187079	0.9183125	0.9179162	0.9175190
0.41	0.9171208	0.9167218	0.9163218	0.9159209	0.9155191	0.9151163	0.9147127	0.9143081	0.9139026	0.9134962
0.42	0.9130889	0.9126807	0.9122716	0.9118616	0.9114506	0.9110387	0.9106260	0.9102123	0.9097977	0.9093822
0.43	0.9089657	0.9085484	0.9081302	0.9077110	0.9072910	0.9068700	0.9064482	0.9060254	0.9056017	0.9051772
0.44	0.9047517	0.9043253	0.9038980	0.9034698	0.9030407	0.9026107	0.9021798	0.9017479	0.9013152	0.9008816
0.45	0.9004471	0.9000117	0.8995754	0.8991382	0.8987000	0.8982610	0.8978211	0.8973803	0.8969386	0.8964960
0.46	0.8960525	0.8956081	0.8951628	0.8947166	0.8942695	0.8938216	0.8933727	0.8929229	0.8924723	0.8920207
0.47	0.8915683	0.8911150	0.8906607	0.8902056	0.8897496	0.8892927	0.8888349	0.8883763	0.8879167	0.8874563
0.48	0.8869949	0.8865327	0.8860696	0.8856056	0.8851407	0.8846749	0.8842083	0.8837408	0.8832723	0.8828030
0.49	0.8823329	0.8818618	0.8813898	0.8809170	0.8804433	0.8799687	0.8794932	0.8790169	0.8785397	0.8780615
0.50	0.8775826	0.8771027	0.8766220	0.8761403	0.8756578	0.8751745	0.8746902	0.8742051	0.8737191	0.8732322
0.51	0.8727445	0.8722559	0.8717664	0.8712761	0.8707848	0.8702927	0.8697998	0.8693059	0.8688112	0.8683156
0.52	0.8678192	0.8673219	0.8668237	0.8663246	0.8658247	0.8653239	0.8648223	0.8643198	0.8638164	0.8633122
0.53	0.8628071	0.8623011	0.8617943	0.8612866	0.8607780	0.8602686	0.8597584	0.8592472	0.8587352	0.8582224
0.54	0.8577087	0.8571941	0.8566787	0.8561624	0.8556453	0.8551273	0.8546084	0.8540887	0.8535682	0.8530468
0.55	0.8525245	0.8520014	0.8514774	0.8509526	0.8504270	0.8499004	0.8493731	0.8488449	0.8483158	0.8477859
0.56	0.8472551	0.8467235	0.8461910	0.8456577	0.8451236	0.8445886	0.8440528	0.8435161	0.8429786	0.8424402
0.57	0.8419010	0.8413609	0.8408200	0.8402783	0.8397357	0.8391923	0.8386480	0.8381030	0.8375570	0.8370103
0.58	0.8364626	0.8359142	0.8353649	0.8348148	0.8342639	0.8337121	0.8331595	0.8326060	0.8320517	0.8314966
0.59	0.8309407	0.8303839	0.8298263	0.8292679	0.8287086	0.8281485	0.8275876	0.8270258	0.8264632	0.8258998
0.60	0.8253356	0.8247706	0.8242047	0.8236380	0.8230704	0.8225021	0.8219329	0.8213629	0.8207921	0.8202205
0.61	0.8196480	0.8190747	0.8185006	0.8179257	0.8173500	0.8167734	0.8161961	0.8156179	0.8150389	0.8144591
0.62	0.8138785	0.8132970	0.8127148	0.8121317	0.8115478	0.8109631	0.8103776	0.8097913	0.8092042	0.8086162
0.63	0.8080275	0.8074380	0.8068476	0.8062564	0.8056645	0.8050717	0.8044781	0.8038837	0.8032885	0.8026926
0.64	0.8020958	0.8014982	0.8008998	0.8003006	0.7997006	0.7990998	0.7984982	0.7978958	0.7972926	0.7966886
0.65	0.7960838	0.7954782	0.7948718	0.7942647	0.7936567	0.7930479	0.7924384	0.7918280	0.7912169	0.7906050
0.66	0.7899922	0.7893787	0.7887644	0.7881493	0.7875335	0.7869168	0.7862993	0.7856811	0.7850621	0.7844423
0.67	0.7838217	0.7832003	0.7825781	0.7819552	0.7813315	0.7807070	0.7800817	0.7794556	0.7788287	0.7782011
0.68	0.7775727	0.7769435	0.7763136	0.7756828	0.7750513	0.7744190	0.7737860	0.7731522	0.7725175	0.7718822
0.69	0.7712460	0.7706091	0.7699714	0.7693329	0.7686937	0.7680537	0.7674129	0.7667714	0.7661291	0.7654860

TABLE 2　Cos

τ	.000	.001	.002	.003	.004	.005	.006	.007	.008	.009
0.70	0.7648422	0.7641976	0.7635522	0.7629061	0.7622592	0.7616116	0.7609631	0.7603140	0.7596640	0.7590133
0.71	0.7583619	0.7577097	0.7570567	0.7564030	0.7557485	0.7550932	0.7544372	0.7537805	0.7531230	0.7524647
0.72	0.7518057	0.7511460	0.7504855	0.7498242	0.7491622	0.7484994	0.7478359	0.7471717	0.7465067	0.7458409
0.73	0.7451744	0.7445072	0.7438392	0.7431704	0.7425010	0.7418308	0.7411598	0.7404881	0.7398157	0.7391425
0.74	0.7384686	0.7377939	0.7371185	0.7364424	0.7357655	0.7350879	0.7344096	0.7337305	0.7330507	0.7323701
0.75	0.7316889	0.7310069	0.7303241	0.7296407	0.7289565	0.7282715	0.7275859	0.7268995	0.7262124	0.7255246
0.76	0.7248360	0.7241467	0.7234567	0.7227660	0.7220745	0.7213824	0.7206895	0.7199958	0.7193015	0.7186064
0.77	0.7179107	0.7172142	0.7165170	0.7158190	0.7151204	0.7144210	0.7137210	0.7130202	0.7123187	0.7116165
0.78	0.7109135	0.7102099	0.7095056	0.7088005	0.7080947	0.7073883	0.7066811	0.7059732	0.7052646	0.7045553
0.79	0.7038453	0.7031346	0.7024232	0.7017111	0.7009983	0.7002848	0.6995706	0.6988556	0.6981400	0.6974237
0.80	0.6967067	0.6959890	0.6952706	0.6945515	0.6938317	0.6931112	0.6923901	0.6916682	0.6909456	0.6902224
0.81	0.6894984	0.6887738	0.6880485	0.6873225	0.6865958	0.6858684	0.6851403	0.6844116	0.6836821	0.6829520
0.82	0.6822212	0.6814897	0.6807576	0.6800247	0.6792912	0.6785570	0.6778221	0.6770865	0.6763503	0.6756134
0.83	0.6748758	0.6741375	0.6733985	0.6726589	0.6719186	0.6711777	0.6704361	0.6696937	0.6689508	0.6682071
0.84	0.6674628	0.6667178	0.6659722	0.6652259	0.6644789	0.6637313	0.6629830	0.6622340	0.6614844	0.6607341
0.85	0.6599831	0.6592315	0.6584793	0.6577263	0.6569728	0.6562185	0.6554635	0.6547081	0.6539518	0.6531950
0.86	0.6524375	0.6516793	0.6509205	0.6501610	0.6494009	0.6486401	0.6478787	0.6471166	0.6463539	0.6455906
0.87	0.6448265	0.6440619	0.6432966	0.6425307	0.6417641	0.6409969	0.6402290	0.6394605	0.6386913	0.6379216
0.88	0.6371511	0.6363801	0.6356084	0.6348361	0.6340631	0.6332895	0.6325153	0.6317404	0.6309649	0.6301888
0.89	0.6294120	0.6286346	0.6278566	0.6270780	0.6262987	0.6255188	0.6247383	0.6239571	0.6231754	0.6223930
0.90	0.6216100	0.6208263	0.6200421	0.6192572	0.6184717	0.6176856	0.6168988	0.6161115	0.6153235	0.6145349
0.91	0.6137457	0.6129559	0.6121655	0.6113745	0.6105828	0.6097906	0.6089977	0.6082042	0.6074101	0.6066155
0.92	0.6058202	0.6050243	0.6042277	0.6034306	0.6026329	0.6018346	0.6010357	0.6002361	0.5994360	0.5986353
0.93	0.5978340	0.5970321	0.5962295	0.5954264	0.5946227	0.5938184	0.5930135	0.5922080	0.5914020	0.5905953
0.94	0.5897880	0.5889802	0.5881717	0.5873627	0.5865531	0.5857429	0.5849321	0.5841207	0.5833088	0.5824962
0.95	0.5816831	0.5808694	0.5800551	0.5792402	0.5784248	0.5776088	0.5767922	0.5759750	0.5751572	0.5743389
0.96	0.5735200	0.5727005	0.5718805	0.5710598	0.5702386	0.5694169	0.5685945	0.5677716	0.5669482	0.5661241
0.97	0.5652995	0.5644744	0.5636486	0.5628223	0.5619955	0.5611681	0.5603401	0.5595115	0.5586824	0.5578528
0.98	0.5570225	0.5561918	0.5553604	0.5545286	0.5536961	0.5528631	0.5520296	0.5511955	0.5503608	0.5495256
0.99	0.5486899	0.5478536	0.5470167	0.5461793	0.5453414	0.5445029	0.5436639	0.5428243	0.5419842	0.5411435
1.00	0.5403023	0.5394606	0.5386183	0.5377755	0.5369321	0.5360882	0.5352438	0.5343988	0.5335533	0.5327073
1.01	0.5318607	0.5310136	0.5301660	0.5293178	0.5284691	0.5276199	0.5267702	0.5259199	0.5250691	0.5242178
1.02	0.5233660	0.5225136	0.5216607	0.5208073	0.5199533	0.5190989	0.5182439	0.5173884	0.5165324	0.5156759
1.03	0.5148188	0.5139613	0.5131032	0.5122446	0.5113855	0.5105259	0.5096658	0.5088052	0.5079441	0.5070824
1.04	0.5062203	0.5053576	0.5044944	0.5036308	0.5027666	0.5019019	0.5010368	0.5001711	0.4993049	0.4984382

TABLE 2   Cos

T	.000	.001	.002	.003	.004	.005	.006	.007	.008	.009
1.05	0.4975710	0.4967034	0.4958352	0.4949665	0.4940974	0.4932277	0.4923576	0.4914869	0.4906159	0.4897443
1.06	0.4888721	0.4879995	0.4871264	0.4862528	0.4853788	0.4845042	0.4836292	0.4827537	0.4818777	0.4810012
1.07	0.4801242	0.4792468	0.4783689	0.4774905	0.4766116	0.4757322	0.4748524	0.4739721	0.4730913	0.4722101
1.08	0.4713284	0.4704462	0.4695635	0.4686804	0.4677968	0.4669127	0.4660282	0.4651432	0.4642577	0.4633718
1.09	0.4624854	0.4615985	0.4607112	0.4598234	0.4589352	0.4580465	0.4571573	0.4562677	0.4553776	0.4544871
1.10	0.4535961	0.4527047	0.4518128	0.4509205	0.4500277	0.4491344	0.4482417	0.4473466	0.4464520	0.4455570
1.11	0.4446615	0.4437656	0.4428692	0.4419724	0.4410752	0.4401775	0.4392794	0.4383808	0.4374818	0.4365823
1.12	0.4356824	0.4347821	0.4338814	0.4329802	0.4320786	0.4311765	0.4302740	0.4293711	0.4284678	0.4275640
1.13	0.4266598	0.4257552	0.4248501	0.4239447	0.4230388	0.4221324	0.4212257	0.4203185	0.4194109	0.4185029
1.14	0.4175945	0.4166857	0.4157764	0.4148667	0.4139566	0.4130461	0.4121352	0.4112239	0.4103122	0.4094000
1.15	0.4084874	0.4075745	0.4066611	0.4057473	0.4048331	0.4039185	0.4030035	0.4020881	0.4011723	0.4002561
1.16	0.3993395	0.3984225	0.3975051	0.3965873	0.3956691	0.3947505	0.3938316	0.3929122	0.3919924	0.3910722
1.17	0.3901517	0.3892307	0.3883094	0.3873877	0.3864656	0.3855431	0.3846202	0.3836969	0.3827733	0.3818492
1.18	0.3809248	0.3800000	0.3790749	0.3781493	0.3772234	0.3762971	0.3753704	0.3744433	0.3735159	0.3725881
1.19	0.3716599	0.3707313	0.3698024	0.3688731	0.3679434	0.3670134	0.3660830	0.3651522	0.3642211	0.3632896
1.20	0.3623578	0.3614255	0.3604930	0.3595600	0.3586267	0.3576930	0.3567590	0.3558247	0.3548899	0.3539548
1.21	0.3530194	0.3520836	0.3511475	0.3502110	0.3492741	0.3483369	0.3473994	0.3464615	0.3455233	0.3445847
1.22	0.3436457	0.3427065	0.3417669	0.3408269	0.3398866	0.3389460	0.3380050	0.3370637	0.3361220	0.3351800
1.23	0.3342377	0.3332951	0.3323521	0.3314088	0.3304651	0.3295211	0.3285768	0.3276322	0.3266872	0.3257419
1.24	0.3247963	0.3238503	0.3229041	0.3219575	0.3210106	0.3200633	0.3191158	0.3181679	0.3172197	0.3162712
1.25	0.3153224	0.3143732	0.3134238	0.3124740	0.3115239	0.3105735	0.3096228	0.3086718	0.3077205	0.3067688
1.26	0.3058169	0.3048647	0.3039121	0.3029593	0.3020061	0.3010527	0.3000989	0.2991448	0.2981905	0.2972358
1.27	0.2962809	0.2953256	0.2943701	0.2934147	0.2924581	0.2915017	0.2905450	0.2895880	0.2886307	0.2876731
1.28	0.2867152	0.2857571	0.2847986	0.2838399	0.2828809	0.2819216	0.2809620	0.2800021	0.2790420	0.2780816
1.29	0.2771209	0.2761599	0.2751987	0.2742371	0.2732753	0.2723133	0.2713509	0.2703883	0.2694254	0.2684623
1.30	0.2674988	0.2665351	0.2655712	0.2646070	0.2636425	0.2626777	0.2617127	0.2607474	0.2597819	0.2588161
1.31	0.2578500	0.2568837	0.2559171	0.2549503	0.2539832	0.2530159	0.2520483	0.2510805	0.2501124	0.2491440
1.32	0.2481755	0.2472066	0.2462375	0.2452682	0.2442986	0.2433288	0.2423587	0.2413884	0.2404179	0.2394471
1.33	0.2384761	0.2375048	0.2365333	0.2355615	0.2345896	0.2336174	0.2326449	0.2316722	0.2306993	0.2297262
1.34	0.2287528	0.2277792	0.2268054	0.2258313	0.2248571	0.2238825	0.2229078	0.2219329	0.2209577	0.2199823
1.35	0.2190067	0.2180309	0.2170548	0.2160785	0.2151021	0.2141254	0.2131484	0.2121713	0.2111940	0.2102164
1.36	0.2092387	0.2082607	0.2072825	0.2063041	0.2053255	0.2043467	0.2033677	0.2023885	0.2014091	0.2004295
1.37	0.1994497	0.1984697	0.1974895	0.1965091	0.1955285	0.1945477	0.1935667	0.1925855	0.1916042	0.1906226
1.38	0.1896408	0.1886589	0.1876767	0.1866944	0.1857119	0.1847292	0.1837463	0.1827633	0.1817800	0.1807966
1.39	0.1798130	0.1788292	0.1778452	0.1768611	0.1758767	0.1748922	0.1739076	0.1729227	0.1719377	0.1709525

TABLE 2   Cos

T	.000	.001	.002	.003	.004	.005	.006	.007	.008	.009
1.40	0.1699671	0.1689816	0.1679959	0.1670100	0.1660240	0.1650378	0.1640514	0.1630649	0.1620782	0.1610913
1.41	0.1601043	0.1591171	0.1581298	0.1571423	0.1561546	0.1551668	0.1541789	0.1531907	0.1522025	0.1512140
1.42	0.1502255	0.1492367	0.1482479	0.1472588	0.1462697	0.1452804	0.1442909	0.1433013	0.1423115	0.1413216
1.43	0.1403316	0.1393414	0.1383511	0.1373607	0.1363701	0.1353793	0.1343885	0.1333975	0.1324064	0.1314151
1.44	0.1304237	0.1294322	0.1284405	0.1274488	0.1264568	0.1254648	0.1244726	0.1234804	0.1224880	0.1214954
1.45	0.1205028	0.1195100	0.1185171	0.1175241	0.1165310	0.1155377	0.1145444	0.1135509	0.1125573	0.1115636
1.46	0.1105698	0.1095759	0.1085818	0.1075877	0.1065934	0.1055991	0.1046046	0.1036100	0.1026154	0.1016206
1.47	0.1006257	0.0996308	0.0986357	0.0976405	0.0966452	0.0956499	0.0946544	0.0936589	0.0926632	0.0916675
1.48	0.0906716	0.0896757	0.0886797	0.0876836	0.0866874	0.0856911	0.0846947	0.0836983	0.0827018	0.0817051
1.49	0.0807084	0.0797117	0.0787148	0.0777179	0.0767209	0.0757238	0.0747266	0.0737294	0.0727320	0.0717347
1.50	0.0707372	0.0697397	0.0687421	0.0677444	0.0667467	0.0657489	0.0647510	0.0637531	0.0627551	0.0617570
1.51	0.0607589	0.0597607	0.0587625	0.0577642	0.0567658	0.0557674	0.0547689	0.0537704	0.0527718	0.0517732
1.52	0.0507745	0.0497757	0.0487770	0.0477781	0.0467792	0.0457803	0.0447813	0.0437823	0.0427833	0.0417842
1.53	0.0407850	0.0397858	0.0387866	0.0377873	0.0367880	0.0357887	0.0347893	0.0337899	0.0327904	0.0317910
1.54	0.0307915	0.0297919	0.0287923	0.0277927	0.0267931	0.0257935	0.0247938	0.0237941	0.0227944	0.0217946
1.55	0.0207948	0.0197950	0.0187952	0.0177954	0.0167955	0.0157957	0.0147958	0.0137959	0.0127960	0.0117961
1.56	0.0107961	0.0097962	0.0087962	0.0077962	0.0067963	0.0057963	0.0047963	0.0037963	0.0027963	0.0017963
1.57	0.0007963	-0.0002037	-0.0012037	-0.0022037	-0.0032037	-0.0042037	-0.0052036	-0.0062036	-0.0072036	-0.0082036
1.58	-0.0092035	-0.0102035	-0.0112034	-0.0122034	-0.0132033	-0.0142032	-0.0152031	-0.0162030	-0.0172029	-0.0182027
1.59	-0.0192025	-0.0202023	-0.0212021	-0.0222018	-0.0232016	-0.0242013	-0.0252010	-0.0262007	-0.0272003	-0.0281999
1.60	-0.0291995	-0.0301991	-0.0311986	-0.0321981	-0.0331976	-0.0341970	-0.0351964	-0.0361958	-0.0371951	-0.0381944
1.61	-0.0391936	-0.0401928	-0.0411920	-0.0421911	-0.0431902	-0.0441893	-0.0451883	-0.0461872	-0.0471861	-0.0481850
1.62	-0.0491838	-0.0501826	-0.0511813	-0.0521800	-0.0531786	-0.0541771	-0.0551756	-0.0561741	-0.0571725	-0.0581708
1.63	-0.0591691	-0.0601673	-0.0611655	-0.0621636	-0.0631616	-0.0641596	-0.0651575	-0.0661553	-0.0671531	-0.0681508
1.64	-0.0691484	-0.0701460	-0.0711435	-0.0721410	-0.0731383	-0.0741356	-0.0751328	-0.0761299	-0.0771270	-0.0781240
1.65	-0.0791209	-0.0801177	-0.0811145	-0.0821111	-0.0831077	-0.0841042	-0.0851006	-0.0860969	-0.0870932	-0.0880893
1.66	-0.0890854	-0.0900814	-0.0910773	-0.0920731	-0.0930688	-0.0940644	-0.0950599	-0.0960553	-0.0970507	-0.0980459
1.67	-0.0990410	-0.1000361	-0.1010310	-0.1020258	-0.1030206	-0.1040152	-0.1050097	-0.1060041	-0.1069984	-0.1079927
1.68	-0.1089868	-0.1099807	-0.1109746	-0.1119684	-0.1129620	-0.1139556	-0.1149490	-0.1159423	-0.1169355	-0.1179286
1.69	-0.1189216	-0.1199144	-0.1209071	-0.1218997	-0.1228922	-0.1238846	-0.1248768	-0.1258689	-0.1268609	-0.1278528
1.70	-0.1288445	-0.1298361	-0.1308276	-0.1318189	-0.1328101	-0.1338012	-0.1347921	-0.1357829	-0.1367736	-0.1377641
1.71	-0.1387545	-0.1397448	-0.1407349	-0.1417249	-0.1427147	-0.1437044	-0.1446940	-0.1456834	-0.1466726	-0.1476617
1.72	-0.1486507	-0.1496395	-0.1506282	-0.1516167	-0.1526051	-0.1535933	-0.1545814	-0.1555692	-0.1565570	-0.1575446
1.73	-0.1585320	-0.1595193	-0.1605064	-0.1614933	-0.1624801	-0.1634668	-0.1644532	-0.1654395	-0.1664257	-0.1674116
1.74	-0.1683974	-0.1693831	-0.1703685	-0.1713538	-0.1723390	-0.1733239	-0.1743087	-0.1752933	-0.1762777	-0.1772620

TABLE 2   Cos

r	.000	.001	.002	.003	.004	.005	.006	.007	.008	.009
1.75	-0.1782461	-0.1792300	-0.1802137	-0.1811972	-0.1821805	-0.1831637	-0.1841467	-0.1851295	-0.1861122	-0.1870946
1.76	-0.1880768	-0.1890589	-0.1900408	-0.1910225	-0.1920039	-0.1929852	-0.1939663	-0.1949473	-0.1959280	-0.1969085
1.77	-0.1978888	-0.1988689	-0.1998489	-0.2008286	-0.2018081	-0.2027874	-0.2037666	-0.2047455	-0.2057242	-0.2067027
1.78	-0.2076810	-0.2086591	-0.2096370	-0.2106147	-0.2115921	-0.2125694	-0.2135464	-0.2145232	-0.2154998	-0.2164762
1.79	-0.2174524	-0.2184284	-0.2194041	-0.2203797	-0.2213550	-0.2223300	-0.2233049	-0.2242795	-0.2252539	-0.2262281
1.80	-0.2272021	-0.2281758	-0.2291493	-0.2301226	-0.2310957	-0.2320685	-0.2330411	-0.2340134	-0.2349855	-0.2359574
1.81	-0.2369290	-0.2379005	-0.2388716	-0.2398426	-0.2408133	-0.2417837	-0.2427539	-0.2437239	-0.2446936	-0.2456631
1.82	-0.2466323	-0.2476013	-0.2485700	-0.2495385	-0.2505068	-0.2514748	-0.2524425	-0.2534100	-0.2543773	-0.2553442
1.83	-0.2563109	-0.2572774	-0.2582436	-0.2592095	-0.2601752	-0.2611407	-0.2621058	-0.2630707	-0.2640354	-0.2649998
1.84	-0.2659639	-0.2669277	-0.2678913	-0.2688546	-0.2698177	-0.2707804	-0.2717430	-0.2727052	-0.2736671	-0.2746288
1.85	-0.2755902	-0.2765514	-0.2775122	-0.2784728	-0.2794331	-0.2803932	-0.2813529	-0.2823124	-0.2832715	-0.2842304
1.86	-0.2851891	-0.2861474	-0.2871054	-0.2880632	-0.2890207	-0.2899778	-0.2909347	-0.2918913	-0.2928476	-0.2938036
1.87	-0.2947594	-0.2957148	-0.2966699	-0.2976247	-0.2985793	-0.2995335	-0.3004874	-0.3014411	-0.3023944	-0.3033474
1.88	-0.3043002	-0.3052526	-0.3062047	-0.3071565	-0.3081080	-0.3090592	-0.3100101	-0.3109607	-0.3119110	-0.3128609
1.89	-0.3138106	-0.3147599	-0.3157089	-0.3166576	-0.3176060	-0.3185540	-0.3195018	-0.3204492	-0.3213963	-0.3223431
1.90	-0.3232896	-0.3242357	-0.3251815	-0.3261270	-0.3270722	-0.3280170	-0.3289615	-0.3299057	-0.3308495	-0.3317931
1.91	-0.3327362	-0.3336791	-0.3346216	-0.3355638	-0.3365057	-0.3374472	-0.3383883	-0.3393292	-0.3402697	-0.3412098
1.92	-0.3421497	-0.3430891	-0.3440283	-0.3449670	-0.3459055	-0.3468436	-0.3477813	-0.3487187	-0.3496558	-0.3505925
1.93	-0.3515288	-0.3524648	-0.3534005	-0.3543358	-0.3552707	-0.3562053	-0.3571395	-0.3580734	-0.3590069	-0.3599401
1.94	-0.3608729	-0.3618053	-0.3627374	-0.3636691	-0.3646004	-0.3655314	-0.3664620	-0.3673923	-0.3683222	-0.3692517
1.95	-0.3701809	-0.3711096	-0.3720380	-0.3729650	-0.3738937	-0.3748210	-0.3757479	-0.3766744	-0.3776006	-0.3785264
1.96	-0.3794518	-0.3803768	-0.3813014	-0.3822257	-0.3831496	-0.3840731	-0.3849962	-0.3859189	-0.3868412	-0.3877632
1.97	-0.3886848	-0.3896059	-0.3905267	-0.3914471	-0.3923671	-0.3932867	-0.3942059	-0.3951248	-0.3960432	-0.3969612
1.98	-0.3978789	-0.3987961	-0.3997130	-0.4006294	-0.4015454	-0.4024611	-0.4033763	-0.4042911	-0.4052056	-0.4061196
1.99	-0.4070332	-0.4079464	-0.4088592	-0.4097716	-0.4106836	-0.4115952	-0.4125063	-0.4134171	-0.4143274	-0.4152373
2.00	-0.4161468	-0.4170559	-0.4179646	-0.4188729	-0.4197807	-0.4206881	-0.4215951	-0.4225017	-0.4234078	-0.4243135
2.01	-0.4252189	-0.4261237	-0.4270282	-0.4279322	-0.4288358	-0.4297390	-0.4306417	-0.4315440	-0.4324459	-0.4333473
2.02	-0.4342483	-0.4351489	-0.4360491	-0.4369488	-0.4378480	-0.4387469	-0.4396453	-0.4405432	-0.4414407	-0.4423378
2.03	-0.4432344	-0.4441306	-0.4450263	-0.4459216	-0.4468165	-0.4477109	-0.4486048	-0.4494983	-0.4503914	-0.4512840
2.04	-0.4521762	-0.4530679	-0.4539591	-0.4548499	-0.4557402	-0.4566301	-0.4575196	-0.4584085	-0.4592970	-0.4601851
2.05	-0.4610727	-0.4619598	-0.4628465	-0.4637327	-0.4646184	-0.4655037	-0.4663885	-0.4672729	-0.4681568	-0.4690402
2.06	-0.4699231	-0.4708056	-0.4716876	-0.4725691	-0.4734502	-0.4743308	-0.4752109	-0.4760905	-0.4769697	-0.4778483
2.07	-0.4787265	-0.4796043	-0.4804815	-0.4813583	-0.4822346	-0.4831104	-0.4839857	-0.4848605	-0.4857349	-0.4866087
2.08	-0.4874821	-0.4883550	-0.4892274	-0.4900993	-0.4909707	-0.4918417	-0.4927121	-0.4935820	-0.4944515	-0.4953205
2.09	-0.4961889	-0.4970569	-0.4979243	-0.4987913	-0.4996578	-0.5005238	-0.5013892	-0.5022542	-0.5031187	-0.5039826

TABLE 2　Cos

T	.000	.001	.002	.003	.004	.005	.006	.007	.008	.009
2.10	-0.5048461	-0.5057001	-0.5065715	-0.5074335	-0.5082949	-0.5091558	-0.5100162	-0.5108762	-0.5117356	-0.5125944
2.11	-0.5134528	-0.5143107	-0.5151680	-0.5160249	-0.5168812	-0.5177370	-0.5185922	-0.5194470	-0.5203013	-0.5211550
2.12	-0.5220082	-0.5228609	-0.5237130	-0.5245646	-0.5254158	-0.5262663	-0.5271164	-0.5279659	-0.5288149	-0.5296634
2.13	-0.5305113	-0.5313588	-0.5322056	-0.5330520	-0.5338978	-0.5347431	-0.5355878	-0.5364320	-0.5372757	-0.5381188
2.14	-0.5389614	-0.5398035	-0.5406450	-0.5414860	-0.5423265	-0.5431663	-0.5440057	-0.5448445	-0.5456829	-0.5465205
2.15	-0.5473577	-0.5481943	-0.5490304	-0.5498659	-0.5507009	-0.5515353	-0.5523692	-0.5532025	-0.5540353	-0.5548675
2.16	-0.5556991	-0.5565303	-0.5573608	-0.5581908	-0.5590202	-0.5599491	-0.5606774	-0.5615052	-0.5623324	-0.5631590
2.17	-0.5639851	-0.5648106	-0.5656355	-0.5664599	-0.5672837	-0.5681069	-0.5689295	-0.5697517	-0.5705732	-0.5713942
2.18	-0.5722146	-0.5730344	-0.5738536	-0.5746723	-0.5754904	-0.5763079	-0.5771249	-0.5779412	-0.5787570	-0.5795722
2.19	-0.5803869	-0.5812009	-0.5820144	-0.5828273	-0.5836396	-0.5844513	-0.5852624	-0.5860730	-0.5868829	-0.5876923
2.20	-0.5885011	-0.5893093	-0.5901169	-0.5909240	-0.5917304	-0.5925362	-0.5933415	-0.5941461	-0.5949502	-0.5957537
2.21	-0.5965565	-0.5973588	-0.5981605	-0.5989615	-0.5997620	-0.6005619	-0.6013612	-0.6021599	-0.6029579	-0.6037554
2.22	-0.6045523	-0.6053485	-0.6061442	-0.6069392	-0.6077337	-0.6085275	-0.6093208	-0.6101134	-0.6109054	-0.6116968
2.23	-0.6124876	-0.6132777	-0.6140673	-0.6148562	-0.6156446	-0.6164323	-0.6172194	-0.6180059	-0.6187917	-0.6195770
2.24	-0.6203616	-0.6211456	-0.6219290	-0.6227118	-0.6234939	-0.6242754	-0.6250563	-0.6258366	-0.6266162	-0.6273952
2.25	-0.6281736	-0.6289514	-0.6297285	-0.6305050	-0.6312809	-0.6320561	-0.6328307	-0.6336047	-0.6343780	-0.6351507
2.26	-0.6359228	-0.6366943	-0.6374650	-0.6382352	-0.6390047	-0.6397736	-0.6405419	-0.6413095	-0.6420764	-0.6428427
2.27	-0.6436084	-0.6443735	-0.6451378	-0.6459016	-0.6466647	-0.6474271	-0.6481889	-0.6489501	-0.6497106	-0.6504705
2.28	-0.6512297	-0.6519882	-0.6527461	-0.6535034	-0.6542600	-0.6550159	-0.6557712	-0.6565258	-0.6572798	-0.6580331
2.29	-0.6587858	-0.6595378	-0.6602891	-0.6610398	-0.6617898	-0.6625392	-0.6632879	-0.6640359	-0.6647833	-0.6655300
2.30	-0.6662760	-0.6670214	-0.6677661	-0.6685101	-0.6692535	-0.6699962	-0.6707382	-0.6714796	-0.6722203	-0.6729603
2.31	-0.6736996	-0.6744383	-0.6751763	-0.6759136	-0.6766503	-0.6773862	-0.6781215	-0.6788561	-0.6795901	-0.6803233
2.32	-0.6810559	-0.6817878	-0.6825190	-0.6832495	-0.6839794	-0.6847085	-0.6854370	-0.6861648	-0.6868919	-0.6876183
2.33	-0.6883440	-0.6890691	-0.6897934	-0.6905171	-0.6912400	-0.6919623	-0.6926839	-0.6934048	-0.6941250	-0.6948445
2.34	-0.6955633	-0.6962814	-0.6969989	-0.6977156	-0.6984316	-0.6991469	-0.6998616	-0.7005755	-0.7012887	-0.7020013
2.35	-0.7027131	-0.7034242	-0.7041346	-0.7048443	-0.7055533	-0.7062616	-0.7069692	-0.7076761	-0.7083823	-0.7090878
2.36	-0.7097926	-0.7104966	-0.7112000	-0.7119026	-0.7126045	-0.7133057	-0.7140062	-0.7147060	-0.7154051	-0.7161034
2.37	-0.7168011	-0.7174980	-0.7181942	-0.7188897	-0.7195844	-0.7202785	-0.7209718	-0.7216644	-0.7223563	-0.7230474
2.38	-0.7237379	-0.7244276	-0.7251166	-0.7258048	-0.7264924	-0.7271792	-0.7278653	-0.7285506	-0.7292353	-0.7299192
2.39	-0.7306023	-0.7312848	-0.7319665	-0.7326474	-0.7333277	-0.7340072	-0.7346860	-0.7353640	-0.7360413	-0.7367179
2.40	-0.7373937	-0.7380688	-0.7387432	-0.7394168	-0.7400897	-0.7407618	-0.7414332	-0.7421039	-0.7427738	-0.7434429
2.41	-0.7441114	-0.7447790	-0.7454460	-0.7461122	-0.7467776	-0.7474423	-0.7481063	-0.7487695	-0.7494319	-0.7500936
2.42	-0.7507546	-0.7514148	-0.7520743	-0.7527330	-0.7533909	-0.7540481	-0.7547046	-0.7553602	-0.7560152	-0.7566693
2.43	-0.7573228	-0.7579754	-0.7586273	-0.7592785	-0.7599289	-0.7605785	-0.7612274	-0.7618755	-0.7625228	-0.7631694
2.44	-0.7638152	-0.7644603	-0.7651045	-0.7657481	-0.7663908	-0.7670328	-0.7676740	-0.7683145	-0.7689542	-0.7695931

TABLE 2   Cos

τ	.000	.001	.002	.003	.004	.005	.006	.007	.008	.009
2.45	-0.7702313	-0.7708686	-0.7715052	-0.7721411	-0.7727761	-0.7734104	-0.7740440	-0.7746767	-0.7753087	-0.7759399
2.46	-0.7765703	-0.7771999	-0.7778288	-0.7784569	-0.7790842	-0.7797107	-0.7803365	-0.7809614	-0.7815856	-0.7822090
2.47	-0.7828317	-0.7834535	-0.7840746	-0.7846948	-0.7853143	-0.7859330	-0.7865509	-0.7871681	-0.7877844	-0.7884000
2.48	-0.7890147	-0.7896287	-0.7902419	-0.7908543	-0.7914659	-0.7920767	-0.7926868	-0.7932960	-0.7939044	-0.7945121
2.49	-0.7951189	-0.7957250	-0.7963303	-0.7969347	-0.7975384	-0.7981413	-0.7987433	-0.7993446	-0.7999451	-0.8005447
2.50	-0.8011436	-0.8017417	-0.8023390	-0.8029354	-0.8035311	-0.8041259	-0.8047200	-0.8053133	-0.8059057	-0.8064973
2.51	-0.8070882	-0.8076782	-0.8082674	-0.8088558	-0.8094434	-0.8100302	-0.8106162	-0.8112014	-0.8117858	-0.8123693
2.52	-0.8129520	-0.8135340	-0.8141151	-0.8146954	-0.8152748	-0.8158535	-0.8164314	-0.8170084	-0.8175846	-0.8181600
2.53	-0.8187346	-0.8193084	-0.8198813	-0.8204534	-0.8210247	-0.8215952	-0.8221649	-0.8227337	-0.8233017	-0.8238689
2.54	-0.8244353	-0.8250008	-0.8255656	-0.8261294	-0.8266925	-0.8272548	-0.8278162	-0.8283768	-0.8289365	-0.8294954
2.55	-0.8300535	-0.8306108	-0.8311672	-0.8317228	-0.8322776	-0.8328316	-0.8333847	-0.8339370	-0.8344884	-0.8350390
2.56	-0.8355888	-0.8361377	-0.8366858	-0.8372331	-0.8377795	-0.8383251	-0.8388699	-0.8394138	-0.8399568	-0.8404991
2.57	-0.8410405	-0.8415810	-0.8421207	-0.8426596	-0.8431976	-0.8437348	-0.8442711	-0.8448066	-0.8453413	-0.8458751
2.58	-0.8464080	-0.8469402	-0.8474714	-0.8480018	-0.8485314	-0.8490601	-0.8495880	-0.8501150	-0.8506412	-0.8511665
2.59	-0.8516910	-0.8522146	-0.8527374	-0.8532593	-0.8537803	-0.8543005	-0.8548199	-0.8553384	-0.8558560	-0.8563728
2.60	-0.8568888	-0.8574038	-0.8579180	-0.8584314	-0.8589439	-0.8594555	-0.8599663	-0.8604762	-0.8609853	-0.8614935
2.61	-0.8620008	-0.8625073	-0.8630129	-0.8635177	-0.8640216	-0.8645246	-0.8650267	-0.8655280	-0.8660285	-0.8665280
2.62	-0.8670267	-0.8675245	-0.8680215	-0.8685176	-0.8690128	-0.8695072	-0.8700007	-0.8704933	-0.8709850	-0.8714759
2.63	-0.8719659	-0.8724550	-0.8729433	-0.8734307	-0.8739172	-0.8744028	-0.8748876	-0.8753715	-0.8758545	-0.8763366
2.64	-0.8768179	-0.8772983	-0.8777778	-0.8782564	-0.8787342	-0.8792110	-0.8796870	-0.8801621	-0.8806364	-0.8811097
2.65	-0.8815822	-0.8820538	-0.8825245	-0.8829943	-0.8834633	-0.8839313	-0.8843985	-0.8848648	-0.8853302	-0.8857947
2.66	-0.8862583	-0.8867211	-0.8871830	-0.8876439	-0.8881040	-0.8885632	-0.8890215	-0.8894789	-0.8899355	-0.8903911
2.67	-0.8908459	-0.8912997	-0.8917527	-0.8922048	-0.8926560	-0.8931063	-0.8935556	-0.8940042	-0.8944518	-0.8948985
2.68	-0.8953443	-0.8957892	-0.8962333	-0.8966764	-0.8971186	-0.8975600	-0.8980004	-0.8984400	-0.8988786	-0.8993164
2.69	-0.8997532	-0.9001892	-0.9006242	-0.9010584	-0.9014916	-0.9019240	-0.9023554	-0.9027859	-0.9032156	-0.9036443
2.70	-0.9040721	-0.9044991	-0.9049251	-0.9053502	-0.9057744	-0.9061977	-0.9066201	-0.9070416	-0.9074622	-0.9078819
2.71	-0.9083007	-0.9087185	-0.9091355	-0.9095515	-0.9099667	-0.9103809	-0.9107942	-0.9112066	-0.9116181	-0.9120287
2.72	-0.9124384	-0.9128471	-0.9132550	-0.9136619	-0.9140679	-0.9144730	-0.9148772	-0.9152805	-0.9156828	-0.9160843
2.73	-0.9164848	-0.9168844	-0.9172831	-0.9176809	-0.9180778	-0.9184737	-0.9188687	-0.9192628	-0.9196560	-0.9200483
2.74	-0.9204396	-0.9208300	-0.9212195	-0.9216081	-0.9219958	-0.9223825	-0.9227683	-0.9231532	-0.9235372	-0.9239203
2.75	-0.9243024	-0.9246836	-0.9250639	-0.9254437	-0.9258216	-0.9261991	-0.9265757	-0.9269513	-0.9273261	-0.9276998
2.76	-0.9280727	-0.9284446	-0.9288157	-0.9291857	-0.9295549	-0.9299231	-0.9302904	-0.9306567	-0.9310222	-0.9313867
2.77	-0.9317502	-0.9321129	-0.9324746	-0.9328353	-0.9331952	-0.9335541	-0.9339120	-0.9342691	-0.9346252	-0.9349804
2.78	-0.9353346	-0.9356879	-0.9360402	-0.9363917	-0.9367422	-0.9370917	-0.9374403	-0.9377880	-0.9381347	-0.9384805
2.79	-0.9388254	-0.9391693	-0.9395123	-0.9398544	-0.9401955	-0.9405356	-0.9408749	-0.9412131	-0.9415505	-0.9418869

TABLE 2   Cos

T	.000	.001	.002	.003	.004	.005	.006	.007	.008	.009
2.80	-0.9422223	-0.9425569	-0.9428904	-0.9432231	-0.9435543	-0.9438855	-0.9442153	-0.9445442	-0.9448721	-0.9451990
2.81	-0.9455251	-0.9458501	-0.9461743	-0.9464974	-0.9468197	-0.9471410	-0.9474613	-0.9477807	-0.9480992	-0.9484167
2.82	-0.9487332	-0.9490488	-0.9493635	-0.9496772	-0.9499899	-0.9503017	-0.9506126	-0.9509225	-0.9512315	-0.9515395
2.83	-0.9518465	-0.9521526	-0.9524578	-0.9527619	-0.9530652	-0.9533675	-0.9536688	-0.9539692	-0.9542586	-0.9545671
2.84	-0.9548646	-0.9551612	-0.9554568	-0.9557514	-0.9560451	-0.9563379	-0.9566297	-0.9569205	-0.9572104	-0.9574993
2.85	-0.9577872	-0.9580742	-0.9583603	-0.9586454	-0.9589295	-0.9592126	-0.9594949	-0.9597761	-0.9600564	-0.9603357
2.86	-0.9606141	-0.9608915	-0.9611679	-0.9614434	-0.9617179	-0.9619915	-0.9622641	-0.9625357	-0.9628064	-0.9630761
2.87	-0.9633449	-0.9636126	-0.9638795	-0.9641453	-0.9644102	-0.9646741	-0.9649371	-0.9651991	-0.9654601	-0.9657202
2.88	-0.9659793	-0.9662374	-0.9664946	-0.9667508	-0.9670061	-0.9672603	-0.9675136	-0.9677660	-0.9680173	-0.9682677
2.89	-0.9685172	-0.9687656	-0.9690131	-0.9692596	-0.9695057	-0.9697498	-0.9699934	-0.9702360	-0.9704777	-0.9707184
2.90	-0.9709582	-0.9711969	-0.9714347	-0.9716715	-0.9719074	-0.9721423	-0.9723762	-0.9726091	-0.9728411	-0.9730721
2.91	-0.9733021	-0.9735311	-0.9737592	-0.9739863	-0.9742124	-0.9744375	-0.9746617	-0.9748849	-0.9751071	-0.9753284
2.92	-0.9755486	-0.9757679	-0.9759863	-0.9762036	-0.9764200	-0.9766354	-0.9768498	-0.9770632	-0.9772757	-0.9774872
2.93	-0.9776977	-0.9779072	-0.9781157	-0.9783233	-0.9785299	-0.9787355	-0.9789402	-0.9791438	-0.9793465	-0.9795482
2.94	-0.9797489	-0.9799487	-0.9801474	-0.9803452	-0.9805420	-0.9807378	-0.9809327	-0.9811265	-0.9813194	-0.9815113
2.95	-0.9817022	-0.9818921	-0.9820811	-0.9822691	-0.9824560	-0.9826420	-0.9828271	-0.9830111	-0.9831942	-0.9833762
2.96	-0.9835573	-0.9837374	-0.9839165	-0.9840947	-0.9842718	-0.9844480	-0.9846232	-0.9847974	-0.9849706	-0.9851428
2.97	-0.9853141	-0.9854843	-0.9856536	-0.9858219	-0.9859892	-0.9861555	-0.9863208	-0.9864852	-0.9866485	-0.9868109
2.98	-0.9869723	-0.9871327	-0.9872921	-0.9874505	-0.9876080	-0.9877644	-0.9879199	-0.9880743	-0.9882278	-0.9883803
2.99	-0.9885318	-0.9886823	-0.9888319	-0.9889804	-0.9891280	-0.9892745	-0.9894201	-0.9895647	-0.9897083	-0.9898509
3.00	-0.9899925	-0.9901331	-0.9902728	-0.9904114	-0.9905491	-0.9906857	-0.9908214	-0.9909561	-0.9910898	-0.9912225
3.01	-0.9913542	-0.9914849	-0.9916146	-0.9917434	-0.9918711	-0.9919978	-0.9921236	-0.9922484	-0.9923721	-0.9924949
3.02	-0.9926167	-0.9927375	-0.9928573	-0.9929761	-0.9930939	-0.9932108	-0.9933266	-0.9934414	-0.9935553	-0.9936681
3.03	-0.9937800	-0.9938909	-0.9940007	-0.9941096	-0.9942175	-0.9943244	-0.9944303	-0.9945352	-0.9946391	-0.9947420
3.04	-0.9948439	-0.9949448	-0.9950447	-0.9951437	-0.9952416	-0.9953386	-0.9954345	-0.9955294	-0.9956234	-0.9957164
3.05	-0.9958083	-0.9958993	-0.9959893	-0.9960782	-0.9961662	-0.9962532	-0.9963392	-0.9964242	-0.9965082	-0.9965912
3.06	-0.9966732	-0.9967542	-0.9968342	-0.9969132	-0.9969912	-0.9970682	-0.9971442	-0.9972193	-0.9972933	-0.9973663
3.07	-0.9974383	-0.9975094	-0.9975794	-0.9976484	-0.9977165	-0.9977835	-0.9978496	-0.9979146	-0.9979787	-0.9980417
3.08	-0.9981038	-0.9981648	-0.9982249	-0.9982839	-0.9983420	-0.9983991	-0.9984551	-0.9985102	-0.9985643	-0.9986173
3.09	-0.9986694	-0.9987205	-0.9987705	-0.9988196	-0.9988677	-0.9989148	-0.9989608	-0.9990059	-0.9990500	-0.9990931
3.10	-0.9991352	-0.9991762	-0.9992163	-0.9992554	-0.9992935	-0.9993306	-0.9993666	-0.9994017	-0.9994358	-0.9994689
3.11	-0.9995010	-0.9995321	-0.9995622	-0.9995913	-0.9996193	-0.9996464	-0.9996725	-0.9996976	-0.9997217	-0.9997448
3.12	-0.9997669	-0.9997880	-0.9998081	-0.9998272	-0.9998453	-0.9998623	-0.9998784	-0.9998935	-0.9999076	-0.9999207
3.13	-0.9999328	-0.9999439	-0.9999540	-0.9999631	-0.9999712	-0.9999783	-0.9999844	-0.9999895	-0.9999935	-0.9999966
3.14	-0.9999987	-0.9999998	-0.9999999	-0.9999990	-0.9999971	-0.9999942	-0.9999903	-0.9999854	-0.9999795	-0.9999726

TABLE 2   Cos

T	.000	.001	.002	.003	.004	.005	.006	.007	.008	.009
3.15	-0.9999647	-0.9999558	-0.9999458	-0.9999349	-0.9999230	-0.9999101	-0.9998962	-0.9998813	-0.9998654	-0.9998485
3.16	-0.9998306	-0.9998117	-0.9997918	-0.9997709	-0.9997490	-0.9997261	-0.9997022	-0.9996773	-0.9996513	-0.9996244
3.17	-0.9995965	-0.9995676	-0.9995377	-0.9995068	-0.9994749	-0.9994420	-0.9994081	-0.9993732	-0.9993373	-0.9993004
3.18	-0.9992625	-0.9992236	-0.9991837	-0.9991428	-0.9991009	-0.9990580	-0.9990142	-0.9989693	-0.9989234	-0.9988765
3.19	-0.9988286	-0.9987797	-0.9987298	-0.9986789	-0.9986270	-0.9985742	-0.9985203	-0.9984654	-0.9984095	-0.9983527
3.20	-0.9982948	-0.9982359	-0.9981760	-0.9981152	-0.9980533	-0.9979904	-0.9979266	-0.9978617	-0.9977958	-0.9977290
3.21	-0.9976611	-0.9975923	-0.9975224	-0.9974516	-0.9973797	-0.9973069	-0.9972331	-0.9971582	-0.9970824	-0.9970055
3.22	-0.9969277	-0.9968489	-0.9967691	-0.9966883	-0.9966064	-0.9965236	-0.9964398	-0.9963550	-0.9962692	-0.9961824
3.23	-0.9960946	-0.9960058	-0.9959160	-0.9958253	-0.9957335	-0.9956407	-0.9955469	-0.9954522	-0.9953564	-0.9952597
3.24	-0.9951619	-0.9950632	-0.9949634	-0.9948627	-0.9947609	-0.9946582	-0.9945545	-0.9944498	-0.9943441	-0.9942374
3.25	-0.9941297	-0.9940210	-0.9939113	-0.9938006	-0.9936889	-0.9935763	-0.9934626	-0.9933480	-0.9932323	-0.9931157
3.26	-0.9929980	-0.9928794	-0.9927598	-0.9926392	-0.9925176	-0.9923950	-0.9922714	-0.9921468	-0.9920212	-0.9918947
3.27	-0.9917671	-0.9916385	-0.9915090	-0.9913785	-0.9912469	-0.9911144	-0.9909809	-0.9908464	-0.9907109	-0.9905745
3.28	-0.9904370	-0.9902985	-0.9901591	-0.9900186	-0.9898772	-0.9897348	-0.9895914	-0.9894470	-0.9893016	-0.9891552
3.29	-0.9890078	-0.9888595	-0.9887101	-0.9885598	-0.9884085	-0.9882562	-0.9881029	-0.9879486	-0.9877933	-0.9876370
3.30	-0.9874798	-0.9873215	-0.9871623	-0.9870021	-0.9868409	-0.9866787	-0.9865155	-0.9863514	-0.9861862	-0.9860201
3.31	-0.9858530	-0.9856849	-0.9855158	-0.9853457	-0.9851746	-0.9850026	-0.9848295	-0.9846555	-0.9844805	-0.9843045
3.32	-0.9841276	-0.9839496	-0.9837707	-0.9835908	-0.9834099	-0.9832280	-0.9830451	-0.9828612	-0.9826764	-0.9824906
3.33	-0.9823038	-0.9821160	-0.9819272	-0.9817375	-0.9815467	-0.9813550	-0.9811623	-0.9809687	-0.9807740	-0.9805784
3.34	-0.9803817	-0.9801841	-0.9799856	-0.9797860	-0.9795855	-0.9793840	-0.9791815	-0.9789780	-0.9787735	-0.9785681
3.35	-0.9783617	-0.9781543	-0.9779459	-0.9777366	-0.9775262	-0.9773149	-0.9771027	-0.9768894	-0.9766752	-0.9764600
3.36	-0.9762438	-0.9760266	-0.9758085	-0.9755894	-0.9753693	-0.9751482	-0.9749262	-0.9747031	-0.9744792	-0.9742542
3.37	-0.9740282	-0.9738013	-0.9735734	-0.9733446	-0.9731148	-0.9728840	-0.9726522	-0.9724194	-0.9721857	-0.9719510
3.38	-0.9717153	-0.9714787	-0.9712411	-0.9710025	-0.9707629	-0.9705224	-0.9702809	-0.9700384	-0.9697950	-0.9695506
3.39	-0.9693052	-0.9690589	-0.9688116	-0.9685633	-0.9683140	-0.9680638	-0.9678126	-0.9675605	-0.9673073	-0.9670533
3.40	-0.9667982	-0.9665422	-0.9662852	-0.9660272	-0.9657683	-0.9655084	-0.9652476	-0.9649857	-0.9647229	-0.9644592
3.41	-0.9641945	-0.9639288	-0.9636622	-0.9633946	-0.9631260	-0.9628565	-0.9625860	-0.9623145	-0.9620421	-0.9617687
3.42	-0.9614944	-0.9612191	-0.9609428	-0.9606656	-0.9603874	-0.9601082	-0.9598281	-0.9595470	-0.9592650	-0.9589820
3.43	-0.9586981	-0.9584132	-0.9581273	-0.9578405	-0.9575527	-0.9572640	-0.9569743	-0.9566836	-0.9563920	-0.9560995
3.44	-0.9558059	-0.9555115	-0.9552160	-0.9549196	-0.9546223	-0.9543240	-0.9540248	-0.9537246	-0.9534234	-0.9531213
3.45	-0.9528182	-0.9525142	-0.9522092	-0.9519033	-0.9515964	-0.9512886	-0.9509798	-0.9506701	-0.9503594	-0.9500478
3.46	-0.9497352	-0.9494217	-0.9491072	-0.9487918	-0.9484754	-0.9481581	-0.9478398	-0.9475206	-0.9472004	-0.9468793
3.47	-0.9465572	-0.9462342	-0.9459103	-0.9455854	-0.9452595	-0.9449327	-0.9446050	-0.9442763	-0.9439467	-0.9436161
3.48	-0.9432846	-0.9429521	-0.9426187	-0.9422844	-0.9419491	-0.9416129	-0.9412757	-0.9409376	-0.9405986	-0.9402586
3.49	-0.9399176	-0.9395758	-0.9392330	-0.9388892	-0.9385445	-0.9381989	-0.9378523	-0.9375048	-0.9371564	-0.9368070

TABLE 2 Cos

T	.000	.001	.002	.003	.004	.005	.006	.007	.008	.009
3.50	-0.9364567	-0.9361054	-0.9357532	-0.9354001	-0.9350461	-0.9346911	-0.9343351	-0.9339783	-0.9336205	-0.9332618
3.51	-0.9329021	-0.9325415	-0.9321800	-0.9318175	-0.9314541	-0.9310898	-0.9307245	-0.9303583	-0.9299912	-0.9296232
3.52	-0.9292542	-0.9288843	-0.9285135	-0.9281417	-0.9277690	-0.9273954	-0.9270208	-0.9266454	-0.9262690	-0.9258916
3.53	-0.9255134	-0.9251342	-0.9247541	-0.9243731	-0.9239911	-0.9236083	-0.9232245	-0.9228397	-0.9224541	-0.9220675
3.54	-0.9216800	-0.9212916	-0.9209023	-0.9205120	-0.9201209	-0.9197288	-0.9193358	-0.9189419	-0.9185470	-0.9181512
3.55	-0.9177545	-0.9173569	-0.9169584	-0.9165589	-0.9161586	-0.9157573	-0.9153551	-0.9149520	-0.9145480	-0.9141431
3.56	-0.9137372	-0.9133304	-0.9129228	-0.9125142	-0.9121047	-0.9116943	-0.9112829	-0.9108707	-0.9104576	-0.9100435
3.57	-0.9096285	-0.9092127	-0.9087959	-0.9083782	-0.9079596	-0.9075401	-0.9071196	-0.9066983	-0.9062761	-0.9058529
3.58	-0.9054289	-0.9050039	-0.9045781	-0.9041513	-0.9037237	-0.9032951	-0.9028656	-0.9024352	-0.9020040	-0.9015718
3.59	-0.9011387	-0.9007047	-0.9002698	-0.8998341	-0.8993974	-0.8989598	-0.8985213	-0.8980819	-0.8976417	-0.8972005
3.60	-0.8967584	-0.8963154	-0.8958716	-0.8954268	-0.8949812	-0.8945346	-0.8940872	-0.8936398	-0.8931896	-0.8927395
3.61	-0.8922884	-0.8918365	-0.8913837	-0.8909300	-0.8904755	-0.8900200	-0.8895636	-0.8891064	-0.8886482	-0.8881892
3.62	-0.8877293	-0.8872684	-0.8868067	-0.8863442	-0.8858807	-0.8854163	-0.8849511	-0.8844850	-0.8840180	-0.8835501
3.63	-0.8830813	-0.8826116	-0.8821411	-0.8816697	-0.8811973	-0.8807242	-0.8802501	-0.8797751	-0.8792993	-0.8788226
3.64	-0.8783450	-0.8778665	-0.8773872	-0.8769070	-0.8764259	-0.8759439	-0.8754611	-0.8749773	-0.8744927	-0.8740072
3.65	-0.8735209	-0.8730337	-0.8725456	-0.8720566	-0.8715668	-0.8710761	-0.8705845	-0.8700920	-0.8695987	-0.8691045
3.66	-0.8686094	-0.8681135	-0.8676167	-0.8671190	-0.8666205	-0.8661211	-0.8656208	-0.8651197	-0.8646177	-0.8641148
3.67	-0.8636111	-0.8631065	-0.8626011	-0.8620948	-0.8615875	-0.8610795	-0.8605706	-0.8600609	-0.8595503	-0.8590388
3.68	-0.8585264	-0.8580132	-0.8574992	-0.8569843	-0.8564685	-0.8559519	-0.8554344	-0.8549160	-0.8543969	-0.8538768
3.69	-0.8533559	-0.8528341	-0.8523115	-0.8517881	-0.8512638	-0.8507386	-0.8502126	-0.8496857	-0.8491580	-0.8486294
3.70	-0.8481000	-0.8475698	-0.8470387	-0.8465067	-0.8459739	-0.8454403	-0.8449058	-0.8443704	-0.8438342	-0.8432972
3.71	-0.8427594	-0.8422206	-0.8416811	-0.8411407	-0.8405995	-0.8400574	-0.8395145	-0.8389707	-0.8384261	-0.8378807
3.72	-0.8373344	-0.8367873	-0.8362393	-0.8356906	-0.8351409	-0.8345905	-0.8340392	-0.8334871	-0.8329341	-0.8323803
3.73	-0.8318257	-0.8312703	-0.8307140	-0.8301569	-0.8295989	-0.8290401	-0.8284805	-0.8279201	-0.8273588	-0.8267968
3.74	-0.8262338	-0.8256701	-0.8251055	-0.8245402	-0.8239739	-0.8234069	-0.8228390	-0.8222703	-0.8217008	-0.8211305
3.75	-0.8205594	-0.8199874	-0.8194146	-0.8188410	-0.8182666	-0.8176913	-0.8171152	-0.8165384	-0.8159607	-0.8153821
3.76	-0.8148028	-0.8142227	-0.8136417	-0.8130599	-0.8124773	-0.8118939	-0.8113097	-0.8107247	-0.8101389	-0.8095522
3.77	-0.8089648	-0.8083765	-0.8077875	-0.8071976	-0.8066069	-0.8060154	-0.8054231	-0.8048300	-0.8042361	-0.8036414
3.78	-0.8030459	-0.8024495	-0.8018524	-0.8012545	-0.8006558	-0.8000563	-0.7994559	-0.7988548	-0.7982529	-0.7976502
3.79	-0.7970466	-0.7964423	-0.7958372	-0.7952313	-0.7946246	-0.7940171	-0.7934088	-0.7927997	-0.7921898	-0.7915792
3.80	-0.7909677	-0.7903555	-0.7897424	-0.7891286	-0.7885140	-0.7878985	-0.7872823	-0.7866654	-0.7860476	-0.7854290
3.81	-0.7848097	-0.7841896	-0.7835686	-0.7829469	-0.7823245	-0.7817012	-0.7810772	-0.7804523	-0.7798267	-0.7792003
3.82	-0.7785732	-0.7779452	-0.7773165	-0.7766870	-0.7760567	-0.7754257	-0.7747939	-0.7741613	-0.7735279	-0.7728937
3.83	-0.7722588	-0.7716231	-0.7709867	-0.7703494	-0.7697114	-0.7690726	-0.7684331	-0.7677928	-0.7671517	-0.7665098
3.84	-0.7658672	-0.7652239	-0.7645797	-0.7639348	-0.7632891	-0.7626427	-0.7619955	-0.7613475	-0.7606988	-0.7600493

TABLE 2   Cos

T	.000	.001	.002	.003	.004	.005	.006	.007	.008	.009
3.85	−0.7593991	−0.7587481	−0.7580963	−0.7574438	−0.7567905	−0.7561365	−0.7554817	−0.7548261	−0.7541598	−0.7535128
3.86	−0.7528549	−0.7521964	−0.7515371	−0.7508770	−0.7502162	−0.7495546	−0.7488923	−0.7482292	−0.7475654	−0.7469009
3.87	−0.7462355	−0.7455695	−0.7449027	−0.7442351	−0.7435669	−0.7428978	−0.7422280	−0.7415575	−0.7408863	−0.7402143
3.88	−0.7395415	−0.7388680	−0.7381938	−0.7375189	−0.7368432	−0.7361667	−0.7354896	−0.7348117	−0.7341330	−0.7334537
3.89	−0.7327736	−0.7320927	−0.7314111	−0.7307288	−0.7300458	−0.7293620	−0.7286776	−0.7279923	−0.7273064	−0.7266197
3.90	−0.7259323	−0.7252442	−0.7245553	−0.7238657	−0.7231754	−0.7224844	−0.7217927	−0.7211002	−0.7204070	−0.7197131
3.91	−0.7190185	−0.7183231	−0.7176270	−0.7169303	−0.7162328	−0.7155345	−0.7148356	−0.7141359	−0.7134356	−0.7127345
3.92	−0.7120327	−0.7113302	−0.7106270	−0.7099231	−0.7092184	−0.7085131	−0.7078070	−0.7071003	−0.7063928	−0.7056846
3.93	−0.7049758	−0.7042662	−0.7035559	−0.7028449	−0.7021332	−0.7014208	−0.7007077	−0.6999939	−0.6992794	−0.6985642
3.94	−0.6978483	−0.6971317	−0.6964144	−0.6956965	−0.6949778	−0.6942584	−0.6935383	−0.6928175	−0.6920961	−0.6913739
3.95	−0.6906511	−0.6899276	−0.6892033	−0.6884784	−0.6877528	−0.6870265	−0.6862996	−0.6855719	−0.6848436	−0.6841145
3.96	−0.6833848	−0.6826544	−0.6819233	−0.6811916	−0.6804591	−0.6797260	−0.6789922	−0.6782577	−0.6775225	−0.6767867
3.97	−0.6760502	−0.6753130	−0.6745751	−0.6738366	−0.6730973	−0.6723575	−0.6716169	−0.6708757	−0.6701339	−0.6693917
3.98	−0.6686479	−0.6679040	−0.6671594	−0.6664142	−0.6656683	−0.6649217	−0.6641745	−0.6634265	−0.6626780	−0.6619287
3.99	−0.6611788	−0.6604283	−0.6596771	−0.6589257	−0.6581726	−0.6574194	−0.6566656	−0.6559111	−0.6551559	−0.6544001
4.00	−0.6536436	−0.6528865	−0.6521287	−0.6513703	−0.6506112	−0.6498515	−0.6490911	−0.6483300	−0.6475683	−0.6468060
4.01	−0.6460430	−0.6452794	−0.6445151	−0.6437502	−0.6429847	−0.6422185	−0.6414516	−0.6406841	−0.6399160	−0.6391473
4.02	−0.6383779	−0.6376078	−0.6368371	−0.6360658	−0.6352939	−0.6345213	−0.6337481	−0.6329742	−0.6321997	−0.6314246
4.03	−0.6306488	−0.6298725	−0.6290954	−0.6283178	−0.6275395	−0.6267606	−0.6259811	−0.6252009	−0.6244202	−0.6236388
4.04	−0.6228567	−0.6220741	−0.6212908	−0.6205069	−0.6197224	−0.6189373	−0.6181515	−0.6173652	−0.6165782	−0.6157906
4.05	−0.6150024	−0.6142135	−0.6134241	−0.6126340	−0.6118434	−0.6110521	−0.6102602	−0.6094677	−0.6086746	−0.6078808
4.06	−0.6070865	−0.6062916	−0.6054960	−0.6046999	−0.6039031	−0.6031058	−0.6023078	−0.6015092	−0.6007101	−0.5999103
4.07	−0.5991099	−0.5983090	−0.5975074	−0.5967052	−0.5959025	−0.5950991	−0.5942952	−0.5934906	−0.5926855	−0.5918798
4.08	−0.5910734	−0.5902665	−0.5894590	−0.5886509	−0.5878422	−0.5870330	−0.5862231	−0.5854127	−0.5846016	−0.5837900
4.09	−0.5829778	−0.5821651	−0.5813517	−0.5805378	−0.5797233	−0.5789081	−0.5780924	−0.5772762	−0.5764594	−0.5756419
4.10	−0.5748239	−0.5740054	−0.5731862	−0.5723665	−0.5715462	−0.5707254	−0.5699040	−0.5690820	−0.5682594	−0.5674363
4.11	−0.5666126	−0.5657883	−0.5649635	−0.5641381	−0.5633121	−0.5624856	−0.5616585	−0.5608308	−0.5600026	−0.5591739
4.12	−0.5583445	−0.5575146	−0.5566842	−0.5558532	−0.5550216	−0.5541895	−0.5533569	−0.5525236	−0.5516899	−0.5508555
4.13	−0.5500207	−0.5491852	−0.5483493	−0.5475127	−0.5466757	−0.5458381	−0.5449999	−0.5441612	−0.5433219	−0.5424821
4.14	−0.5416418	−0.5408009	−0.5399595	−0.5391175	−0.5382750	−0.5374320	−0.5365884	−0.5357443	−0.5348997	−0.5340545
4.15	−0.5332088	−0.5323625	−0.5315157	−0.5306684	−0.5298205	−0.5289722	−0.5281233	−0.5272739	−0.5264239	−0.5255734
4.16	−0.5247224	−0.5238709	−0.5230188	−0.5221662	−0.5213131	−0.5204595	−0.5196053	−0.5187507	−0.5178955	−0.5170398
4.17	−0.5161836	−0.5153268	−0.5144696	−0.5136118	−0.5127535	−0.5118947	−0.5110354	−0.5101756	−0.5093153	−0.5084545
4.18	−0.5075931	−0.5067313	−0.5058689	−0.5050061	−0.5041427	−0.5032788	−0.5024144	−0.5015496	−0.5006842	−0.4998183
4.19	−0.4989519	−0.4980850	−0.4972177	−0.4963498	−0.4954814	−0.4946126	−0.4937432	−0.4928733	−0.4920030	−0.4911322

TABLE 2   Cos

T	.000	.001	.002	.003	.004	.005	.006	.007	.008	.009
4.20	-0.4902608	-0.4893890	-0.4885167	-0.4876439	-0.4867705	-0.4858968	-0.4850226	-0.4841478	-0.4832726	-0.4823969
4.21	-0.4815207	-0.4806440	-0.4797669	-0.4788892	-0.4780111	-0.4771325	-0.4762535	-0.4753739	-0.4744939	-0.4736134
4.22	-0.4727324	-0.4718510	-0.4709691	-0.4700867	-0.4692038	-0.4683205	-0.4674367	-0.4665524	-0.4656677	-0.4647825
4.23	-0.4638969	-0.4630107	-0.4621242	-0.4612371	-0.4603496	-0.4594616	-0.4585732	-0.4576843	-0.4567950	-0.4559052
4.24	-0.4550149	-0.4541242	-0.4532331	-0.4523414	-0.4514494	-0.4505568	-0.4496639	-0.4487704	-0.4478766	-0.4469823
4.25	-0.4460875	-0.4451923	-0.4442966	-0.4434005	-0.4425040	-0.4416070	-0.4407096	-0.4398117	-0.4389134	-0.4380146
4.26	-0.4371154	-0.4362158	-0.4353158	-0.4344153	-0.4335143	-0.4326130	-0.4317112	-0.4308089	-0.4299063	-0.4290032
4.27	-0.4280997	-0.4271957	-0.4262914	-0.4253866	-0.4244813	-0.4235757	-0.4226696	-0.4217631	-0.4208562	-0.4199489
4.28	-0.4190411	-0.4181329	-0.4172243	-0.4163153	-0.4154059	-0.4144961	-0.4135858	-0.4126751	-0.4117640	-0.4108525
4.29	-0.4099406	-0.4090283	-0.4081156	-0.4072025	-0.4062889	-0.4053750	-0.4044606	-0.4035459	-0.4026307	-0.4017151
4.30	-0.4007992	-0.3998828	-0.3989660	-0.3980489	-0.3971313	-0.3962134	-0.3952950	-0.3943762	-0.3934571	-0.3925376
4.31	-0.3916176	-0.3906973	-0.3897766	-0.3888555	-0.3879340	-0.3870121	-0.3860899	-0.3851672	-0.3842441	-0.3833207
4.32	-0.3823969	-0.3814727	-0.3805482	-0.3796232	-0.3786979	-0.3777722	-0.3768461	-0.3759196	-0.3749928	-0.3740656
4.33	-0.3731380	-0.3722100	-0.3712817	-0.3703530	-0.3694239	-0.3684944	-0.3675646	-0.3666345	-0.3657039	-0.3647730
4.34	-0.3638417	-0.3629101	-0.3619781	-0.3610457	-0.3601130	-0.3591799	-0.3582464	-0.3573126	-0.3563785	-0.3554439
4.35	-0.3545091	-0.3535738	-0.3526383	-0.3517023	-0.3507660	-0.3498294	-0.3488924	-0.3479551	-0.3470174	-0.3460793
4.36	-0.3451410	-0.3442022	-0.3432632	-0.3423238	-0.3413840	-0.3404439	-0.3395035	-0.3385627	-0.3376216	-0.3366801
4.37	-0.3357384	-0.3347962	-0.3338538	-0.3329110	-0.3319679	-0.3310244	-0.3300806	-0.3291365	-0.3281921	-0.3272473
4.38	-0.3263022	-0.3253567	-0.3244110	-0.3234649	-0.3225185	-0.3215718	-0.3206247	-0.3196774	-0.3187297	-0.3177817
4.39	-0.3168334	-0.3158847	-0.3149358	-0.3139865	-0.3130369	-0.3120870	-0.3111368	-0.3101863	-0.3092355	-0.3082843
4.40	-0.3073329	-0.3063811	-0.3054291	-0.3044767	-0.3035240	-0.3025710	-0.3016178	-0.3006642	-0.2997103	-0.2987561
4.41	-0.2978016	-0.2968469	-0.2958918	-0.2949364	-0.2939808	-0.2930248	-0.2920685	-0.2911120	-0.2901552	-0.2891980
4.42	-0.2882406	-0.2872829	-0.2863249	-0.2853667	-0.2844081	-0.2834493	-0.2824901	-0.2815307	-0.2805710	-0.2796111
4.43	-0.2786508	-0.2776903	-0.2767295	-0.2757684	-0.2748070	-0.2738454	-0.2728835	-0.2719213	-0.2709588	-0.2699961
4.44	-0.2690331	-0.2680698	-0.2671063	-0.2661425	-0.2651784	-0.2642141	-0.2632495	-0.2622847	-0.2613195	-0.2603541
4.45	-0.2593885	-0.2584226	-0.2574564	-0.2564900	-0.2555233	-0.2545564	-0.2535892	-0.2526218	-0.2516541	-0.2506862
4.46	-0.2497180	-0.2487495	-0.2477808	-0.2468119	-0.2458427	-0.2448733	-0.2439036	-0.2429337	-0.2419635	-0.2409931
4.47	-0.2400225	-0.2390516	-0.2380804	-0.2371091	-0.2361375	-0.2351656	-0.2341936	-0.2332213	-0.2322487	-0.2312759
4.48	-0.2303029	-0.2293297	-0.2283562	-0.2273826	-0.2264086	-0.2254345	-0.2244601	-0.2234855	-0.2225107	-0.2215357
4.49	-0.2205604	-0.2195849	-0.2186092	-0.2176333	-0.2166572	-0.2156808	-0.2147042	-0.2137274	-0.2127504	-0.2117732
4.50	-0.2107958	-0.2098182	-0.2088403	-0.2078623	-0.2068840	-0.2059055	-0.2049269	-0.2039480	-0.2029689	-0.2019896
4.51	-0.2010101	-0.2000304	-0.1990505	-0.1980705	-0.1970902	-0.1961097	-0.1951290	-0.1941481	-0.1931671	-0.1921858
4.52	-0.1912043	-0.1902227	-0.1892412	-0.1882588	-0.1872766	-0.1862942	-0.1853116	-0.1843289	-0.1833459	-0.1823658
4.53	-0.1813794	-0.1803959	-0.1794123	-0.1784284	-0.1774444	-0.1764601	-0.1754757	-0.1744912	-0.1735064	-0.1725215
4.54	-0.1715364	-0.1705511	-0.1695657	-0.1685801	-0.1675943	-0.1666084	-0.1656223	-0.1646360	-0.1636496	-0.1626630

TABLE 2   Cos

T	.000	.001	.002	.003	.004	.005	.006	.007	.008	.009
4.55	-0.1616762	-0.1606893	-0.1597022	-0.1587150	-0.1577276	-0.1567400	-0.1557523	-0.1547644	-0.1537764	-0.1527882
4.56	-0.1517999	-0.1508114	-0.1498227	-0.1488339	-0.1478450	-0.1468559	-0.1458667	-0.1448773	-0.1438878	-0.1428981
4.57	-0.1419083	-0.1409184	-0.1399283	-0.1389380	-0.1379477	-0.1369572	-0.1359665	-0.1349757	-0.1339848	-0.1329938
4.58	-0.1320026	-0.1310113	-0.1300198	-0.1290283	-0.1280365	-0.1270447	-0.1260528	-0.1250607	-0.1240685	-0.1230761
4.59	-0.1220837	-0.1210911	-0.1200984	-0.1191056	-0.1181126	-0.1171196	-0.1161264	-0.1151331	-0.1141397	-0.1131462
4.60	-0.1121525	-0.1111588	-0.1101649	-0.1091710	-0.1081769	-0.1071827	-0.1061884	-0.1051940	-0.1041995	-0.1032049
4.61	-0.1022102	-0.1012154	-0.1002204	-0.0992254	-0.0982303	-0.0972351	-0.0962398	-0.0952444	-0.0942489	-0.0932533
4.62	-0.0922576	-0.0912618	-0.0902659	-0.0892700	-0.0882739	-0.0872778	-0.0862816	-0.0852853	-0.0842889	-0.0832924
4.63	-0.0822958	-0.0812992	-0.0803024	-0.0793056	-0.0783087	-0.0773118	-0.0763147	-0.0753176	-0.0743204	-0.0733231
4.64	-0.0723258	-0.0713284	-0.0703309	-0.0693333	-0.0683357	-0.0673380	-0.0663402	-0.0653424	-0.0643445	-0.0633465
4.65	-0.0623485	-0.0613504	-0.0603523	-0.0593541	-0.0583558	-0.0573575	-0.0563591	-0.0553607	-0.0543622	-0.0533636
4.66	-0.0523650	-0.0513664	-0.0503677	-0.0493689	-0.0483701	-0.0473713	-0.0463723	-0.0453734	-0.0443744	-0.0433754
4.67	-0.0423763	-0.0413772	-0.0403780	-0.0393788	-0.0383796	-0.0373803	-0.0363810	-0.0353816	-0.0343822	-0.0333828
4.68	-0.0323833	-0.0313838	-0.0303843	-0.0293847	-0.0283852	-0.0273856	-0.0263859	-0.0253863	-0.0243866	-0.0233868
4.69	-0.0223871	-0.0213873	-0.0203876	-0.0193878	-0.0183879	-0.0173881	-0.0163882	-0.0153884	-0.0143885	-0.0133886
4.70	-0.0123887	-0.0113887	-0.0103888	-0.0093888	-0.0083889	-0.0073889	-0.0063889	-0.0053890	-0.0043890	-0.0033890
4.71	-0.0023890	-0.0013890	-0.0003890	0.0006110	0.0016110	0.0026110	0.0036110	0.0046110	0.0056110	0.0066110
4.72	0.0076109	0.0086109	0.0096109	0.0106108	0.0116108	0.0126107	0.0136106	0.0146105	0.0156104	0.0166103
4.73	0.0176101	0.0186099	0.0196098	0.0206096	0.0216093	0.0226091	0.0236088	0.0246085	0.0256082	0.0266079
4.74	0.0276075	0.0286071	0.0296067	0.0306067	0.0316058	0.0326052	0.0336047	0.0346041	0.0356035	0.0366028
4.75	0.0376022	0.0386014	0.0396007	0.0405999	0.0415990	0.0425981	0.0435972	0.0445962	0.0455952	0.0465941
4.76	0.0475930	0.0485919	0.0495907	0.0505894	0.0515881	0.0525868	0.0535853	0.0545839	0.0555824	0.0565808
4.77	0.0575792	0.0585775	0.0595757	0.0605739	0.0615720	0.0625701	0.0635681	0.0645661	0.0655640	0.0665618
4.78	0.0675595	0.0685572	0.0695548	0.0705524	0.0715498	0.0725472	0.0735446	0.0745418	0.0755390	0.0765361
4.79	0.0775331	0.0785301	0.0795270	0.0805237	0.0815205	0.0825171	0.0835136	0.0845101	0.0855065	0.0865028
4.80	0.0874990	0.0884951	0.0894911	0.0904871	0.0914829	0.0924787	0.0934744	0.0944699	0.0954654	0.0964608
4.81	0.0974561	0.0984513	0.0994464	0.1004414	0.1014363	0.1024310	0.1034257	0.1044203	0.1054148	0.1064092
4.82	0.1074034	0.1083976	0.1093917	0.1103856	0.1113794	0.1123732	0.1133668	0.1143603	0.1153537	0.1163469
4.83	0.1173401	0.1183331	0.1193260	0.1203188	0.1213115	0.1223040	0.1232965	0.1242888	0.1252810	0.1262730
4.84	0.1272650	0.1282568	0.1292484	0.1302400	0.1312314	0.1322227	0.1332138	0.1342049	0.1351957	0.1361865
4.85	0.1371771	0.1381676	0.1391579	0.1401481	0.1411382	0.1421281	0.1431179	0.1441075	0.1450970	0.1460864
4.86	0.1470756	0.1480646	0.1490535	0.1500423	0.1510309	0.1520193	0.1530076	0.1539958	0.1549838	0.1559716
4.87	0.1569593	0.1579468	0.1589342	0.1599214	0.1609084	0.1618953	0.1628821	0.1638686	0.1648550	0.1658413
4.88	0.1668273	0.1678132	0.1687990	0.1697845	0.1707699	0.1717552	0.1727402	0.1737251	0.1747098	0.1756943
4.89	0.1766787	0.1776629	0.1786469	0.1796307	0.1806143	0.1815978	0.1825811	0.1835642	0.1845471	0.1855298

TABLE 2　Cos

r	.000	.001	.002	.003	.004	.005	.006	.007	.008	.009
4.90	0.1865124	0.1874947	0.1884769	0.1894589	0.1904407	0.1914223	0.1924037	0.1933849	0.1943659	0.1953468
4.91	0.1963274	0.1973078	0.1982881	0.1992681	0.2002480	0.2012276	0.2022071	0.2031863	0.2041653	0.2051442
4.92	0.2061228	0.2071012	0.2080794	0.2090575	0.2100353	0.2110128	0.2119902	0.2129674	0.2139443	0.2149211
4.93	0.2158976	0.2168739	0.2178500	0.2188259	0.2198015	0.2207770	0.2217522	0.2227272	0.2237019	0.2246765
4.94	0.2256508	0.2266249	0.2275988	0.2285724	0.2295458	0.2305190	0.2314920	0.2324647	0.2334372	0.2344094
4.95	0.2353814	0.2363532	0.2373248	0.2382961	0.2392672	0.2402380	0.2412086	0.2421789	0.2431491	0.2441189
4.96	0.2450885	0.2460579	0.2470271	0.2479959	0.2489646	0.2499330	0.2509011	0.2518690	0.2528366	0.2538040
4.97	0.2547711	0.2557380	0.2567046	0.2576710	0.2586371	0.2596029	0.2605685	0.2615338	0.2624989	0.2634637
4.98	0.2644282	0.2653925	0.2663565	0.2673203	0.2682837	0.2692469	0.2702099	0.2711726	0.2721349	0.2730971
4.99	0.2740589	0.2750205	0.2759818	0.2769428	0.2779036	0.2788640	0.2798242	0.2807841	0.2817439	0.2827031
5.00	0.2836622	0.2846210	0.2855795	0.2865377	0.2874956	0.2884532	0.2894106	0.2903677	0.2913244	0.2922809
5.01	0.2932371	0.2941930	0.2951486	0.2961039	0.2970589	0.2980136	0.2989630	0.2999221	0.3008759	0.3018295
5.02	0.3027827	0.3037356	0.3046882	0.3056405	0.3065925	0.3075442	0.3084955	0.3094466	0.3103974	0.3113478
5.03	0.3122980	0.3132478	0.3141973	0.3151465	0.3160954	0.3170440	0.3179922	0.3189401	0.3198874	0.3208351
5.04	0.3217820	0.3227287	0.3236750	0.3246210	0.3255667	0.3265121	0.3274571	0.3284018	0.3293462	0.3302902
5.05	0.3312339	0.3321773	0.3331204	0.3340631	0.3350055	0.3359475	0.3368892	0.3378306	0.3387716	0.3397123
5.06	0.3406527	0.3415927	0.3425324	0.3434717	0.3444107	0.3453494	0.3462877	0.3472256	0.3481632	0.3491005
5.07	0.3500374	0.3509740	0.3519102	0.3528460	0.3537815	0.3547167	0.3556515	0.3565859	0.3575200	0.3584537
5.08	0.3593871	0.3603201	0.3612527	0.3621850	0.3631170	0.3640485	0.3649797	0.3659106	0.3668410	0.3677711
5.09	0.3687009	0.3696302	0.3705592	0.3714878	0.3724161	0.3733440	0.3742715	0.3751986	0.3761254	0.3770517
5.10	0.3779777	0.3789034	0.3798286	0.3807535	0.3816780	0.3826021	0.3835253	0.3844491	0.3853721	0.3862947
5.11	0.3872168	0.3881386	0.3890600	0.3899811	0.3909017	0.3918219	0.3927418	0.3936612	0.3945803	0.3954989
5.12	0.3964172	0.3973351	0.3982526	0.3991696	0.4000863	0.4010026	0.4019185	0.4028339	0.4037490	0.4046637
5.13	0.4055779	0.4064918	0.4074052	0.4083183	0.4092309	0.4101432	0.4110550	0.4119664	0.4128774	0.4137879
5.14	0.4146981	0.4156079	0.4165172	0.4174261	0.4183345	0.4192427	0.4201504	0.4210576	0.4219644	0.4228708
5.15	0.4237768	0.4246874	0.4255875	0.4264922	0.4273965	0.4283003	0.4292038	0.4301067	0.4310093	0.4319114
5.16	0.4328131	0.4337144	0.4346152	0.4355156	0.4364156	0.4373151	0.4382142	0.4391129	0.4400111	0.4409089
5.17	0.4418062	0.4427031	0.4435995	0.4444955	0.4453911	0.4462862	0.4471809	0.4480751	0.4489689	0.4498622
5.18	0.4507551	0.4516475	0.4525394	0.4534310	0.4543220	0.4552126	0.4561028	0.4569925	0.4578817	0.4587705
5.19	0.4596588	0.4605467	0.4614341	0.4623211	0.4632075	0.4640936	0.4649791	0.4658642	0.4667488	0.4676330
5.20	0.4685167	0.4693999	0.4702826	0.4711649	0.4720467	0.4729281	0.4738089	0.4746893	0.4755692	0.4764487
5.21	0.4773276	0.4782061	0.4790841	0.4799617	0.4808387	0.4817153	0.4825914	0.4834670	0.4843421	0.4852167
5.22	0.4860909	0.4869646	0.4878377	0.4887104	0.4895825	0.4904543	0.4913256	0.4921963	0.4930665	0.4939363
5.23	0.4948055	0.4956743	0.4965425	0.4974103	0.4982776	0.4991443	0.5000106	0.5008764	0.5017416	0.5026064
5.24	0.5034707	0.5043344	0.5051977	0.5060604	0.5069227	0.5077844	0.5086457	0.5095064	0.5103666	0.5112263

TABLE 2   Cos

r	.000	.001	.002	.003	.004	.005	.006	.007	.008	.009
5.25	0.5120855	0.5129442	0.5138023	0.5146600	0.5155171	0.5163737	0.5172298	0.5180854	0.5189405	0.5197950
5.26	0.5206491	0.5215026	0.5223556	0.5232080	0.5240600	0.5249114	0.5257623	0.5266127	0.5274625	0.5283118
5.27	0.5291606	0.5300089	0.5308566	0.5317038	0.5325505	0.5333966	0.5342422	0.5350872	0.5359318	0.5367758
5.28	0.5376192	0.5384621	0.5393045	0.5401464	0.5409877	0.5418284	0.5426686	0.5435083	0.5443475	0.5451860
5.29	0.5460241	0.5468616	0.5476985	0.5485349	0.5493708	0.5502061	0.5510409	0.5518750	0.5527087	0.5535418
5.30	0.5543743	0.5552063	0.5560378	0.5568686	0.5576990	0.5585287	0.5593579	0.5601866	0.5610147	0.5618422
5.31	0.5626692	0.5634956	0.5643214	0.5651467	0.5659714	0.5667955	0.5676191	0.5684421	0.5692645	0.5700864
5.32	0.5709077	0.5717284	0.5725486	0.5733682	0.5741872	0.5750056	0.5758235	0.5766408	0.5774575	0.5782736
5.33	0.5790892	0.5799041	0.5807185	0.5815323	0.5823456	0.5831582	0.5839703	0.5847818	0.5855927	0.5864030
5.34	0.5872127	0.5880219	0.5888304	0.5896384	0.5904457	0.5912525	0.5920587	0.5928643	0.5936693	0.5944737
5.35	0.5952775	0.5960808	0.5968834	0.5976854	0.5984869	0.5992877	0.6000879	0.6008876	0.6016866	0.6024850
5.36	0.6032829	0.6040801	0.6048767	0.6056727	0.6064681	0.6072629	0.6080571	0.6088507	0.6096437	0.6104361
5.37	0.6112278	0.6120190	0.6128095	0.6135994	0.6143887	0.6151774	0.6159655	0.6167530	0.6175393	0.6183261
5.38	0.6191117	0.6198967	0.6206810	0.6214648	0.6222479	0.6230304	0.6238123	0.6245936	0.6253742	0.6261542
5.39	0.6269336	0.6277124	0.6284905	0.6292680	0.6300449	0.6308211	0.6315967	0.6323717	0.6331461	0.6339198
5.40	0.6346929	0.6354653	0.6362371	0.6370083	0.6377788	0.6385487	0.6393180	0.6400866	0.6408546	0.6416220
5.41	0.6423887	0.6431547	0.6439201	0.6446849	0.6454490	0.6462125	0.6469753	0.6477375	0.6484991	0.6492600
5.42	0.6500202	0.6507798	0.6515387	0.6522970	0.6530547	0.6538116	0.6545680	0.6553237	0.6560787	0.6568330
5.43	0.6575867	0.6583398	0.6590922	0.6598439	0.6605950	0.6613454	0.6620952	0.6628442	0.6635927	0.6643404
5.44	0.6650875	0.6658340	0.6665797	0.6673248	0.6680693	0.6688130	0.6695561	0.6702985	0.6710403	0.6717814
5.45	0.6725218	0.6732615	0.6740006	0.6747390	0.6754767	0.6762138	0.6769501	0.6776858	0.6784208	0.6791552
5.46	0.6798848	0.6806218	0.6813541	0.6820857	0.6828166	0.6835469	0.6842765	0.6850053	0.6857335	0.6864610
5.47	0.6871879	0.6879140	0.6886394	0.6893642	0.6900883	0.6908117	0.6915343	0.6922563	0.6929776	0.6936983
5.48	0.6944182	0.6951374	0.6958559	0.6965738	0.6972909	0.6980073	0.6987231	0.6994381	0.7001525	0.7008661
5.49	0.7015791	0.7022913	0.7030028	0.7037137	0.7044238	0.7051332	0.7058420	0.7065500	0.7072573	0.7079639
5.50	0.7086698	0.7093750	0.7100794	0.7107832	0.7114863	0.7121886	0.7128902	0.7135912	0.7142914	0.7149909
5.51	0.7156896	0.7163877	0.7170850	0.7177817	0.7184776	0.7191728	0.7198672	0.7205610	0.7212540	0.7219463
5.52	0.7226379	0.7233288	0.7240189	0.7247083	0.7253970	0.7260850	0.7267722	0.7274588	0.7281445	0.7288296
5.53	0.7295139	0.7301975	0.7308804	0.7315625	0.7322440	0.7329246	0.7336046	0.7342838	0.7349623	0.7356400
5.54	0.7363170	0.7369933	0.7376688	0.7383436	0.7390177	0.7396910	0.7403635	0.7410354	0.7417065	0.7423768
5.55	0.7430464	0.7437153	0.7443834	0.7450508	0.7457174	0.7463833	0.7470485	0.7477129	0.7483765	0.7490394
5.56	0.7497016	0.7503630	0.7510236	0.7516835	0.7523427	0.7530011	0.7536587	0.7543156	0.7549717	0.7556271
5.57	0.7562817	0.7569356	0.7575887	0.7582411	0.7588927	0.7595435	0.7601936	0.7608429	0.7614915	0.7621392
5.58	0.7627863	0.7634325	0.7640781	0.7647228	0.7653668	0.7660100	0.7666524	0.7672941	0.7679350	0.7685752
5.59	0.7692145	0.7698531	0.7704910	0.7711280	0.7717643	0.7723999	0.7730346	0.7736686	0.7743018	0.7749342

TABLE 2 Cos

T	.000	.001	.002	.003	.004	.005	.006	.007	.008	.009
5.60	0.7755659	0.7761968	0.7768269	0.7774562	0.7780847	0.7787125	0.7793395	0.7799657	0.7805911	0.7812158
5.61	0.7818397	0.7824628	0.7830851	0.7837066	0.7843273	0.7849473	0.7855664	0.7861848	0.7868024	0.7874192
5.62	0.7880353	0.7886505	0.7892649	0.7898786	0.7904915	0.7911035	0.7917148	0.7923253	0.7929350	0.7935439
5.63	0.7941521	0.7947594	0.7953659	0.7959716	0.7965766	0.7971807	0.7977841	0.7983866	0.7989883	0.7995893
5.64	0.8001894	0.8007888	0.8013873	0.8019851	0.8025820	0.8031782	0.8037735	0.8043680	0.8049618	0.8055547
5.65	0.8061468	0.8067381	0.8073286	0.8079183	0.8085072	0.8090953	0.8096826	0.8102690	0.8108547	0.8114395
5.66	0.8120236	0.8126068	0.8131892	0.8137708	0.8143516	0.8149315	0.8155107	0.8160890	0.8166665	0.8172432
5.67	0.8178191	0.8183942	0.8189684	0.8195418	0.8201145	0.8206862	0.8212572	0.8218274	0.8223967	0.8229652
5.68	0.8235329	0.8240997	0.8246658	0.8252310	0.8257954	0.8263589	0.8269216	0.8274835	0.8280446	0.8286049
5.69	0.8291643	0.8297229	0.8302806	0.8308376	0.8313937	0.8319489	0.8325034	0.8330570	0.8336097	0.8341617
5.70	0.8347128	0.8352631	0.8358125	0.8363611	0.8369088	0.8374558	0.8380019	0.8385471	0.8390915	0.8396351
5.71	0.8401708	0.8407197	0.8412608	0.8418010	0.8423403	0.8428789	0.8434165	0.8439534	0.8444894	0.8450245
5.72	0.8455588	0.8460923	0.8466249	0.8471567	0.8476876	0.8482177	0.8487469	0.8492753	0.8498028	0.8503295
5.73	0.8508553	0.8513803	0.8519044	0.8524276	0.8529501	0.8534716	0.8539923	0.8545122	0.8550312	0.8555494
5.74	0.8560667	0.8565831	0.8570987	0.8576134	0.8581273	0.8586403	0.8591524	0.8596637	0.8601741	0.8606837
5.75	0.8611924	0.8617003	0.8622073	0.8627134	0.8632186	0.8637230	0.8642266	0.8647292	0.8652310	0.8657320
5.76	0.8662321	0.8667313	0.8672296	0.8677271	0.8682237	0.8687194	0.8692143	0.8697083	0.8702014	0.8706937
5.77	0.8711851	0.8716756	0.8721653	0.8726540	0.8731419	0.8736290	0.8741151	0.8746004	0.8750848	0.8755683
5.78	0.8760510	0.8765328	0.8770137	0.8774937	0.8779729	0.8784511	0.8789285	0.8794050	0.8798807	0.8803554
5.79	0.8808293	0.8813023	0.8817744	0.8822456	0.8827160	0.8831854	0.8836540	0.8841217	0.8845885	0.8850545
5.80	0.8855195	0.8859837	0.8864469	0.8869093	0.8873708	0.8878314	0.8882912	0.8887500	0.8892080	0.8896650
5.81	0.8901212	0.8905765	0.8910309	0.8914843	0.8919370	0.8923887	0.8928395	0.8932894	0.8937385	0.8941866
5.82	0.8946338	0.8950802	0.8955257	0.8959702	0.8964139	0.8968567	0.8972985	0.8977395	0.8981796	0.8986188
5.83	0.8990570	0.8994944	0.8999309	0.9003665	0.9008012	0.9012349	0.9016678	0.9020998	0.9025309	0.9029611
5.84	0.9033903	0.9038187	0.9042462	0.9046727	0.9050984	0.9055231	0.9059470	0.9063699	0.9067919	0.9072131
5.85	0.9076333	0.9080526	0.9084710	0.9088885	0.9093051	0.9097207	0.9101355	0.9105494	0.9109623	0.9113743
5.86	0.9117855	0.9121957	0.9126050	0.9130134	0.9134208	0.9138274	0.9142330	0.9146378	0.9150416	0.9154445
5.87	0.9158465	0.9162475	0.9166477	0.9170469	0.9174453	0.9178427	0.9182392	0.9186347	0.9190294	0.9194231
5.88	0.9198159	0.9202078	0.9205988	0.9209888	0.9213779	0.9217662	0.9221534	0.9225398	0.9229252	0.9233098
5.89	0.9236934	0.9240760	0.9244578	0.9248386	0.9252185	0.9255975	0.9259755	0.9263526	0.9267288	0.9271041
5.90	0.9274784	0.9278518	0.9282243	0.9285959	0.9289665	0.9293362	0.9297050	0.9300728	0.9304397	0.9308057
5.91	0.9311708	0.9315349	0.9318981	0.9322603	0.9326216	0.9329820	0.9333415	0.9337000	0.9340576	0.9344143
5.92	0.9347700	0.9351248	0.9354786	0.9358315	0.9361835	0.9365346	0.9368847	0.9372339	0.9375821	0.9379294
5.93	0.9382757	0.9386211	0.9389656	0.9393092	0.9396518	0.9399934	0.9403341	0.9406739	0.9410128	0.9413507
5.94	0.9416876	0.9420236	0.9423587	0.9426929	0.9430260	0.9433583	0.9436896	0.9440200	0.9443494	0.9446778

TABLE 2   Cos

T	.000	.001	.002	.003	.004	.005	.006	.007	.008	.009
5.95	0.9450054	0.9453320	0.9456576	0.9459823	0.9463060	0.9466288	0.9469507	0.9472716	0.9475915	0.9479106
5.96	0.9482286	0.9485457	0.9488619	0.9491771	0.9494914	0.9498047	0.9501171	0.9504285	0.9507390	0.9510485
5.97	0.9513570	0.9516646	0.9519713	0.9522770	0.9525818	0.9528856	0.9531884	0.9534903	0.9537913	0.9540913
5.98	0.9543903	0.9546884	0.9549855	0.9552817	0.9555769	0.9558712	0.9561645	0.9564569	0.9567482	0.9570387
5.99	0.9573282	0.9576167	0.9579043	0.9581909	0.9584765	0.9587612	0.9590449	0.9593277	0.9596095	0.9598904
6.00	0.9601703	0.9604492	0.9607272	0.9610042	0.9612803	0.9615554	0.9618295	0.9621027	0.9623749	0.9626461
6.01	0.9629164	0.9631857	0.9634541	0.9637215	0.9639879	0.9642533	0.9645178	0.9647814	0.9650440	0.9653056
6.02	0.9655662	0.9658259	0.9660846	0.9663423	0.9665991	0.9668549	0.9671098	0.9673636	0.9676165	0.9678685
6.03	0.9681195	0.9683695	0.9686185	0.9688666	0.9691137	0.9693598	0.9696049	0.9698491	0.9700924	0.9703346
6.04	0.9705759	0.9708162	0.9710555	0.9712939	0.9715313	0.9717677	0.9720032	0.9722377	0.9724712	0.9727037
6.05	0.9729353	0.9731659	0.9733955	0.9736241	0.9738518	0.9740785	0.9743042	0.9745290	0.9747527	0.9749755
6.06	0.9751974	0.9754182	0.9756381	0.9758570	0.9760749	0.9762919	0.9765078	0.9767228	0.9769368	0.9771499
6.07	0.9773619	0.9775730	0.9777831	0.9779923	0.9782004	0.9784076	0.9786138	0.9788190	0.9790232	0.9792265
6.08	0.9794288	0.9796301	0.9798304	0.9800297	0.9802281	0.9804255	0.9806219	0.9808173	0.9810117	0.9812052
6.09	0.9813977	0.9815892	0.9817797	0.9819692	0.9821578	0.9823453	0.9825319	0.9827175	0.9829021	0.9830858
6.10	0.9832684	0.9834501	0.9836308	0.9838105	0.9839892	0.9841670	0.9843437	0.9845195	0.9846943	0.9848681
6.11	0.9850409	0.9852127	0.9853835	0.9855534	0.9857223	0.9858902	0.9860571	0.9862230	0.9863879	0.9865518
6.12	0.9867148	0.9868768	0.9870377	0.9871977	0.9873568	0.9875148	0.9876718	0.9878278	0.9879828	0.9881370
6.13	0.9882901	0.9884421	0.9885933	0.9887434	0.9888925	0.9890406	0.9891878	0.9893339	0.9894791	0.9896233
6.14	0.9897665	0.9899087	0.9900499	0.9901901	0.9903294	0.9904676	0.9906048	0.9907411	0.9908764	0.9910107
6.15	0.9911439	0.9912762	0.9914075	0.9915379	0.9916672	0.9917955	0.9919229	0.9920492	0.9921745	0.9922989
6.16	0.9924223	0.9925447	0.9926660	0.9927864	0.9929058	0.9930242	0.9931417	0.9932581	0.9933735	0.9934879
6.17	0.9936014	0.9937138	0.9938253	0.9939357	0.9940452	0.9941537	0.9942612	0.9943676	0.9944731	0.9945776
6.18	0.9946811	0.9947836	0.9948851	0.9949856	0.9950852	0.9951837	0.9952812	0.9953778	0.9954733	0.9955678
6.19	0.9956614	0.9957539	0.9958455	0.9959361	0.9960256	0.9961142	0.9962018	0.9962883	0.9963739	0.9964585
6.20	0.9965421	0.9966247	0.9967063	0.9967869	0.9968665	0.9969451	0.9970227	0.9970993	0.9971749	0.9972495
6.21	0.9973232	0.9973958	0.9974674	0.9975380	0.9976077	0.9976763	0.9977439	0.9978106	0.9978762	0.9979408
6.22	0.9980045	0.9980671	0.9981288	0.9981894	0.9982491	0.9983077	0.9983654	0.9984220	0.9984777	0.9985323
6.23	0.9985860	0.9986387	0.9986903	0.9987410	0.9987906	0.9988393	0.9988870	0.9989336	0.9989793	0.9990240
6.24	0.9990677	0.9991103	0.9991520	0.9991927	0.9992324	0.9992710	0.9993087	0.9993454	0.9993811	0.9994157
6.25	0.9994494	0.9994821	0.9995138	0.9995445	0.9995741	0.9996029	0.9996305	0.9996572	0.9996829	0.9997075
6.26	0.9997312	0.9997539	0.9997756	0.9997963	0.9998160	0.9998347	0.9998523	0.9998690	0.9998847	0.9998994
6.27	0.9999131	0.9999258	0.9999374	0.9999491	0.9999578	0.9999665	0.9999742	0.9999809	0.9999866	0.9999912
6.28	0.9999949	0.9999976	0.9999993	1.0000000	0.9999997	0.9999984	0.9999960	0.9999927	0.9999884	0.9999831
6.29	0.9999768	0.9999695	0.9999612	0.9999518	0.9999415	0.9999302	0.9999179	0.9999046	0.9998903	0.9998750

TABLE 2   Cos

r	.000	.001	.002	.003	.004	.005	.006	.007	.008	.009
6.30	0.9998586	0.9998413	0.9998230	0.9998037	0.9997834	0.9997621	0.9997398	0.9997164	0.9996921	0.9996668
6.31	0.9996405	0.9996132	0.9995849	0.9995556	0.9995253	0.9994940	0.9994616	0.9994283	0.9993940	0.9993587
6.32	0.9993224	0.9992851	0.9992468	0.9992075	0.9991672	0.9991259	0.9990836	0.9990403	0.9989960	0.9989507
6.33	0.9989044	0.9988571	0.9988088	0.9987595	0.9987092	0.9986579	0.9986056	0.9985523	0.9984981	0.9984428
6.34	0.9983865	0.9983292	0.9982709	0.9982116	0.9981514	0.9980901	0.9980278	0.9979645	0.9979003	0.9978350
6.35	0.9977687	0.9977015	0.9976332	0.9975639	0.9974937	0.9974224	0.9973502	0.9972768	0.9972027	0.9971274
6.36	0.9970512	0.9969740	0.9968957	0.9968165	0.9967363	0.9966550	0.9965728	0.9964896	0.9964054	0.9963202
6.37	0.9962340	0.9961468	0.9960586	0.9959694	0.9958797	0.9957880	0.9956958	0.9956026	0.9955085	0.9954133
6.38	0.9953171	0.9952200	0.9951218	0.9950226	0.9949225	0.9948214	0.9947192	0.9946161	0.9945120	0.9944068
6.39	0.9943007	0.9941936	0.9940855	0.9939764	0.9938663	0.9937552	0.9936432	0.9935301	0.9934160	0.9933010
6.40	0.9931849	0.9930679	0.9929498	0.9928308	0.9927108	0.9925898	0.9924678	0.9923447	0.9922208	0.9920958
6.41	0.9919698	0.9918428	0.9917149	0.9915859	0.9914559	0.9913250	0.9911931	0.9910602	0.9909263	0.9907914
6.42	0.9906555	0.9905186	0.9903807	0.9902418	0.9901020	0.9899611	0.9898193	0.9896765	0.9895327	0.9893879
6.43	0.9892421	0.9890953	0.9889475	0.9887988	0.9886490	0.9884983	0.9883465	0.9881938	0.9880401	0.9878854
6.44	0.9877298	0.9875731	0.9874154	0.9872568	0.9870972	0.9869365	0.9867749	0.9866124	0.9864488	0.9862842
6.45	0.9861187	0.9859521	0.9857846	0.9856161	0.9854466	0.9852761	0.9851047	0.9849322	0.9847588	0.9845844
6.46	0.9844090	0.9842326	0.9840552	0.9838769	0.9836975	0.9835172	0.9833359	0.9831536	0.9829703	0.9827861
6.47	0.9826008	0.9824146	0.9822274	0.9820392	0.9818500	0.9816599	0.9814688	0.9812767	0.9810836	0.9808895
6.48	0.9806944	0.9804984	0.9803014	0.9801034	0.9799044	0.9797044	0.9795035	0.9793016	0.9790987	0.9788948
6.49	0.9786900	0.9784841	0.9782773	0.9780695	0.9778608	0.9776510	0.9774403	0.9772286	0.9770159	0.9768023
6.50	0.9765876	0.9763720	0.9761554	0.9759379	0.9757193	0.9754998	0.9752793	0.9750579	0.9748354	0.9746120
6.51	0.9743876	0.9741623	0.9739359	0.9737086	0.9734803	0.9732511	0.9730209	0.9727896	0.9725575	0.9723243
6.52	0.9720902	0.9718551	0.9716190	0.9713820	0.9711440	0.9709050	0.9706651	0.9704241	0.9701823	0.9699394
6.53	0.9696956	0.9694508	0.9692050	0.9689583	0.9687105	0.9684619	0.9682122	0.9679616	0.9677100	0.9674575
6.54	0.9672040	0.9669495	0.9666940	0.9664376	0.9661802	0.9659219	0.9656625	0.9654023	0.9651410	0.9648788
6.55	0.9646156	0.9643515	0.9640864	0.9638203	0.9635533	0.9632853	0.9630163	0.9627464	0.9624755	0.9622037
6.56	0.9619308	0.9616571	0.9613823	0.9611066	0.9608300	0.9605524	0.9602738	0.9599942	0.9597137	0.9594323
6.57	0.9591499	0.9588665	0.9585821	0.9582968	0.9580106	0.9577234	0.9574352	0.9571461	0.9568560	0.9565650
6.58	0.9562730	0.9559800	0.9556861	0.9553912	0.9550954	0.9547986	0.9545009	0.9542022	0.9539026	0.9536020
6.59	0.9533004	0.9529979	0.9526945	0.9523901	0.9520847	0.9517784	0.9514712	0.9511629	0.9508538	0.9505437
6.60	0.9502326	0.9499206	0.9496076	0.9492937	0.9489788	0.9486630	0.9483463	0.9480285	0.9477099	0.9473903
6.61	0.9470697	0.9467482	0.9464258	0.9461024	0.9457780	0.9454527	0.9451265	0.9447993	0.9444712	0.9441422
6.62	0.9438121	0.9434812	0.9431493	0.9428164	0.9424827	0.9421479	0.9418123	0.9414757	0.9411381	0.9407996
6.63	0.9404602	0.9401198	0.9397785	0.9394362	0.9390930	0.9387489	0.9384038	0.9380578	0.9377109	0.9373630
6.64	0.9370142	0.9366644	0.9363137	0.9359621	0.9356095	0.9352560	0.9349016	0.9345462	0.9341899	0.9338326

TABLE 2 Cos

T	.000	.001	.002	.003	.004	.005	.006	.007	.008	.009
6.65	0.9334745	0.9331154	0.9327553	0.9323943	0.9320324	0.9316696	0.9313058	0.9309411	0.9305755	0.9302089
6.66	0.9298414	0.9294730	0.9291036	0.9287334	0.9283621	0.9279900	0.9276169	0.9272429	0.9268680	0.9264922
6.67	0.9261154	0.9257377	0.9253591	0.9249795	0.9245990	0.9242176	0.9238353	0.9234520	0.9230679	0.9226828
6.68	0.9222967	0.9219098	0.9215219	0.9211331	0.9207434	0.9203528	0.9199613	0.9195688	0.9191754	0.9187811
6.69	0.9183859	0.9179897	0.9175927	0.9171947	0.9167958	0.9163960	0.9159952	0.9155936	0.9151910	0.9147875
6.70	0.9143831	0.9139778	0.9135716	0.9131645	0.9127564	0.9123475	0.9119376	0.9115268	0.9111151	0.9107025
6.71	0.9102890	0.9098746	0.9094592	0.9090430	0.9086258	0.9082078	0.9077888	0.9073689	0.9069481	0.9065264
6.72	0.9061038	0.9056803	0.9052559	0.9048306	0.9044044	0.9039772	0.9035492	0.9031203	0.9026904	0.9022597
6.73	0.9018280	0.9013955	0.9009620	0.9005277	0.9000924	0.8996563	0.8992192	0.8987813	0.8983424	0.8979027
6.74	0.8974621	0.8970205	0.8965781	0.8961347	0.8956905	0.8952454	0.8947994	0.8943525	0.8939046	0.8934559
6.75	0.8930063	0.8925559	0.8921045	0.8916522	0.8911990	0.8907450	0.8902900	0.8898342	0.8893775	0.8889198
6.76	0.8884613	0.8880019	0.8875416	0.8870805	0.8866184	0.8861555	0.8856916	0.8852269	0.8847613	0.8842948
6.77	0.8838275	0.8833592	0.8828901	0.8824201	0.8819492	0.8814774	0.8810047	0.8805311	0.8800567	0.8795814
6.78	0.8791052	0.8786282	0.8781502	0.8776714	0.8771917	0.8767111	0.8762297	0.8757473	0.8752641	0.8747800
6.79	0.8742951	0.8738092	0.8733225	0.8728350	0.8723465	0.8718572	0.8713670	0.8708759	0.8703840	0.8698912
6.80	0.8693975	0.8689029	0.8684075	0.8679112	0.8674141	0.8669161	0.8664172	0.8659174	0.8654168	0.8649153
6.81	0.8644130	0.8639098	0.8634057	0.8629007	0.8623949	0.8618883	0.8613807	0.8608723	0.8603631	0.8598530
6.82	0.8593420	0.8588302	0.8583175	0.8578039	0.8572895	0.8567743	0.8562582	0.8557412	0.8552233	0.8547047
6.83	0.8541851	0.8536647	0.8531435	0.8526214	0.8520984	0.8515746	0.8510499	0.8505244	0.8499981	0.8494709
6.84	0.8489428	0.8484139	0.8478841	0.8473535	0.8468221	0.8462898	0.8457566	0.8452226	0.8446878	0.8441521
6.85	0.8436156	0.8430782	0.8425400	0.8420010	0.8414611	0.8409203	0.8403787	0.8398363	0.8392931	0.8387490
6.86	0.8382040	0.8376583	0.8371116	0.8365642	0.8360159	0.8354668	0.8349168	0.8343660	0.8338144	0.8332619
6.87	0.8327086	0.8321545	0.8315996	0.8310438	0.8304871	0.8299297	0.8293714	0.8288123	0.8282524	0.8276916
6.88	0.8271300	0.8265676	0.8260043	0.8254402	0.8248753	0.8243096	0.8237431	0.8231757	0.8226075	0.8220385
6.89	0.8214686	0.8208980	0.8203265	0.8197542	0.8191810	0.8186071	0.8180323	0.8174567	0.8168803	0.8163031
6.90	0.8157251	0.8151463	0.8145666	0.8139861	0.8134048	0.8128227	0.8122398	0.8116561	0.8110715	0.8104862
6.91	0.8099000	0.8093130	0.8087253	0.8081367	0.8075473	0.8069571	0.8063660	0.8057742	0.8051816	0.8045882
6.92	0.8039939	0.8033989	0.8028031	0.8022064	0.8016090	0.8010107	0.8004117	0.7998118	0.7992112	0.7986097
6.93	0.7980075	0.7974044	0.7968006	0.7961959	0.7955905	0.7949843	0.7943772	0.7937694	0.7931608	0.7925514
6.94	0.7919412	0.7913302	0.7907184	0.7901058	0.7894925	0.7888783	0.7882634	0.7876476	0.7870311	0.7864138
6.95	0.7857957	0.7851768	0.7845572	0.7839367	0.7833155	0.7826935	0.7820707	0.7814471	0.7808227	0.7801976
6.96	0.7795717	0.7789450	0.7783175	0.7776892	0.7770602	0.7764304	0.7757998	0.7751684	0.7745363	0.7739034
6.97	0.7732697	0.7726352	0.7720000	0.7713640	0.7707272	0.7700896	0.7694513	0.7688122	0.7681724	0.7675317
6.98	0.7668903	0.7662482	0.7656052	0.7649616	0.7643171	0.7636719	0.7630259	0.7623792	0.7617316	0.7610834
6.99	0.7604343	0.7597845	0.7591340	0.7584827	0.7578306	0.7571777	0.7565242	0.7558698	0.7552147	0.7545589

TABLE 2 Cos

τ	.000	.001	.002	.003	.004	.005	.006	.007	.008	.009
7.00	0.7539023	0.7532449	0.7525868	0.7519279	0.7512683	0.7506079	0.7499468	0.7492849	0.7486223	0.7479589
7.01	0.7472948	0.7466299	0.7459643	0.7452980	0.7446309	0.7439630	0.7432944	0.7426251	0.7419550	0.7412842
7.02	0.7406126	0.7399403	0.7392673	0.7385935	0.7379190	0.7372437	0.7365677	0.7358910	0.7352135	0.7345353
7.03	0.7338564	0.7331767	0.7324963	0.7318152	0.7311333	0.7304507	0.7297674	0.7290833	0.7283985	0.7277130
7.04	0.7270268	0.7263398	0.7256521	0.7249637	0.7242745	0.7235846	0.7228940	0.7222027	0.7215107	0.7208179
7.05	0.7201244	0.7194307	0.7187353	0.7180397	0.7173433	0.7166462	0.7159484	0.7152499	0.7145507	0.7138507
7.06	0.7131501	0.7124487	0.7117466	0.7110438	0.7103403	0.7096361	0.7089312	0.7082256	0.7075192	0.7068122
7.07	0.7061044	0.7053960	0.7046868	0.7039769	0.7032664	0.7025551	0.7018431	0.7011304	0.7004170	0.6997030
7.08	0.6989882	0.6982727	0.6975565	0.6968396	0.6961221	0.6954038	0.6946848	0.6939652	0.6932448	0.6925237
7.09	0.6918020	0.6910796	0.6903565	0.6896326	0.6889081	0.6881829	0.6874571	0.6867305	0.6860032	0.6852753
7.10	0.6845467	0.6838174	0.6830874	0.6823567	0.6816253	0.6808933	0.6801606	0.6794272	0.6786931	0.6779583
7.11	0.6772229	0.6764868	0.6757500	0.6750125	0.6742743	0.6735355	0.6727960	0.6720559	0.6713150	0.6705735
7.12	0.6698314	0.6690885	0.6683450	0.6676008	0.6668559	0.6661104	0.6653642	0.6646174	0.6638699	0.6631217
7.13	0.6623729	0.6616233	0.6608732	0.6601224	0.6593709	0.6586187	0.6578659	0.6571124	0.6563583	0.6556035
7.14	0.6548481	0.6540920	0.6533353	0.6525779	0.6518198	0.6510611	0.6503018	0.6495418	0.6487811	0.6480198
7.15	0.6472579	0.6464953	0.6457321	0.6449682	0.6442036	0.6434385	0.6426726	0.6419062	0.6411391	0.6403713
7.16	0.6396029	0.6388339	0.6380643	0.6372940	0.6365230	0.6357514	0.6349792	0.6342064	0.6334329	0.6326588
7.17	0.6318840	0.6311087	0.6303327	0.6295560	0.6287787	0.6280008	0.6272223	0.6264432	0.6256634	0.6248830
7.18	0.6241019	0.6233203	0.6225380	0.6217551	0.6209716	0.6201874	0.6194027	0.6186173	0.6178313	0.6170447
7.19	0.6162574	0.6154696	0.6146811	0.6138920	0.6131023	0.6123120	0.6115211	0.6107296	0.6099374	0.6091447
7.20	0.6083513	0.6075573	0.6067628	0.6059676	0.6051718	0.6043754	0.6035784	0.6027808	0.6019826	0.6011838
7.21	0.6003844	0.5995843	0.5987837	0.5979825	0.5971807	0.5963783	0.5955753	0.5947717	0.5939675	0.5931627
7.22	0.5923573	0.5915514	0.5907448	0.5899377	0.5891299	0.5883216	0.5875127	0.5867032	0.5858931	0.5850824
7.23	0.5842711	0.5834593	0.5826468	0.5818338	0.5810202	0.5802060	0.5793913	0.5785759	0.5777600	0.5769435
7.24	0.5761264	0.5753088	0.5744906	0.5736718	0.5728524	0.5720325	0.5712119	0.5703909	0.5695692	0.5687470
7.25	0.5679242	0.5671008	0.5662769	0.5654524	0.5646273	0.5638017	0.5629755	0.5621487	0.5613214	0.5604935
7.26	0.5596651	0.5588361	0.5580065	0.5571764	0.5563458	0.5555145	0.5546827	0.5538504	0.5530175	0.5521841
7.27	0.5513501	0.5505155	0.5496804	0.5488448	0.5480086	0.5471718	0.5463345	0.5454967	0.5446583	0.5438194
7.28	0.5429799	0.5421399	0.5412993	0.5404582	0.5396166	0.5387744	0.5379317	0.5370984	0.5362446	0.5354003
7.29	0.5345554	0.5337100	0.5328641	0.5320176	0.5311706	0.5303231	0.5294750	0.5286265	0.5277773	0.5269277
7.30	0.5260775	0.5252268	0.5243756	0.5235238	0.5226716	0.5218188	0.5209655	0.5201116	0.5192573	0.5184024
7.31	0.5175470	0.5166911	0.5158346	0.5149777	0.5141202	0.5132623	0.5124038	0.5115449	0.5106853	0.5098252
7.32	0.5089647	0.5081037	0.5072421	0.5063801	0.5055175	0.5046544	0.5037909	0.5029268	0.5020622	0.5011971
7.33	0.5003315	0.4994654	0.4985989	0.4977318	0.4968642	0.4959961	0.4951276	0.4942585	0.4933889	0.4925189
7.34	0.4916483	0.4907773	0.4899057	0.4890337	0.4881612	0.4872882	0.4864147	0.4855408	0.4846663	0.4837914

TABLE 2   Cos

T	.000	.001	.002	.003	.004	.005	.006	.007	.008	.009
7.35	0.4829159	0.4820400	0.4811636	0.4802868	0.4794094	0.4785316	0.4776533	0.4767745	0.4758952	0.4750155
7.36	0.4741353	0.4732546	0.4723734	0.4714918	0.4706097	0.4697271	0.4688441	0.4679605	0.4670766	0.4661921
7.37	0.4653072	0.4644218	0.4635360	0.4626497	0.4617629	0.4608757	0.4599880	0.4590998	0.4582112	0.4573221
7.38	0.4564326	0.4555426	0.4546522	0.4537613	0.4528699	0.4519781	0.4510859	0.4501931	0.4493000	0.4484064
7.39	0.4475123	0.4466178	0.4457229	0.4448275	0.4439315	0.4430354	0.4421386	0.4412415	0.4403439	0.4394458
7.40	0.4385473	0.4376484	0.4367490	0.4358492	0.4349490	0.4340483	0.4331472	0.4322457	0.4313437	0.4304413
7.41	0.4295385	0.4286352	0.4277315	0.4268274	0.4259228	0.4250179	0.4241125	0.4232067	0.4223004	0.4213937
7.42	0.4204867	0.4195791	0.4186712	0.4177629	0.4168541	0.4159449	0.4150353	0.4141253	0.4132149	0.4123040
7.43	0.4113928	0.4104811	0.4095691	0.4086566	0.4077437	0.4068304	0.4059167	0.4050026	0.4040880	0.4031731
7.44	0.4022578	0.4013421	0.4004259	0.3995094	0.3985925	0.3976752	0.3967574	0.3958393	0.3949208	0.3940019
7.45	0.3930826	0.3921629	0.3912428	0.3903223	0.3894014	0.3884802	0.3875585	0.3866365	0.3857140	0.3847912
7.46	0.3838680	0.3829445	0.3820205	0.3810962	0.3801714	0.3792463	0.3783208	0.3773950	0.3764687	0.3755421
7.47	0.3746151	0.3736878	0.3727600	0.3718319	0.3709034	0.3699746	0.3690453	0.3681157	0.3671858	0.3662554
7.48	0.3653247	0.3643937	0.3634623	0.3625305	0.3615983	0.3606658	0.3597329	0.3587997	0.3578661	0.3569321
7.49	0.3559978	0.3550632	0.3541281	0.3531928	0.3522570	0.3513210	0.3503845	0.3494478	0.3485106	0.3475731
7.50	0.3466353	0.3456971	0.3447586	0.3438198	0.3428806	0.3419410	0.3410011	0.3400609	0.3391203	0.3381794
7.51	0.3372381	0.3362966	0.3353546	0.3344124	0.3334698	0.3325269	0.3315836	0.3306401	0.3296961	0.3287518
7.52	0.3278072	0.3268623	0.3259171	0.3249715	0.3240257	0.3230794	0.3221329	0.3211861	0.3202389	0.3192914
7.53	0.3183436	0.3173954	0.3164470	0.3154982	0.3145491	0.3135997	0.3126500	0.3117000	0.3107497	0.3097990
7.54	0.3088481	0.3078968	0.3069452	0.3059933	0.3050411	0.3040887	0.3031359	0.3021928	0.3012294	0.3002757
7.55	0.2993217	0.2983674	0.2974128	0.2964579	0.2955027	0.2945472	0.2935914	0.2926353	0.2916789	0.2907223
7.56	0.2897653	0.2888081	0.2878506	0.2868927	0.2859346	0.2849762	0.2840176	0.2830586	0.2820994	0.2811398
7.57	0.2801800	0.2792199	0.2782596	0.2772989	0.2763380	0.2753768	0.2744153	0.2734536	0.2724916	0.2715293
7.58	0.2705667	0.2696039	0.2686408	0.2676774	0.2667137	0.2657498	0.2647857	0.2638212	0.2628565	0.2618915
7.59	0.2609263	0.2599608	0.2589951	0.2580291	0.2570628	0.2560963	0.2551295	0.2541625	0.2531952	0.2522276
7.60	0.2512598	0.2502918	0.2493235	0.2483550	0.2473862	0.2464171	0.2454478	0.2444783	0.2435085	0.2425385
7.61	0.2415682	0.2405977	0.2396270	0.2386560	0.2376848	0.2367133	0.2357416	0.2347697	0.2337975	0.2328251
7.62	0.2318525	0.2308796	0.2299065	0.2289332	0.2279596	0.2269859	0.2260118	0.2250376	0.2240631	0.2230885
7.63	0.2221135	0.2211384	0.2201631	0.2191875	0.2182117	0.2172357	0.2162595	0.2152830	0.2143064	0.2133295
7.64	0.2123524	0.2113751	0.2103976	0.2094199	0.2084419	0.2074638	0.2064855	0.2055069	0.2045281	0.2035492
7.65	0.2025700	0.2015906	0.2006111	0.1996313	0.1986513	0.1976712	0.1966908	0.1957102	0.1947295	0.1937485
7.66	0.1927674	0.1917860	0.1908045	0.1898228	0.1888409	0.1878588	0.1868765	0.1858940	0.1849113	0.1839285
7.67	0.1829454	0.1819622	0.1809788	0.1799953	0.1790115	0.1780276	0.1770435	0.1760592	0.1750747	0.1740901
7.68	0.1731052	0.1721202	0.1711351	0.1701498	0.1691642	0.1681786	0.1671927	0.1662067	0.1652206	0.1642342
7.69	0.1632477	0.1622610	0.1612742	0.1602872	0.1593001	0.1583128	0.1573253	0.1563377	0.1553499	0.1543620

TABLE 2   Cos

T	.000	.001	.002	.003	.004	.005	.006	.007	.008	.009
7.70	0.1533739	0.1523856	0.1513972	0.1504087	0.1494200	0.1484311	0.1474421	0.1464530	0.1454637	0.1444742
7.71	0.1434847	0.1424950	0.1415051	0.1405151	0.1395249	0.1385346	0.1375442	0.1365536	0.1355629	0.1345721
7.72	0.1335811	0.1325900	0.1315988	0.1306074	0.1296159	0.1286243	0.1276325	0.1266407	0.1256486	0.1246565
7.73	0.1236642	0.1226719	0.1216794	0.1206867	0.1196940	0.1187011	0.1177081	0.1167150	0.1157218	0.1147284
7.74	0.1137350	0.1127414	0.1117477	0.1107539	0.1097600	0.1087660	0.1077719	0.1067777	0.1057833	0.1047889
7.75	0.1037944	0.1027997	0.1018050	0.1008101	0.0998151	0.0988201	0.0978249	0.0968297	0.0958343	0.0948389
7.76	0.0938433	0.0928477	0.0918520	0.0908562	0.0898603	0.0888643	0.0878682	0.0868720	0.0858757	0.0848794
7.77	0.0838829	0.0828864	0.0818898	0.0808931	0.0798964	0.0788995	0.0779026	0.0769056	0.0759085	0.0749114
7.78	0.0739142	0.0729169	0.0719195	0.0709220	0.0699245	0.0689269	0.0679293	0.0669316	0.0659338	0.0649359
7.79	0.0639380	0.0629400	0.0619420	0.0609438	0.0599457	0.0589474	0.0579492	0.0569508	0.0559524	0.0549539
7.80	0.0539554	0.0529569	0.0519582	0.0509596	0.0499608	0.0489621	0.0479632	0.0469644	0.0459654	0.0449665
7.81	0.0439675	0.0429684	0.0419693	0.0409702	0.0399710	0.0389718	0.0379725	0.0369732	0.0359739	0.0349745
7.82	0.0339751	0.0329757	0.0319762	0.0309767	0.0299771	0.0289776	0.0279780	0.0269784	0.0259787	0.0249790
7.83	0.0239793	0.0229796	0.0219799	0.0209801	0.0199803	0.0189805	0.0179807	0.0169809	0.0159810	0.0149811
7.84	0.0139812	0.0129813	0.0119813	0.0109814	0.0099815	0.0089815	0.0079815	0.0069816	0.0059816	0.0049816
7.85	0.0039816	0.0029816	0.0019816	0.0009816	-0.0000184	-0.0010184	-0.0020184	-0.0030184	-0.0040184	-0.0050183
7.86	-0.0060183	-0.0070183	-0.0080183	-0.0090182	-0.0100182	-0.0110181	-0.0120181	-0.0130180	-0.0140179	-0.0150178
7.87	-0.0160177	-0.0170175	-0.0180174	-0.0190172	-0.0200170	-0.0210168	-0.0220166	-0.0230163	-0.0240161	-0.0250158
7.88	-0.0260154	-0.0270151	-0.0280147	-0.0290143	-0.0300139	-0.0310134	-0.0320129	-0.0330124	-0.0340118	-0.0350112
7.89	-0.0360106	-0.0370099	-0.0380092	-0.0390085	-0.0400077	-0.0410069	-0.0420060	-0.0430051	-0.0440042	-0.0450032
7.90	-0.0460021	-0.0470010	-0.0479999	-0.0489987	-0.0499975	-0.0509962	-0.0519949	-0.0529935	-0.0539921	-0.0549906
7.91	-0.0559891	-0.0569875	-0.0579858	-0.0589841	-0.0599823	-0.0609805	-0.0619786	-0.0629767	-0.0639746	-0.0649726
7.92	-0.0659704	-0.0669682	-0.0679659	-0.0689636	-0.0699612	-0.0709587	-0.0719561	-0.0729535	-0.0739508	-0.0749480
7.93	-0.0759452	-0.0769422	-0.0779392	-0.0789362	-0.0799330	-0.0809298	-0.0819264	-0.0829230	-0.0839196	-0.0849160
7.94	-0.0859123	-0.0869086	-0.0879048	-0.0889008	-0.0898968	-0.0908927	-0.0918886	-0.0928843	-0.0938799	-0.0948755
7.95	-0.0958709	-0.0968662	-0.0978615	-0.0988566	-0.0998517	-0.1008466	-0.1018415	-0.1028362	-0.1038309	-0.1048254
7.96	-0.1058199	-0.1068142	-0.1078084	-0.1088025	-0.1097966	-0.1107905	-0.1117842	-0.1127779	-0.1137715	-0.1147649
7.97	-0.1157583	-0.1167515	-0.1177446	-0.1187376	-0.1197304	-0.1207232	-0.1217158	-0.1227083	-0.1237007	-0.1246930
7.98	-0.1256851	-0.1266771	-0.1276690	-0.1286607	-0.1296524	-0.1306438	-0.1316352	-0.1326264	-0.1336175	-0.1346085
7.99	-0.1355993	-0.1365900	-0.1375806	-0.1385710	-0.1395613	-0.1405514	-0.1415414	-0.1425313	-0.1435210	-0.1445106
8.00	-0.1455000	-0.1464893	-0.1474785	-0.1484674	-0.1494563	-0.1504450	-0.1514335	-0.1524219	-0.1534102	-0.1543983
8.01	-0.1553862	-0.1563740	-0.1573616	-0.1583490	-0.1593363	-0.1603235	-0.1613105	-0.1622973	-0.1632840	-0.1642704
8.02	-0.1652568	-0.1662429	-0.1672289	-0.1682148	-0.1692005	-0.1701859	-0.1711713	-0.1721564	-0.1731414	-0.1741262
8.03	-0.1751109	-0.1760953	-0.1770796	-0.1780637	-0.1790476	-0.1800314	-0.1810150	-0.1819984	-0.1829816	-0.1839646
8.04	-0.1849474	-0.1859301	-0.1869126	-0.1878948	-0.1888769	-0.1898589	-0.1908406	-0.1918221	-0.1928034	-0.1937846

TABLE 2   Cos

τ	.000	.001	.002	.003	.004	.005	.006	.007	.008	.009
8.05	-0.1947655	-0.1957463	-0.1967268	-0.1977072	-0.1986873	-0.1996673	-0.2006471	-0.2016266	-0.2026060	-0.2035851
8.06	-0.2045641	-0.2055428	-0.2065214	-0.2074997	-0.2084779	-0.2094558	-0.2104335	-0.2114110	-0.2123883	-0.2133654
8.07	-0.2143422	-0.2153189	-0.2162953	-0.2172715	-0.2182475	-0.2192233	-0.2201989	-0.2211742	-0.2221494	-0.2231243
8.08	-0.2240989	-0.2250734	-0.2260476	-0.2270216	-0.2279954	-0.2289690	-0.2299423	-0.2309154	-0.2318882	-0.2328608
8.09	-0.2338332	-0.2348054	-0.2357773	-0.2367490	-0.2377205	-0.2386917	-0.2396627	-0.2406334	-0.2416039	-0.2425741
8.10	-0.2435442	-0.2445139	-0.2454834	-0.2464527	-0.2474218	-0.2483905	-0.2493591	-0.2503274	-0.2512954	-0.2522632
8.11	-0.2532307	-0.2541980	-0.2551650	-0.2561318	-0.2570983	-0.2580646	-0.2590306	-0.2599963	-0.2609618	-0.2619270
8.12	-0.2628919	-0.2638566	-0.2648211	-0.2657852	-0.2667491	-0.2677128	-0.2686761	-0.2696392	-0.2706021	-0.2715646
8.13	-0.2725269	-0.2734889	-0.2744506	-0.2754121	-0.2763733	-0.2773342	-0.2782948	-0.2792552	-0.2802153	-0.2811751
8.14	-0.2821346	-0.2830938	-0.2840528	-0.2850114	-0.2859698	-0.2869279	-0.2878857	-0.2888432	-0.2898005	-0.2907574
8.15	-0.2917141	-0.2926704	-0.2936265	-0.2945823	-0.2955379	-0.2964929	-0.2974478	-0.2984024	-0.2993567	-0.3003107
8.16	-0.3012644	-0.3022178	-0.3031709	-0.3041236	-0.3050761	-0.3060283	-0.3069802	-0.3079317	-0.3088830	-0.3098339
8.17	-0.3107846	-0.3117349	-0.3126849	-0.3136346	-0.3145840	-0.3155331	-0.3164818	-0.3174303	-0.3183784	-0.3193262
8.18	-0.3202737	-0.3212208	-0.3221677	-0.3231142	-0.3240604	-0.3250063	-0.3259518	-0.3268971	-0.3278419	-0.3287865
8.19	-0.3297308	-0.3306747	-0.3316182	-0.3325615	-0.3335044	-0.3344470	-0.3353892	-0.3363311	-0.3372727	-0.3382140
8.20	-0.3391549	-0.3400954	-0.3410356	-0.3419755	-0.3429151	-0.3438543	-0.3447931	-0.3457316	-0.3466698	-0.3476076
8.21	-0.3485451	-0.3494822	-0.3504189	-0.3513554	-0.3522914	-0.3532271	-0.3541625	-0.3550975	-0.3560322	-0.3569665
8.22	-0.3579004	-0.3588340	-0.3597672	-0.3607001	-0.3616326	-0.3625647	-0.3634965	-0.3644279	-0.3653589	-0.3662896
8.23	-0.3672199	-0.3681499	-0.3690795	-0.3700087	-0.3709375	-0.3718660	-0.3727941	-0.3737218	-0.3746492	-0.3755762
8.24	-0.3765028	-0.3774290	-0.3783548	-0.3792803	-0.3802054	-0.3811301	-0.3820544	-0.3829784	-0.3839020	-0.3848251
8.25	-0.3857479	-0.3866703	-0.3875924	-0.3885140	-0.3894353	-0.3903561	-0.3912766	-0.3921967	-0.3931163	-0.3940356
8.26	-0.3949545	-0.3958730	-0.3967911	-0.3977089	-0.3986262	-0.3995431	-0.4004595	-0.4013757	-0.4022914	-0.4032067
8.27	-0.4041216	-0.4050361	-0.4059502	-0.4068639	-0.4077772	-0.4086901	-0.4096026	-0.4105146	-0.4114263	-0.4123375
8.28	-0.4132483	-0.4141588	-0.4150687	-0.4159783	-0.4168875	-0.4177962	-0.4187046	-0.4196125	-0.4205200	-0.4214271
8.29	-0.4223337	-0.4232399	-0.4241457	-0.4250511	-0.4259561	-0.4268606	-0.4277647	-0.4286684	-0.4295716	-0.4304745
8.30	-0.4313768	-0.4322788	-0.4331803	-0.4340814	-0.4349821	-0.4358823	-0.4367821	-0.4376814	-0.4385803	-0.4394788
8.31	-0.4403768	-0.4412744	-0.4421716	-0.4430683	-0.4439646	-0.4448604	-0.4457558	-0.4466507	-0.4475452	-0.4484392
8.32	-0.4493328	-0.4502259	-0.4511186	-0.4520109	-0.4529027	-0.4537940	-0.4546849	-0.4555753	-0.4564653	-0.4573548
8.33	-0.4582438	-0.4591324	-0.4600206	-0.4609082	-0.4617955	-0.4626822	-0.4635685	-0.4644543	-0.4653397	-0.4662246
8.34	-0.4671090	-0.4679930	-0.4688765	-0.4697595	-0.4706421	-0.4715242	-0.4724058	-0.4732869	-0.4741676	-0.4750478
8.35	-0.4759275	-0.4768068	-0.4776856	-0.4785638	-0.4794417	-0.4803190	-0.4811958	-0.4820722	-0.4829481	-0.4838235
8.36	-0.4846984	-0.4855729	-0.4864468	-0.4873203	-0.4881933	-0.4890658	-0.4899378	-0.4908093	-0.4916803	-0.4925508
8.37	-0.4934209	-0.4942904	-0.4951595	-0.4960280	-0.4968961	-0.4977636	-0.4986307	-0.4994973	-0.5003633	-0.5012289
8.38	-0.5020940	-0.5029585	-0.5038226	-0.5046861	-0.5055492	-0.5064117	-0.5072738	-0.5081353	-0.5089963	-0.5098568
8.39	-0.5107168	-0.5115763	-0.5124353	-0.5132938	-0.5141517	-0.5150092	-0.5158661	-0.5167225	-0.5175784	-0.5184338

TABLE 2 Cos

τ	.000	.001	.002	.003	.004	.005	.006	.007	.008	.009
8.40	-0.5192887	-0.5201430	-0.5209968	-0.5218501	-0.5227029	-0.5235551	-0.5244069	-0.5252581	-0.5261088	-0.5269589
8.41	-0.5278085	-0.5286576	-0.5295062	-0.5303542	-0.5312018	-0.5320488	-0.5328952	-0.5337411	-0.5345865	-0.5354313
8.42	-0.5362756	-0.5371194	-0.5379627	-0.5388054	-0.5396475	-0.5404891	-0.5413302	-0.5421708	-0.5430107	-0.5438502
8.43	-0.5446891	-0.5455275	-0.5463653	-0.5472026	-0.5480393	-0.5488755	-0.5497111	-0.5505462	-0.5513807	-0.5522147
8.44	-0.5530481	-0.5538810	-0.5547133	-0.5555451	-0.5563763	-0.5572069	-0.5580370	-0.5588666	-0.5596955	-0.5605240
8.45	-0.5613518	-0.5621791	-0.5630059	-0.5638320	-0.5646576	-0.5654827	-0.5663072	-0.5671311	-0.5679544	-0.5687772
8.46	-0.5695994	-0.5704210	-0.5712421	-0.5720626	-0.5728825	-0.5737019	-0.5745206	-0.5753388	-0.5761565	-0.5769735
8.47	-0.5777900	-0.5786059	-0.5794212	-0.5802359	-0.5810501	-0.5818637	-0.5826767	-0.5834891	-0.5843009	-0.5851122
8.48	-0.5859228	-0.5867329	-0.5875424	-0.5883513	-0.5891596	-0.5899673	-0.5907745	-0.5915810	-0.5923369	-0.5931923
8.49	-0.5939971	-0.5948012	-0.5956048	-0.5964078	-0.5972102	-0.5980120	-0.5988131	-0.5996137	-0.6004137	-0.6012131
8.50	-0.6020119	-0.6028101	-0.6036077	-0.6044047	-0.6052010	-0.6059968	-0.6067920	-0.6075865	-0.6083805	-0.6091739
8.51	-0.6099665	-0.6107587	-0.6115502	-0.6123411	-0.6131314	-0.6139210	-0.6147101	-0.6154985	-0.6162864	-0.6170736
8.52	-0.6178602	-0.6186462	-0.6194315	-0.6202163	-0.6210004	-0.6217839	-0.6225668	-0.6233490	-0.6241306	-0.6249117
8.53	-0.6256920	-0.6264718	-0.6272509	-0.6280294	-0.6288073	-0.6295846	-0.6303612	-0.6311372	-0.6319125	-0.6326872
8.54	-0.6334613	-0.6342348	-0.6350076	-0.6357798	-0.6365513	-0.6373223	-0.6380925	-0.6388622	-0.6396312	-0.6403995
8.55	-0.6411673	-0.6419343	-0.6427008	-0.6434666	-0.6442317	-0.6449962	-0.6457601	-0.6465233	-0.6472859	-0.6480478
8.56	-0.6488091	-0.6495697	-0.6503297	-0.6510890	-0.6518477	-0.6526057	-0.6533631	-0.6541198	-0.6548759	-0.6556313
8.57	-0.6563860	-0.6571401	-0.6578936	-0.6586464	-0.6593985	-0.6601499	-0.6609007	-0.6616509	-0.6624004	-0.6631492
8.58	-0.6638973	-0.6646448	-0.6653917	-0.6661378	-0.6668833	-0.6676281	-0.6683723	-0.6691158	-0.6698586	-0.6706008
8.59	-0.6713423	-0.6720831	-0.6728232	-0.6735627	-0.6743015	-0.6750396	-0.6757770	-0.6765138	-0.6772499	-0.6779853
8.60	-0.6787200	-0.6794541	-0.6801875	-0.6809202	-0.6816522	-0.6823835	-0.6831142	-0.6838442	-0.6845734	-0.6853020
8.61	-0.6860300	-0.6867572	-0.6874837	-0.6882096	-0.6889348	-0.6896592	-0.6903830	-0.6911061	-0.6918285	-0.6925502
8.62	-0.6932713	-0.6939916	-0.6947112	-0.6954307	-0.6961484	-0.6968660	-0.6975828	-0.6982990	-0.6990144	-0.6997292
8.63	-0.7004433	-0.7011566	-0.7018693	-0.7025812	-0.7032925	-0.7040030	-0.7047129	-0.7054220	-0.7061304	-0.7068382
8.64	-0.7075452	-0.7082515	-0.7089571	-0.7096620	-0.7103662	-0.7110697	-0.7117724	-0.7124745	-0.7131758	-0.7138765
8.65	-0.7145764	-0.7152756	-0.7159741	-0.7166718	-0.7173689	-0.7180652	-0.7187608	-0.7194557	-0.7201499	-0.7208434
8.66	-0.7215361	-0.7222281	-0.7229194	-0.7236100	-0.7242999	-0.7249890	-0.7256774	-0.7263650	-0.7270520	-0.7277382
8.67	-0.7284237	-0.7291084	-0.7297925	-0.7304758	-0.7311584	-0.7318402	-0.7325213	-0.7332017	-0.7338813	-0.7345602
8.68	-0.7352384	-0.7359159	-0.7365926	-0.7372685	-0.7379438	-0.7386183	-0.7392920	-0.7399650	-0.7406373	-0.7413088
8.69	-0.7419796	-0.7426497	-0.7433190	-0.7439876	-0.7446554	-0.7453225	-0.7459888	-0.7466544	-0.7473192	-0.7479833
8.70	-0.7486466	-0.7493092	-0.7499711	-0.7506322	-0.7512925	-0.7519521	-0.7526110	-0.7532691	-0.7539264	-0.7545830
8.71	-0.7552388	-0.7558939	-0.7565482	-0.7572017	-0.7578545	-0.7585066	-0.7591579	-0.7598084	-0.7604582	-0.7611072
8.72	-0.7617554	-0.7624029	-0.7630496	-0.7636956	-0.7643408	-0.7649852	-0.7656289	-0.7662718	-0.7669139	-0.7675553
8.73	-0.7681959	-0.7688357	-0.7694748	-0.7701131	-0.7707506	-0.7713873	-0.7720233	-0.7726585	-0.7732930	-0.7739266
8.74	-0.7745595	-0.7751916	-0.7758230	-0.7764535	-0.7770833	-0.7777123	-0.7783405	-0.7789680	-0.7795947	-0.7802206

TABLE 2   Cos

T	.000	.001	.002	.003	.004	.005	.006	.007	.008	.009
8.75	-0.7808457	-0.7814700	-0.7820936	-0.7827163	-0.7833383	-0.7839595	-0.7845799	-0.7851995	-0.7858184	-0.7864365
8.76	-0.7870538	-0.7876703	-0.7882860	-0.7889009	-0.7895150	-0.7901283	-0.7907409	-0.7913526	-0.7919636	-0.7925738
8.77	-0.7931832	-0.7937918	-0.7943995	-0.7950065	-0.7956127	-0.7962182	-0.7968228	-0.7974266	-0.7980296	-0.7986318
8.78	-0.7992332	-0.7998339	-0.8004337	-0.8010327	-0.8016309	-0.8022283	-0.8028250	-0.8034208	-0.8040158	-0.8046100
8.79	-0.8052034	-0.8057960	-0.8063878	-0.8069788	-0.8075689	-0.8081583	-0.8087469	-0.8093346	-0.8099216	-0.8105077
8.80	-0.8110930	-0.8116775	-0.8122612	-0.8128441	-0.8134262	-0.8140074	-0.8145879	-0.8151675	-0.8157463	-0.8163243
8.81	-0.8169015	-0.8174779	-0.8180535	-0.8186282	-0.8192021	-0.8197752	-0.8203475	-0.8209189	-0.8214896	-0.8220594
8.82	-0.8226284	-0.8231965	-0.8237639	-0.8243304	-0.8248961	-0.8254610	-0.8260250	-0.8265882	-0.8271506	-0.8277122
8.83	-0.8282729	-0.8288328	-0.8293919	-0.8299502	-0.8305076	-0.8310642	-0.8316200	-0.8321749	-0.8327290	-0.8332822
8.84	-0.8338347	-0.8343863	-0.8349370	-0.8354870	-0.8360361	-0.8365843	-0.8371317	-0.8376783	-0.8382241	-0.8387690
8.85	-0.8393130	-0.8398563	-0.8403987	-0.8409402	-0.8414809	-0.8420208	-0.8425598	-0.8430980	-0.8436353	-0.8441718
8.86	-0.8447075	-0.8452423	-0.8457762	-0.8463093	-0.8468416	-0.8473730	-0.8479036	-0.8484333	-0.8489622	-0.8494902
8.87	-0.8500174	-0.8505438	-0.8510692	-0.8515939	-0.8521176	-0.8526406	-0.8531626	-0.8536838	-0.8542042	-0.8547237
8.88	-0.8552424	-0.8557602	-0.8562771	-0.8567932	-0.8573084	-0.8578228	-0.8583363	-0.8588490	-0.8593608	-0.8598717
8.89	-0.8603818	-0.8608910	-0.8613994	-0.8619069	-0.8624135	-0.8629193	-0.8634242	-0.8639283	-0.8644314	-0.8649338
8.90	-0.8654352	-0.8659358	-0.8664355	-0.8669344	-0.8674324	-0.8679295	-0.8684257	-0.8689211	-0.8694156	-0.8699093
8.91	-0.8704021	-0.8708940	-0.8713850	-0.8718752	-0.8723645	-0.8728529	-0.8733404	-0.8738271	-0.8743129	-0.8747978
8.92	-0.8752819	-0.8757651	-0.8762474	-0.8767288	-0.8772093	-0.8776890	-0.8781678	-0.8786457	-0.8791227	-0.8795989
8.93	-0.8800742	-0.8805486	-0.8810221	-0.8814947	-0.8819665	-0.8824373	-0.8829073	-0.8833764	-0.8838447	-0.8843120
8.94	-0.8847784	-0.8852440	-0.8857087	-0.8861725	-0.8866354	-0.8870974	-0.8875586	-0.8880188	-0.8884782	-0.8889367
8.95	-0.8893942	-0.8898509	-0.8903067	-0.8907617	-0.8912157	-0.8916688	-0.8921211	-0.8925724	-0.8930229	-0.8934724
8.96	-0.8939211	-0.8943689	-0.8948158	-0.8952618	-0.8957069	-0.8961510	-0.8965944	-0.8970368	-0.8974783	-0.8979189
8.97	-0.8983586	-0.8987974	-0.8992353	-0.8996723	-0.9001084	-0.9005437	-0.9009780	-0.9014114	-0.9018439	-0.9022755
8.98	-0.9027062	-0.9031360	-0.9035649	-0.9039929	-0.9044200	-0.9048462	-0.9052715	-0.9056959	-0.9061194	-0.9065419
8.99	-0.9069636	-0.9073843	-0.9078042	-0.9082231	-0.9086412	-0.9090583	-0.9094745	-0.9098898	-0.9103042	-0.9107177
9.00	-0.9111303	-0.9115419	-0.9119527	-0.9123625	-0.9127714	-0.9131795	-0.9135866	-0.9139927	-0.9143980	-0.9148024
9.01	-0.9152058	-0.9156084	-0.9160100	-0.9164107	-0.9168104	-0.9172093	-0.9176073	-0.9180043	-0.9184004	-0.9187956
9.02	-0.9191899	-0.9195832	-0.9199757	-0.9203672	-0.9207578	-0.9211474	-0.9215362	-0.9219240	-0.9223109	-0.9226969
9.03	-0.9230820	-0.9234661	-0.9238493	-0.9242316	-0.9246130	-0.9249935	-0.9253730	-0.9257516	-0.9261292	-0.9265060
9.04	-0.9268818	-0.9272567	-0.9276307	-0.9280037	-0.9283758	-0.9287470	-0.9291172	-0.9294865	-0.9298549	-0.9302224
9.05	-0.9305889	-0.9309545	-0.9313192	-0.9316829	-0.9320457	-0.9324076	-0.9327686	-0.9331286	-0.9334876	-0.9338458
9.06	-0.9342030	-0.9345593	-0.9349146	-0.9352690	-0.9356225	-0.9359750	-0.9363266	-0.9366773	-0.9370270	-0.9373758
9.07	-0.9377236	-0.9380706	-0.9384165	-0.9387616	-0.9391057	-0.9394488	-0.9397910	-0.9401323	-0.9404727	-0.9408121
9.08	-0.9411505	-0.9414880	-0.9418246	-0.9421602	-0.9424949	-0.9428287	-0.9431615	-0.9434934	-0.9438243	-0.9441543
9.09	-0.9444833	-0.9448114	-0.9451385	-0.9454647	-0.9457900	-0.9461143	-0.9464376	-0.9467600	-0.9470815	-0.9474020

TABLE 2 Cos

T	.000	.001	.002	.003	.004	.005	.006	.007	.008	.009
9.10	-0.9477216	-0.9480402	-0.9483579	-0.9486746	-0.9489904	-0.9493052	-0.9496191	-0.9499321	-0.9502440	-0.9505551
9.11	-0.9508651	-0.9511743	-0.9514825	-0.9517897	-0.9520960	-0.9524013	-0.9527057	-0.9530091	-0.9533115	-0.9536130
9.12	-0.9539136	-0.9542132	-0.9545119	-0.9548096	-0.9551063	-0.9554021	-0.9556969	-0.9559908	-0.9562837	-0.9565757
9.13	-0.9568667	-0.9571567	-0.9574458	-0.9577339	-0.9580211	-0.9583073	-0.9585926	-0.9588769	-0.9591602	-0.9594426
9.14	-0.9597241	-0.9600045	-0.9602840	-0.9605626	-0.9608402	-0.9611168	-0.9613924	-0.9616671	-0.9619409	-0.9622137
9.15	-0.9624855	-0.9627563	-0.9630262	-0.9632951	-0.9635631	-0.9638301	-0.9640961	-0.9643612	-0.9646253	-0.9648885
9.16	-0.9651506	-0.9654118	-0.9656721	-0.9659314	-0.9661897	-0.9664470	-0.9667034	-0.9669588	-0.9672133	-0.9674668
9.17	-0.9677193	-0.9679708	-0.9682214	-0.9684710	-0.9687197	-0.9689673	-0.9692140	-0.9694598	-0.9697045	-0.9699483
9.18	-0.9701912	-0.9704330	-0.9706739	-0.9709138	-0.9711528	-0.9713907	-0.9716277	-0.9718638	-0.9720988	-0.9723329
9.19	-0.9725660	-0.9727982	-0.9730293	-0.9732595	-0.9734887	-0.9737170	-0.9739443	-0.9741706	-0.9743959	-0.9746202
9.20	-0.9748436	-0.9750660	-0.9752875	-0.9755079	-0.9757274	-0.9759459	-0.9761634	-0.9763800	-0.9765955	-0.9768101
9.21	-0.9770237	-0.9772364	-0.9774480	-0.9776587	-0.9778684	-0.9780772	-0.9782849	-0.9784917	-0.9786975	-0.9789023
9.22	-0.9791062	-0.9793090	-0.9795109	-0.9797118	-0.9799117	-0.9801107	-0.9803086	-0.9805056	-0.9807016	-0.9808966
9.23	-0.9810907	-0.9812837	-0.9814758	-0.9816669	-0.9818570	-0.9820461	-0.9822343	-0.9824215	-0.9826076	-0.9827929
9.24	-0.9829771	-0.9831603	-0.9833426	-0.9835238	-0.9837041	-0.9838834	-0.9840617	-0.9842391	-0.9844154	-0.9845908
9.25	-0.9847652	-0.9849386	-0.9851110	-0.9852824	-0.9854529	-0.9856223	-0.9857908	-0.9859583	-0.9861248	-0.9862903
9.26	-0.9864548	-0.9866183	-0.9867809	-0.9869425	-0.9871030	-0.9872626	-0.9874212	-0.9875789	-0.9877355	-0.9878911
9.27	-0.9880458	-0.9881995	-0.9883521	-0.9885038	-0.9886545	-0.9888042	-0.9889530	-0.9891007	-0.9892474	-0.9893932
9.28	-0.9895380	-0.9896817	-0.9898245	-0.9899663	-0.9901071	-0.9902470	-0.9903858	-0.9905236	-0.9906605	-0.9907963
9.29	-0.9909312	-0.9910651	-0.9911979	-0.9913298	-0.9914607	-0.9915907	-0.9917196	-0.9918475	-0.9919744	-0.9921004
9.30	-0.9922253	-0.9923493	-0.9924772	-0.9925947	-0.9927152	-0.9928352	-0.9929542	-0.9930722	-0.9931892	-0.9933052
9.31	-0.9934202	-0.9935343	-0.9936473	-0.9937593	-0.9938704	-0.9939804	-0.9940895	-0.9941976	-0.9943046	-0.9944107
9.32	-0.9945158	-0.9946199	-0.9947230	-0.9948251	-0.9949262	-0.9950263	-0.9951254	-0.9952235	-0.9953207	-0.9954168
9.33	-0.9955119	-0.9956061	-0.9956992	-0.9957914	-0.9958825	-0.9959727	-0.9960618	-0.9961500	-0.9962372	-0.9963233
9.34	-0.9964085	-0.9964927	-0.9965759	-0.9966580	-0.9967392	-0.9968194	-0.9968986	-0.9969768	-0.9970540	-0.9971302
9.35	-0.9972054	-0.9972796	-0.9973529	-0.9974251	-0.9974963	-0.9975665	-0.9976357	-0.9977040	-0.9977712	-0.9978374
9.36	-0.9979026	-0.9979669	-0.9980301	-0.9980923	-0.9981536	-0.9982138	-0.9982731	-0.9983313	-0.9983886	-0.9984448
9.37	-0.9985001	-0.9985543	-0.9986076	-0.9986598	-0.9987111	-0.9987613	-0.9988106	-0.9988589	-0.9989061	-0.9989524
9.38	-0.9989976	-0.9990419	-0.9990852	-0.9991274	-0.9991687	-0.9992090	-0.9992482	-0.9992865	-0.9993238	-0.9993600
9.39	-0.9993953	-0.9994296	-0.9994629	-0.9994951	-0.9995264	-0.9995567	-0.9995859	-0.9996142	-0.9996415	-0.9996678
9.40	-0.9996930	-0.9997173	-0.9997406	-0.9997629	-0.9997841	-0.9998044	-0.9998237	-0.9998420	-0.9998593	-0.9998755
9.41	-0.9998908	-0.9999051	-0.9999184	-0.9999306	-0.9999419	-0.9999522	-0.9999615	-0.9999698	-0.9999770	-0.9999833
9.42	-0.9999886	-0.9999929	-0.9999961	-0.9999984	-0.9999997	-1.0000000	-0.9999993	-0.9999977	-0.9999948	-0.9999911
9.43	-0.9999864	-0.9999807	-0.9999740	-0.9999662	-0.9999575	-0.9999478	-0.9999370	-0.9999253	-0.9999126	-0.9998999
9.44	-0.9998841	-0.9998684	-0.9998517	-0.9998340	-0.9998153	-0.9997955	-0.9997748	-0.9997531	-0.9997304	-0.9997067

TABLE 2

Cos

T	.000	.001	.002	.003	.004	.005	.006	.007	.008	.009
9.45	-0.9996819	-0.9996562	-0.9996295	-0.9996018	-0.9995731	-0.9995433	-0.9995126	-0.9994809	-0.9994482	-0.9994145
9.46	-0.9993798	-0.9993441	-0.9993073	-0.9992696	-0.9992309	-0.9991912	-0.9991505	-0.9991088	-0.9990661	-0.9990224
9.47	-0.9989777	-0.9989320	-0.9988852	-0.9988375	-0.9987888	-0.9987391	-0.9986884	-0.9986367	-0.9985840	-0.9985303
9.48	-0.9984757	-0.9984200	-0.9983633	-0.9983056	-0.9982469	-0.9981872	-0.9981265	-0.9980648	-0.9980022	-0.9979385
9.49	-0.9978738	-0.9978081	-0.9977414	-0.9976738	-0.9976051	-0.9975354	-0.9974648	-0.9973931	-0.9973205	-0.9972468
9.50	-0.9971722	-0.9970965	-0.9970199	-0.9969422	-0.9968636	-0.9967839	-0.9967033	-0.9966217	-0.9965390	-0.9964554
9.51	-0.9963708	-0.9962852	-0.9961986	-0.9961110	-0.9960224	-0.9959328	-0.9958422	-0.9957506	-0.9956580	-0.9955644
9.52	-0.9954698	-0.9953742	-0.9952777	-0.9951801	-0.9950815	-0.9949820	-0.9948814	-0.9947799	-0.9946773	-0.9945738
9.53	-0.9944693	-0.9943637	-0.9942572	-0.9941497	-0.9940412	-0.9939317	-0.9938212	-0.9937097	-0.9935972	-0.9934838
9.54	-0.9933693	-0.9932538	-0.9931374	-0.9930199	-0.9929015	-0.9927820	-0.9926616	-0.9925402	-0.9924178	-0.9922944
9.55	-0.9921700	-0.9920446	-0.9919182	-0.9917908	-0.9916624	-0.9915331	-0.9914027	-0.9912714	-0.9911391	-0.9910057
9.56	-0.9908714	-0.9907361	-0.9905998	-0.9904625	-0.9903243	-0.9901850	-0.9900447	-0.9899035	-0.9897612	-0.9896180
9.57	-0.9894738	-0.9893286	-0.9891824	-0.9890352	-0.9888870	-0.9887379	-0.9885877	-0.9884366	-0.9882845	-0.9881313
9.58	-0.9879772	-0.9878221	-0.9876661	-0.9875090	-0.9873509	-0.9871919	-0.9870319	-0.9868708	-0.9867088	-0.9865458
9.59	-0.9863819	-0.9862169	-0.9860509	-0.9858840	-0.9857161	-0.9855472	-0.9853773	-0.9852064	-0.9850345	-0.9848617
9.60	-0.9846879	-0.9845130	-0.9843372	-0.9841604	-0.9839827	-0.9838039	-0.9836242	-0.9834435	-0.9832617	-0.9830791
9.61	-0.9828954	-0.9827107	-0.9825251	-0.9823385	-0.9821509	-0.9819623	-0.9817727	-0.9815822	-0.9813906	-0.9811981
9.62	-0.9810046	-0.9808101	-0.9806147	-0.9804183	-0.9802208	-0.9800224	-0.9798231	-0.9796227	-0.9794214	-0.9792191
9.63	-0.9790158	-0.9788115	-0.9786062	-0.9784000	-0.9781928	-0.9779846	-0.9777754	-0.9775653	-0.9773542	-0.9771421
9.64	-0.9769290	-0.9767149	-0.9764999	-0.9762839	-0.9760669	-0.9758490	-0.9756300	-0.9754101	-0.9751892	-0.9749674
9.65	-0.9747445	-0.9745207	-0.9742959	-0.9740702	-0.9738435	-0.9736158	-0.9733871	-0.9731574	-0.9729268	-0.9726952
9.66	-0.9724626	-0.9722291	-0.9719946	-0.9717591	-0.9715226	-0.9712852	-0.9710468	-0.9708074	-0.9705670	-0.9703257
9.67	-0.9700834	-0.9698402	-0.9695960	-0.9693508	-0.9691046	-0.9688575	-0.9686094	-0.9683603	-0.9681102	-0.9678592
9.68	-0.9676073	-0.9673543	-0.9671004	-0.9668455	-0.9665897	-0.9663329	-0.9660751	-0.9658163	-0.9655566	-0.9652960
9.69	-0.9650343	-0.9647717	-0.9645081	-0.9642436	-0.9639781	-0.9637116	-0.9634442	-0.9631758	-0.9629065	-0.9626362
9.70	-0.9623649	-0.9620926	-0.9618194	-0.9615453	-0.9612701	-0.9609941	-0.9607170	-0.9604390	-0.9601600	-0.9598801
9.71	-0.9595992	-0.9593174	-0.9590345	-0.9587508	-0.9584660	-0.9581804	-0.9578937	-0.9576061	-0.9573176	-0.9570280
9.72	-0.9567376	-0.9564461	-0.9561537	-0.9558603	-0.9555661	-0.9552708	-0.9549746	-0.9546775	-0.9543794	-0.9540803
9.73	-0.9537803	-0.9534793	-0.9531773	-0.9528744	-0.9525706	-0.9522658	-0.9519601	-0.9516534	-0.9513457	-0.9510371
9.74	-0.9507276	-0.9504171	-0.9501056	-0.9497932	-0.9494799	-0.9491655	-0.9488503	-0.9485341	-0.9482169	-0.9478988
9.75	-0.9475798	-0.9472598	-0.9469389	-0.9466170	-0.9462941	-0.9459704	-0.9456456	-0.9453200	-0.9449934	-0.9446658
9.76	-0.9443373	-0.9440078	-0.9436774	-0.9433461	-0.9430138	-0.9426806	-0.9423464	-0.9420113	-0.9416753	-0.9413383
9.77	-0.9410003	-0.9406615	-0.9403216	-0.9399809	-0.9396392	-0.9392966	-0.9389530	-0.9386085	-0.9382630	-0.9379166
9.78	-0.9375693	-0.9372210	-0.9368718	-0.9365217	-0.9361706	-0.9358186	-0.9354656	-0.9351117	-0.9347569	-0.9344012
9.79	-0.9340445	-0.9336869	-0.9333283	-0.9329688	-0.9326084	-0.9322470	-0.9318847	-0.9315215	-0.9311574	-0.9307923

TABLE 2 Cos

T	.000	.001	.002	.003	.004	.005	.006	.007	.008	.009
9.80	-0.9304263	-0.9300593	-0.9296915	-0.9293226	-0.9289529	-0.9285823	-0.9282107	-0.9278381	-0.9274647	-0.9270903
9.81	-0.9267150	-0.9263388	-0.9259616	-0.9255836	-0.9252046	-0.9248246	-0.9244438	-0.9240620	-0.9236793	-0.9232957
9.82	-0.9229111	-0.9225256	-0.9221392	-0.9217519	-0.9213637	-0.9209745	-0.9205844	-0.9201934	-0.9198015	-0.9194087
9.83	-0.9190149	-0.9186202	-0.9182246	-0.9178281	-0.9174306	-0.9170323	-0.9166330	-0.9162329	-0.9158317	-0.9154297
9.84	-0.9150268	-0.9146229	-0.9142182	-0.9138125	-0.9134059	-0.9129984	-0.9125900	-0.9121806	-0.9117704	-0.9113592
9.85	-0.9109472	-0.9105342	-0.9101203	-0.9097055	-0.9092898	-0.9088732	-0.9084556	-0.9080372	-0.9076179	-0.9071976
9.86	-0.9067765	-0.9063544	-0.9059314	-0.9055075	-0.9050828	-0.9046571	-0.9042305	-0.9038030	-0.9033746	-0.9029453
9.87	-0.9025151	-0.9020840	-0.9016519	-0.9012190	-0.9007852	-0.9003505	-0.8999149	-0.8994784	-0.8990410	-0.8986026
9.88	-0.8981634	-0.8977233	-0.8972823	-0.8968404	-0.8963976	-0.8959539	-0.8955093	-0.8950638	-0.8946174	-0.8941702
9.89	-0.8937220	-0.8932729	-0.8928229	-0.8923721	-0.8919203	-0.8914677	-0.8910142	-0.8905598	-0.8901044	-0.8896482
9.90	-0.8891912	-0.8887332	-0.8882743	-0.8878145	-0.8873539	-0.8868924	-0.8864299	-0.8859666	-0.8855025	-0.8850374
9.91	-0.8845714	-0.8841046	-0.8836368	-0.8831682	-0.8826987	-0.8822283	-0.8817571	-0.8812849	-0.8808119	-0.8803380
9.92	-0.8798632	-0.8793875	-0.8789110	-0.8784336	-0.8779553	-0.8774761	-0.8769960	-0.8765151	-0.8760333	-0.8755506
9.93	-0.8750670	-0.8745826	-0.8740973	-0.8736111	-0.8731240	-0.8726361	-0.8721473	-0.8716576	-0.8711671	-0.8706756
9.94	-0.8701833	-0.8696902	-0.8691961	-0.8687012	-0.8682055	-0.8677088	-0.8672113	-0.8667130	-0.8662137	-0.8657136
9.95	-0.8652126	-0.8647108	-0.8642081	-0.8637045	-0.8632001	-0.8626948	-0.8621886	-0.8616816	-0.8611737	-0.8606650
9.96	-0.8601554	-0.8596449	-0.8591336	-0.8586214	-0.8581084	-0.8575945	-0.8570797	-0.8565641	-0.8560477	-0.8555303
9.97	-0.8550122	-0.8544931	-0.8539732	-0.8534525	-0.8529309	-0.8524084	-0.8518851	-0.8513610	-0.8508360	-0.8503101
9.98	-0.8497834	-0.8492559	-0.8487275	-0.8481982	-0.8476681	-0.8471371	-0.8466053	-0.8460727	-0.8455392	-0.8450049
9.99	-0.8444697	-0.8439337	-0.8433968	-0.8428591	-0.8423205	-0.8417811	-0.8412409	-0.8406999	-0.8401579	-0.8396151

Section 1.1   Page 5

1. (a) $(9, 6, 1)$ (b) $(1, 2, 1, 5)$ (c) $(0, 0, 0, 0, 0)$ (d) $(1, 0, 4)$
   (e) $(1, 11)$ (f) (-14)
3. Use Lemma 1.1.4.   5. Use Lemma 1.1.3, Lemma 1.1.1, and Lemma 1.1.2.
7. Use the fact that $(a + b)c = ac + bc$ whenever $\{a, b, c\} \subset R$.
9. $1 \circ (a_1, \ldots, a_n) = (1 \cdot a_1, \ldots, 1 \cdot a_n) = (a_1, \ldots, a_n)$.
11. $(a_1, \ldots, a_n) + -1(a_1, \ldots, a_n) = (0, \ldots, 0) = \mathbf{0}$.
13. Now, $a \circ \beta = \gamma$; so $(1/a) \circ (a \circ \beta) = (1/a) \circ \gamma$. By Lemma 1.1.7 $(1/a) \circ (a \circ \beta) = [(1/a) \cdot a] \circ \beta = 1 \circ \beta = \beta$ so $\beta = (1/a) \circ \gamma$.
15. The operations are carried out on the coefficients of the unknowns; but the coefficients are real numbers. Thus, addition of equations is associative and commutative, and the zero equation is an additive identity. The result of adding the equations $a_1 x_1 + \cdots + a_n x_n = b_1$ and $(-a_1)x_1 + \cdots + (-a_n)x_n = -b_1$ is $\mathbf{0}$. This verifies that addition of equations has the properties given in the first four lemmas. In a similar way it can be shown that multiplication by a scalar has the properties given in the remaining four lemmas.

Section 1.2   Page 11

1. $\{(1, -1)\}$ 3. $\varnothing$ 5. $(2/3, 4/3, 0), (4/3, 11/3, 1), (0, -1, -1)$
7. Each linear system has solution set $\{(1, -2, 3)\}$.   9. Consider Definition 1.2.1.
11. If $k = 0$ the two matrices are the same. If $k \neq 0$ then multiply the second row of the given matrix by k, and add the resulting second row to the first row.

13. $\begin{pmatrix} 1 & 0 & 1 \\ 0 & 1 & -1 \\ 0 & 0 & 1 \\ 0 & 0 & 0 \end{pmatrix}$ 15. $\{(2, 0, -1, -3)\}$

Section 1.3   Page 16

1. 11   3. 30   5. 4   7. 0   9. 0

Section 1.4   Page 23

1. 172   3. 60   5. −150   7. $a = -32$

9. (0) is the only 1×1 matrix for which **0** is a column vector. But $|0| = 0$, so 1 has the property. Assume that k is a natural number with the property, i.e. if A is a $k \times k$ matrix such that $_iA = \mathbf{0}$ for some i, then $|A| = 0$. Let B be any $k + 1 \times k + 1$ matrix such that $_iB = \mathbf{0}$ for some i. By Definition 1.3.1

$$|B| = b_{11} B_{11} + \cdots + b_{1n} B_{1n} = 0$$

since zero is a factor of each term on the right, by assumption. Thus, by mathematical induction, each natural number has the property. So $|A| = 0$ whenever A is a square matrix for which **0** is a column vector.

Section 1.5   Page 26

1. (a) $2(4|1|) - |1| + 3(-4|-2|) = 31$

(b) $3\left(-10\begin{vmatrix} 2 & 1 \\ 1 & -1 \end{vmatrix} + 5\begin{vmatrix} 2 & 0 \\ 1 & 0 \end{vmatrix}\right) - 2\left(4\begin{vmatrix} 0 & 1 \\ 0 & -1 \end{vmatrix} - 10\begin{vmatrix} -1 & 1 \\ 1 & -1 \end{vmatrix} + 5\begin{vmatrix} -1 & 0 \\ 1 & 0 \end{vmatrix}\right)$

$- 1\left(4\begin{vmatrix} 2 & 0 \\ 1 & 0 \end{vmatrix} + 10\begin{vmatrix} -1 & 2 \\ 1 & 1 \end{vmatrix}\right) = 120$

Section 1.6   Page 31

1. For each i, the ith row vector of $(A^t)^t$ is A_i. Thus $(A^t)^t = A$.

3. (a) Let B be the matrix obtained from an $n \times n$ matrix A by replacing $_1A$ by an n-vector β, and let C be the matrix obtained from A by replacing $_1A$ by $_1A + \beta$. Then $|C| = |A| + |B|$.

(c) Let C be the matrix obtained from a square matrix A by replacing $_iA$ by $_iA + _jA$ where $i \neq j$. Then $|C| = |A|$.

5. (a) $\begin{vmatrix} 2 & 4 & 1 \\ 5 & 2 & 0 \\ -3 & 0 & 0 \end{vmatrix} = 1\begin{vmatrix} 5 & 2 \\ -3 & 0 \end{vmatrix} - 0\begin{vmatrix} 2 & 4 \\ -3 & 0 \end{vmatrix} + 0\begin{vmatrix} 2 & 4 \\ 5 & 2 \end{vmatrix} = 6$ (here $r = 3$)

(c) $\begin{vmatrix} 7 & 1 & -2 & 1 \\ -1 & 5 & 0 & 6 \\ 3 & 0 & 0 & 4 \\ 4 & 0 & 0 & -2 \end{vmatrix} = -2\begin{vmatrix} -1 & 5 & 6 \\ 3 & 0 & 4 \\ 4 & 0 & -2 \end{vmatrix}$ (here $r = 3$)

$= 10\begin{vmatrix} 3 & 4 \\ 4 & -2 \end{vmatrix}$ (here $r = 2$)

$= -220$

7. (a) 0 , (b) −54

9. $\det(k\alpha + \beta , \gamma) = \det(k\alpha , \gamma) + \det(\beta , \gamma) = k \det(\alpha , \gamma) + \det(\beta , \gamma)$.

Section 2.1   Page 36

1. This set is a nonempty subset of R_3. Let α and β be members; so, there are scalars s_1 , t_1 , s_1 , t_2 such that $\alpha = (s_1 , t_1 , 0)$ and $\beta = (s_2 , t_2 , 0)$. Thus $\alpha + \beta = (s_1 + s_2 , t_1 + t_2 , 0)$ and it is clear that $\alpha + \beta$ is also a member of our set. Next, let $k \in R$, then $k\alpha = (ks_1 , kt_1 , 0)$; thus $k\alpha$ is a member of our set. We conclude that this set is a subspace of $\mathcal{R}_3$.

3. (a) $\{(a, 0) \mid a \in R\}$ is a nonempty subset of R_2; also $(a, 0) + (b, 0) = (a + b, 0)$, so this set is closed under vector addition. Moreover, $k(a, 0) = (ka, 0)$ whenever $k \in R$; so this set is closed under scalar multiplication.

(c) If $m = 0$ the given set is $\{(a, 0) \mid a \in R\}$ which is a subspace of $\Re_2$. Assume $m \neq 0$. Clearly $W = \{(a, b) \mid (a, b) \in R_2$ and $b = ma\}$ is a nonempty subset of R_2. Let $b_1 = ma_1$ and let $b_2 = ma_2$; now, $(a_1, b_1) + (a_2, b_2) = (a_1 + a_2, b_1 + b_2)$, but $b_1 + b_2 = ma_1 + ma_2 = m(a_1 + a_2)$, so $(a_1 + a_2, b_1 + b_2) \in W$. Let $k \in R$; now, $k(a_1, b_1) = (ka_1, kb_1)$. But $kb_1 = m(ka_1)$; so $k(a_1, b_1) \in W$. This proves that W is a subspace of $\Re_2$.

5. Let $W = \{(a, b, c) \mid (a, b, c) \in R_3$ and $2a - b + c = 0\}$; clearly $\mathbf{0} \in W$ so W is a nonempty subset of R_3. Let $2a_1 - b_1 + c_1 = 0$ and let $2a_2 - b_2 + c_2 = 0$. Now

$$(a_1, b_1, c_1) + (a_2, b_2, c_2) = (a_1 + a_2, b_1 + b_2, c_1 + c_2)$$

and $2(a_1 + a_2) - (b_1 + b_2) + (c_1 + c_2) = (2a_1 - b_1 + c_1) + (2a_2 - b_2 + c_2) = 0$ so W is closed under vector addition. Let $k \in R$; now, $k(a, b, c) = (ka, kb, kc)$. Let $(a, b, c) \in W$; then

$$2ka - kb + kc = k(2a - b + c) = 0$$

so $k(a, b, c) \in W$. We conclude that W is a subspace of $\Re_3$.

7. Follow the pattern of Exercise 5.

9. (a) Now $\mathbf{0} \in W_1$ and $\mathbf{0} \in W_2$, so $\mathbf{0} \in W_1 \cap W_2$; thus, $W_1 \cap W_2$ is a nonempty subset of R_n. Let $\alpha \in W_1 \cap W_2$ and let $\beta \in W_1 \cap W_2$; then $\{\alpha, \beta\} \subset W_1$ and $\{\alpha, \beta\} \subset W_2$, thus $\alpha + \beta \in W_1$ and $\alpha + \beta \in W_2$, so $\alpha + \beta \in W_1 \cap W_2$. Let $k \in R$ and let $\alpha \in W_1 \cap W_2$; then $k\alpha \in W_1$ and $k\alpha \in W_2$. Thus $k\alpha \in W_1 \cap W_2$. We conclude that $W_1 \cap W_2$ is a subspace of $\Re_n$.

(b) Let $W = \{\alpha_1 + \alpha_2 \mid \alpha_1 \in W_1$ and $\alpha_2 \in W_2\}$. Clearly, W is a nonempty subset of R_n. Let $\{\alpha, \beta\} \subset W$; then $\alpha = \alpha_1 + \alpha_2$ and $\beta = \beta_1 + \beta_2$ where $\{\alpha_1, \beta_1\} \subset W_1$ and $\{\alpha_2, \beta_2\} \subset W_2$. Now,

$$\alpha + \beta = (\alpha_1 + \beta_1) + (\alpha_2 + \beta_2) \in W$$

since $\alpha_1 + \beta_1 \in W_1$ and $\alpha_2 + \beta_2 \in W_2$. Let $k \in R$; then $k(\alpha_1 + \alpha_2) = k\alpha_1 + k\alpha_2 \in W$ since $k\alpha_1 \in W_1$ and $k\alpha_2 \in W_2$. Thus, W is a subspace of $\Re_n$.

11. $(1, 1, 0) = 1(1, 0, 0) + 1(0, 1, 0)$, i.e. $(1, 1, 0)$ is a linear combination of $(1, 0, 0)$ and $(0, 1, 0)$. Thus, $(1, 0, 0), (0, 1, 0), (1, 1, 0)$ are linearly dependent.

13. $k = 0$

15. We seek scalars x_1, x_2, x_3, x_4 such that

$$x_1(-1, 2, 0) + x_2(3, 1, 2) + x_3(4, -1, 0) + x_4(0, 1, -1) = (5, 6, 0).$$

So, we must solve the linear system

$$\begin{cases} -x_1 + 3x_2 + 4x_3 \qquad\ = 5 \\ \ 2x_1 + \ x_2 - \ x_3 + x_4 = 6 \\ \qquad\ 2x_2 \qquad - x_4 = 0. \end{cases}$$

Notice that $(29/7, 0, 16/7, 0)$ is a member of its solution set. Thus, $(5, 6, 0)$ is a linear combination of the given vectors.

17. Let a, b, c, d be any scalars; now,

$$a(1, 0, 0, 0) + b(0, 1, 0, 0) + c(0, 0, 1, 0) + d(0, 0, 0, 1) = (a, b, c, d)$$

and $(a, b, c, d) \neq \mathbf{0}$ if and only if the given scalars are not each 0. So, by the Test for Linear Independence, the given list is linearly independent.

Section 2.2   Page 42

1. $A \subset LA$, so $LA \subset LLA$. We must show that $LLA \subset LA$. Let $\gamma \in LLA$, so $\gamma = \sum_{i=1}^{s} k_i \alpha_i$ where the k's are scalars and $\{\alpha_1, \ldots, \alpha_s\} \subset LA$. Now, $\alpha_j = \sum_{i=1}^{m} c_i \beta_i, j = 1, \ldots, s$, where the c's are scalars and $\{\beta_1, \ldots, \beta_m\} \subset A$. Substituting for $\alpha_1, \ldots, \alpha_s$ in $\gamma = \sum_{i=1}^{s} k_i \alpha_i$, we see that $\gamma \in LA$. Thus, $LLA \subset LA$, so $LLA = LA$.

3. $\alpha \neq \mathbf{0}$, so by Definition 2.2.3, $\{\alpha\}$ is linearly dependent if and only if $\alpha \in L\varnothing$. But $\alpha \notin L\varnothing$; we conclude that $\{\alpha\}$ is linearly independent.

5. Let $A = \{(1, 0, 0), (0, 1, 0), (0, 0, 1), (1, 0, 0)\} = \{(1, 0, 0), (0, 1, 0), (0, 0, 1)\}$. Now, $\mathbf{0} \notin A$; moreover, if $\gamma \in A$ then $\gamma \notin L(A - \{\gamma\})$. Thus, A is linearly independent.

7. (a) $\{(1, 3)\}$ is a basis for W.   (b) dim $W = 1$

9. (a) $\{(1, -1, 0), (0, 0, 1)\}$ is a basis for W.   (b) dim $W = 2$

11. Let A be linearly independent and let B be a linearly dependent subset of A. If $\mathbf{0} \in B$ then $\mathbf{0} \in A$, so A is linearly dependent. Otherwise, there is a member of B, say γ, such that $\gamma \in L(B - \{\gamma\})$, and it follows that $\gamma \in L(A - \{\gamma\})$; so, A is linearly dependent. This proves that B does not exist.

13. Assume that $A \cup \{\beta\}$ is linearly dependent. Clearly $\beta \neq \mathbf{0}$; therefore, there is a member of $A \cup \{\beta\}$, say γ, such that $\gamma \in L((A \cup \{\beta\}) - \{\gamma\})$. If $\gamma = \beta$ then $\beta \in LA$. But $\beta \notin LA$. Thus $\gamma \neq \beta$. So, $\gamma \in A$. Thus

$$\gamma = k\beta + \sum_{i=1}^{s} k_i \alpha_i \qquad \text{where } \alpha_i \neq \gamma, \, i = 1, \ldots, s$$

If $k \neq 0$ then $\beta \in LA$; so $k = 0$. Thus $\gamma = \sum_{i=1}^{s} k_i \alpha_i$. We conclude that $\gamma \in L(A - \{\gamma\})$ where $\gamma \in A$. Thus A is linearly dependent. This contradiction proves that $A \cup \{\beta\}$ is linearly independent.

Section 2.3   Page 45

1. 2   3. 3   5. 2

7. Rank of coefficient matrix is 1; rank of augmented matrix is 2. Thus, linear system has no solution.

9. Linear system is $x + 2y = 4$, $2x + y = -1$, $-x = 2$. Now, $(-2, 3)$ is a solution of this linear system. Thus, $(4, -1, 2) \in L\{(1, 2, -1), (2, 1, 0)\}$.

Section 2.4   Page 50

1. Let W be the solution set of (3); certainly, $\mathbf{0} \in W$, so W is a nonempty subset of R_n. Let $(c_1, \ldots, c_n) \in W$ and let $(d_1, \ldots, d_n) \in W$. We show that $(c_1, \ldots, c_n) + (d_1, \ldots, d_n) \in W$. Now,

$$(c_1 + d_1)\,{}_1A + \cdots + (c_n + d_n)\,{}_nA = (c_1\,{}_1A + \cdots + c_n\,{}_nA) + (d_1\,{}_1A + \cdots + d_n\,{}_nA)$$
$$= \mathbf{0} + \mathbf{0}$$
$$= \mathbf{0}.$$

So, by Lemma 2.4.1, $(c_1 + d_1, \ldots, c_n + d_n) \in W$. Similarly, it is easy to prove that $k(c_1, \ldots, c_n) \in W$ whenever $k \in R$. So, W is a subspace of $\mathfrak{R}_n$.

3. $\{(1/2, 7/2, 0)\}$

5. $\{(1, 7/3, 0, 4/3, 0) + \gamma \mid \gamma \in W\}$ where $W = L\{(1, -3, -2, 0, 0), (-3, 17, 0, 2, -6)\}$.

7. $\mathbf{0}$ is the only vector with the stated property.

Section 2.5   Page 53

1. 3   3. 2   5. 3   7. Yes, e.g. $(1/2, -3/2, 0, 0, 0)$.

Section 2.6   Page 56

1. (1), (0), (3), (2), (−1), (4), $\begin{pmatrix}1\\2\end{pmatrix}$, $\begin{pmatrix}0\\-1\end{pmatrix}$, $\begin{pmatrix}3\\4\end{pmatrix}$, (1 0), (1 3), (0 3), (2 −1), (2 4),

(−1 4), $\begin{pmatrix}1&0\\2&-1\end{pmatrix}$, $\begin{pmatrix}1&3\\2&4\end{pmatrix}$, $\begin{pmatrix}0&3\\-1&4\end{pmatrix}$, (1 0 3), (2 −1 4), $\begin{pmatrix}1&0&3\\2&-1&4\end{pmatrix}$.

3. By Theorem 2.4.4 this linear system has a unique solution if and only if its coefficient matrix and augmented matrix both have rank 4. But the coefficient matrix is nonsingular, so its rank is 4. Clearly, the rank of the augmented matrix is greater than or equal to that of the coefficient matrix; also, since the vectors involved are members of R_4, the rank of the augmented matrix cannot exceed 4. We conclude that 4 is the rank of the augmented matrix. This proves that the given linear system has a unique solution for any choice of b_1, b_2, b_3, and b_4.

5. By assumption, rank $\begin{pmatrix}a_1&b_1&c_1\\a_2&b_2&c_2\\a_3&b_3&c_3\end{pmatrix} < 3$; thus, by Corollary 2.6.3, rank $\begin{pmatrix}a_1&a_2&a_3\\b_1&b_2&b_3\\c_1&c_2&c_3\end{pmatrix} < 3$.

So, if $\{(a_1, b_1, c_1),(a_2, b_2, c_2),(a_3, b_3, c_3)\}$ has three members, then this set is linearly dependent.

7. Let $\{(a_{11}, \ldots, a_{1n}), \ldots, (a_{n1}, \ldots, a_{nn})\}$ have n members and be linearly independent. Then, by Corollary 2.6.3, the coefficient matrix of the homogeneous linear system

$$(1)\begin{cases}a_{11}x_1 +\cdots+ a_{1n}x_n = 0\\ \qquad\quad\vdots\\ a_{n1}x_1 +\cdots+ a_{nn}x_n = 0\end{cases}$$

has rank n. Therefore, by Theorem 2.4.2, the dimension of the solution set of (1) is 0; so this solution set is $\{0\}$. Thus, $\mathbf{0}$ is the only vector orthogonal to each of the given vectors.

Section 3.1   Page 61

1. Let $\alpha = (a_1, \ldots, a_n)$, $\beta = (b_1, \ldots, b_n)$, and let $\gamma = (c_1, \ldots, c_n)$. Then
   (i) $\alpha\cdot\beta = a_1 b_1 +\cdots+ a_n b_n = b_1 a_1 +\cdots+ b_n a_n = \beta\cdot\alpha$.
   (ii) $\alpha\cdot(\beta + \gamma) = a_1(b_1 + c_1) +\cdots+ a_n(b_n + c_n)$
                   $= (a_1 b_1 +\cdots+ a_n b_n) + (a_1 c_1 +\cdots+ a_n c_n)$
                   $= \alpha\cdot\beta + \alpha\cdot\gamma$.
   (iii) $(k\alpha)\cdot\beta = (ka_1)b_1 +\cdots+ (ka_n)b_n = k(a_1 b_1) +\cdots+ k(a_n b_n) = k(\alpha\cdot\beta)$.
   (iv) $\alpha\cdot\alpha = a_1^2 +\cdots+ a_n^2 > 0$ if $\alpha \neq \mathbf{0}$; $\mathbf{0}\cdot\mathbf{0} = 0 +\cdots+ 0 = 0$.

3. If $t = 1$ there is nothing to prove. Assume that k has the property, i.e. $\alpha\cdot(\beta_1 +\cdots+ \beta_k)$ $= \alpha\cdot\beta_1 +\cdots+ \alpha\cdot\beta_k$. We show that $k + 1$ has the property. Now,
    $\alpha\cdot(\beta_1 +\cdots+ \beta_{k+1}) = \alpha\cdot(\beta_1 +\cdots+ \beta_k) + \alpha\cdot\beta_{k+1}$ by Theorem 3.1.1 (*iii*)
                          $= (\alpha\cdot\beta_1 +\cdots+ \alpha\cdot\beta_k) + \alpha\cdot\beta_{k+1}$ by assumption
                          $= \alpha\cdot\beta_1 +\cdots+ \alpha\cdot\beta_k + \alpha\cdot\beta_{k+1}$
so $k + 1$ has the property whenever k has the property. Thus, by mathematical induction, each natural number has the property.

5. Now, $\zeta = (x_1, x_2, x_3)$ is orthogonal to the given vectors if and only if $x_1 = 0$, $x_2 = 0$, and $x_3 = 0$. Thus $\zeta = \mathbf{0}$.

7. Let $W = \{\alpha \mid \alpha \perp \gamma\}$. Clearly $\mathbf{0} \in W$; so W is a nonempty subset of R_n. Let $\{\alpha, \beta\} \subset W$; now $\gamma\cdot(\alpha + \beta) = \gamma\cdot\alpha + \gamma\cdot\beta$ by Theorem 3.1.1, hence $\gamma\cdot(\alpha + \beta) = 0 + 0 = 0$, i.e. $(\alpha + \beta) \perp \gamma$, thus $\alpha + \beta \in W$. Let $k \in R$; then $(k\alpha)\cdot\gamma = k(\alpha\cdot\gamma) = 0$; so $k\alpha \perp \gamma$. Thus $k\alpha \in W$. We conclude that W is a subspace of $\mathcal{R}_n$.

9. By Exercise 8, $W = \{\zeta \mid \zeta \perp \alpha_i, i = 1, \ldots, m\}$ is a subspace of $\mathcal{R}_n$. We must show that $\dim W = n - m$. Now, W is the solution set of the following homogeneous linear system:
(1) $\alpha_1\cdot(x_1, \ldots, x_n) = 0, \ldots, \alpha_m\cdot(x_1, \ldots, x_n) = 0$.

Thus, by Theorem 2.4.2, dim $W = n - r$ where r is the rank of the coefficient matrix of (1). Clearly, the subspace spanned by the row vectors of this coefficient matrix is $L\{\alpha_1, \ldots, \alpha_m\}$, whose dimension is m, by assumption. So, by Corollary 2.6.3, m is the rank of the coefficient matrix of (1). Thus, dim $W = n - m$.

11. $\{(1, 2, -1, 0), (-5, 2, -1, 3), (-23, 4, -15, -46)\}$

13. (a) Show that $\mathbf{0} \in A^\perp$, that $A^\perp$ is closed under vector addition, and that $A^\perp$ is closed under scalar multiplication. (b) $\{(2, 0, -1, 0, 0), (0, 1, 0, -1, 0), (3, 0, 0, 0, -1)\}$

15. (a) Let $k_1, \ldots, k_n$ be scalars such that

$$k_1(\beta_1 \cdot \beta_1, \ldots, \beta_n \cdot \beta_1) + \cdots + k_n(\beta_1 \cdot \beta_n, \ldots, \beta_n \cdot \beta_n) = \mathbf{0}$$

then $\beta_1 \cdot (k_1 \beta_1 + \cdots + k_n \beta_n) = 0, \ldots, \beta_n \cdot (k_1 \beta_1 + \cdots + k_n \beta_n) = 0$. But $\{\beta_1, \ldots, \beta_n\}$ is a basis for R_n, so $\{\beta_1, \ldots, \beta_n\}^\perp = \{\mathbf{0}\}$; thus $k_1 \beta_1 + \cdots + k_n \beta_n = \mathbf{0}$. Now, $\{\beta_1, \ldots, \beta_n\}$ is linearly independent and has n members; so $k_1 = 0, \ldots, k_n = 0$. This proves that the given set is linearly independent.

(b) Consider the linear system $\beta_1 \cdot \gamma = k_1, \ldots, \beta_n \cdot \gamma = k_n$. Clearly the rank of its coefficient matrix and augmented matrix is n. So, by Theorem 2.4.4, this linear system has a unique solution.

17. Assume that there are scalars k_1 and k_2, not both zero, such that $k_1(\beta_1 \cdot \beta_1, -\beta_2 \cdot \beta_1) + k_2(\beta_1 \cdot \beta_2, -\beta_2 \cdot \beta_2) = \mathbf{0}$. Then $\beta_1 \cdot (k_1 \beta_1 + k_2 \beta_2) = 0$ and $\beta_2 \cdot (k_1 \beta_1 + k_2 \beta_2) = 0$. But $\mathbf{0}$ is the only member of $L\{\beta_1, \beta_2\}$ which is also a member of $\{\beta_1, \beta_2\}^\perp$. Therefore, $k_1 \beta_1 + k_2 \beta_2 = \mathbf{0}$; we conclude that $k_1 = k_2 = 0$. This contradiction establishes our result.

Section 3.2   Page 70

1. (a) Let $\alpha = (a_1, a_2)$ and consider the triangle whose hypotenuse is the line-segment with endpoints $\mathbf{0}$ and α, whose remaining vertex is $(a_1, 0)$. Apply the Theorem of Pythagoras. (b) Let $\alpha = (a_1, a_2)$ and let $\beta = (b_1, b_2)$. Apply the Theorem of Pythagoras to the triangle with vertices α, β, and (a_1, b_2).

3. Apply Theorem 3.1.1.

5. $\alpha \neq \mathbf{0}$ so $\|\alpha\| \neq 0$. Now, $\|(1/\|\alpha\|)\alpha\|^2 = (1/\|\alpha\|)\alpha \cdot (1/\|\alpha\|)\alpha = (1/\|\alpha\|^2)(\alpha \cdot \alpha) = 1$.

7. $\|\alpha - \beta\|^2 = \|\alpha + (-\beta)\|^2 = \|\alpha\|^2 + \|-\beta\|^2 + 2\alpha \cdot (-\beta)$ by Theorem 3.2.1
$= \|\alpha\|^2 + \|\beta\|^2 - 2(\alpha \cdot \beta)$.

9. Clearly, $|\mathbf{0} \cdot \beta| = 0$ and $\|\mathbf{0}\|\|\beta\| = 0$. Let $\beta = k\alpha$; then $|\alpha \cdot \beta| = |k(\alpha \cdot \alpha)| = |k|\|\alpha\|^2 = |k|\|\alpha\|^2$ and $\|\alpha\|\|\beta\| = \|\alpha\|\|k\alpha\| = |k|\|\alpha\|^2$ by Lemma 3.2.2.

11. $\arccos .01 = \pi/2 - \int_0^{.01} (1 - x^2)^{-\frac{1}{2}}$

$\approx 1.5708 - \dfrac{.01}{6} [1 + 4(1 - .000025)^{-\frac{1}{2}} + (1 - .0001)^{-\frac{1}{2}}]$

$\approx 1.5708 - \dfrac{.01}{6} [1 + 4(1 + .0000125) + (1 + .00005)]$

by the Binomial Theorem

≈ 1.5608

13. 1.107

15. (i) If $\alpha \perp \beta$ then angle $(\alpha, \beta) = \arccos 0 = \pi/2$. If angle $(\alpha, \beta) = \pi/2$, then $\alpha \cdot \beta = 0$, i.e. $\alpha \perp \beta$.

(ii) angle $(\beta, \alpha) = \arccos \dfrac{\beta \cdot \alpha}{\|\beta\|\|\alpha\|} = \arccos \dfrac{\alpha \cdot \beta}{\|\alpha\|\|\beta\|} = $ angle (α, β).

(iii) angle $(\alpha, \alpha) = \arccos \dfrac{\alpha \cdot \alpha}{\|\alpha\|^2} = \arccos \dfrac{\alpha \cdot \alpha}{\alpha \cdot \alpha} = \arccos 1 = 0$.

(iv) angle $(\alpha, k\alpha) = \arccos \dfrac{k(\alpha \cdot \alpha)}{\|\alpha\|\|k\alpha\|} = \arccos \dfrac{k(\alpha \cdot \alpha)}{|k|(\alpha \cdot \alpha)} = \arccos 1 = 0$ since $k > 0$.

(v) angle (α, $-\alpha$) = arccos $\dfrac{-\alpha \cdot \alpha}{\|\alpha\|\|-\alpha\|}$ = arccos $\dfrac{-\alpha \cdot \alpha}{\alpha \cdot \alpha}$ = arccos -1 = π.

(vi) angle (α, $k\alpha$) = arccos $\dfrac{k(\alpha \cdot \alpha)}{|k|(\alpha \cdot \alpha)}$ = arccos -1 = π, since $k < 0$.

Section 3.3   Page 76

1. Let $A = (a_{ij})$; by Definition 3.3.3, $(AB)_i = a_{i1} B_1 + \cdots + a_{in} B_n$. Now, the jth entry of the vector on the right is

$$a_{i1} \times j\text{th entry of } B_1 + \cdots + a_{in} \times j\text{th entry of } B_n$$

But the jth entries of the row vectors of a matrix constitute the jth column vector of that matrix. Thus, the jth entry of $(AB)_i$ is the dot product $A_i \cdot {}_jB$. So, $AB = (A_i \cdot {}_jB)$.

3. $(-1, 14, 13)$

5. $A(B + C) = (A_i \cdot {}_j[B + C]) = (A_i \cdot [{}_jB + {}_jC]) = (A_i \cdot {}_jB + A_i \cdot {}_jC) = AB + AC$.

7. $A_i + A_j$

9. $(CA)_i = C_i \cdot A = (k\epsilon_i) \cdot A = k A_i$; if $j \neq i$ then $(CA)_j = C_j \cdot A = \epsilon_j \cdot A = A_j$. So CA is the matrix obtained from A by replacing A_i by $k A_i$.

11. Exercise 8 asserts that BA is the matrix obtained from A by interchanging A_i and A_j. So $(BA)^t$ is the transpose of the matrix obtained from A by interchanging A_i and A_j. Thus, $A^t \cdot B^t$ is the matrix obtained from A^t by interchanging ${}_i(A^t)$ and ${}_j(A^t)$. So, $A \cdot B^t$ is the matrix obtained from A by interchanging ${}_iA$ and ${}_jA$.

13. Use the method of Exercise 11.

Section 3.4   Page 80

1. Let $A = (a_{ij})$ be $n \times n$; now,

$$(A \cdot I_n)_i = a_{i1} \epsilon_1 + \cdots + a_{in} \epsilon_n = (a_{i1}, \ldots, a_{in}) = A_i$$

So, $A \cdot I_n = A$. To show that $I_n \cdot A = A$, notice that $(I_n \cdot A)_i = 0 A_1 + \cdots + 1 A_i + \cdots + 0 A_n = A_i$ by Definition 3.3.3. Thus, $I_n \cdot A = A$.

3. (a) $\begin{pmatrix} 3 & -1 \\ 1 & 2 \end{pmatrix}$ (c) $\begin{pmatrix} 9 & -4 & 1 \\ 1 & 8 & -2 \\ -2 & 3 & 4 \end{pmatrix}$ (e) $\begin{pmatrix} 7 & 3 & 22 & 27 \\ -1 & -6 & -31 & -15 \\ 8 & 9 & 14 & 3 \\ -5 & 9 & 1 & 3 \end{pmatrix}$

5. If $AB = I_n$ then $A(BC) = C$; so $AX = C$ if $X = A^{-1} \cdot C$. Hence, $X = \dfrac{1}{7}\begin{pmatrix} 11 & 1 \\ 6 & 5 \end{pmatrix}$.

7. Use the method of Exercise 5.   9. $39^3 = 59{,}319$

11. (a) $[(A + B)^t]_i = {}_i(A + B) = {}_iA + {}_iB$; $(A^t + B^t)_i = {}_iA + {}_iB$

(b) $(A + A^t)^t = A^t + A^{tt} = A + A^t$

13. Notice that the proof of Theorem 3.4.4 does not use Theorem 3.4.3; so we are entitled to use Theorem 3.4.4 in proving Theorem 3.4.3. Let A be any nonsingular $n \times n$ matrix. By Theorem 3.4.2, A has an inverse, say B. Assume that A has another inverse, say C. Then $AB = I_n$ and $AC = I_n$, so $AB = AC$. Thus, $B(AB) = B(AC)$; so, by the associative law, $(BA)B = (BA)C$, i.e. $I_n \cdot B = I_n \cdot C$, so $B = C$. We conclude that A has a unique inverse.

15. $(AB)(B^{-1} \cdot A^{-1}) = A(B \cdot B^{-1})A^{-1} = A \cdot I_n \cdot A^{-1} = A \cdot A^{-1} = I_n$; so $(AB)^{-1} = B^{-1} \cdot A^{-1}$.

17. Let $B = P \cdot A \cdot P^{-1}$; then

(a) trace B = trace $(P \cdot A \cdot P^{-1})$ = trace $(A \cdot P \cdot P^{-1})$ by Exercise 16(b)

= trace A

(b) rank B = rank $(P \cdot A \cdot P^{-1})$ = rank A by Exercise 18(c).

Section 3.5   Page 87

1. $\dfrac{1}{19}\begin{pmatrix} 9 & -4 & 1 \\ 1 & 8 & -2 \\ -2 & 3 & 4 \end{pmatrix}$

3. $\dfrac{1}{39}\begin{pmatrix} 7 & 3 & 22 & 27 \\ -1 & -6 & -31 & -15 \\ 8 & 9 & 14 & 3 \\ -5 & 9 & 1 & 3 \end{pmatrix}$

5. $\begin{pmatrix} 1 & -2 & 1 & 1 \\ 1 & 1 & 0 & 0 \\ 0 & 4 & -2 & -1 \\ 0 & -2 & 1 & 1 \end{pmatrix}$

7. $\dfrac{1}{68}\begin{pmatrix} 2 & -14 & -14 & 20 & 6 & -22 \\ 115 & 11 & 130 & 79 & 22 & 78 \\ 14 & 38 & 4 & -30 & 8 & 16 \\ 105 & 13 & 98 & 13 & 26 & 86 \\ 41 & -15 & 36 & 19 & 4 & 8 \\ -38 & -6 & -40 & -6 & -12 & -24 \end{pmatrix}$

9. $\begin{pmatrix} 1 & 5 & 2 & -6 \\ 1 & -6 & 3 & 12 \end{pmatrix}$

11. $\begin{pmatrix} -5/2 \\ 9/2 \\ 0 \\ 0 \end{pmatrix}$

13. $\begin{pmatrix} -13/2 & -2 \\ 7/2 & 2 \\ 0 & 0 \\ 0 & 0 \end{pmatrix}$

15. $\begin{pmatrix} 3 & -1 \\ 0 & 1 \end{pmatrix}$

Section 4.1   Page 91

1. $44^{\frac12}$ 3. $(5, -2, 5)$ 5. $\{(0, a, 0) \mid a \in R\} = \{\mathbf{0} + \gamma \mid \gamma \in L\{\epsilon_2\}\}$
7. $\{(3 - a, 2, 1) \mid a \in R\} = \{(3, 2, 1) + \gamma \mid \gamma \in L\{\epsilon_1\}\}$
9. $\{(2, -1, 3) + \gamma \mid \gamma \in L\{(2, 1, -2)\}\}$
11. $\{(a, b, c) \mid c = 0\} = \mathcal{P}$. Note that $L\{\epsilon_1\} \subset \mathcal{P}$ and $L\{\epsilon_2\} \subset \mathcal{P}$.
13. (a) Let $L = \{\alpha + \gamma \mid \gamma \in W\}$ where $\alpha \in R_2$ and $W = L\{\beta\}$ is a one-dimensional sub-space of $\mathcal{R}_2$. Let $\beta_1 \in W^{\perp} - \{\mathbf{0}\}$, so $\beta \cdot \beta_1 = 0$, and let $\mathcal{K}$ be the set of all points equidistant from $\alpha - \beta_1$ and $\alpha + \beta_1$. It is easy to verify that $\gamma \in \mathcal{K} \Leftrightarrow (\gamma - \alpha) \cdot \beta_1 = 0$ (see the proof of Lemma 5.1.2). Now, $\gamma \in L \Leftrightarrow \gamma - \alpha \in W$; also, β_1 is orthogonal to each member of W. So, $\gamma \in \mathcal{K} \Leftrightarrow \gamma \in L$. Thus, $L = \mathcal{K}$.
13. (b) See the proof of Lemma 5.1.3.
15. $\{(2, 0, 1, 1) + \gamma \mid \gamma \in L\{(2, -1, 0, 0)\}\}$; no.
17. (a) $\{\alpha + t\beta \mid t \in R\} = \{\alpha + \gamma \mid \gamma \in L\{\beta\}\}$
    (b) $\{\alpha + t(k\beta) \mid t \in R\} = \{\alpha + \gamma \mid \gamma \in L\{k\beta\}\}$

Section 4.2   Page 95

1. $\{(2, -3, 1) + t(1, -3, -4) \mid t \in R\}$ 3. Yes.   5. No.
7. Yes, at $(2, -1, 0)$.   9. No.
11. The linear system $1 - t = 3t$, $t + 1 = 1 - t$, $t + 2 = 2 + 3t$ has no solution.
13. $\|\alpha + t_1\beta - \alpha\| = \|t_1\beta\| = |t_1|$ if $\|\beta\| = 1$. So, $|t_1|$ is the distance between α and $\alpha + t_1\beta$.

Section 4.3   Page 99

1. 2.598 (arccos $-.864$)   3. π 5. $\pi/2$

7. $\beta_1 \equiv \beta_2 \Leftrightarrow \beta_2 = k\beta_1$ and $k > 0$. But arccos $\dfrac{\beta_1 \cdot k\beta_1}{\|\beta_1\|\|k\beta_1\|} = $ arccos $1 = 0$ since $|k| = k$.

9. Yes.   11. $\{(1, 0, 2) + t(1, 2, 0) \mid t \in R\}$

Section 4.4   Page 101

1. (a) 3   (b) -3 (c) 3   (d) $(3, 6, -6)$

3. The given line is $\{(1, 0, 1) + \dfrac{t}{\sqrt{11}}(1, -1, -3) \mid t \in R\}$; so the required point is

$(1, 0, -1) - \dfrac{3}{\sqrt{11}}(1, -1, -3).$

5. (a) $\{\alpha + t(\beta - \alpha) \mid t \in [0, 1]\} = \{(1 - t)\alpha + t\beta \mid t \in [0, 1]\}$ which is the set of all convex combinations of α and β. Notice that $1 - t \in [0, 1]$ if and only if $t \in [0, 1]$.

(b) Each point on the boundary of the triangle is yielded by taking a convex combination of α, β, and γ for which one or two of the scalars are zero. Consider any convex combination of α, β, and γ, say

$$\lambda = k_1\alpha + k_2\beta + k_3\gamma = k_1\alpha + (k_2 + k_3)\left(\frac{k_2}{k_2 + k_3}\beta + \frac{k_3}{k_2 + k_3}\gamma\right)$$

where $k_1 \neq 0$, $k_2 \neq 0$, and $k_3 \neq 0$. Now, $\delta = \dfrac{k_2}{k_2 + k_3}\beta + \dfrac{k_3}{k_2 + k_3}\gamma$ is a convex combination of β and γ; so δ is on one side of the triangle. But $\lambda = k_1\alpha + (k_2 + k_3)\delta$ is a convex combination of α and δ, so λ is on the line-segment with endpoints α and δ, which is an interior point of the triangle. So, each convex combination of α, β, and γ is a member of the triangle. Notice that this argument is reversible.

Section 4.5   Page 106

1. Yes.   3. $\{t(3, 9, 2) \mid t \in R\}$ 5. $\{(2, 5, -1) + t(21, -14, 11) \mid t \in R\}$

7. Consider the matrix obtained from A by replacing A_1 by $(A_{11}, \ldots, A_{1n})$.

9. $(-3, 6, 1, 17, 4)$

11. By assumption, the matrix product $A \cdot A^t = I_n$, so $|A \cdot A^t| = |A||A^t| = |I_n| = 1$. But $|A^t| = |A|$, thus $|A|^2 = 1$.

13. The terms of $\alpha \times \beta$ are the cofactors of positions in the first row of a matrix whose second row is α and whose third row is β. Since each cofactor is essentially the determinant of a submatrix, each term of $\beta \times \alpha$ is the negative of the corresponding term of $\alpha \times \beta$; so $\alpha \times \beta = -(\beta \times \alpha)$. Again, considering cofactors, we see that $(-\beta) \times \alpha = -(\beta \times \alpha)$.

15. Use the "cofactor" approach.

17. (a) Let $\alpha = (a_1, a_2, a_3)$ and let $\beta = (b_1, b_2, b_3)$; then
$\|\alpha \times \beta\|^2 = (a_2b_3 - a_3b_2)^2 + (a_3b_1 - a_1b_3)^2 + (a_1b_2 - a_2b_1)^2$
$= a_1^2(b_2^2 + b_3^2) + a_2^2(b_1^2 + b_3^2) + a_3^2(b_1^2 + b_2^2) - 2(a_2b_3a_3b_2 + a_3b_1a_1b_3 + a_1b_2a_2b_1)$
and $\|\alpha\|^2\|\beta\|^2 - (\alpha \cdot \beta)^2 = (a_1^2 + a_2^2 + a_3^2)(b_1^2 + b_2^2 + b_3^2) - (a_1b_1 + a_2b_2 + a_3b_3)^2$
$= \|\alpha \times \beta\|^2$

(b) Let $\theta = $ angle (α, β); then $\cos\theta = \dfrac{\alpha \cdot \beta}{\|\alpha\|\|\beta\|}$, so

$$\sin^2\theta = 1 - \frac{(\alpha \cdot \beta)^2}{\|\alpha\|^2\|\beta\|^2} = \frac{\|\alpha\|^2\|\beta\|^2 - (\alpha \cdot \beta)^2}{\|\alpha\|^2\|\beta\|^2}$$

thus $\|\alpha\|^2\|\beta\|^2 - (\alpha \cdot \beta)^2 = \|\alpha\|^2\|\beta\|^2\sin^2\theta$

therefore $\|\alpha \times \beta\|^2 = \|\alpha\|^2\|\beta\|^2\sin^2\theta$

so $\|\alpha \times \beta\| = \|\alpha\|\|\beta\|\sin\theta$, since $0 \leq \theta \leq \pi$ (i.e. $\sin\theta \geq 0$).

19. $\alpha = (1, 0, 0)$, $\beta = (0, 1, 0) = \gamma$ 21. Use Exercise 17(b).

23. (a) Use Theorem 1.4.3.   (b) Use Theorem 1.4.2.   (c) Use Lemma 1.4.7.

25. (a) 0   (b) 0   (c) $\times (\alpha, \beta, \gamma)$ (d) $0 \times (\alpha, \beta, \gamma)$ (e) $\times (\alpha, \beta, \gamma)$
27. Use Lemma 1.4.6.

Section 5.1   Page 111

1. (a) $\mathcal{P} = \{\gamma \mid \epsilon_3 \cdot (\gamma - (2, 0, 3)) = 0\}$ (b) $\mathcal{P} = \{\gamma \mid \|\gamma - (2, 0, 4)\| = \|\gamma - (2, 0, 2)\|\}$
3. $\{\gamma \mid (1, -1, -1) \cdot (\gamma - (3, -1, 0)) = 0\}$ 5. $(2, 4, 6)$
7. Each point on the line.   9. $\{\gamma \mid (6, 2, -1) \cdot (\gamma - (1, 2, -2)) = 0\}$
11. $\{(3, 2, 0), (5, 0, -2)\}$

Section 5.2   Page 115

1. $\{t(2, -1, 1) \mid t \in R\}$ 3. $\{t(2, 0, -3) \mid t \in R\}$
5. (a) $[(3, -1, 2)]$ (b) $\{\gamma \mid (3, -1, 2) \cdot \gamma = 7\}$ 7. $\{\gamma \mid (1, 1, 0) \cdot \gamma = 4\}$
9. $\{\gamma \mid (1, 1, 1) \cdot \gamma = 1\}$ 11. $\{\gamma \mid (29, -1, 12) \cdot \gamma = 107\}$
13. $\{\gamma \mid (1, -1, 0) \cdot \gamma = -1\}$ 15. $\{\gamma \mid (1, -1, 0) \cdot \gamma = 0\}, \{\gamma \mid (0, 1, 0) \cdot \gamma = 1\}$

Section 5.3   Page 118

1. Apply Theorem 5.3.1.
3. Each normal to $\mathcal{P}_1$ has directions $[\beta_1]$ and $[-\beta_1]$; also, each normal to $\mathcal{P}_2$ has directions $[\beta_2]$ and $[-\beta_2]$. Thus, $\mathcal{P}_1$ and $\mathcal{P}_2$ have a common normal if and only if $\beta_2 \in L\{\beta_1\}$.

5. Assume that $l_2 m_1 = l_1 m_2$ and that $l_2 n_1 = l_1 n_2$; then $(l_2, m_2, n_2) = \frac{l_2}{l_1}(l_1, m_1, n_1)$. So, by Theorem 5.3.1, the given planes are parallel.
7. See the solution to Exercise 5.   9. $\{(0, -1, -5) + t(2, 1, 5) \mid t \in R\}$
11. $\{t(1, 1, 1) \mid t \in R\}$ 13. $\{\gamma \mid (1, -2, 1) \cdot \gamma = 0\} \cap \{\gamma \mid (1, -3, 2) \cdot \gamma = 1\}$.

Section 5.4   Page 121

1. By Theorem 4.4.1, d is the directed distance from $\mathbf{0}$ to $d\beta$ along (L, β).   3. 2

5. By Theorem 5.4.2, the distance between α and $\{\gamma \mid \frac{\beta}{\|\beta\|} \cdot \gamma = d/\|\beta\|\}$ is $|(\beta/\|\beta\|) \cdot \alpha - d/\|\beta\||$, i.e. $|\beta \cdot \alpha - d|/\|\beta\|$.
7. $1/\sqrt{6}$ 9. $\frac{1}{3}\sqrt{14}$ 11. $3/\sqrt{5}$ 13. $\gamma = \alpha + t\beta$ where $t = d - \beta \cdot \alpha$. So, by Theorem 4.4.1, the directed distance from α to γ along (L, β) is $d - \beta \cdot \alpha$; thus $\beta \cdot \alpha - d$ is the directed distance from $\mathcal{P}$ to α.
15. $\epsilon_2 \cdot (\alpha - \alpha_0)$

Section 6.1   Page 127

1. (a) $\{2\}$ (b) $\{1, 2, 3, 4\}$ (c) $\{1, 2, 4\}$ (d) $A \doteq B = \{t \mid t \in A \text{ or else } t \in B\} = (A \cup B) - (A \cap B) = A \cup B$ (e) $A \doteq B = (A \cup B) - (A \cap B) = A - B$ since $B \subset A$.
(f) $A \doteq \varnothing = (A \cup \varnothing) - (A \cap \varnothing) = A$ (g) $A \doteq B = (A \cup B) - (A \cap B) = (B \cup A) - (B \cap A) = B \doteq A$ (h) $A \doteq A = \varnothing$

3. The *difference* operation is not associative; we mention that $A - (B - C) = A \cap (B' \cup C)$ whereas $(A - B) - C = A \cap B' \cap C'$.

5. (a) It is easy to verify that composition of mappings is associative. (b) Use Theorem 6.1.1.

Section 6.2   Page 134

1. Here, $x + (y + z) = (x + y) + z$ if one or more of x, y, z is 0. But $1 + (1 + 1) = 1$ and $(1 + 1) + 1 = 1$. So, $+$ is associative. Also, 0 is a right identity, 0 is a right inverse of 0, and 1 is a right inverse of 1.   3. (a) See Section 1.1.

3. (b) $A \doteq (B \doteq C) = [A - (B \doteq C)] \cup [(B \doteq C) - A]$
$$= (A \cap B \cap C) \cup (A \cap B' \cap C') \cup (B \cap C' \cap A') \cup (B' \cap C \cap A')$$
$(A \doteq B) \doteq C = [(A \doteq B) - C] \cup [C - (A \doteq B)]$
$$= (A \cap B' \cap C') \cup (A' \cap B \cap C') \cup (C \cap A \cap B) \cup (C \cap A' \cap B')$$
So, $\doteq$ is associative. Clearly, $A \doteq \varnothing = A$, so $\varnothing$ is a right identity. Finally, $A \doteq A = \varnothing$, so the right inverse of A is A.

(c) By Theorem 3.3.5, the product of nonsingular matrices is nonsingular; so $\cdot$ is a binary operation on G. Matrix multiplication is associative by Theorem 3.3.2; clearly, I_n is a right identity; by Theorem 3.4.2, each member of G has a right inverse.

5. Use the hints of the text.

7. By Lemma 6.2.3, e is a left identity. Let a be another left identity; then $a \circ e = e$. But e is also a right identity, so $a \circ e = a$. Thus, $a = e$.

9. Now, $-x + -(-x) = 0$. But $x + -x = 0$; so, by Lemma 6.2.2, $-x + x = 0$. Thus, $-x + -(-x) = -x + x$. Now, apply Theorem 6.2.3.

11. $(x + y) + (y + x) = x + (y + y) + x = 0$; so $[(x + y) + (y + x)] + (y + x) = y + x$, i.e. $x + y = y + x$.

13. (a) $+$ is commutative since its table is symmetric. 0 is a right identity; notice that $-1 = 3$, $-2 = 2$, and $-3 = 1$. To show that $+$ is associative, consider a circle whose circumference is divided into four equal parts by means of four points labelled 0, 1, 2, and 3

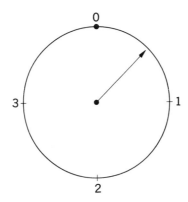

A pointer is pivoted at the center of the circle so that it can point at each of the four labels on the circumference. We can now interpret the binary operation of G as follows. Let $\{x, y\} \subset \{0, 1, 2, 3\}$; then $x + y$ is found by first setting the pointer at 0, then moving it through x parts clockwise, and then through y parts clockwise. The pointer now points at $x + y$. This is easy to verify. Now, to show that $x + (y + z) = (x + y) + z$, use the fact that $+$ is commutative, so $x + (y + z) = (y + z) + x$. Using the pointer, it is easy to verify that $(y + z) + x = (x + y) + z$. For $(y + z) + x$ is found by setting the pointer at 0, moving it through y parts and then through z parts, and finally through x parts. On the other hand, $(x + y) + z$ is found by setting the pointer at 0, moving it through x parts, then through y

parts, and finally through z parts. In each case, the pointer is moved through the same number of parts.

13. (b)

$-$	0	1	2	3
0	0	3	2	1
1	1	0	3	2
2	2	1	0	3
3	3	2	1	0

15. (a) $x - (y - z) = x - (y + -z) = x + (-(-z) + -y) = x + (z - y)$

(b) $x + (y - z) = x + (y + -z) = (x + y) + -z = (x + y) - z$

(c) $x - (y + z) = x + -(y + z) = x + (-z + -y) = x + (-z) + -y = (x - z) - y$.

17. Now, G' is nonempty; let $x \in G'$. By assumption, $x \circ' e' = x$ and $x \circ e = x$. But $\circ' \subset \circ$, so $x \circ e' = x$. Thus, by Theorem 6.2.3, $e = e'$.

Section 6.3   Page 139

1. Expand the four conditions of Definition 6.3.1.

3. (a)

$\dot{-}$	$\{a, b\}$	$\{a\}$	$\{b\}$	$\varnothing$
$\{a, b\}$	$\varnothing$	$\{b\}$	$\{a\}$	$\{a, b\}$
$\{a\}$	$\{b\}$	$\varnothing$	$\{a, b\}$	$\{a\}$
$\{b\}$	$\{a\}$	$\{a, b\}$	$\varnothing$	$\{b\}$
$\varnothing$	$\{a, b\}$	$\{a\}$	$\{b\}$	$\varnothing$

$\cap$	$\{a, b\}$	$\{a\}$	$\{b\}$	$\varnothing$
$\{a, b\}$	$\{a, b\}$	$\{a\}$	$\{b\}$	$\varnothing$
$\{a\}$	$\{a\}$	$\{a\}$	$\varnothing$	$\varnothing$
$\{b\}$	$\{b\}$	$\varnothing$	$\{b\}$	$\varnothing$
$\varnothing$	$\varnothing$	$\varnothing$	$\varnothing$	$\varnothing$

5. $x \cdot 0 = x \cdot (0 + 0) = x \cdot 0 + x \cdot 0$; adding the inverse of $x \cdot 0$ to both sides of the equation $x \cdot 0 = x \cdot 0 + x \cdot 0$, we conclude that $x \cdot 0 = 0$.

7. (a) $x + (-x) \cdot x = e \cdot x + (-e) \cdot x = (e + (-e)) \cdot x = 0 \cdot x = 0$; so $(-e) \cdot x = -x$. (b) $(-e) \cdot (-e) = -(-e) = e$. (c) First, notice that $x \cdot (-e) = -x$ see the proof of Exercise 7 (a). Now, $(-x) \cdot (-y) = [x \cdot (-e)] \cdot [(-e) \cdot y] = x \cdot [(-e) \cdot (-e)] \cdot y = x \cdot e \cdot y = x \cdot y$.   9. Obvious.

11. (a) Use the "pointer" device involved in the solution to Exercise 13(a) of Section 6.2. (b) If k is composite, say $k = ab$, then a and b are proper divisors of 0. If k is prime and if $ab = mk$, where m is an integer, then k is a divisor of a or b. This can be established by considering the prime factors of ab. So, if k is prime, 0 has no proper divisors.

13. An infinite set possesses a proper subset equinumerous with it. For example, there are as many even integers as integers, so I is infinite. Thus, it is fallacious to conclude that $\{z \cdot x \mid z \in B\} = B$ merely because these sets are equinumerous and one is a subset of the other.

15. (a) Let $x \in B$, where $x \neq 0$. If k is the characteristic of 1 then k is the smallest natural number for which $0 = 1 + \cdots + 1$ (k 1's); now $x \cdot 0 = x \cdot (1 + \cdots + 1)$, hence $0 = x \cdot 1 + \cdots + x \cdot 1 = x + \cdots + x$ (k x's). So, the characteristic of x does not exceed k. If the characteristic of x is less than k, say k_1, then $0 = x + \cdots + x$ (k_1 x's), so $0 = x \cdot 1 + \cdots + x \cdot 1 = x \cdot (1 + \cdots + 1)$, ($k_1$ 1's). But $x \neq 0$ and 0 has no proper divisors; thus, $0 = 1 + \cdots + 1$ (k_1 1's). This means that the characteristic of 1 does not exceed k_1; so k is not the characteristic of 1. This contradiction proves that k is the characteristic of each nonzero member of B. Our proof also yields that the characteristic of each nonzero member of B is zero if zero is the characteristic of 1.

(b) Let k be composite, say $k = mn$. Now,

$$0 = 1 + \cdots + 1 \ (mn \text{ 1's})$$
$$= (1 + \cdots + 1) + \cdots + (1 + \cdots + 1) \qquad n \text{ terms, each with } m \text{ 1's}$$
$$= m1 + \cdots + m1$$

Thus, the characteristic of $m1$ is at most n, which is less than k. This contradicts Exercise 15(a).
17. $(\{x \mid x \text{ is an even integer}\}, +, \cdot, 0)$ is a ring, where $+$ and $\cdot$ are the operations of addition and multiplication of integers, restricted to even integers. This ring does not have an identity.

Section 6.4   Page 144

1. See Exercises 11 and 14, Section 6.3.   3. See Exercises 11 and 14, Section 6.3.
5. Clearly $x \cdot (x^{-1} \cdot y) = y$ whenever $x \neq 0$; using a cancellation law we easily deduce that z is unique.   7. Use the hints of the text.   9. (a) 5   (b) k (c) 0
11. $(\{0, 1, a, b\}, +, \cdot, 0, 1)$ where $+$ and $\cdot$ are defined by the following tables:

$+$	0	1	a	b		$\cdot$	0	1	a	b
0	0	1	a	b		0	0	0	0	0
1	1	0	b	a		1	0	1	a	b
a	a	b	0	1		a	0	a	b	1
b	b	a	1	0		b	0	b	1	a

13. Assume that zero is the characteristic of $\mathcal{F}$. Now, $k1 \in \mathcal{F}$ whenever $k \in N$; by assumption, $k1 \neq 0$. Since $\mathcal{F}$ is finite, there are natural numbers m and n such that $m1 = n1$. Let a be the natural number such that $n = m + a$ (we assume that $m < n$). Then $m1 = (m + a)1 = m1 + a1$, so $a1 = 0$. Thus, the characteristic of $\mathcal{F}$ is not zero.

Section 6.5   Page 146

1. $(\{a, b, c\}, \{(a, b), (a, c), (b, c)\})$ 3. (a) Let $\mu = \{(0, 1), (1, 0)\}$; then $\mu S = (\{0, 1\}, \{(1, 1, 1), (1, 0, 0), (0, 1, 0), (0, 0, 1)\}, 1) = \mathcal{3}.$ (b) $\mu = \{(0, 1), (1, 0)\}$ 5. (a) $(\{0, 1\}, \{(0, 0, 0), (0, 1, 1), (1, 0, 1), (1, 1, 0)\}, 0)$
(b) $(\{0, a, b\}, +, 0)$ where $+$ is defined by the following table:

$+$	0	a	b
0	0	a	b
a	a	b	0
b	b	0	a

Section 7.1   Page 155

1. (a) This is so by assumption.   (b) Consider Definition 7.1.1.   (c) $\{1\}$ (d) One.
2. (b) $\{f_1, \ldots, f_n\}$ where, for each i, f_i is the mapping of $\{1, \ldots, n\}$ into $\mathcal{F}$ such that $f_i(t) = 1$ if $t = i$, whereas $f_i(t) = 0$ if $t \neq i$. Notice that $\sum_{i=1}^{n} k_i f_i = \{(1, k_1), \ldots, (n, k_n)\}$.
3. (a) This is so by assumption.   (b) Consider Definition 7.1.1.   (c) $\{(1, 0), (0, 1)\}$
(d) Two.   5. Use Lemma 7.1.2.   7. If $k \circ \alpha = 0$ then $\alpha = k^{-1} \circ 0$ by Lemma 7.1.4, so $\alpha = 0$ by Lemma 7.1.3. If $\alpha = 0$ then $k \circ \alpha = 0$ by Lemma 7.1.3.   9. True for 1. Assume true for n, and it follows that it is true for $n + 1$ by Definition 7.1.1(iii).   11. The details are straightforward.   13. Use the hints of the text.   15. Let C be a proper subset of B. So, there is a vector γ such that $\gamma \in B - C$. If C is a basis for the vector space, then $\gamma \in LC$; thus $\gamma \in L(B - \{\gamma\})$. So, B is linearly dependent. Contradiction!
17. $\mathcal{V} = (\{0\}, \{(0, 0, 0)\}, 0)$

Section 7.2   Page 162

1. Use Theorem 7.2.1 (see the proof of the Steinitz Replacement Theorem).
3. $\{(0, 2, 3, -1), (1, 0, 1, 0), \epsilon_3, \epsilon_4\}$.   5. Follow the proof of Lemma 2.2.7.
7. (a) $T(0) = T(0 + 0) = T(0) + T(0)$; so $T(0) = 0$
   (b) $T(\alpha + \beta) = T(1\alpha + \beta) = 1T(\alpha) + T(\beta) = T(\alpha) + T(\beta)$
   (c) $T(k\alpha) = T(k\alpha + 0) = k\,T(\alpha) + T(0) = k\,T(\alpha)$
   (d) Let $W = \{\gamma \mid T(\gamma) = 0\}$. Now, $0 \in W$ by part (a) so W is a nonempty subset of $\mathcal{V}$. Let $\{\alpha, \beta\} \subset W$; then $T(\alpha + \beta) = T(\alpha) + T(\beta) = 0$, so $\alpha + \beta \in W$. Also, $T(k\alpha) = k\,T(\alpha) = k0 = 0$ if $k \in R$.

Section 7.3   Page 169

1. (a) $\{(2, 0, 1), (1, 1, -1), (0, 0, 1)\}$ is linearly independent.   (b) $(3, -1, -1)$
3. I_n 5. (a) $(2, 1, 2, 1)$ (b) $(2, -2, 2, -3)$

(c) $\begin{pmatrix} 3 & -1 & -1 & 3 \\ 4 & -2 & -1 & 4 \\ -2 & 1 & 1 & -2 \\ -2 & 1 & 1 & -3 \end{pmatrix}$ (d) $(2, -1, 0, 2)$

7. The $n \times n$ matrix whose ith row vector is $\epsilon_{\pi(i)}$, $i = 1, \ldots, n$.
9. (a) $\{\alpha \mid 5/4$ is the first term of $[\alpha]_{\mathcal{B}}\}$ where $\mathcal{B} = ((1, 1, -2), (1, -1, 0), (1, 1, 1))$.
(b) $\{\alpha \mid$ there are scalars y' and z' such that $[\alpha]_{\mathcal{B}} = (5/4, y', z')$ and $y'^2 + z'^2 + 11y'z' - 5y' - (35/4)z' = -315/16\}$.
11. The argument assumes that if $\gamma B = \gamma$ then $B = I_n$. To see that this is false, note that $(2, 1)\begin{pmatrix} 0 & 0 \\ 2 & 1 \end{pmatrix} = (2, 1)$.
13. Let $\alpha_1, \ldots, \alpha_m$ be distinct members of S, and let $k_1, \ldots, k_m$ be scalars. Clearly, $\sum_{i=1}^{m} k_i \alpha_i = 0$ if and only $\sum_{i=1}^{m} k_i [\alpha_i]_{\mathcal{B}} = 0$.
15. The ith row vector of $[\mathcal{B}]_{\alpha}$ is $[\beta_i]_{\alpha}$, whereas the ith row vector of $[\mathcal{B}][\alpha]^{-1}$ is $\beta_i [\alpha]^{-1}$. To see that $[\beta_i]_{\alpha} = \beta_i [\alpha]^{-1}$, apply Theorems 7.3.2 and 7.3.3.

Section 8.1   Page 176

1. (a) $(2, 1, -3)$ (b) (4) (c) $(0, 5, -5)$ (d) (0) (e) $(2, 4, -6)$
3. (a) $(0, 0, 1), (0, 1, 1), (1, 0, 1), (1, 1, 1)$.   (b) $(0, 0, 0, 1)$ (c) $(0, 1)$
   (d) $(1, 1)$ (e) $(0, 1, 1)$ (f) $(1, 0, 1)$ (g) $(0, 1, 1)$
5. Let $p = (a_0, \ldots, a_s)$ and let $q = (b_0, \ldots, b_t)$, where $s \leq t$. If $s \neq t$, then $\deg(p + q) = t$. Now, assume that $s = t$. If $a_s + b_t \neq 0$, then $\deg(p + q) = t$; whereas, if $a_s + b_t = 0$ then $\deg(p + q) < t$ or else $p + q = 0$.

Section 8.2   Page 182

1. $(8, 12, 6, 19, 7, 7, -3)$ 3. $(0, -1, 1)$ 5. See Lemma 8.2.2.
7. Each integral domain can be extended to a field by forming ordered pairs. Do this.

Section 8.3   Page 184

1. (a) $\{(a, b) \mid a \in R \text{ and } b = 2 + 3a^2\}$ (b) No.
3. (a) $\{(a, b) \mid a \in R \text{ and } b = 2 + 3a + 5a^3 - 3a^4\}$ (b) Yes, between 0 and -1.
5. (a) $\{(0, 1), (1, 1), (2, 1)\}$ (b) $\{(0, 2), (1, 2), (2, 2)\}$ (c) 0   (d) 0
   (e) $(2, 2, 0, 1)$ and $(2, 0, 1, 0, 2)$
7. Assume $p \neq q \Rightarrow p_f \neq q_f$; then certainly $r_f \neq 0_f$ if $r \neq 0$. Assume $r \neq 0 \Rightarrow r_f \neq 0_f$.
Let $p \neq q$; then $p - q \neq 0$, so $(p - q)_f \neq 0_f$. But $(p - q)_f = p_f - q_f$, so $p_f \neq q_f$.

Section 8.4   Page 189

1. (a) $q = (0, 1), r = (-6)$ (b) $q = (4, -1, -1, 2), r = 0$
3. (a) $q = (0, 1, 2), r = (0, 2, 1, 1)$ (b) $q = (0, 2, 1, 0, 1), r = (1, 2)$
5. (a) $(5, 1), (1, 1)$ (b) $(1, 1), (-2, 1)$ (c) $(-1, 1)$
7. By assumption, $a_1 + a_2(r/s) + \cdots + a_n(r/s)^{n-1} = 0$; thus
(1) $a_1 s^{n-1} + a_2 r s^{n-2} + \cdots + a_{n-1} r^{n-2} s + a_n r^{n-1} = 0$
Put $a_n r^{n-1}$ alone on one side of this equation. Observe that s is a factor of the other side. So
$s \mid a_n r^{n-1}$; deduce that $s \mid a_n$. Also, from (1), $a_1 s^{n-1} = -r(a_2 s^{n-2} + \cdots + a_{n-1} r^{n-3} s + a_n r^{n-2})$;
so $r \mid a_1 s^{n-1}$, thus $r \mid a_1$. The rational zeros of $(2, 3, 0, -1)$ are 2 and -1; $-1/3$ is the only
rational zero of $(1, 4, 12, 29, 6)$.   9. (a) Obvious.   (b) Use Exercise 8.

Section 8.5   Page 194

1. (a) $(0) \in I[x]$ and each tuple of integers with nonzero final term is a polynomial over I.
(b) See Section 8.1.   (c) See Section 8.1.   (d) Clearly (1) is a multiplicative identity and
$(0) \neq (1)$. There are no divisors of zero.   (e) Take $p_1 = (0, 2)$ and $p_2 = (0, 3)$.   (f) See
the proof of Lemma 8.4.1.

3. $\begin{pmatrix} 1 & 0 \\ -1 & 1 \end{pmatrix}\begin{pmatrix} 0 & 1 \\ 1 & 2 \end{pmatrix} \neq \begin{pmatrix} 0 & 1 \\ 1 & 2 \end{pmatrix}\begin{pmatrix} 1 & 0 \\ -1 & 1 \end{pmatrix}$;

$\begin{pmatrix} 0 & 1 \\ 0 & 0 \end{pmatrix}\begin{pmatrix} 1 & 0 \\ 0 & 0 \end{pmatrix} = \begin{pmatrix} 0 & 0 \\ 0 & 0 \end{pmatrix}$

5. (a) Take $A = \begin{pmatrix} 1 & 0 \\ -1 & 1 \end{pmatrix}$ and $B = \begin{pmatrix} 0 & 1 \\ 1 & 2 \end{pmatrix}$.

(b) $[D - E][D + E] = D^2 + DE - ED - E^2$ by a distributive law
$= D^2 - E^2$ by assumption.

(c) First, prove that $DE^n = E^n \cdot D$ whenever $n \in N$. Using mathematical induction, observe that $D^{n+1} - E^{n+1} = D^{n+1} - D \cdot E^n + D \cdot E^n - E^{n+1}$. The rest is easy.   (d) Let

$p = \sum_{i=0}^{s} b_i x^i$; then

$$p(D) - p(E) = \sum_{i=0}^{s} b_i D^i - \sum_{i=0}^{s} b_i E^i$$

$$= \sum_{i=0}^{s} b_i (D^i - E^i) \qquad \text{by properties of matrix addition and scalar multiplication}$$

$$= \sum_{i=0}^{s} b_i (D - E)Q_i \qquad \text{by part } (c)$$

$$= (D - E)\sum_{i=0}^{s} b_i Q_i \qquad \text{by a distributive law.}$$

Section 9.1   Page 200

1. (a) Let $\alpha = (a_1, a_2, a_3)$ and let $\gamma = (c_1, c_2, c_3)$; then $T(\alpha + \gamma) = T(a_1 + c_1, a_2 + c_2, a_3 + c_3) = (a_2 + c_2, 0) = (a_2, 0) + (c_2, 0) = T(\alpha) + T(\gamma)$. Also, $T(k\alpha) = T(ka_1, ka_2, ka_3) = (ka_2, 0) = kT(\alpha)$.   (b) dim $T(R_3) = 1$ since $\{(1, 0)\}$ is a basis for $T(R_3)$.   3. (a) Follow the pattern of the solution to Exercise 1(a).   (b) dim $T(R_3) = 1$
5. (a) Follow the pattern of the solution to Exercise 1(a).   (b) $\{(1, 0, 0), (0, 1, 0), (0, 0, 1)\}$ 7. Follow the pattern of the solution to Exercise 1.   9. Follow the pattern of the solution to Exercise 1.   11. $5T(1, 0, 0) = (10, 0, 0)$ whereas $T(5, 0, 0) = (6, 0, 0)$.   13. (a) $T(0 + 0) = T(0) +'T(0)$, so $T(0) = T(0) +'T(0)$; thus, $T(0) = 0'$.
   (b) $T(\alpha) = T((\alpha - \gamma) + \gamma) = T(\alpha - \gamma) + T(\gamma)$; so $T(\alpha - \gamma) = T(\alpha) -'T(\gamma)$ (c) Let $\{\alpha', \beta'\} \subset T(W)$, where $\alpha' = T(\alpha)$ and $\beta' = T(\beta)$. Now, $T(\alpha + \beta) = T(\alpha) +'T(\beta) = \alpha' +' \beta'$; thus $\alpha' +' \beta' \in T(W)$. Also, $T(k \circ \alpha) = k \circ' T(\alpha) = k \circ' \alpha'$; so $k' \circ' \alpha' \in T(W)$.
   (d) By part (c), $T(V)$ is a subspace of V'.
15. (a) $T(a, b, c) = (2a + b + 4c, -b + 5c)$ (b) $T(0, 0, 1) = (4, 5)$
17. Let $[\gamma]_\mathfrak{B} = (a, b, c)$; then $T(\gamma) = (5a + 5b + 4c, a + 3b + 9c, a + 2b, 2a + 5b + 2c)$.
19. See the proof of Lemma 9.1.1.

Section 9.2   Page 206

1. See Exercise 13(a), Section 9.1.   3. Use mathematical induction.

5. (a) $\begin{pmatrix} 2 & 0 & 1 \\ 1 & 1 & 0 \\ 0 & 1 & -1 \end{pmatrix}$ (b) $(7, 0, 4)$ (c) $(8, 2, 2)$

7. $\begin{pmatrix} -1 & 8 & -7 \\ 0 & 1 & 0 \\ 0 & -2 & 2 \end{pmatrix}$ 9. Lemmas 9.2.5 and 7.3.4.

11. First, assume that T is orthogonal. Let $\{\alpha, \gamma\} \subset R_n$; then $T(\alpha + \gamma) \cdot T(\alpha + \gamma) = (\alpha + \gamma) \cdot (\alpha + \gamma)$ by assumption. Here,
   $LHS = \alpha \cdot \alpha + \gamma \cdot \gamma + 2T(\alpha) \cdot T(\gamma)$ and
   $RHS = \alpha \cdot \alpha + \gamma \cdot \gamma + 2\alpha \cdot \gamma$
so $T(\alpha) \cdot T(\gamma) = \alpha \cdot \gamma$. Next, assume that $T(\alpha) \cdot T(\gamma) = \alpha \cdot \gamma$ whenever $\{\alpha, \gamma\} \subset R_n$. In particular, $T(\gamma) \cdot T(\gamma) = \gamma \cdot \gamma$ whenever $\gamma \in R_n$; so $\|T(\gamma)\| = \|\gamma\|$, i.e. T is orthogonal.

Section 9.3   Page 211

1. (a) $\begin{pmatrix} 1 & 2 & 3 \\ 4 & 2 & -2 \\ 4 & 2 & -2 \end{pmatrix}$ (b) $\begin{pmatrix} 10 & 0 & 5 \\ 5 & 5 & -10 \\ 15 & 5 & -5 \end{pmatrix}$ (c) $(1, 2, 3)$
   (d) $T(\epsilon_1) + U(\epsilon_1) = (2, 0, 1) + (-1, 2, 2) = (1, 2, 3)$
3. $(T + U)(\alpha + \beta) = T(\alpha + \beta) + U(\alpha + \beta) = T(\alpha) + T(\beta) + U(\alpha) + U(\beta) = (T + U)(\alpha) + (T + U)(\beta)$ and $(T + U)(k\alpha) = T(k\alpha) + U(k\alpha) = k(T(\alpha) + U(\alpha)) = k(T + U)(\alpha)$. So, $T + U \in \mathcal{L}(V)$ whenever $\{T, U\} \subset \mathcal{L}(V)$; thus, $+$ is a binary operation on $\mathcal{L}(V)$.
5. 0 is the mapping of V into V that associates 0 with each member of V. So, $0(\alpha + \beta) = 0$ and $0(\alpha) + 0(\beta) = 0 + 0 = 0$; also, $0(k\alpha) = 0$ and $k \, 0(\alpha) = k0 = 0$ whenever k is a scalar. Thus, $0 \in \mathcal{L}(V)$.   7. The details are straightforward.

9. (a) $\begin{pmatrix} 11 & 7 & 4 & 0 \\ -1 & 6 & 3 & 2 \\ -1 & 7 & 3 & 3 \\ 1 & 8 & 2 & 3 \end{pmatrix}$ (b) $(20, 13, 9, 0)$

(c) $(T \cdot U)(2, 0, 1, -1) = U(T(2, 0, 1, -1)) = U(7, 1, -1, -1) = (20, 13, 9, 0).$
11. $[kT]_\mathfrak{G} = C$ where $C_i = [k\, T(\beta_i)]_\mathfrak{G}$ for each i. But $[k\, T(\beta_i)]_\mathfrak{G} = k[T(\beta_i)]_\mathfrak{G}$ by Lemma 7.3.2,
so $C_i = k[T(\beta_i)]_\mathfrak{G}$. Thus, $C = k[T]_\mathfrak{G}$.

Section 10.1   Page 217

1. 0 and 1 are the characteristic roots of T; each nonzero member of $L\{\epsilon_2\}$ and each nonzero
member of $L\{\epsilon_1, \epsilon_3\}$ is a characteristic vector of T.
3. -1 is the only characteristic root of T; each nonzero vector is a characteristic vector of T.
5. Show that $T(\epsilon_1) = 4\epsilon_1$.   7. (a) $-x(x+1)^2$ (b) $0, -1$; $t(3, 1, -1)$ if $t \neq 0$,
and each nonzero member of $L\{(2, 1, 0), (0, 0, 1)\}$.

Section 10.2   Page 219

1. (a) x^4 (b) 0   (c) $t\epsilon_1$ if $t \neq 0$ 3. (a) Assume that 0 is a characteristic root of
A; then $|A - 0\, I_n| = 0$, i.e. $|A| = 0$. Contradiction!   (b) Let k be a characteristic root of
A; then there is a nonzero vector α such that $\alpha A = k\alpha$. Multiplying both sides of this equation by A^{-1} yields $\alpha I_n = (k\alpha)A^{-1}$, so $\alpha A^{-1} = (1/k)\alpha$.   (c) It is enough to show that each
characteristic vector of a nonsingular matrix is also a characteristic vector of its inverse. This
has already been shown in the solution to part (b).   5. (a) By assumption, there are scalars
k_1 and k_2 such that $\alpha A = k_1\alpha$ and $\alpha B = k_2\alpha$. So, by the associative law, $\alpha(AB) = (\alpha A)B =$
$(k_1\alpha)B = k_1(\alpha B) = k_1(k_2\alpha) = (k_1 k_2)\alpha$.   (b) Let k be a scalar such that $\alpha A = k\alpha$. Using
mathematical induction it follows that $\alpha A^n = k^n\alpha$ whenever $n \in N$.   (c) See part (b).

Section 10.3   Page 222

1. If there is a nonsingular matrix P such that $P\begin{pmatrix} 1 & 0 & 0 \\ 2 & 0 & 0 \\ 3 & -1 & 0 \end{pmatrix} = \begin{pmatrix} 2 & 0 & 0 \\ 2 & 0 & 0 \\ 3 & -1 & 0 \end{pmatrix}P$, then

$P_1\begin{pmatrix} 1 & 0 & 0 \\ 2 & 0 & 0 \\ 3 & -1 & 0 \end{pmatrix} = 2\,P_1$; so 2 is a characteristic root of $\begin{pmatrix} 1 & 0 & 0 \\ 2 & 0 & 0 \\ 3 & -1 & 0 \end{pmatrix}$. But $x^2(1-x)$ is the
characteristic polynomial of this matrix, so its characteristic roots are 0 and 1.
3. It is easy to verify that if A and B are similar matrices, then both A and B are singular or
neither is singular. Here, the first matrix is singular whereas the second matrix is nonsingular.
5. $(2 - x)(x - 2)(x - 3)$ is the characteristic polynomial of the given matrix, so its characteristic roots are 2 and 3. Now ϵ_3 and $(2, 1, 0)$ are characteristic vectors corresponding to
2, and $(3, 1, -1)$ is a characteristic vector corresponding to 3; moreover, $\{\epsilon_3, (2, 1, 0),$
$(3, 1, -1)\}$ is linearly independent. Thus, the given matrix is similar to diag$(2, 2, 3)$
and $P = \begin{pmatrix} 0 & 0 & 1 \\ 2 & 1 & 0 \\ 3 & 1 & -1 \end{pmatrix}$.   7. Take $\mathfrak{C} = (P_1, \ldots, P_n)$.
9. Let A and B be similar $n \times n$ matrices; then there is a nonsingular matrix P such that
$B = P^{-1}AP$. Now, the characteristic polynomial of B is $|B - x\, I_n| = |P^{-1}AP - P^{-1}x\, I_nP| =$
$|P^{-1}(A - x\, I_n)P| = |P^{-1}||A - x\, I_n||P| = |A - x\, I_n|$, which is the characteristic polynomial
of A.

11. By Exercise 9, A and A^{-1} have the same characteristic roots. Apply Exercise 3(b), Section 10.2.

Section 10.4   Page 225

1. (a) $(-17, -4, 1)$ (b) $\begin{pmatrix} -17 & 0 \\ 0 & -17 \end{pmatrix} + \begin{pmatrix} 4 & -12 \\ -16 & -20 \end{pmatrix} + \begin{pmatrix} 13 & 12 \\ 16 & 37 \end{pmatrix} = \begin{pmatrix} 0 & 0 \\ 0 & 0 \end{pmatrix}$

3. (a) $(24, 19, -9, -3, 1)$.

(b) $A^2 = \begin{pmatrix} 7 & 2 & 2 & -4 \\ 1 & 4 & 1 & 6 \\ -2 & -6 & 11 & 12 \\ 0 & 0 & 2 & 5 \end{pmatrix}$, $A^3 = \begin{pmatrix} 9 & 10 & 4 & 8 \\ 19 & 0 & 13 & -10 \\ -8 & -26 & 39 & 44 \\ 5 & -4 & 11 & 3 \end{pmatrix}$, and

$A^4 = \begin{pmatrix} 47 & 10 & 30 & -12 \\ 9 & 12 & 29 & 62 \\ -42 & -94 & 135 & 164 \\ -4 & -12 & 32 & 49 \end{pmatrix}$, so $f(A) = \begin{pmatrix} 24 & 0 & 0 & 0 \\ 0 & 24 & 0 & 0 \\ 0 & 0 & 24 & 0 \\ 0 & 0 & 0 & 24 \end{pmatrix}$

$+ \begin{pmatrix} 19 & 38 & 0 & 0 \\ 57 & 0 & 19 & -38 \\ 0 & -38 & 57 & 76 \\ 19 & 0 & 19 & -19 \end{pmatrix} + \begin{pmatrix} -63 & -18 & -18 & 36 \\ -9 & -36 & -9 & -54 \\ 18 & 54 & -99 & -108 \\ 0 & 0 & -18 & -45 \end{pmatrix}$

$+ \begin{pmatrix} -27 & -30 & -12 & -24 \\ -57 & 0 & -39 & 30 \\ 24 & 78 & -117 & -132 \\ -15 & 12 & -33 & -9 \end{pmatrix} + \begin{pmatrix} 47 & 10 & 30 & -12 \\ 9 & 12 & 29 & 62 \\ -42 & -94 & 135 & 164 \\ -4 & -12 & 32 & 49 \end{pmatrix}$

$= \begin{pmatrix} 0 & 0 & 0 & 0 \\ 0 & 0 & 0 & 0 \\ 0 & 0 & 0 & 0 \\ 0 & 0 & 0 & 0 \end{pmatrix}$.

5. (a) Apply the Cayley-Hamilton Theorem.   (b) By the Cayley-Hamilton Theorem, $(-1)^{n+1} A^n = c_0 I_n + c_1 A + \cdots + c_{n-1} A^{n-1}$ and $(-1)^{n+1} A^{n+1} = c_0 A + c_1 A^2 + \cdots + c_{n-2} A^{n-1} + c_{n-1} A^n$. The required result now follows.   (c) Apply part (b).   (d) Notice that $A^{-s} = (A^{-1})^s = (A^s)^{-1}$ since $A^s \cdot (A^{-1})^s = I_n$. It follows from part (a) that $(A^{-1})^2 \in L\{I_n, A, \ldots, A^{n-1}\}$ (multiply both sides of the equation of (a) by A^{-1}). So, by mathematical induction, we obtain (d).   7. (a) See the proof of Theorem 10.4.1.   (b) Note that $A - 0 I_n = A$.   (c) Recall that $A^{-1} = \dfrac{1}{|A|} \text{adj } A$, so $A^{-1} = \dfrac{-1}{|A|}(c_1 I_n + c_2 A + \cdots + c_n A^{n-1})$.   (d) $(A - I_n)^{-1} = \dfrac{-1}{|A - I_n|}[c_1 I_n + c_2(A + I_n) + c_3(A^2 + A + I_n) + \cdots + c_n(A^{n-1} + A^{n-2} + \cdots + A + I_n)]$.

(e) $(A + I_n)^{-1} = \dfrac{-1}{|A + I_n|}[c_1 I_n + c_2(A - I_n) + \cdots + c_n(A^{n-1} - A^{n-2} + A^{n-3} + \cdots + (-1)^{n-2} A + (-1)^{n-1} I_n)]$

Section 10.5   Page 230

1. (a) Apply Lemma 1.4.6   (b) 16   3. (a) $(-13, -18, 4, -1)$
   (c) $(-33, -2, 6, -5, 1)$ (e) $(145, 23, -11, -2, 3, -1)$

Section 11.1   Page 238

1. (a) The details are straightforward.   (b) $\begin{pmatrix} 1 & 0 \\ 0 & 0 \end{pmatrix}$ (c) $\begin{matrix} c_1 & c_2 \\ a_1 \\ a_2 \end{matrix}\begin{pmatrix} 1 & 0 \\ 0 & 0 \end{pmatrix}$

(d) $\begin{pmatrix} 1 & 1 \\ 1 & 1 \end{pmatrix}$ (e) Yes.   3. No.   5. The details are straightforward.

7. (a) $\begin{pmatrix} 3 & -1 \\ 1 & 2 \end{pmatrix}$ (b) $\begin{pmatrix} 29 & -11 \\ -3 & 5 \end{pmatrix}$ 9. See Theorem 11.1.4.

11. (a) Consider $B(\alpha + \gamma, \alpha + \gamma)$.   (b) Consider $B(\alpha, \gamma) + B(\gamma, \alpha)$.

Section 11.2   Page 242

1. The details are straightforward.   3. Notice that $-2 + -2 < 0$, so (ii) of Definition 11.2.1 is violated.   5. $\alpha * \alpha = 0$; so (ii) of Definition 11.2.1 is violated.   7. Take $f \ne 0$ such that $f(0) = f(1) = 0$; then $f * f = 0$.   9. Here $(V, +, 0)$ is not an abelian group since the sum of two members of V is not necessarily a member of V; e.g. $(1, 3, 7) + (-4, -1, -2) = (-3, 2, 5)$.   11. The details are straightforward.

Section 11.3   Page 246

1. Straightforward.   3. See the proof of Theorem 3.2.2.   5. Apply the generalized form of Lemma 3.2.4 to the real inner product space of Example 3, Section 11.2.   7. (a) $\{(1, 1, 0), \epsilon_3\}$ (b) $\{(1, 1, 1)\}$ 9. Follow the proof of Theorem 3.1.3.
11. By Theorem 11.3.4, $\gamma_1 * \gamma_2 = [\gamma_1]_\alpha \cdot [\gamma_2]_\alpha$ and $\gamma_1 * \gamma_2 = [\gamma_1]_\mathfrak{B} \cdot [\gamma_2]_\mathfrak{B}$.

Section 11.4   Page 251

1. The associated bilinear form is B, where $[B] = \begin{pmatrix} 3 & -1 \\ -1 & 0 \end{pmatrix}$.

3. Straightforward.   5. Let $[Q] = \begin{pmatrix} 1 & -3 \\ -3 & 9 \end{pmatrix}$ and $\mathfrak{B} = ((1, -3), (3, 1))$; then $[Q]_\mathfrak{B} = \begin{pmatrix} 100 & 0 \\ 0 & 0 \end{pmatrix}$. So the given set is $\{\alpha \mid x'$ and y' exist such that $[\alpha]_\mathfrak{B} = (x', y')$ and $x'^2 = .01\}$.
7. Take $\mathfrak{B} = ((4, 0, 3), \epsilon_2, (3, 0, -4))$; then $[Q]_\mathfrak{B} = \text{diag}(1250, 1, -625)$. The given set is $\{\alpha \mid x', y'$, and z' exist such that $[\alpha]_\mathfrak{B} = (x', y', z')$ and $1250x'^2 + y'^2 - 625z'^2 = 1\}$.
9. Take $\mathfrak{B} = ((1, 0, 1, 0), (1, 0, -1, 0), (0, 1, 0, 1), (0, 1, 0, -1))$; then $[Q]_\mathfrak{B} = \text{diag}(0, -4, 8, 4)$. The given set is $\{(x, y, z, w) \mid x', y', z'$, and w' exist such that $[\alpha]_\mathfrak{B} = (x', y', z', w')$ and $-4y'^2 + 8z'^2 + 4w'^2 = 1\}$.
11. See Exercise 18, Section 3.4.

Section 12.1   Page 260

1. $\begin{pmatrix} 2 & 0 & 0 \\ 0 & -1 & 3 \\ 0 & 3 & 0 \end{pmatrix}$, $(-2, 1, 0)$, -1. .   3. $\begin{pmatrix} -1 & 2 & 0 \\ 2 & 3 & 0 \\ 0 & 0 & 0 \end{pmatrix}$, $\mathbf{0}$, 0.

5. $\begin{pmatrix} 5 & -1 & 0 \\ -1 & -3 & 0 \\ 0 & 0 & 1 \end{pmatrix}$, $(0, 2, 0)$, 5.   7. $\begin{pmatrix} 2 & -1 & 0 \\ -1 & 0 & 0 \\ 0 & 0 & 1 \end{pmatrix}$, $(0, 2, -1)$, 0.

9. (a) $\begin{pmatrix} 0 & -2 & 0 \\ -2 & 3 & 0 \\ 0 & 0 & 1 \end{pmatrix}$, ϵ_3, -3.   (b) $\begin{pmatrix} 0 & -2 & 0 & 0 \\ -2 & 3 & 0 & 0 \\ 0 & 0 & 1 & 1 \\ 0 & 0 & 1 & -3 \end{pmatrix}$ (c) No.   (d) Yes.

(e) 24   (f) 16   11. Ellipsoid.   13. Hyperboloid of one sheet.
15. Hyperbolic paraboloid.   17. Two parallel planes.
19. (a) Here $C = \{(x, y, 0) \mid x^2 + y^2 = 9\}$ which is the intersection of the given surface and the XY-plane. It is easy to verify that $\{(x, y, z) \mid x^2 + y^2 = 9\}$ is the union of all lines with direction $[\epsilon_3]$ through a point of C.   (b) Straightforward.
21. No; e.g. consider the quadric surface $\{0\}$.

Section 12.2   Page 264

1. $\{(0, -t_1, 8 + 3t_1), (0, -t_2, 8 + 3t_2)\}$ where $t_1 = -.5 + 22^{\frac{1}{2}}$ and $t_2 = -.5 - 22^{\frac{1}{2}}$.
3. Apply Theorem 12.2.1; notice that a, b, and c are the coefficients of the quadratic equation involved.

Section 12.3   Page 269

1. Endpoints of line-segment are $(-1, -1, 0)$ and $(1, 1, 0)$; these points are members of the given quadric surface. So, this line-segment is a chord of this quadric surface.
3. YZ-plane.   5. $\{(x, y, z) \mid x - y = 0\}$
7. Clearly, $(\gamma[Q] + \beta) \cdot k\beta_0 = 0 \Leftrightarrow (\gamma[Q] + \beta) \cdot \beta_0 = 0$.   9. Obvious.
11. $(1, -2, 2)$ 13. No centers.   15. $\{(x, y, z) \mid x + y + z = 2\}$
17. Apply Theorem 2.3.1.   19. (a) Apply Theorem 12.3.2.
    (b) $Q(\alpha_1 + \alpha_2) = Q(\alpha_1) + Q(\alpha_2) + 2B(\alpha_1, \alpha_2)$ by Lemma 11.4.2, and $Q(\alpha_2 + \alpha_1) = Q(\alpha_2) + Q(\alpha_1) + 2B(\alpha_2, \alpha_1)$; so $B(\alpha_1, \alpha_2) = B(\alpha_2, \alpha_1)$.   (c) $(\alpha_1[Q] + \beta) \cdot \alpha_1 = 0$ and $(\alpha_2[Q] + \beta) \cdot \alpha_2 = 0$; so $Q(\alpha_1) + \beta \cdot \alpha_1 = Q(\alpha_2) + \beta \cdot \alpha_2$, but $\beta \cdot \alpha_1 = \beta \cdot \alpha_2$ by Lemma 12.3.4.

Section 12.4   Page 274

1. The diametral plane of the given quadric surface with respect to ϵ_1 is the given plane. Moreover, $[\epsilon_1]$ is a direction of a normal to this plane.   3. (a) $(0, 27, -6, -1)$.
    (b) $0, 3, -9$ (c) $\{(x, y, z) \mid x - y = 1.5\}$, $\{(x, y, z) \mid x + y - 4z = .5\}$.

5. (a) $\begin{pmatrix} 1 & -3 & 0 \\ -3 & 9 & 0 \\ 0 & 0 & 0 \end{pmatrix}$ (b) $(0, 0, 10, -1)$ (c) $0, 10$

    (d) $\{(x, y, z) \mid x = 3y\}$ 7. (a) $\begin{pmatrix} 9 & -6 & 0 \\ -6 & 5 & 0 \\ 0 & 0 & -1 \end{pmatrix}$ (b) $(-9, 5, 13, -1)$

    (c) $-1, 7 + 40^{\frac{1}{2}}, 7 - 40^{\frac{1}{2}}$.   (d) $\{(x, y, z) \mid z = -2\}$, $\{(x, y, z) \mid (1 + 10^{\frac{1}{2}})x - 3y = (2/3)10^{\frac{1}{2}} - 7/3\}$, $\{(x, y, z) \mid (10^{\frac{1}{2}} - 1)x + 3y = 7/3 + (2/3)10^{\frac{1}{2}}\}$.
9. $\{(x, y, z) \mid -6x + (7 + 73^{\frac{1}{2}})y + .5(5 + 73^{\frac{1}{2}})z = 0\}$, $\{(x, y, z) \mid 6x + (-7 + 73^{\frac{1}{2}})y + .5(-5 + 73^{\frac{1}{2}})z = 0\}$.   11. $\{(x, y, z) \mid 2x + y + z = -3\}$, $\{(x, y, z) \mid y - z = 1\}$.

INDEX OF MATHEMATICAL EXPRESSIONS

Symbol	Meaning/Page
R	set of all real numbers 1
N	set of all natural numbers 1
$\in$	is a member of 1
R_n	set of all ordered n-tuples of real numbers 1
$+$	vector addition 2
$\circ$	scalar multiplication 2
$\mathbf{0}$	$(0, \ldots, 0)$ 2
$\mathcal{R}_n$	vector space for which vectors are members of R_n 4, 150
$\varnothing$	empty set 6
$\sim$	equivalent 8
$\|A\|$	determinant of A 13
M_{ij}	minor of (i, j) 13, 19
(a_{ij})	matrix 15
$\displaystyle\sum_{i \in I} a_i$	summation convention 15
$\displaystyle\prod_{i \in I} a_i$	product convention 15
C_n	$\{1, \ldots, n\} \times \{1, \ldots, n\}$ 16
$\displaystyle\sum_{i<j} a_{ij}$	index set is $\{(i, j) \mid i < j \text{ and } (i, j) \in C_n\}$ 16
$\mathrm{diag}(a_1, \ldots, a_n)$	the $n \times n$ matrix (a_{ij}) where $a_{ij} = \begin{cases} a_i & \text{if } i = j \\ 0 & \text{if } i \neq j \end{cases}$ 18
A_i	the ith row vector of A 18
$_jA$	the jth column vector of A 18
A_{ij}	cofactor of (i, j) in A; $(-1)^{i+j}M_{ij}$ 19
a_{ij}	the entry of A occupying position (i, j) 19
M_i^j	minor of $(1, i)$ and $(2, j)$ 25
A^t	(a_{ji}) if $A = (a_{ij})$ 27
$\mathfrak{D}(P)$	the dual of P 27
$\det(\alpha_1, \ldots, \alpha_n)$	$\|A\|$ where $A_i = \alpha_i$, $i = 1, \ldots, n$ 29
ϵ_i	$(0, \ldots, 1(i\text{th term}), \ldots, 0)$ 30
M_n	the set of all mappings of $\{1, \ldots, n\}$ into $\{1, \ldots, n\}$ 30
P_n	the set of all mappings of $\{1, \ldots, n\}$ onto $\{1, \ldots, n\}$ 30

Symbol	Meaning/Page
sgn Π	$\det(\epsilon_{\Pi(1)}, \ldots, \epsilon_{\Pi(n)})$ 31
I_n	$\mathrm{diag}(1, \ldots, 1)$ 31
$W_1 + W_2$	$\{\alpha_1 + \alpha_2 \mid \alpha_1 \in W_1 \text{ and } \alpha_2 \in W_2\}$ 37
LA	the set of all linear combinations of A 38
rank A	$\dim L\{\gamma \mid \gamma \text{ is a column vector of } A\}$ 43
$\alpha \cdot \gamma$	$a_1 c_1 + \cdots + a_n c_n$ if $\alpha = (a_1, \ldots, a_n)$ and $\gamma = (c_1, \ldots, c_n)$ 51, 57
$\alpha \perp \beta$	$\alpha \cdot \beta = 0$ 58
$A^\perp$	$\{\gamma \mid \gamma \perp \alpha \text{ whenever } \alpha \in A\}$ 58
$\|\alpha\|$	$\sqrt{\alpha \cdot \alpha}$ 62
$A + B$	matrix addition 71
kA	scalar multiplication 71
$A \cdot B$	matrix multiplication 71

$$\begin{array}{cc} & c_1 \quad\;\; c_n \\ \begin{matrix} a_1 \\ \cdot \\ \cdot \\ \cdot \\ a_m \end{matrix} & \begin{pmatrix} b_{11} \cdots b_{1n} \\ \cdot \\ \cdot \\ \cdot \\ b_{m1} \cdots b_{mn} \end{pmatrix} \end{array}$$

Symbol	Meaning/Page
	matrix with multipliers 73
adj A	(A_{ji}) 77
A^{-1}	the inverse of A 79
trace A	$a_{11} + \cdots + a_{nn}$ if $A = (a_{ij})$ and is $n \times n$ 81
E_3	three-dimensional Euclidean space 89
XY-plane	the plane containing $L\{\epsilon_1\}$ and $L\{\epsilon_2\}$ 90
YZ-plane	the plane containing $L\{\epsilon_2\}$ and $L\{\epsilon_3\}$ 90
ZX-plane	the plane containing $L\{\epsilon_3\}$ and $L\{\epsilon_1\}$ 90
E_n	n-dimensional Euclidean space 91
$\alpha \equiv \beta$	$\beta = k\alpha$ where $k > 0$ 96
$[\beta]$	$\{\alpha \mid \alpha \equiv \beta\}$ 96
$(L, [\beta])$	directed line 97
(L, β)	$(L, [\beta])$ 97
X	$(L\{\epsilon_1\}, \epsilon_1)$ 98
Y	$(L\{\epsilon_2\}, \epsilon_2)$ 98
Z	$(L\{\epsilon_3\}, \epsilon_3)$ 98
$\alpha \times \beta$	cross product of α and β 103
$\times (\alpha_2, \ldots, \alpha_n)$	cross product of $\alpha_2, \ldots, \alpha_n$ 104
$\wp S$	set of all subsets of S 124
$A \doteq B$	$\{t \mid t \in A \text{ or else } t \in B\}$ 124
$A - B$	$\{t \mid t \in A \text{ and } t \notin B\}$ 124
na	see Definition 6.2.4 133
a^n	see Definition 6.2.4 133
$\mathfrak{C}$	$(C, +, \cdot, 0, 1)$, the complex number field 143
$\mathfrak{S} \cong \mathfrak{J}$	$\mathfrak{S}$ is isomorphic to $\mathfrak{J}$ 145
V	set of all vectors of a vector space 149
$\mathfrak{V}$	$(V, +, 0)$ 149
$\mathfrak{F}$	$(F, +, \cdot, 0, 1)$ 149
$(\mathfrak{F}, \mathfrak{V}, \circ)$	vector space 149
$\mathfrak{R}$	$(R, +, \cdot, 0, 1)$, the real number field 150
$\mathfrak{C}_n$	vector space for which vectors are n-tuples of complex numbers 150
$\mathbf{v}$	$(\mathfrak{F}, \mathfrak{V}, \circ)$ 153

Symbol	Meaning/Page
$\mathcal{B}$	ordered basis 163
$[\gamma]_\mathcal{B}$	$(c_1, \ldots, c_n)$ if $\gamma = c_1\beta_1 + \cdots + c_n\beta_n$ and $\mathcal{B} = (\beta_1, \ldots, \beta_n)$ 163
$[\mathcal{B}]_\alpha$	the matrix M such that $M_i = [\beta_i]_\alpha$, if $\mathcal{B} = (\beta_1, \ldots, \beta_n)$ 164
$[\mathcal{B}]$	$[\mathcal{B}]_\alpha$ provided $\alpha = (\epsilon_1, \ldots, \epsilon_n)$ 164
δ_{ij}	1 if $i = j$, 0 if $i \neq j$ 168
$F[x]$	the set of all polynomials over F 175
$\mathcal{P}[F]$	$F[x]$ 175
$\deg p$	the degree of the polynomial p 175
$(a_n)\cdot(b_n)$	$\left(\sum_{i+j=n+1} a_i b_j \right)$ 177
x	the polynomial $(0, 1)$ 179
x^{n+1}	$x^n \cdot x$ 179
x^0	(1) 179
p_f	the polynomial function associated with p 183
$p(t)$	$(a_0, a_1, \ldots, a_m)\cdot(1, t, \ldots, t^m)$ if $p = (a_0, a_1, \ldots, a_m)$ 183
$q \mid p$	q is a divisor of p 189
$[T]_\mathcal{B}$	matrix of T with respect to $\mathcal{B}$ 203, 204
$[T]$	matrix of T with respect to $(\epsilon_1, \ldots, \epsilon_n)$ 204
$\mathcal{L}(V)$	the set of all linear operators on V 207
$T + U$	$\{(\alpha, \beta) \mid \alpha \in V \text{ and } \beta = T(\alpha) + U(\alpha)\}$ 207
kT	$\{(\alpha, \beta) \mid \alpha \in V \text{ and } \beta = kT(\alpha)\}$ 207
0	$\{(\alpha, \mathbf{0}) \mid \alpha \in V\}$ 208
$T \cdot U$	$\{(\alpha, \beta) \mid \alpha \in V \text{ and } \beta = U(T(\alpha))\}$ 208
1	$\{(\alpha, \alpha) \mid \alpha \in V\}$ 209
$[B]_\mathcal{B}$	$(B(\beta_i, \beta_j))$ if $\mathcal{B} = (\beta_1, \ldots, \beta_n)$ 236
$[B]$	$[B]_\mathcal{B}$ provided $\mathcal{B} = (\epsilon_1, \ldots, \epsilon_n)$ 236
$*$	inner product 239
$(V, *)$	real inner product space 240
$\|\alpha\|$	$\sqrt{\alpha * \alpha}$ 244
$A^\perp$	$\{\gamma \mid \gamma \in V \text{ and } \gamma * \alpha = 0 \text{ whenever } \alpha \in A\}$ 246
$[Q]_\mathcal{B}$	see Definition 11.4.2 249
$[Q]$	$[Q]_\mathcal{B}$ provided $\mathcal{B} = (\epsilon_1, \ldots, \epsilon_n)$ 249
$[\mathcal{Q}]$	$\begin{pmatrix} a & h & g & q \\ h & b & f & r \\ g & f & c & s \\ q & r & s & d \end{pmatrix}$ if $[Q] = \begin{pmatrix} a & h & g \\ h & b & f \\ g & f & c \end{pmatrix}$, $\beta = (q, r, s)$, and $\mathcal{Q} = \{\gamma \mid Q(\gamma) + 2\beta\cdot\gamma + d = 0\}$ 253, 254
γ^1	$(x, y, z, 1)$ if $\gamma = (x, y, z)$ 254
Q'	the quadratic form on $\mathcal{R}_4$ such that $[Q'] = [\mathcal{Q}]$ 262

INDEX

Abelian group, 4, 132
Adjoint matrix, 77
Algebraic system, 123
  basic set, 123
  extension, 146
  subsystem, 153
  supporting set, 123
Angle, 64, 66
  between directed lines, 97
Arccos, 67
  graph, 67
  table, 68, 277- 282
Augmented matrix, 43

Basis, 39, 155
  ordered, 161, 162
  orthogonal, 60
  orthonormal, 62
Bilinear form, 233
  matrix, 236
  skew-symmetric, 239
  symmetric, 237
Binary relation
  reflexive, 12
  symmetric, 12
  transitive, 12

Cauchy-Schwarz Inequality, 63
Cayley-Hamilton Theorem 78, 223
Center of quadric surface, 267
Characteristic
  polynomial, 30, 215, 217
  root, 213, 218
  value, 213
  vector, 213, 218
Chord, 264
Closed interval, 66
Coefficient matrix, 43
Cofactor, 19

Collinear points, 94
Column vector, 11, 18
Combination
  convex, 101
  linear, 34, 154
Complex
  number field, 143
  vector space, 161
Composite, 208
Convex combination, 101
Cos
  graph, 66
  table, 69, 283- 312
Cross product, 103, 104
Cylinder, 261
  elliptic, 258
  hyperbolic, 258
  parabolic, 258
  right, 261

Degree of polynomial, 175
Det, 29
Determinant, 13
  polynomial matrix, 193
Diametral plane, 265
Difference, 124
  symmetric, 124
Dimension, 40, 155
Directed
  angle, 97
  distance, 99, 120
  line, 97
Direction, 96
  angles, 98
  cosines, 98
  of line, 96
Distance, 90, 91
  directed, 99
Division Theorem, 186
Domain of vector function, 197

Dot product, 57
Duality principle, 27

Eigenvalue, 213
Eigenvector, 213
Elementary matrix, 83
Ellipsoid, 255
Elliptic
    cone, 257
    cylinder, 258
    paraboloid, 257
Equivalent
    linear systems, 6
    matrices, 11
    vectors, 96
Euclid, 89, 92
Euclidean space, 89
Exchange Theorem, 158
Extension, 146

Factor Theorem, 189
Field, 4, 141
    characteristic, 144
Form
    bilinear, 233
    quadratic, 247
Function
    polynomial, 183
    vector, 197
    zero, 184
Fundamental Theorem of Algebra, 184, 190

Gram-Schmidt Theorem, 60, 244
Group, 3, 128
    abelian, 4, 132
    characteristic, 135
    commutative, 132
    postulates, 128

Homogeneous linear system, 46
Hyperbolic
    cylinder, 258
    paraboloid, 257
Hyperboloid
    of one sheet, 256
    of two sheets, 257
Hyperplane, 91

Identity
    left, 130
    multiplicative, 4

Identity (*Cont.*)
    right, 3
    ring, 138
Image of vector function, 197
Index set, 15
Inequality
    Cauchy-Schwarz, 63
    Triangle, 64
Inner product, 58, 239
Integral domain, 138
Interval
    closed, 66
    open, 66
Inverse
    left, 129
    matrix, 77
    right, 3, 129
Isomorphic, 145
Isomorphism, 145

Kronecker delta, 168

Left
    identity, 130
    inverse, 129
Length of vector, 62
Line
    directed, 97
    direction, 96
    orthogonal, 99, 102
    parallel, 98, 99
    perpendicular, 99, 102
Line-segment, 62, 100
    endpoints, 100
Linear combination, 34, 38, 154
Linear dependence test, 35, 39
Linear independence test, 36
Linear operator, 202
    characteristic polynomial, 215
    matrix, 203
    orthogonal, 206
    symmetric, 207
Linear system, 6
    equivalent, 6
    homogeneous, 46
    inconsistent, 11
    redundant, 11
Linear transformation, 198
Linearly
    dependent, 34, 39, 154
    independent, 35, 39, 155

Main diagonal, 9
Matric polynomial, 191

Matrix, 7
  adjoint, 77
  augmented, 43
  bilinear form, 236
  characteristic polynomial, 217
  characteristic root, 218
  characteristic vector, 218
  coefficient, 43
  determinant, 13
  elementary, 83
  equivalent, 11
  inverse, 77
  linear operator, 203
  lower triangular, 18
  main diagonal, 9
  mixed, 84
  nonsingular, 53
  ordered basis, 164
  quadratic form, 249
  quadric surface, 254
  rank, 43
  similar, 82, 220
  singular, 53
  sub, 14
  symmetric, 32, 81
  trace, 81
  transformation, 11
  transpose, 27
  triangular, 18
  upper triangular, 18
  vector, 163
  with multipliers, 73
  zero, 54
Minkowski Inequality, 244
Minor, 19
  (j-1)-level, 26
  second-level, 24
Mixed matrix, 84
Multiplicative identity, 4
Multiplicity m, 190

Natural number system, 124
Nonsingular matrix, 53
Norm, 62, 244
Normal to plane, 112
n-vector, 2

Open interval, 66
Ordered basis, 161, 162
Orthogonal, 53, 58, 244
  basis, 60
  complement, 58, 246
  linear operator, 206
  lines, 99, 102

Orthonormal
  basis, 62
  set, 62, 244

Parabolic cylinder, 258
Paraboloid
  elliptic, 257
  hyperbolic, 257
Parallel
  directed lines, 98
  lines, 99
  planes, 116
Partition, 96
Permutation, 30
Perpendicular lines, 99, 102
Pivot, 9
Plane, 89, 91
  curve, 261
  parallel, 116
Point, 89, 91
  collinear, 94
Postulates
  field, 142
  group, 128
  integral domain, 138
  ring, 136
  semigroup, 124
  vector space, 149
Polynomial, 173
  characteristic, 30, 215, 217
  degree, 175
  divisor, 188
  factor, 188
  function, 183
  matrix, 191
  over F, 173
  zero, 175, 184
Power set, 124
Principal
  plane, 271
  submatrix, 228
Principle of Duality, 27

Quadratic form, 247
  matrix, 249
  nonzero, 251
Quadric surface, 253
  center, 267
  chord, 264
  diametral plane, 265
  imaginary, 255
  matrix, 253–4
  principal plane, 271
  real, 255

Rank, 43
Real
  inner product space, 240
  vector space, 161
Reduced matrix, 8
Remainder Theorem, 188
Replacement Theorem, 40, 159
Right
  cylinder, 261
  identity, 3
  inverse, 3, 129
Ring, 136
  commutative, 138
  identity, 138
  postulates, 136

Scalar, 2, 150
  multiplication, 2
Schmidt, 60
Schwarz, 63, 244
Schwarz Inequality, 244
Semigroup, 123
  postulate, 124
Set
  index, 15
  orthogonal, 60
  power, 124
Sgn, 31
Similar matrices, 82, 220
Similarity, 220
Singular matrix, 53
Skew-symmetric, 239
Span, 34, 38
Standard form of equation, 259
Steinitz Replacement Theorem, 40, 159
Subgroup, 133, 135
Submatrix, 14, 53
  principal, 228
Subspace, 33, 153
  basis, 39
  dimension, 40
  sum, 37, 162
  trivial, 40, 155
Subsystem, 153
Subtraction, 132
Sum of subspaces, 37, 162
Symmetric
  bilinear form, 237

Symmetric (*Cont.*)
  difference, 124
  linear operator, 207
  matrix, 32, 81
System of integers, 124

Tables,
  arccos, 68, 277- 283
  cos, 69, 283- 312
Test for
  linear dependence, 35, 39, 154, 155
  linear independence, 36
Trace, 81, 199, 255
Transpose, 27
Triangle Inequality, 64, 244
Triangular matrix, 18
  lower, 18
  upper, 18
Trivial
  solution, 48
  subspace, 40, 155

Vector, 2, 150
  characteristic, 213
  column, 11, 18
  dot product, 57
  equivalent, 96
  inner product, 58
  length, 62
  norm, 62, 244
  orthogonal, 53, 244
  orthonormal, 244
  product, 103
  row, 11, 18
Vector function, 197
  domain, 197
  image, 197
Vector space, 4, 149
  complex, 161
  real, 161
  subspace, 153
  subsystem, 153

Zero
  matrix, 54
  polynomial, 175